A new first-year algebra course from McDougal, Littell

ALGEBRA 1: The Language and Skills of Algebra provides students with the fundamental vocabulary and skills of algebra. The **Student Text** and the **Teacher's Edition** are designed for flexibility in providing content coverage and student challenge for three levels of courses:

Basic courses
Average courses
Advanced courses

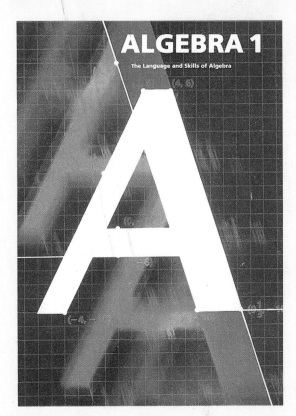

Students learn the vocabulary and skills of first-year algebra. They learn to read mathematical language, solve equations and problems, and describe algebraic properties.

ALGEBRA 1: The Language and Skills of Algebra has a clean, open format. The text invites all students to read well-organized material, provides students with problem sets of appropriate difficulty and challenge, and reviews and maintains students' skills.

The text provides an abundance of student-interest features: **Projects** and **Applications** for independent student work, **After-School Mathematics** and **Math History** for reading about mathematics, and many problems for calculators and computers.

Components of the
McDougal, Littell Mathematics Program

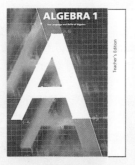

Publication: Spring 1983

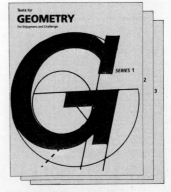

Revised Edition
Publication: Spring 1983

The Geometry program includes a complete **Solution Manual** with every problem completely solved.

ISBN: 0–88343–912–3

ALGEBRA 1: The Language and Skills of Algebra

ALGEBRA 2: Functions and Techniques

GEOMETRY for Enjoyment and Challenge

The three courses of the McDougal, Littell Mathematics Program provide a complete three-year series for high school mathematics.

- Each **Student Text** combines clear, accessible reading and flexible sets of problems. Exposition consists of brief introductory material and completely worked-through **Sample Problems**. Extensive **Problem Sets** contain an abundance of problems for practice and for challenge. End-of-chapter **Study Guides**, student-interest features, and end-of-text material help students learn to work independently.

- Each **Teacher's Edition** provides commentary for the text and contains on-page answers and solutions. It also provides conveniently located recommendations for using the text with three different ability levels. For each section, **Section Schedules** and **Assignment Guides** recommend ways to adjust content coverage and homework assignments for Basic, Average, and Advanced courses.

- In conjunction with the three levels of recommendations in the Teacher's Edition, each course is accompanied by three **Series of Tests**. These provide each text with a flexible program of tests appropriate for students at all ability levels, a flexibility that could not be possible with a single set of tests.

Special Features of ALGEBRA 1:
The Language and Skills of Algebra

The features of the **Student Text** are described on the following six pages of this **Teacher's Edition**. The features are designed so students learn to work independently and solve problems.

- Students learn how to read mathematical exposition and analyze and solve problems.

   Each section contains a brief introduction. Most of the exposition is in the form of **Sample Problems** which help students learn to analyze problems and prepare students for the **Problem Sets** (p. T5).

- Students develop skills to solve problems, and maintain their algebraic skills.

   Three-level **Problem Sets** follow each section, each with problems that progress from A (easy), to B (moderate), to C (advanced). The last few A problems in every set are review problems, providing a continuous maintenance of skills (p. T6).

- Students are led to extend their study to related topics.

   In each chapter, features called **Xtending the topic** and **Problem Set X** extend the ideas of the section and provide related material (p. T7).

- Students can periodically review and test their skills.

   End-of-chapter materials include **Chapter Study Guides**, **Chapter Tests**, and **Problem Sets**. Chapters 3, 7, 10, 12, and 14 are followed by **Cumulative Review Problem Sets** (pp. T8 – T10).

- Students investigate mathematics through individual activities.

   Each chapter includes student-interest features, presented on tinted text pages. These include independent students **Projects** and opportunities to use algebra in **After-School Mathematics** and **Applications** (p. T11).

Sample Problems

Most of the exposition is in the **Sample Problems**, so the students' reading is relevant and task-directed. The **Sample Problems** illustrate the technique of the section, so students learn how to analyze problems. The **Sample Problems** are similar to the homework, so students prepare for the **Problem Sets**.

The text is designed for students to read. To this end, the format is open and uncluttered, the reading level is appropriate, and the tone is informal but accurate.

A functional use of color and a clear, uncluttered format provide a readable text.

Sample Problems detail how to apply the concepts and techniques of the section.

Section 8.2   Using Fractions in Proportions

The scale on a map is a ratio. For this map, the scale is that 1 cm represents 100 km. This may be written several ways, including:

1 cm : 100 km

$$\frac{1 \text{ cm}}{100 \text{ km}}$$

Map of the
Great Desert

On the map, the distance between points A and B is 3.5 cm:

$$\frac{1}{100} = \frac{3.5}{x}$$

The value of x must be 350, and thus the actual distance represented is 350 km.
The equation $\frac{1}{100} = \frac{3.5}{350}$ is called a **proportion**.

Definition

   A PROPORTION is a mathematical statement that two ratios are equal.

   EXAMPLES

   • $\frac{2}{5} = \frac{4}{10}$ • $\frac{7}{10} = \frac{700}{1000}$

   Proportions usually occur in problems with a variable, such as:

   • $\frac{3}{4} = \frac{6}{x}$

   One way to solve for the variable is to multiply both sides of the equation by the common denominator:

$$\frac{3}{4} = \frac{6}{x}$$

   MULTBY $4x$: $4x\left(\frac{3}{4}\right) = 4x\left(\frac{6}{x}\right)$

   $3x = 24$

   MULTBY $\frac{1}{3}$: $x = 8$

   Thus $x = 8$.

8.2 Fractions in Proportions   **315**

Sample Problems

1   Rewrite the following proportion without fractions: $\frac{a}{b} = \frac{c}{d}$

   PROCEDURE   Multiply both sides by the common denominator bd:

$$\frac{a}{b} = \frac{c}{d}$$

   MULTBY bd: $bd\left(\frac{a}{b}\right) = bd\left(\frac{c}{d}\right)$

$$\frac{bda}{b} = \frac{bdc}{d}$$

$$ad = bc$$

   The equation $ad = bc$ is called the **cross-product** of the original proportion. Notice how the cross-product pattern is used in the next Sample Problem.

2   Solve the following proportions:

   a $\frac{x}{5} = \frac{6}{15}$ b $\frac{3}{4} = \frac{2t}{13}$ c $\frac{7}{2w - 3} = \frac{8}{3w + 4}$

   PROCEDURE   Write the cross-product for each proportion, and solve:

   a $\frac{x}{5} = \frac{6}{15}$
        $15x = 30$
        $x = 2$

   b $\frac{3}{4} = \frac{2t}{13}$
        $39 = 8t$
        $\frac{39}{8} = t$

   c $\frac{7}{2w - 3} = \frac{8}{3w + 4}$
        $7(3w + 4) = 8(2w - 3)$
        $21w + 28 = 16w - 24$
        $5w + 28 = -24$
        $5w = -52$
        $w = \frac{-52}{5}$

316   *8.2 Fractions in Proportions*

New terms are developed by first using the term in context, next presenting the definition, and then providing several examples.

Problem Sets

Each **Problem Set** consists of three levels of problems: A (easy), B (moderate), and C (advanced). Thus each **Problem Set** contains many easy problems as well as problems that will challenge any student. Throughout the year, students respond to problems that are multiple choice, fill-in, verbal, and numerical computation.

Problem Set A

1   Name two uses of the Distributive Property.

2   Explain how the Distributive Property can be used to remove the parentheses in $3 + (4y + 2)$.

Copy the following exercises and replace each __?__ with the correct expression.

3   $5(x + 3) = 5x + 5 \cdot$ __?__   8   __?__ $(y + 8) = xy + 8x$

4   $6(y - 2) = 6y - 6 \cdot$ __?__   9   __?__ $(2x - 5) = 6x^2 - 15x$

5   $x(y + 7) = xy +$ __?__   10 $2($ __?__ $+ 7) = 6x + 14$

6   $(b + c) \cdot a = ba + c \cdot$ __?__   11 $5(x +$ __?__ $) = 5x + 5$

7   $(4 + m)(-3) = -12 - 3 \cdot$ __?__   12   __?__ $(3x^2 + 2x) = 3x^2 + 2x$

Use the Distributive Property to remove the parentheses.

13   $6(x + 3)$ 15 $8(x^2 + 3x - 2)$

14   $-5(3x + 2)$ 16 $-(4x^2 - 5x + 1)$

Translate the verbal phrases into variable expressions containing parentheses. Then distribute to remove the parentheses.

17   The product of $4x$ and the difference $2x$ minus $5y$.

18   The sum $-3x$ plus $2x^2$; that sum multiplied by x.

19   5 added to $11x$ and then that sum multiplied by $3x$.

20   $2m$ subtracted from $7a$ and that difference multiplied by $-5am$.

Rewrite each of the following subtraction problems as a sum. (Review: Section 2.4)

21   $12x - 30$ 23 $5x^2 - 12x$

22   $91 - 215y$ 24 $-7 - ab$

170   *4.4 Removing Parentheses*

Problem Set B

In problems 25–32, remove the parentheses and then combine the like terms.

25   $2(x + 9) + 7x$ 29 $8x(2x + 10) - 16x^2$

26   $6 + 4(2x - 8)$ 30 $6x^2 + 5(12x^2 - 3x)$

27   $-(2x + 5) + 3x$ 31 $-3(2x + 9) + 2(4x + 7)$

28   $-(5x^2 + 2x) - 4x$ 32 $4(5x^2 - 2x + 1) + 6(9 - 3x)$

Problem Set C

Remove the parentheses, combine the like terms, and then evaluate the expression for the given value of x.

33   $2x(3x - 5) + 6(2x^2 - 5x)$ $x = 6$

34   $6x^3 + 5x(x^2 - 3x + 2) - 7x^2$ $x = 5$

35   $-(4x^3 - 5x^2 - 2x - 6) + 2(x^2 - 5x)$ $x = -2$

36   $-3x^2(2x - 5) + 7x^2 + (4x^3 - 5x)$ $x = 3$

When using a calculator to evaluate expressions such as those in problems 33–36, a memory key is not necessary.

- In problem 33, after the first two steps, the problem becomes $18x^2 - 40x = (18x - 40)x$. To evaluate for $x = 6$, enter:

  18 ⊠ 6 ⊟ ⊟ 40 ⊟ ⊠ 6 ⊟

  The result is 408.

- Problem 34 simplifies to $11x^3 - 22x^2 + 10x = ((11x - 22)x + 10)x$. To evaluate for $x = 5$, enter:

  11 ⊠ 5 ⊟ ⊟ 22 ⊟ ⊠ 5 ⊟ ⊞ 10 ⊟ ⊠ 5 ⊟

  The result is 875.

4.4 Removing Parentheses   171

Answers to the odd-numbered problems are at the end of the student text.

The first problems can be used as in-class, oral exercises.

Even-numbered problems in Sets A and B are similar to the preceding odd-numbered problems.

Translating between verbal phrases and variable expressions is a constant theme throughout the text.

The last problems of every **Problem Set A** are review problems.

Calculator problems are located in C-level **Problem Sets**. Thus every student can be assigned some C problems (assuming, of course, access to calculators).

Xtending the topic

Several sections in each chapter are followed by sections called **Xtending the topic**. These sections, which extend ideas or provide related material, are not necessary to the development of skills and concepts through the chapter. They can be used to increase the content coverage for individuals or groups of students. Brighter students especially can study these sections independently.

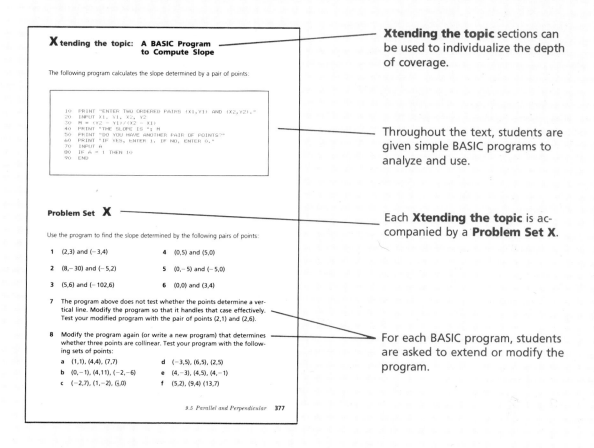

X tending the topic: **A BASIC Program to Compute Slope**

The following program calculates the slope determined by a pair of points:

```
10  PRINT "ENTER TWO ORDERED PAIRS (X1,Y1) AND (X2,Y2)."
20  INPUT X1, Y1, X2, Y2
30  M = (Y2 - Y1)/(X2 - X1)
40  PRINT "THE SLOPE IS "; M
50  PRINT "DO YOU HAVE ANOTHER PAIR OF POINTS?"
60  PRINT "IF YES, ENTER 1. IF NO, ENTER 0."
70  INPUT A
80  IF A = 1 THEN 10
90  END
```

Problem Set X

Use the program to find the slope determined by the following pairs of points:

1 (2,3) and (−3,4)   4 (0,5) and (5,0)

2 (8,−30) and (−5,2)   5 (0,−5) and (−5,0)

3 (5,6) and (−102,6)   6 (0,0) and (3,4)

7 The program above does not test whether the points determine a vertical line. Modify the program so that it handles that case effectively. Test your modified program with the pair of points (2,1) and (2,6).

8 Modify the program again (or write a new program) that determines whether three points are collinear. Test your program with the following sets of points:
   a (1,1), (4,4), (7,7)   d (−3,5), (6,5), (2,5)
   b (0,−1), (4,11), (−2,−6)   e (4,−3), (4,5), (4,−1)
   c (−2,7), (1,−2), (½,0)   f (5,2), (9,4) (13,7)

9.5 Parallel and Perpendicular **377**

Xtending the topic sections can be used to individualize the depth of coverage.

Throughout the text, students are given simple BASIC programs to analyze and use.

Each **Xtending the topic** is accompanied by a **Problem Set X**.

For each BASIC program, students are asked to extend or modify the program.

Chapter Study Guide

Each chapter includes a **Chapter Study Guide**, which is a summary of the vocabulary and skills of the chapter. Definitions are restated, with examples. Skills are presented in **Sample Problem** format.

The **Chapter Study Guide** helps students recapitulate and synthesize the language and skills of the chapter.

The **Vocabulary** section restates each of the definitions in the chapter.

In addition to review, **Chapter Study Guides** can be used as a statement of objectives to introduce the chapter.

Examples are provided along with each definition.

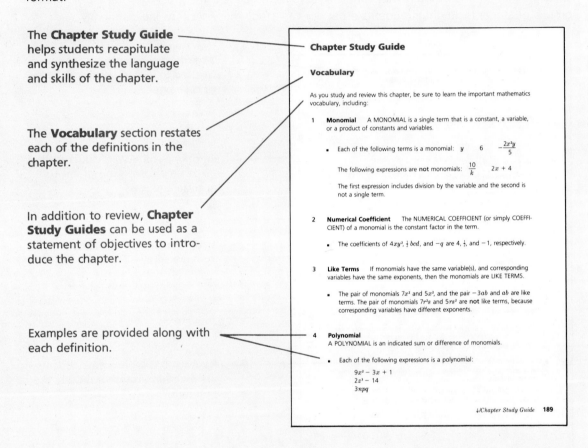

Chapter Study Guide

Vocabulary

As you study and review this chapter, be sure to learn the important mathematics vocabulary, including:

1 **Monomial**   A MONOMIAL is a single term that is a constant, a variable, or a product of constants and variables.

  ▪ Each of the following terms is a monomial: y 6 $-\dfrac{2x^2y}{5}$

    The following expressions are **not** monomials: $\dfrac{10}{k}$ $2x + 4$

    The first expression includes division by the variable and the second is not a single term.

2 **Numerical Coefficient**   The NUMERICAL COEFFICIENT (or simply COEFFICIENT) of a monomial is the constant factor in the term.

  ▪ The coefficients of $4xy^2$, $\frac{1}{2}bcd$, and $-q$ are 4, $\frac{1}{2}$, and -1, respectively.

3 **Like Terms**   If monomials have the same variable(s), and corresponding variables have the same exponents, then the monomials are LIKE TERMS.

  ▪ The pair of monomials $7x^2$ and $5x^2$, and the pair $-3ab$ and ab are like terms. The pair of monomials $7r^2s$ and $5rs^2$ are **not** like terms, because corresponding variables have different exponents.

4 **Polynomial**
    A POLYNOMIAL is an indicated sum or difference of monomials.

  ▪ Each of the following expressions is a polynomial:

    $9x^2 - 3x + 1$
    $2z^3 - 14$
    $3npq$

4/Chapter Study Guide **189**

The **Skills** section highlights each of the techniques in the chapter.

Skills are reviewed in **Sample Problem** format.

Skills

Be sure you build the useful algebraic skills, including:

5   Multiplying monomials   Find the product $(5x^2)(-3x^4)$.

PROCEDURE
Multiply the coefficients and then determine the exponent for the variable:

$$(5x^2)(-3x^4)$$
$$(5)(-3)(x^2)(x^4)$$
$$(-15)(x \cdot x)(x \cdot x \cdot x \cdot x)$$
$$-15x^6$$

6   Using the Distributive Property
Explain how to perform the following:
a   subtract: $4t - 9t$
b   remove the parentheses in $7z(z^2 + 5)$

PROCEDURE   The Distributive Property states that the following pairs of expressions have the same value:

$$ab - ac \qquad\qquad a(b + c)$$
$$a(b - c) \qquad\qquad ab + ac$$

a $4t - 9t$ b $7z(z^2 + 5)$
   $t(4 - 9)$ $(7z)(z^2) + (7z)(5)$
   $t(-5)$ $7z^3 + 35z$
   $-5t$

7   Adding or subtracting polynomials
Find the difference: $(5y^2 + 3y - 2) - (8y^2 - 6y + 1)$

PROCEDURE   Rewrite the subtraction problem as an addition problem, distribute to remove the parentheses, and then combine the like terms:

$$(5y^2 + 3y - 2) - (8y^2 - 6y + 1)$$
$$(1)[5y^2 + 3y + (-2)] + (-1)[8y^2 + (-6y) + 1]$$
$$(1)(5y^2) + (1)(3y) + (1)(-2) + (-1)(8y^2) + (-1)(-6y) + (-1)(1)$$
$$5y^2 + 3y - 2 - 8y^2 + 6y - 1$$
$$5y^2 - 8y^2 + 3y + 6y - 2 - 1$$
$$-3y^2 + 9y - 3$$

8   Finding the Greatest Common Factor   Find the GCF of $8x^2y^3$ and $12xy^5$

PROCEDURE
For the coefficients 8 and 12, the GCF is 4.
For the factors x^2 and x, the GCF is x.
For the factors y^3 and y^5, the GCF is y^3.
Therefore the GCF of $8x^2y^3$ and $12xy^5$ is $4xy^3$.

9   Solving equations containing parentheses
Solve for p and check: $7(p - 6) = 5p - 12$

PROCEDURE

	$7(p - 6) = 5p - 12$	*To check* $7(p - 6) = 5p - 12$
distribute:	$7p - 42 = 5p - 12$	$7(15 - 6) \overset{?}{=} 5(15) - 12$
ADD $-5p$:	$2p - 42 = -12$	$7(9) \overset{?}{=} 75 - 12$
ADD 42:	$2p = 30$	$63 \overset{?}{=} 63$ ✓
MULTBY $\frac{1}{2}$:	$p = 15$	

Math History: Descartes and Fermat

In the seventeenth century, two French amateur mathematicians, René Descartes and Pierre de Fermat, independently developed coordinate geometry. Fermat was first, and was also more modern and thorough, but his work was not published until after his death. Consequently, the coordinate system was named the Cartesian plane, after Descartes.

   Descartes thought of himself as a scientist and philosopher, but he enjoyed solving problems in geometry. In the process of solving such problems, he used a coordinate system as a tool. When Descartes published his major work on the scientific method, he illustrated the method with three appendices at the back of the book. One appendix showed techniques for applying the ideas of algebra to solve problems of geometry. These techniques developed into the branch of mathematics called coordinate geometry.

Math History provides interesting material about mathematicians whose work greatly affected the content of first-year algebra.

Additional Features

A **Chapter Test** follows each chapter, and a **Cumulative Review Problem Set** follows chapters 3, 7, 10, 12, and 14. The student text provides answers to the odd-numbered problems on tests and cumulative reviews so that students can assess their skills.

Chapters without cumulative reviews are followed by **Problem Sets** that apply the concepts of the chapter. No answers are provided in the student text for these nine **Problem Sets**, which can be used for classwork, additional assignments, or extra credit projects.

Chapter Test

Replace each __?__ with <, >, or =.

1. 4 __?__ -2 4. -5 __?__ 0 7. -8 __?__ $8 \cdot \left(-\frac{1}{4}\right)$

2. -3 __?__ -6 5. -8.1 __?__ -8.2 8. -6 __?__ $(3)(-2)$

3. $\frac{3}{4}$ __?__ $-\frac{1}{2}$ 6. $\frac{10}{3}$ __?__ $3\frac{1}{3}$ 9. $\frac{9}{10}$ __?__ $\frac{10}{11}$

Translate each inequality into words.

10. $10 \geq -3$ 12. $-3 < x < 2$ 14. $-5 < x \leq 2$

11. $-9 < 4$ 13. $0 \leq x \leq 1$ 15. $-5 \leq x < 2$

Graph each inequality on a number line.

16. $x \geq 1$ 19. $x \leq -4 \ or \ x = 2$

17. $y < -2$ 20. $x \leq -4 \ or \ x \geq 2$

18. $z \leq 0$ 21. $x \geq -4 \ and \ x \leq 2$

Solve for each variable.

22. $3x > -18$ 25. $3y + 5 \geq y - 7$

23. $(x + 12) \div 2 < 7$ 26. $2(-y + 3) \leq (y - 4)$

24. $-\frac{1}{2}x + 12 < 7$ 27. $y - 1 \leq 3y + 1 \leq 7 + y$

28. Ron has at most three dollars to spend for lunch. If he buys a milkshake for seventy cents and fries for fifty-five cents, how many eighty-cent hamburgers can he buy?

29. Rona walks her dog two or three times each day, and each walk lasts between fifteen and twenty-five minutes. Write a compound inequality that represents the time Rona spends each day walking her dog.

230   *5/Chapter Test*

About half the problems in the **Chapter Test** are at the level of **Problem Set A**.

In addition to reviewing the order of operations, this end-of-chapter **Problem Set** reviews order symbols and computation.

Problem Set: The Order of Operations

The order for performing operations in mathematics is: parentheses, exponentiation, multiplication and division (left to right), and addition and subtraction (left to right). Fill in each blank with <, =, or >.

1. $-8 + 9 \cdot 10 \div 5$ __?__ 10 11. $(-8 + 9 \cdot 10) \div 5$ __?__ 16

2. $-(8 + 9 \cdot 10 \div 5)$ __?__ -20 12. $(-8 + 9) \cdot 10 \div 5$ __?__ 2

3. $3 \cdot 12 \div 6 - 10 + 2$ __?__ 0 13. $3 \cdot (12 \div 6 - 10) + 2$ __?__ -18

4. $3 \cdot (12 \div 6) - 10 + 2$ __?__ -2 14. $3 \cdot 12 \div (6 - 10) + 2$ __?__ 10

5. $4 - 7^2 + 5 \cdot 8 - 24$ __?__ -15 15. $4 - 7^2 + 5 \cdot (8 - 24)$ __?__ -30

6. $(4 - 7)^2 + 5 \cdot (8 - 24)$ __?__ 89 16. $((4 - 7)^2 + 5) \cdot 8 - 24$ __?__ 100

7. $15 \div 3 \cdot 8 - 5 + 7 \cdot 2$ __?__ 45 17. $15 \div 3 \cdot (8 - 5) + 7 \cdot 2$ __?__ 25

8. $15 \div 3 \cdot (8 - 5 + 7) \cdot 2$ __?__ 75 18. $15 \div (3 \cdot 8) - (5 + 7) \cdot 2$ __?__ -24

9. $15 - 10 + 3^2 \cdot 14 \div 7$ __?__ 33 19. $(15 - 10 + 3)^2 \cdot 14 \div 7$ __?__ 128

10. $(15 - 10 + 3^2 \cdot 14) \div 7$ __?__ 15 20. $15 - (10 + 3)^2 \cdot 14 \div 7$ __?__ 210

In problems 21–26, $a = 7$ and $b = -3$. Evaluate each expression.

21. $3a - (6 \div 2) + b$ 24. $(b - 9) \div (a + 2b)$

22. $(3a - 6) \div 2 + b$ 25. $(b - (9 \div a)) + 2b$

23. $3a - 6 \div (2 + b)$ 26. $b - (9 \div (a + 2b))$

Use parentheses and operation symbols to express the given number. (Problem 27 is done.)

27. Use 1, 2, 8, 12, 20; make 4   29. Use 4, 8, 10, 19; make 17.

   ■ $1 + 2 + (20 - 12) \div 8 = 4$ 30. Use 3, 5, 10, 12, 16; make 14.

28. Use 6, 9, 10, 18, 20; make 8.   31. Use 2, 7, 9, 16, 19; make 2.

Order of Operations   **231**

T10

Each chapter contains features for independent use by students.

- Each **Project** asks students to answer specific questions, and often leads students through a series of more open-ended questions.

- Each **After-School Mathematics** shows students using mathematics in their after-school activities. The Teacher's Edition contains suggestions for investigating the mathematics involved in these activities.

- Using a detail of the chapter-opening photograph as a point of departure, each **Application** asks students to use algebraic ideas.

A brief exposition allows students to work independently on the **Project**.

Students read about their peers in **After-School Mathematics** activities.

After-School Mathematics: Bakery Assistant

Vivian has an after-school job at a bakery. Several afternoons each week she helps close the store by putting away breads, cakes, and cookies and by cleaning the glass shelves. On Saturday mornings she helps out in the back room.

One Saturday, she was given the job of decorating a birthday cake. She was to put twenty-one yellow frosting roses around the circumference of the cake. The problem was to space them evenly along the circumference.

She solved the problem in this way. She knew that twenty-one was divisible by three, so she put three roses equally spaced around the circumference. She then had eighteen remaining roses to place between those already on the cake, or six roses in each of the three sections. For each section, she carefully noted the point that divided that section in half, and put three roses into that half. When she finished the cake, she counted the roses twice to be sure!

Application: License Plates

License plates in state A have two letters followed by four numbers. To determine the number of different license plates that can be made, consider the number of choices for each position on the plates:

$$\left(\substack{26\\\text{choices}}\right) \cdot \left(\substack{26\\\text{choices}}\right) \cdot \left(\substack{10\\\text{choices}}\right) \cdot \left(\substack{10\\\text{choices}}\right) \cdot \left(\substack{10\\\text{choices}}\right) \cdot \left(\substack{10\\\text{choices}}\right)$$

There are 6,760,000 or 6.76×10^6 different license numbers.

License numbers in state B have three letters followed by three numbers, but no letter can be used more than once. License numbers in state C are three letters followed by three numbers, but no number can be used more than once. Which of the three states has the greatest number of different license plate numbers? Which state has the least number?

499

Project: Patterns and Guesses

Trace a few paths through the word **MATHEMATICS**.
a Start at any **M** along the main diagonal.
b Move down or right to **A**.
c Move down or right to **T**.
d Continue moving down or right, letter by letter, until you finish at the lower right corner with **S**.

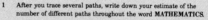

1   After you trace several paths, write down your estimate of the number of different paths throughout the word **MATHEMATICS**.

2   Explain how you made your estimate. (For example, did you count the number of **M**'s in the diagonal, then the number of **A**'s, etc.?)

Often in mathematics (and in many problem situations) you can find a solution to a "large" problem by looking at similar problems that are "small." Consider paths through **TU**, **TRE**, and **FORE**:

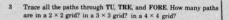

3   Trace all the paths through **TU**, **TRE**, and **FORE**. How many paths are in a 2 × 2 grid? in a 3 × 3 grid? in a 4 × 4 grid?

4   Do your answers to problem 3 suggest a pattern? Make a prediction for the number of paths in a 5 × 5 grid, and then test your guess. Then make another prediction for **MATHEMATICS**. How does this prediction compare with your answer to problem 1?

5   How many squares are there in a 10 × 10 grid?

6   There are 19 circles. Write the numbers 1–19 in the circles so that any three numbers in a row will have the same sum.

118

Students are expected to solve "small" problems, and look for patterns that can answer "large" problems.

Applications utilize a detail of the chapter-opening photograph.

Special Features of the Teacher's Edition

The extra-wide margins of the **Teacher's Edition** provide articulation between parts of the text and commentary on the material. The commentary is clearly differentiated from the student material.

The margins also contain conveniently-located information on how to adjust the text for Basic, Average, and Advanced courses. For each section, **Section Schedules** and **Assignment Guides** recommend how to use **Xtending the topic** sections and how to adjust homework assignments.

The **Chapter Schedule** summarizes the time-scheduling recommendations for the chapter.

Section Schedules recommend the number of days for each section.

TE notes provide a conversation with the teacher about students and the text.

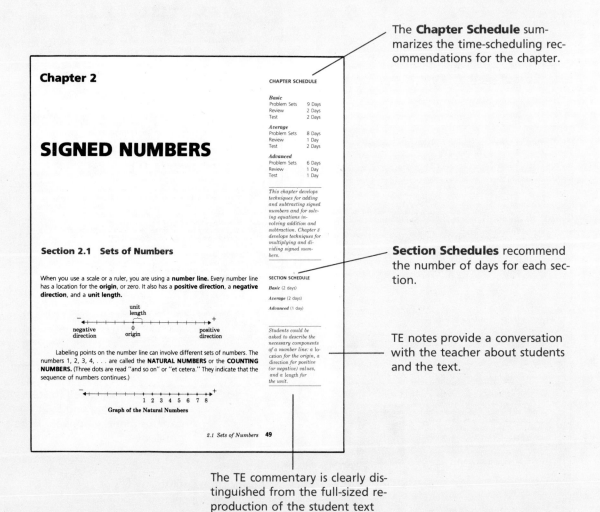

The TE commentary is clearly distinguished from the full-sized reproduction of the student text pages.

Accompanying each section's **Problem Set** and each **Chapter Study Guide** is an **Assignment Guide**. When several days are recommended in the **Section Schedule**, a separate assignment is recommended for each of those days.

All answers are provided in the body of the Teacher's Edition. (Answers to odd-numbered problems are supplied on pages 610–631 of the student text and Teacher's Edition.) The Teacher's Edition also provides complete solutions, where needed, for the B and C problems.

Assignments are suggested for each of the days recommended in the **Section Schedule**.

The TE points out the regular use of the review problems to preview the subsequent sections.

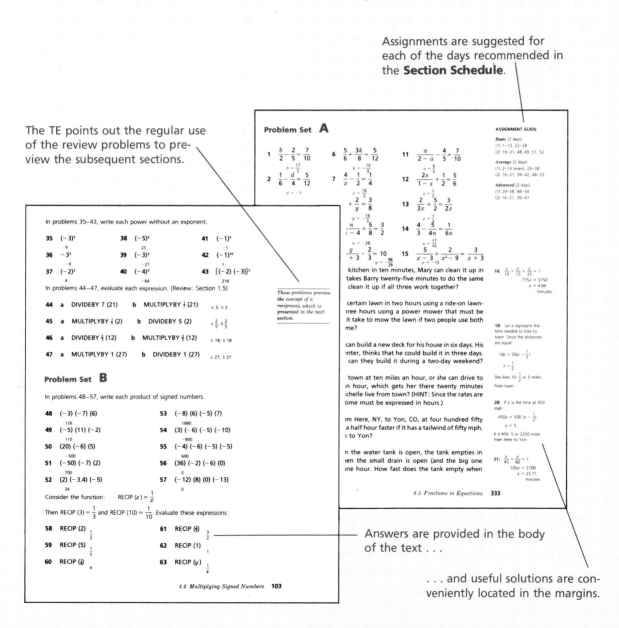

Answers are provided in the body of the text . . .

. . . and useful solutions are conveniently located in the margins.

T13

Time-Scheduling Recommendations

Recommendations for Reviewing and Testing

CHAPTER SCHEDULE	
Basic	
Problem Sets	9 Days
Review	2 Days
Test	2 Days
Average	
Problem Sets	8 Days
Review	1 Day
Test	2 Days
Advanced	
Problem Sets	6 Days
Review	1 Day
Test	1 Day

The time-scheduling information in the **Chapter Schedules** allows two days' review for Basic courses and one day for Average and Advanced courses. Many students in Basic courses need more than one day to fully recapitulate and synthesize the language and skills of a chapter.

The **Chapter Schedules** include two days for midyear and for end-of-year cumulative reviews and one day for other cumulative reviews. The text assumes that Basic courses will have midyear and end-of-year reviews after chapters 6 and 12, respectively. For Average courses, the reviews are expected to be after chapters 7 and 13; for Advanced courses, after chapters 8 and 14.

The **Chapter Schedules** allow two days for testing in Basic and Average courses. These recommendations are to accommodate teachers who use a class period to have students analyze, discuss, and correct their errors.

Summary of Chapter Schedule Recommendations

Chapter	Basic Course	Average Course	Advanced Course
1	12 days	10 days	9 days
2	13	11	8
3	16	14	14
4	16	13	12
5	10	10	11
6	16	12	11
7	12	14	11
8	12	11	11
9	17	14	14
10	12	13	12
11	16	13	13
12	13	17	17
13	4 (optional)	16	15
14	3 (optional)	3 (optional)	13
TOTALS:	**165**	**168**	**171**
	7 (optional)	**3** (optional)	

The Cover of the Text

The following compound inequality represents the solid **A** on the cover:

$(y \leq 2x + 2)$ and $(y \leq -3x + 18)$ and $(-10 \leq y \leq 6)$
and $[(y \geq 2x - 2)$ or $(y \geq -3 + 8)$ or $(-6 \leq y \leq -4)]$

In addition, the graphed rays are:

$$y = -6, x \leq \frac{14}{3}$$

$$y = -10, x \geq 6$$

$$y = -3x + 8, x \leq 6$$

$$y = -3x + 18, x \geq 4$$

Students with access to computer graphics programs could use these equations and inequalities to print out a replica of the cover. For capable students, the project could include generating the equations and inequalities from the information on the cover.

ALGEBRA 1

The Language and Skills of Algebra

Teacher's Edition

ALGEBRA 1

The Language and Skills of Algebra

By

Bryan H. Bunch
Teacher and writer, Briarcliff Manor, New York

Delphine Dupee
Formerly, New Trier High School, Winnetka, Illinois

Laird Marshall
University of Wisconsin, Madison, Wisconsin

J. Peter Westergard
Evanston Township High School, Evanston, Illinois

McDougal, Littell & Company
Evanston, Illinois
New York   Sacramento

ALGEBRA 1

The Language and Skills of Algebra

By

Bryan H. Bunch
Teacher and writer   Briarcliff Manor, New York

Delphine Dupee
(Formerly) New Trier High School   Winnetka, Illinois

Laird Marshall
University of Wisconsin   Madison, Wisconsin

J. Peter Westergard
Evanston Township High School   Evanston, Illinois

McDougal, Littell & Company

Evanston, Illinois
New York   Sacramento

Consultants

Siegfried Baum   Venice High School
Venice, California

David Joshpe   Venice High School
Venice, California

Bob McFarland   Alameda County Schools
Hayward, California

Michael Pomerantz   Mathematics Department Chairperson, Venice High School
Venice, California

Susan Porter   Evanston Township High School
Evanston, Illinois

Phillip Rambikur   Johnston High School
Austin, Texas

JoAnn Rebollar   Mathematics Department Chairperson, Winnebago High School
Winnebago, Illinois

ISBN: 0-88343-911-5   TE ISBN: 0-88343-912-3

Copyright © 1983 by McDougal, Littell & Company
Box 1667, Evanston, Illinois 60204

CONTENTS

Chapter 1

VARIABLES

CHAPTER SCHEDULE

Basic
Problem Sets   8 Days
Review   2 Days
Test   2 Days

Average
Problem Sets   7 Days
Review   1 Day
Test   2 Days

Advanced
Problem Sets   7 Days
Review   1 Day
Test   1 Day

The introduction to this Teacher's Edition (p. T14) describes the philosophy behind scheduling 2 days for review in Basic courses and 2 days for testing in Basic and Average courses.

Section 1.1   Mystery Numbers

SECTION SCHEDULE

Basic (1 day)

Average (1 day)

Advanced ($\frac{1}{2}$ day)

What number goes in the blank?

> 1, 3, 5, __?__, 9, 11

Most people quickly tell what is missing, but it can look like a mystery number at first. With the blank filled in, the list is a **sequence** of numbers.

Advanced courses can cover Sections 1.1 and 1.2 in one day.

Definition

A SEQUENCE is a list of numbers in a particular order. There is usually a pattern or rule to get from one number to the next.

The emphasis of this chapter is translating between verbal and algebraic expressions. Most students should find the initial material fairly easy.

EXAMPLE

- 1, 3, 5, 7, 9, 11 is a sequence. The rule may be written as "add 2 to the previous number."

Often in algebra you will see a "mystery number," which is a number that is unknown until you can find its value. In algebra, the symbol that takes the place of a mystery number can be almost anything, like __?__, $\square$, x, or A. However, letters are used more often than other symbols.

Throughout the text, definitions are always followed by one or more examples.

1   In each sequence, see if you can tell the mystery number before you look at the clue. (Cover the **clues** and **mystery numbers** with your hand, and then check to see if you are correct.)

sequence	clue	mystery number
0, 5, 10, __?__, 20, 25	ADD 5	15
3, 6, 12, □, 48, 96	MULTIPLYBY 2	24
128, 64, 32, __?__, 8, 4	DIVIDEBY 2	16
20, 17, 14, y, 8, 5	SUBTRACT 3	11

2   What is the fourth **term** (fourth number) in the sequence where the first term is 38 and the clue is SUBTRACT 6?

PROCEDURE

The sequence is 38, 32, 26, 20, 14, and so on. The fourth term is 20.

3   What is the first term of the sequence where the clue is ADD 4 and the fourth term is 30?

PROCEDURE   The sequence is __?__, __?__, __?__, 30.
Work backwards: the term before 30 must be 26. Before 26 must be 22 and before 22 is 18. So the sequence is 18, 22, 26, 30, and the first term is 18.

4   Find the mystery number in these sequences (these sequences are more difficult). Cover the **clues** and **mystery numbers**, and use them to check your answers.

sequence	clue	mystery number
1, 2, 4, 7, 11, x, 22, 29	ADD 1; ADD 2; ADD 3; . . .	16
2, 3, 5, 9, 17, □, 65, 129	MULTIPLYBY 2 and SUBTRACT 1; . . .	33
8, 4, 12, 6, w, 9, 27	DIVIDEBY 2; MULTIPLYBY 3; DIVIDEBY 2; MULTIPLYBY 3; . . .	18

Problem Set **A**

ASSIGNMENT GUIDE

Basic (1 day)
1–6, 8, 9, 12, 13, 19–22

Average (1 day)
8, 9, 12, 13, 23–32

Advanced ($\frac{1}{2}$ day)
See p. 7.

In problems 1–6, fill in the blanks.

1 The numbers 1, 4, 7, 10, 13 form a(n) ____?____ of five terms. The clue is ____?____ __?__ .

sequence, ADD 3

2 In the sequence 15, 12, 9, 6, the clue is ____?____ __?__ . The next term after 6 is __?__ .

SUBTRACT 3, 3

3 State the clue and the mystery number for the following sequence:

   3, 7, 11, 15, __?__ , 23, 27

ADD 4, 19

4 State the clue and the mystery number for the following sequence:

   51, 44, 37, x, 23, 16

SUBTRACT 7, 30

5 What is the fourth term in the sequence where the first term is 8 and the clue is ADD 4?

20

6 What is the first term in the sequence where the third term is 24 and the clue is MULTIPLYBY 2?

6

Find the clue and the mystery number for each sequence.

7 10, 16, 22, 28, x, 40, 46
ADD 6, 34

8 6, 11, 16, 21, y, 31, 36
ADD 5, 26

9 39, 32, 25, 18, A, 4
SUBTRACT 7, 11

10 65, 54, 43, B, 21, 10
SUBTRACT 11, 32

11 $\frac{1}{4}, \frac{1}{2}$, 1, 2, r, 8
MULTIPLYBY 2, 4

12 $\frac{1}{8}, \frac{1}{2}$, 2, 8, s, 128
MULTIPLYBY 4, 32

13 162, 54, 18, p, 2
DIVIDEBY 3, 6

14 216, 36, 6, q, $\frac{1}{6}, \frac{1}{36}$
DIVIDEBY 6, 1

Find each sum or difference. (Review: Addition and subtraction of decimals)

15 1.47 + 2.81
4.28

16 6.04 + 1.97
8.01

17 6.28 − 3.59
2.69

18 8.05 − 4.44
3.61

19 3.17 + 3.17 + 3.17
9.51

20 5.61 + 5.61 + 5.61
16.83

21 7.83 − 2.16 + 3.42
9.09

22 2.58 + 3.14 − 1.69
4.03

Throughout the text, the first few problems can be used as in-class oral exercises.

Answers to odd-numbered problems are given in the back of the student text (pp. 610–631). Some algebra students may need guidance in learning to use text-supplied answers to check their work rather than to replace their work!

The last few problems in every Problem Set A provide a review of previous material. The first sections of the text review numerical computation.

Problem Set B

Write the first six terms of each sequence, given the clue and the fifth term.

	clue	5th term		clue	5th term
23	ADD 6	31	**27**	SUBTRACT $2\frac{1}{2}$	11
	7, 13, 19, 25, 31, 37			21, $18\frac{1}{2}$, 16, $13\frac{1}{2}$, 11, $8\frac{1}{2}$	
24	ADD 9	38	**28**	SUBTRACT $3\frac{1}{2}$	6
	2, 11, 20, 29, 38, 47			20, $16\frac{1}{2}$, 13, $9\frac{1}{2}$, 6, $2\frac{1}{2}$	
25	MULTIPLYBY 3	324	**29**	DIVIDEBY 10	0.017
	4, 12, 36, 108, 324, 972			170, 17, 1.7, 0.17, 0.017, 0.0017	
26	MULTIPLYBY 4	64	**30**	DIVIDEBY 100	0.0002
	$\frac{1}{4}$, 1, 4, 16, 64, 256			20,000, 200, 2, 0.02, 0.0002, 0.000002	

Find the clue and the missing terms of each sequence.

31 1, 8, 14, 19, __?__ , __?__ , 28

ADD 7, ADD 6, ADD 5, . . . ; 23, 26

32 4, 5, 7, 8, 10, __?__ , __?__ , 14

ADD 1, ADD 2, ADD 1, ADD 2, . . . ; 11, 13

Problem Set C

33 Find the clue and the mystery number for the sequence:

$\frac{1}{4}$, $\frac{1}{2}$, $1\frac{1}{2}$, 6, a, 180, 1260   MULTIPLYBY 2, MULTIPLYBY 3, MULTIPLYBY 4, . . . ; $a = 30$

34 The fifth term of a sequence is 31 and the clue is **MULTIPLYBY 2 and ADD 1**. Write the first 6 terms of the sequence. 1, 3, 7, 15, 31, 63

35 The fifth term of a sequence is 9 and the clue is **DIVIDEBY 2; ADD 4**. What is the first term? 12

36 Here is a sequence: 3, 5, 11, 29, __?__ , 245, 731. Find the clue, and use that same clue to make up a sequence of five terms that starts with:

MULTIPLYBY 3 and SUBTRACT 4; missing term is 83

a 4   **b** 2

4, 8, 20, 56, 164   2, 2, 2, 2, 2

37 For the sequence 3, 4, 6, 10, y, 34, 66, find the clue and use it to write five terms of a sequence that starts with $3\frac{1}{2}$.

ADD 1, ADD 2, ADD 4, . . . ; $y = 18$; $3\frac{1}{2}$, $4\frac{1}{2}$, $6\frac{1}{2}$, $10\frac{1}{2}$, $18\frac{1}{2}$

38 For the sequence 80, 48, 32, 24, 20, 18, find the clue and use it to write five terms of a sequence that starts with 16.

SUBTRACT 32, SUBTRACT 16, SUBTRACT 8, . . . ; 16, −16, −32, −40, −44

Section 1.2   Using Letters to Represent Numbers

SECTION SCHEDULE

Basic (1 day)

Average (1 day)

Advanced ($\frac{1}{2}$ day)

An object on the moon weighs approximately one sixth of what it weighs on Earth.

The C problems in this section introduce students to evaluating formulas.

- A medium sized apple of 180 grams would weigh 30 grams on the moon; that is about the weight of a strawberry.

- A 180-kilogram gorilla would weigh 30 kilograms on the moon; that is about the weight of a large dog.

You can use algebraic symbols to express the weight of an object on the moon. ("Algebraic" is a form of the word "algebra.") If w represents the weight of the object on Earth, then $w \div 6$ represents its weight on the moon.

A certain rocket will fire for 4 seconds after the switch is turned off.

- If the switch is on for 7 seconds, the rocket fires for 11 seconds.

- A pilot who wants the rocket to fire for 6 seconds must turn the switch on for only 2 seconds.

In algebraic symbols, if the switch is on for s seconds, the rocket will fire for $s + 4$ seconds.

In the expressions $w \div 6$ and $s + 4$,   the letters w and s were used to represent numbers. Such letters are called **variables**, and the expressions $w \div 6$ and $s + 4$ are called **variable expressions.**

Definition

A VARIABLE is a symbol that may be replaced by any number or numbers from a specified set of numbers.

The specified set of numbers is frequently called the "replacement set" for the variable.

EXAMPLE

- If a fashion model weighs 48 kilograms on Earth, the variable expression $w \div 6$ can be used to calculate the model's weight on the moon. Replace the variable w by 48, which is called the **value** of the variable.

$$w \div 6$$
$$48 \div 6$$
$$8$$

On the moon, the model's scale would read "8 kilograms." This procedure of replacing a variable by its value and calculating the result is called **evaluating an expression.**

The following two expressions have the same meaning:

$$w \div 6 \qquad w \times \tfrac{1}{6}$$

The multiplication symbol, $\times$, can be confused with the letter x. A raised dot is often used to indicate multiplication.

$\tfrac{1}{6} \times w$	becomes	$\tfrac{1}{6} \cdot w$
10×2	becomes	$10 \cdot 2$
$a \times b$	becomes	$a \cdot b$
$4 \times (n + 8)$	becomes	$4 \cdot (n + 8)$

The raised dot was made popular late in the 17th century by the German mathematician and philosopher Gottfried Wilheim von Leibnitz.

Sample Problems

1   These three expressions follow a pattern: $2 \cdot 13$ $2 \cdot 8$ $2 \cdot 150$

Use a variable to describe the pattern.

PROCEDURE   The first number in each expression is 2, but the second number changes, or varies. The general pattern is **two multiplied by a variable**. In algebra, the pattern can be written as $2 \cdot n$. In this problem, the variable n can be replaced by the numbers 13, 8, or 150.

The order of operations is treated in Section 3.4.

2   If the value of n is 5, evaluate the expression $3 \cdot n + 2$.

PROCEDURE

$$3 \cdot n + 2$$
$$3 \cdot 5 + 2$$
$$15 + 2$$
$$17$$

Note that in $3 \cdot 5 + 2$, the multiplication was done before the addition.

3 Evaluate the variable expression $a \cdot b - 2 \cdot b$, if the value of a is 3 and the value of b is 6.

PROCEDURE

$$a \cdot b - 2 \cdot b = 3 \cdot 6 - 2 \cdot 6 \quad \text{(replace } a \text{ by 3 and } b \text{ by 6)}$$
$$= 18 - 12$$
$$= 6$$

Note that the multiplications $3 \cdot 6$ and $2 \cdot 6$ were performed before the subtraction.

Problem Set **A**

ASSIGNMENT GUIDE

Basic (1 day)
1–10, 15–22, 36–39

Average (1 day)
23–35, 40, 42, 44, 46

Advanced ($\frac{1}{2}$ day)

23–38, 48–52
4: 24, 26, 33–35

1 In an algebraic expression such as $5 \times c$, the letter is called a(n) __?__ .

variable

2 The number that the variable stands for is called the __?__ of the variable.

value

3 In a variable expression, instead of using $\times$ as a multiplication symbol, use a(n) __?__ . raised dot

4 Use a variable to describe the general pattern found in the three expressions:
$$3 \cdot 9 \qquad 3 \cdot 22 \qquad 3 \cdot 1$$

$3x$

5 What is the general pattern for:
$$4 + 8 \qquad 22 + 8 \qquad 8 + 8$$

$x + 8$

6 If the value of n is 2, evaluate the expression $8 \cdot n$. 16

The assignment for
Advanced courses is
for Sections 1.1 and
1.2.

Problems 1–6 can be
used as oral exercises.

Rewrite each expression replacing the multiplication symbol with a raised dot.

7 $5 \times k$

$5 \cdot k$

8 $t \times 7$

$t \cdot 7$

9 $8 \times c + 4$

$8 \cdot c + 4$

10 $a + b \times c$

$a + b \cdot c$

11 $q \times q + 9 \times q + 5$

$q \cdot q + 9 \cdot q + 5$

12 $y \times y + 6 \times y + 7$

$y \cdot y + 6 \cdot y + 7$

13 $(3 - n) \times (4 \times n)$

$(3 - n) \cdot (4 \cdot n)$

14 $(5 \times t) \times (t - 2)$

$(5 \cdot t) \cdot (t - 2)$

15 If the value of n is 3, evaluate $12 \cdot n$.

36

16 Evaluate $4 \cdot t$, if $t = 13$.

52

17 Evaluate $9 + x$, if the value of x is 5.6.

14.6

18 If the value of y is $1\frac{1}{2}$, evaluate $y + 4\frac{1}{2}$.

6

19 Let $m = 12$. Evaluate the expression $m - 9.3$.

2.7

20 Let $r = 7$. Evaluate the expression $r - 5.7$.

1.3

21 Evaluate $32 - w$, if $w = 32$.

0

22 Evaluate $y - 14$, if $y = 14$.

0

In problems 23–28, use the values given for r and s to evaluate the expressions $r + s, r - s, r \cdot s$, and $r \div s$. (Review: Computation)

23 $r = 8, s = 2$

10, 6, 16, 4

24 $r = \frac{1}{2}, s = \frac{1}{4}$

$\frac{3}{4}, \frac{1}{4}, \frac{1}{8}, 2$

25 $r = 0.6, s = 0.2$

0.8, 0.4, 0.12, 3

26 $r = 5, s = 5$

26   10, 0, 25, 1

27 $r = 100, s = 10$

27   110, 90, 1000, 10

28 $r = 10, s = 0$

28   10, 10, 0, undefined

Problem Set **B**

29 Evaluate $6 + 2 \cdot x$ when $x = 8$.

22

30 If the value of y is 7, evaluate the expression $9 \cdot y + 2 \cdot y$.

77

31 Evaluate $14 \cdot p - 6 \cdot p$ if the value of p is $\frac{1}{2}$.

4

32 Calculate $a \cdot b$ if $a = 18$ and $b = \frac{5}{6}$.

15

33 Calculate $x \cdot y$ if $x = 20$ and $y = 0.3$.

6.0

34 If $x = 5$ and $y = 8$, evaluate the expression $2 \cdot x - \frac{1}{2} \cdot y$.

6

35 If $x = 4$ and $y = 3$, evaluate the expression $0.3 \cdot x - 0.05 \cdot y$.

1.05

Problem Set C

The equation for the perimeter of a rectangle is $p = 2\ell + 2w$, and the equation for the area of a rectangle is $A = \ell \cdot w$.

Basic and Average
courses should not
omit these problems
on evaluating formu-
las.

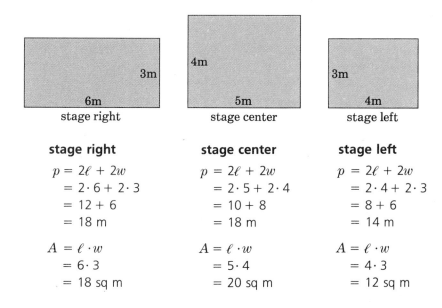

stage right	stage center	stage left
$p = 2\ell + 2w$	$p = 2\ell + 2w$	$p = 2\ell + 2w$
$= 2 \cdot 6 + 2 \cdot 3$	$= 2 \cdot 5 + 2 \cdot 4$	$= 2 \cdot 4 + 2 \cdot 3$
$= 12 + 6$	$= 10 + 8$	$= 8 + 6$
$= 18$ m	$= 18$ m	$= 14$ m
$A = \ell \cdot w$	$A = \ell \cdot w$	$A = \ell \cdot w$
$= 6 \cdot 3$	$= 5 \cdot 4$	$= 4 \cdot 3$
$= 18$ sq m	$= 20$ sq m	$= 12$ sq m

The equations $p = 2\ell + 2w$ and $A = \ell \cdot w$ are called **formulas**. A formula uses variables to state a rule among numbers and measurements. There is at least one variable on each side of a formula.

To show multiplication of two numbers, such as $2 \cdot 6$, the raised dot is used so that the expression will not be confused with the number 26. To show multiplication of two variables, or to show a number multiplied by a variable, the raised dot is not necessary.

36 Use the formula $p = 4s$ (the perimeter of a square) and find the value of p when $s = 7$ feet.　　　$p = 28$ feet

37 Use the formula $p = 3s$ (the perimeter of an equilateral triangle) and the value of p when $s = 12$ cm.　　　$p = 36$ cm

38 Using the formula $E = IR$ (voltage equals current times resistance), find the value of E when $I = 2$ and $R = 4$.　　$E = 8$

39 Use $d = rt$ (uniform motion), and find the distance d in miles when $r = 55$ miles per hour and $t = 6$ hours.　　$d = 330$ miles

Students would not
need to memorize any
of the formulas that
are unfamiliar to
them. The formulas
are intended only as a
device for substituting
values and evaluating
expressions. It may be
helpful, however, to
explain the meaning
of unfamiliar formu-
las.

For problems 40 and 41, use the formula $A = \frac{1}{2}bh$ (the area of a triangle) and find the value of A when:

40 $b = 4, h = 15$

$A = 30$ square units

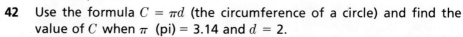

41 $b = 9, h = 6$

$A = 27$ square units

42 Use the formula $C = \pi d$ (the circumference of a circle) and find the value of C when π (pi) = 3.14 and $d = 2$.

$C = 6.28$

43 Use the formula $C = 2\pi r$ (the circumference of a circle) and find the value of C when $\pi = 3.14$ and $r = 100$.

$C = 628$

44 Use the formula $\ell = a + 5d$ (an arithmetic progression) and find the value of ℓ when $a = 4$ and $d = 13$.

$\ell = 69$

45 Use the formula $\ell = a + 7d$ and find the value of ℓ when $a = 13$ and $d = 4$.

$\ell = 41$

In problems 46 and 47, use the formula $A = \frac{1}{2}hB + \frac{1}{2}hb$ (the area of a trapezoid) and find the value of A when:

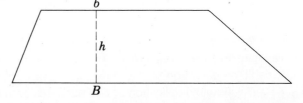

46 $h = 12, B = 9, b = 3$

$A = 72$ square units

47 $h = 5, B = 30, b = 12$

$A = 105$ square units

48 Use the formula $i = prt$ and find the value of i when $p = 30000, r = \frac{7}{100},$ and $t = 20$.

$i = 42{,}000$

49 Use the formula $V = e \cdot e \cdot e$ (the volume of a cube) and find the value of V when $e = 2$.

$V = 8$ cubic units

In problems 50–55, use the formula $S = 2 \cdot \pi \cdot r \cdot r + 2 \cdot \pi \cdot r \cdot h$ (the total surface area of a can) to find the value of S when:

50 $\pi = 3\frac{1}{7}, r = 7, h = 12$

$S = 836$

51 $\pi = 3.14, r = 6, h = 2\frac{1}{2}$

$S = 320.28$

52 $\pi = 3.14, r = 6.25, h = 15$

$S = 834.0625$

53 $\pi = 3\frac{1}{7}, r = 20, h = 21$

$S = 5154\frac{2}{7}$

54 $\pi = 3\frac{1}{7}, r = 4, h = 35$

$S = 980\frac{4}{7}$

55 $\pi = 3.14, r = 1, h = 1$

$S = 12.56$

Project: (Super) Market Research

Which would you buy: soft drinks in cans or soft drinks in returnable bottles? Each has advantages and disadvantages. Cans can be carried easily and cooled quickly, but they should be recycled, not simply thrown away. Bottles are usually less expensive (assuming you collect your deposit), but they are heavier than cans and they can break.

1   What is your immediate opinion: Which is worth more to you, convenience with cans or savings with bottles?

2   Select a particular soft drink that is available in both cans and returnable bottles (in the same size). What is the cost of each? (Do not use a special "sale" price.)

3   Suppose Benito drinks one can or bottle each day, Bonnie drinks twelve cans or bottles each week, and Jessie drinks a case (twenty-four) of cans or bottles each month. How much would each person save per month with the lower-priced container? How much would each save per year?

4   Do you get about the same results for problem 3 for different types of soft drinks?

5   What would you answer if your friends ask you, "Should we buy soft drinks in cans or in bottles?"

6   Soft drinks (and many other products) are available in many different-sized containers. In recent years the label "economy size" has often been replaced with a label such as "family size." Might this mean that the largest package is not the most economical? Can you find specific items in a supermarket for which the larger size does not have the lowest unit price?

7   Compare the cost of a standard refrigerator to one that fits under a counter. Why is the small one more expensive?

8   Problem 1 asked whether cost or convenience was worth more to you. It is easy to measure cost, but how would you try to measure "convenience"?

3) Answers may vary. Benito drinks 31 per month, 365 per year. Bonnie drinks about 54 per month, 624 per year. Jessie drinks 24 per month, 288 per year.

8) "Measures" of convenience could consider the amount of time or energy saved, the number of features only available with the "convenient" item, etc.

Section 1.3 Translating Between English and Algebra

Algebra can help solve puzzles and problems. This section introduces how to translate between **verbal expressions** and **variable expressions.**

Two more than a number can be written as $n + 2$. The expressions **the sum of a number and two** and **two added to a number** can also be written as $n + 2$. Many different verbal phrases can be translated to the same variable expression.

EXAMPLES

in words	in symbols
■ a number plus nine the sum of a number and nine add nine to a number nine more than a number a number increased by nine	$m + 9$
■ a number minus seven the difference between a number and seven subtract seven from a number seven fewer than a number a number decreased by seven	$n - 7$

In translating to algebra, the order of symbols is usually important. The phrase **a number minus seven** is represented $n - 7$. The phrase **seven minus a number** is $7 - n$. The two expressions, $n - 7$ and $7 - n$, do not have the same value (unless $n = 7$). The order of symbols does not affect value for addition; the expressions $n + 9$ and $9 + n$ will always have the same value.

in words	in symbols
■ two times a number the product of two and a number multiply two and a number twice as much as a number double a number	$2p$
■ a number divided by three the quotient of a number and three one third of a number	$\dfrac{q}{3}$

In division, the order of the symbols is important, because $q \div 3$ does not have the same value as $3 \div q$ except when $q = 3$. Some verbal translations for $3 \div q$ are **three divided by a number** and **the quotient of three and a number**.

When the operation is multiplication, such as for the variable expressions $2 \cdot p$ and $p \cdot 2$, the two expressions will always have the same value.

Sample Problems

1   Indicate all the correct answers. **Six more than a number** can be translated as:

a $x - 6$ c $A + 6$ e $6 + G$
b $x + 6$ d $t \cdot 6$ f $6 + 6$

PROCEDURE   Check each choice separately:

a $x - 6$ No   "More than" is represented by addition ($+$), not by subtraction ($-$).

b $x + 6$ Yes

c $A + 6$ Yes   The letter used doesn't matter.

d $t \cdot 6$ No   The raised dot indicates multiplication, not addition.

e $6 + G$ Yes   The sum of two numbers is the same regardless of their order.

f $6 + 6$ No   The words **a number** must be represented by a variable.

2   Translate into algebra: **twice as much as Q**.

PROCEDURE   The words can be translated as $2Q$ or $2 \cdot Q$. You could also write $Q \cdot 2$ since $2 \cdot Q$ and $Q \cdot 2$ will always have the same value.

3   Which of the following has an algebraic translation that is different from the others?
a   three fewer than a particular number
b   pick a number and decrease it by 3
c   a number with 3 subtracted from it
d   a number fewer than 3

PROCEDURE   Choices **a**, **b**, and **c** can all be translated to $x - 3$, but choice **d** should be translated $3 - x$.

ASSIGNMENT GUIDE

Basic (2 days)
(1) 1–20
(2) 21, 22, 25–27, 35–37
    19: 1–5

Average (1 day)
21, 22, 25–37, 41–47

Advanced (1 day)
21, 22, 30–37, 41–43,
50–58

*Assignments are sug-
gested for each of the
days recommended in
the section schedule.*

*As oral exercises, stu-
dents could translate
all four algebraic ex-
pressions in problems
1–15.*

Problem Set A

Indicate which choices are correct algebraic translations. (There may be more than one correct answer for each problem.)

1 Seven added to a number
    a $7 + y$ **b** $7 - y$ **c** $7 \cdot y$ **d** $y + 7$
      a,d

2 Four times a number
    a $4n$ **b** $4 + n$ **c** $4 \cdot n$ **d** $n \cdot 4$
      a,c,d

3 One third of a number
    a $\frac{1}{3} + x$ **b** $\frac{1}{3} \div x$ **c** $\frac{1}{3}x$ **d** $\frac{x}{3}$
      c,d

4 A number minus eleven
    a $11 - a$ **b** $a - 11$ **c** $a + 11$ **d** $a \div 11$
      b

5 A number plus itself
    a $N + N$ **b** $N - N$ **c** $2N$ **d** $N \cdot N$
      a,c

6 A number increased by five
    a $p + 5$ **b** $5 + p$ **c** $5p$ **d** $p \cdot 5$
      a,b

7 A number divided by 3
    a $\frac{3}{Q}$ **b** $3 \div Q$ **c** $\frac{Q}{3}$ **d** $\frac{1}{3}Q$
      c,d

8 Twice as much as B
    a $2 \cdot B$ **b** $B + 2$ **c** $B \cdot 2$ **d** $2B$
      a,c,d

9 The sum of one half and a number
    a $\frac{1}{2}x$ **b** $\frac{1}{2} + x$ **c** $x + \frac{1}{2}$ **d** $x \cdot \frac{1}{2}$
      b,c

10 The quotient of a number and 2
    a $N + 2$ **b** $N \div 2$ **c** $2 \div N$ **d** $\frac{N}{2}$
      b,d

11 Three times as much as a number
    a $3 - D$ **b** $3 \cdot D$ **c** $3 + D$ **d** $3D$
      b,d

12 A number decreased by nine

    a $t - 9$ **b** $t \div 9$ **c** $9 - t$ **d** $9 + t$

       a

13 Four fewer than a number

    a $4 - y$ **b** $y - 4$ **c** $4 + y$ **d** $y + 4$

       b

14 Twenty more than a number

    a $20 + n$ **b** $20 - n$ **c** $20n$ **d** $n + 20$

       a,b

15 Half of a number

    a $\frac{1}{2} + r$ **b** $\frac{1}{2}r$ **c** $\frac{1}{2} - r$ **d** $\dfrac{r}{2}$

       b,d

Indicate which choices are correct verbal translations.

16 $x + 7$

    a seven more than a number   **d** a number increased by 7

    b the product of a number   **e** seven times a number

       and 7

    c seven added to a number   *a,c,d*

17 $\dfrac{Q}{2}$

    a 2 divided by a number   **d** half as much as a number

    b half of a number   **e** the quotient of 2 and

    c a number divided by 2   a number

                         b,c,d

18 $3n$

    a a number plus 3   **d** 3 more than a number

    b a number times 3   **e** the product of a number and 3

    c triple a number   *b,c,e*

19 $8 + q$

    a a number increased by 8   **d** 8 increased by a number

    b 8 more than a number   **e** a number added to 8

    c the sum of 8 and a number   *all*

20 $y - 1$

    a a number decreased by 1   **d** 1 fewer than a number

    b a number subtracted from 1 **e** the difference between

    c the difference between   a number and 1

       1 and a number   *a,d,e*

In problems 21–22, the three expressions follow a pattern. Use the variable x to describe the pattern. (Review: Section 1.2)

21 $15 - 6$ $15 - 2$ $15 - 14$ $\quad _{15 - n}$

22 $22 \cdot \dfrac{3}{4} - 5$ $22 \cdot \dfrac{21}{5} - 5$ $22 \cdot \dfrac{14}{3} - 5$ $\quad _{22n - 5}$

In problems 23–24, find the value of p in the formula $p = 2\ell + 2w$. (Review: Section 1.2)

23 $\ell = 6.4$ and $w = 2.3$ $\quad _{p\ =\ 17.4\ units}$

24 $\ell = 16\frac{1}{2}$ and $w = 5\frac{1}{4}$ $\quad _{p\ =\ 43\frac{1}{2}\ units}$

Problem Set **B**

Translate to a variable expression:

25 some number n, minus eight
$\quad _{n\ -\ 8}$

26 one fourth of some number x
$\quad _{\frac{1}{4}x,\ \frac{x}{4}}$

27 eleven added to a number k
$\quad _{11\ +\ k}$

28 twice as much as P
$\quad _{2P}$

29 three subtracted from a number J
$\quad _{J\ -\ 3}$

30 four more than L
$\quad _{4\ +\ L}$

31 half of B
$\quad _{\frac{B}{2}}$

32 5 fewer than x
$\quad _{x\ -\ 5}$

33 the product of x and 5
$\quad _{x \cdot 5,\ 5x}$

34 the quotient of x and 5
$\quad _{\frac{x}{5}}$

Translate to a verbal expression:

35–40) answers will vary

35 $x + 5$

36 $\dfrac{y}{6}$

37 $4N$

38 $W - 2$

39 $\dfrac{6}{y}$

40 $2 - W$

In each problem, which phrase has an algebraic translation that is different from the others?

41 **a** four fewer than a certain number
     b a number minus 4
     c pick a number and take away 4
     d four minus a number
     e the difference between a number and 4
          d

42 **a** six times a number
     b the sum of a number and six
     c pick a number and add six
     d six added to a certain number
     e a number plus six
          a

43 **a** think of a number and then take half of it
     b some number divided by $\frac{1}{2}$
     c half of a number
     d a number divided by 2
     e the quotient of a number and 2
          b

PUZZLE   The Martian words for the numbers 1–9 are:

1	2	3	4	5	6	7	8	9
bip	dub	tri	qot	funf	shil	bek	nunk	crun

The arithmetic operations are: +   −   ×   ÷
                           hup   den   milt   ver

The phrase **a number** is translated as **blz**.

Translate these Martian phrases into our own algebraic symbols:

44 blz hup dub
       $n + 2$

45 blz den funf
       $n - 5$

46 nunk hup qot
       $8 + 4$

47 bek hup bip den tri
       $7 + 1 - 3$

48 blz milt shil
       $x \cdot 6$

49 qot ver blz
       $4 \div y$

50 tri milt blz den bek
       $3 \cdot n - 7$

51 crun den funf milt blz
       $9 - 5x$

52 blz ver shil hup dub milt blz
       $n \div 6 + 2 \cdot n$

53 bek milt blz den qot milt blz
       $7m - 4m$

54 blz milt blz ver dub hup tri
     milt blz den nunk
       $m \cdot m \div 2 + 3 \cdot m - 8$

Problem Set C

Translate from words to symbols.

55 five more than four times a number

$5 + 4n$

56 the sum of seven and twice the product of six and a number

$7 + 2 \cdot 6w$

57 three times a number decreased by the quotient of the number and four

$3n - \dfrac{n}{4}$

58 the total number of square centimeters in the surface area of a cube that has an edge of e centimeters

$A = 6e \cdot e$

X tending the topic: The Commutative Property

For every value of the variable a, the expressions $a + 9$ and $9 + a$ have the same value. The expressions $a - 9$ and $9 - a$ do **not** have the same value (except if $a = 9$).

Similarly, $a \cdot 9 = 9 \cdot a$, but $a \div 9 \neq 9 \div a$ (except if $a = 9$). These are examples of the **Commutative Property of Addition** and the **Commutative Property of Multiplication**.

Properties

If a and b are any numbers, the **COMMUTATIVE PROPERTY OF ADDITION** is that the following two expressions have the same value:

$a + b$

$b + a$

If a and b are any numbers, the **COMMUTATIVE PROPERTY OF MULTIPLICATION** is that the following two expressions have the same value:

$a \cdot b$

$b \cdot a$

The two properties are usually written as equations:

$a + b = b + a$

$a \cdot b = b \cdot a$

EXAMPLES

- Examples of the Commutative properties are "obvious" statements such as $4 + 7 = 7 + 4$ or $3 \cdot x = x \cdot 3$. It is often more important to be aware of situations that are not commutative:

$$x - y \neq y - \text{x} \qquad \text{(except if } x = y\text{)}$$

$$\frac{x}{y} \neq \frac{y}{x} \qquad \text{(except if } x = y \text{ and neither equals zero)}$$

Problem Set X

Write a commutated form of each expression. Then state whether that commutated form must have the same value as the original form.

1 $14 + 7y$

    $y \cdot 7 + 14$, yes

2 $a \cdot b$

    $b \cdot a$, yes

3 $17 - 12x$

    $x \cdot 12 - 17$, no

4 $9 \div t$

    $t \div 9$, no

5 $(a + b) + (b + c)$

    $(c + b) + (a + a)$, yes

6 $(x - y) + (r - s)$

    $(s - r) + (y - x)$, no

7 $a \cdot (b + c)$

    $(c + b) \cdot a$, yes

8 $\dfrac{r}{s} \cdot \dfrac{u}{v}$

    $\frac{v}{u} \cdot \frac{s}{r}$, no

9 $a \cdot b + c$

    $c + b \cdot a$, yes

Section 1.4   Building Variable Expressions

An important skill in algebra is translating words into symbols. This section gives more practice.

Sample Problems

1 Translate into algebra:
Name a variable and double it. Then subtract 5.

PROCEDURE

Name a variable: n
Double it: $2n$
Then subtract 5: $2n - 5$

This section involves expressions that combine at least two operations.

2   Translate into words: $5y - 8$

   PROCEDURE   Start with the phrase **Name a variable**:
   Name a variable, multiply it by 5, and then subtract 8.

3   Name a variable and add 28. The result is 35. What number did you start with?

   PROCEDURE

   Draw a simple diagram:

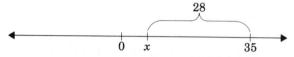

   The value of x must be 7 because $7 + 28 = 35$.

Problem Set **A**

Translate into algebra: **Name a variable. Then:**

1   multiply it by 2, and subtract 7
   $2x - 7$

2   divide it by 3, then add 5
   $\frac{n}{3} + 5$

3   add 6, then add 5 more
   $n + 6 + 5$

4   double it, and subtract 9
   $2x - 9$

5   find the quotient of it and 5, and then add 6
   $\frac{n}{5} + 6$

6   multiply it by 7 and add the variable
   $7x + x$

7   add it to 16
   $x + 16$

8   add it to itself
   $x + x$

9   add 17, then subtract 10
   $x + 17 - 10$

10   take half of it and subtract 6
   $\frac{1}{2}x - 6$

11   multiply it by $\frac{1}{3}$, and add that to the original variable
   $\frac{1}{3}x + x$

12   triple it, then subtract 1
   $3x - 1$

Write each variable expression in words. Start each description with the phrase **Name a variable:**

13–14)   Answers may vary

13 $b + 7$

14 $\frac{c}{8}$

15 $2y - 3$

16 $3x + 15$

17 $\frac{1}{2}A + 2$

18 $\frac{1}{3}w - 1$

19 $b + 2b$

20 $3r - \frac{1}{2}r$

15-20) Answers may vary.

In problems 21–26, what is the value of the variable?

21 Name a variable and double it. The result is 16.
Hint: double the value of the variable is 16.
    8

22 Name a variable and divide it by 3. The result is 9.
    27

23 Name a variable and add 51. The result is 81.
    30

24 Name a variable and add 108. The result is 321.
    213

25 The result is 16 when you name a variable and subtract 5.
    21

26 The result is 41 when you name a variable and subtract 19.
    60

Use the variable to evaluate each expression. (Review: Section 1.2)

27 If $y = 0$ then $y + 17 = $ __?__
    17

28 If $a = 7$ then $32 - a = $ __?__
    25

29 If $x = \frac{1}{4}$ then $6x = $ __?__
    $\frac{3}{2}$

30 If $z = 203$ then $\frac{z}{7} = $ __?__
    29

31 If $w = 17$, $2w + 5 = $ __?__
    39

32 If $x = 15$, $3x - 12 = $ __?__
    33

33 If $r = 2$, $2r + 3r - 1 = $ __?__
    9

34 If $q = 10$, $8q + 5 - 2q = $ __?__
    65

Problem Set **B**

Write each variable expression in words. Start each description with the phrase
Name a variable:

35 $8z + 13 - 4$

36 $11a - a + 9$

37 $y \cdot y - y$

38 $g + \dfrac{1}{g}$

35-38) Answers may vary.

1.4 Building Variable Expressions **21**

In problems 39–44, what number did you start with?

	Name a variable and:	The final result is:
39	add $3\frac{3}{8}$	$6\frac{1}{4}$
		$2\frac{7}{8}$
40	divide by 5	90.2
		451.0
41	multiply it by 12	10.8
		0.9
42	double it; then add 9	63
		27
43	subtract 19; then triple the result	15
		24
44	add it to 7; then take half; then add 19	28
		11

Problem Set C

What number did you start with?

45) One informal method could be to use successive guesses:

Try 10:
2(10+23) + 14 = 2(33) + 14
                    = 66 + 14
                    = 80
Too low.

Try 20:
2(20+23) + 14 = 2(43) + 14
                    = 86 + 14
                    = 100
Too high.

Try 17:
2(17+23) + 14 = 2(40) + 14
                    = 80 + 14
                    = 94

	Name a variable and:	The final result is:
45	take twice the sum of it and 23; and then add 14	94
		17
46	add it to itself; then add 11 and quadruple the result	68
		3
47	add three times the sum of it and 9 to four times the difference of 19 and the variable; then double the result	212
		−3
48	add five times the sum of 3 and double the variable to the product of 6 and the sum of 8 and triple the variable	147
		3
49	subtract the product of three and the sum of a variable and seven from the product of four times the same variable and the number five	41
		42

Xtending the topic: **The Associative Property of Multiplication**

Use the formula $i = prt$ and compute the value of i for $p = 4000$, $r = \frac{1}{10}$, and $t = 2$:

$$i = p \cdot r \cdot t$$
$$= (4000 \cdot \tfrac{1}{10})\, 2$$
$$= 400 \cdot 2$$
$$= 800$$

The calculation could have been performed in a different order, first multiplying r and t:

$$i = p \cdot r \cdot t$$
$$= 4000\,(\tfrac{1}{10} \cdot 2)$$
$$= 4000 \cdot \tfrac{1}{5}$$
$$= 800$$

The final result is the same whether the product $p \cdot r$ is calculated first or whether the product $r \cdot t$ is calculated first. This is an example of the **Associative Property of Multiplication**.

Property

If a, b, and c are any three numbers, then the ASSOCIATIVE PROPERTY OF MULTIPLICATION is that the following two algebraic expressions have the same value:

$$(a \cdot b) \cdot c$$

$$a \cdot (b \cdot c)$$

This property is usually written as an equation:

$$(a \cdot b) \cdot c = a \cdot (b \cdot c)$$

EXAMPLE

- The parentheses indicate which pairs of numbers to "associate." Consider the product $25 \cdot 4 \cdot 7$:

$$(25 \cdot 4) \cdot 7 = 100 \cdot 7 = 700$$
$$25 \cdot (4 \cdot 7) = 25 \cdot 28 = 700$$

Both products are 700, but the first association, $(25 \cdot 4) \cdot 7$, is probably easier to calculate.

Problem Set X

Rewrite each product using parentheses so that the calculation is most simple.

1 $4 \cdot \frac{1}{4} \cdot 7$
$(4 \cdot \frac{1}{4}) \cdot 7 = 1 \cdot 7$

2 $5 \cdot 20 \cdot 17$
$(5 \cdot 20) \cdot 17 = 100 \cdot 17$

3 $14 \cdot 5 \cdot 2$
$14 \cdot (5 \cdot 2) = 14 \cdot 10$

4 $3\frac{1}{2} \cdot 2 \cdot 8$
$(3\frac{1}{2} \cdot 2) \cdot 8 = 7 \cdot 8$

5 $\frac{1}{9} \cdot \frac{1}{6} \cdot 6$
$\frac{1}{9} \cdot (\frac{1}{6} \cdot 6) = \frac{1}{9} \cdot 1$

6 $\frac{1}{4} \cdot 40 \cdot 9$
$(\frac{1}{4} \cdot 40) \cdot 9 = 10 \cdot 9$

7 $3.2 \cdot 10 \cdot \frac{1}{2}$
$(3.2 \cdot 10)\frac{1}{2} = 32 \cdot \frac{1}{2}$

8 $\frac{1}{2} \cdot \frac{1}{4} \cdot \frac{1}{5}$
same either way

9 $1.71523 \cdot 2.51432 \cdot 0$
$1.71523 \cdot (2.51432 \cdot 0) = 1.71523$

SECTION SCHEDULE

Basic (1 day)

Average (1 day)

Advanced (1 day)

While the material in this section is simple, it will probably be novel to all of the students. The "computer talk" will be used throughout the text (in abbreviated form) to describe the steps of solving equations.

Section 1.5 Computer Talk

Some computer programs contain symbols like the following:

```
ABS(C)          SIN(X+2)
EXP(B-3)        COS(T)
```

These are ways to give directions to a computer. The variable expressions inside the parentheses stand for numbers, and the letters outside the parentheses tell the computer what to do with those numbers. This section introduces expressions that look like "computer talk." These expressions will be used throughout this book; familiar words will be used at first.

The expressions will be written in capital letters and are called **functions**.

Definition

A FUNCTION is a rule involving numbers and variables. The rule is applied to one number or variable and results in a single value.

EXAMPLES

- A function can be pictured by a "function machine."

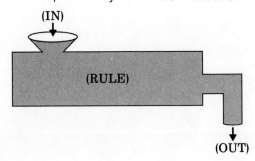

If the rule is ADD 3, and the number 28 is put in the machine, 31 comes out.

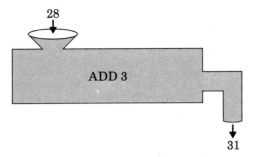

The "computer talk" expression for this machine is ADD 3 (28), which means "start with the number 28 and add 3 to it." The result is 31.

■ The machine for the function SUBTRACT 5 (12) would look like:

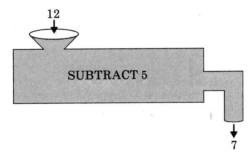

Start with the number 12 (the number inside the parentheses). Apply the rule SUBTRACT 5 to the number 12. The result is 7.

Sample Problems

1 Find the number represented by each function.

PROCEDURE

a DIVIDEBY 6 (24)　　a Start with 24, divide it by 6. The result is 4.

b TRIPLE (11)　　b Start with 11, triple it (multiply 11 by 3). The result is 33.

c SUBTRACT 7 (15)　　c Start with 15, subtract 7. The final value is 8.

d SQUARE (5)　　d Start with 5, square it (multiply 5 by itself). The final value is 25.

Some students may need additional emphasis that they "start with" the expression within the parentheses and then perform the capitalized instruction.

2 Write the variable expression represented by MULTIPLYBY 3 (a).

PROCEDURE MULTIPLYBY 3 (a) means start with a, multiply it by 3, to get $a \cdot 3$. It is usual to write this as $3a$, without the dot. In general, when a variable is multiplied by a number, write the number before the variable.

3 Translate the variable expression $y - 2$ into "computer talk."

PROCEDURE The verbal expression for $y - 2$ is **subtract 2 from a number**. Therefore the rule is SUBTRACT 2, and the number to start with is the variable y. In "computer talk," the function is SUBTRACT 2 (y).

ASSIGNMENT GUIDE

Basic (1 day)
2–38 (even), 39, 40

Average (1 day)
8–26 (even), 35, 37,
43–48, 51–54

Advanced (1 day)
19–22, 47–62

Problem Set A

Find the number represented by each function.

1	ADD 4 (6) 10	**7**	SQUARE (8) 64	**13**	DOUBLE (10) 20
2	ADD 6 (1) 7	**8**	SQUARE (12) 144	**14**	DOUBLE (4) 8
3	MULTIPLYBY 9 (3) 27	**9**	SUBTRACT 5 (12) 7	**15**	TRIPLE (5) 15
4	MULTIPLYBY 1 (19) 19	**10**	SUBTRACT 7 (7) 0	**16**	TRIPLE (1) 3
5	DIVIDEBY 4 (20) 5	**11**	HALF (6) 3	**17**	TWICE (14) 28
6	DIVIDEBY 5 (35) 7	**12**	HALF (5) $2\frac{1}{2}$ or $\frac{5}{2}$	**18**	TWICE (9) 18

Write the variable expression for each computer function.

19	MULTIPLYBY 6 (x) $6x$	**23**	DIVIDEBY 2 (x) $\frac{x}{2}$	**27**	SUBTRACT 11 (k) $k - 11$
20	SUBTRACT 2 (A) $A - 2$	**24**	HALF (X) $\frac{1}{2}X$	**28**	ADD 6 (n) $n + 6$
21	MULTIPLYBY 3 (p) $3p$	**25**	DOUBLE (x) $2x$	**29**	TWICE (Y) $2Y$
22	TRIPLE (y) $3y$	**26**	ADD 4 (N) $4 + N$	**30**	DIVIDEBY 4 (A) $\frac{A}{4}$

Write each verbal phrase as a variable expression. (Review: Section 1.4)

31 a number increased by 8
$$n + 8$$

35 12 decreased by a number
$$12 - n$$

32 a number divided by 3
$$\frac{n}{3}$$

36 5 divided by a number
$$\frac{5}{n}$$

33 twice as much as a number r
$$2r$$

37 q times as much as 7
$$7q$$

34 6 fewer than a number
$$n - 6$$

38 a number fewer than 15
$$15 - N$$

Problem Set **B**

Write each expression as "computer talk."

39 $x + 3$
ADD 3 (x)

43 $c - 11$
SUBTRACT 11 (c)

40 $y - 6$
SUBTRACT 6 (y)

44 $y + 9$
ADD 9 (y)

41 $x \cdot 4$
MULTIPLYBY 4 (x)

45 $\dfrac{b}{2}$
DIVIDEBY 2 (b) or HALF (b)

42 $\dfrac{y}{7}$
DIVIDEBY 7 (y)

46 $2x$
MULTIPLYBY 2 (x) or DOUBLE (x)

In problems 47–50, write each verbal phrase as a variable expression, and then write it as a computer function.

47 a number increased by 12
$n + 12$, ADD 12 (n)

49 double a number n
$2n$, DOUBLE (n)

48 the difference between a number and 8
$n - 8$, SUBTRACT 8 (n)

50 a number divided by 57
$\frac{n}{57}$, DIVIDEBY 57 (n)

Find the value of each variable.

51 ADD 2 $(M) = 9$
Hint: What number plus 2 gives 9?
$$M = 4\tfrac{1}{2}$$

53 TWICE $(P) = 6$
$$P = 3$$

52 SUBTRACT 5 $(Q) = 13$
$$Q = 18$$

54 DIVIDEBY 4 $(N) = 2$
$$N = 8$$

Problem Set C

Problems 55–58 involve the important concept that functions which result in the same value are not necessarily the same function.

55 Which of the following functions does not have the same meaning as the other three?

a MULTIPLYBY 2 (15)   **c** ADD 15 (15)

b TWICE (15)   **d** DOUBLE (15)   *c*

PROCEDURE   All four choices give the same result, 30. However, notice what happens if the number inside the parentheses is 10:

a MULTIPLYBY 2 (10) = 20   **c** ADD 15 (10) = 25

b TWICE (10) = 20   **d** DOUBLE (10) = 20

Choices **a**, **b**, and **d** always give the same result, whatever number is inside the parentheses, but choice **c** does not. Thus choice **c** is a different function from the other three.

In problems 56–58, tell which function is different from the other three choices.

56 **a** HALF (12)   **c** SUBTRACT 6 (12)

 b DIVIDEBY 2 (12)   **d** MULTIPLYBY $\frac{1}{2}$ (12)   *c*

57 **a** DOUBLE (2)   **c** TWICE (2)

 b SQUARE (2)   **d** MULTIPLYBY 2 (2)   *b*

58 **a** TRIPLE (4)   **c** MULTIPLYBY 3 (4)

 b DIVIDEBY $\frac{1}{3}$ (4)   **d** ADD 8 (4)   *d*

Find the value of each variable.

59 SUBTRACT 5 (MULTIPLYBY 4 (N)) = 7   Hint: Rewrite the problem as SUBTRACT 5 (_?_) = 7.   What number must go inside the parentheses?
 $N = 3$

60 ADD 7 (DIVIDEBY 3 (T)) = 9
 $T = 6$

61 TWICE (ADD 8 (S)) = 38
 $S = 11$

62 DOUBLE (SUBTRACT Q (12)) = 10
 $Q = 7$

After-School Mathematics: Stock Clerk

Mike works part-time in a grocery store as a clerk. He usually stocks shelves, bags groceries for customers, and gathers shopping carts from the parking lot. Occasionally he sets up special sale displays.

One day the store manager asked Mike to make a pyramid with tunafish cans in the store window. The manager gave Mike six cases of tuna cans, twenty-four cans per case, for a total of one hundred forty-four cans. He then told Mike to figure out how many cans high it would be and to tell him before he built it.

This problem puzzled Mike for a while because he didn't even know how many cans should be in the base of the pyramid. All he knew was that the top of the pyramid should be one can. He pulled out a piece of notebook paper and drew one can. He knew that the layer under it would be two cans; the third layer, three cans; and so on. Mike noticed a pattern: each layer added one can.

Mike tried different numbers of layers:

5 layers high: $1 + 2 + 3 + 4 + 5 = 15$	(too few cans)
10 layers high: $1 + 2 + 3 + \ldots + 9 + 10 = 55$	(still too few cans)
15 layers high: $1 + 2 + \ldots + 14 + 15 = 120$	(getting closer)
16 layers high: $1 + 2 + \ldots + 16 = 136$	(very close)
17 layers high: $1 + 2 + \ldots + 17 = 153$	(too many cans)

Mike gave the manager the answer. The pyramid would be sixteen cans high, and there would be eight cans left over.

Application: Pencil Sharpener

How many new pencils will a pencil sharpener sharpen before the pencil sharpener shavings fill the sharpener? Here are some steps to take to calculate the answer.

   a To find the volume shaved from each pencil, subtract the volume of the sharpened pencil from the volume of a new pencil.

        volume of new pencil: $V = Bh$
        volume of sharpened cone: $V = \frac{1}{3}Bh$

   where B is the area of the base and h is the height.

   b Then find the volume of the pencil sharpener, and divide that by the volume per sharpening.

Some students may generate the formula for the sum of the integers 1 —n:

$$S_n = \frac{n(n+1)}{2}$$

The project on Polygonal Numbers (p. 539) develops this formula through triangular numbers.

a) measurements:

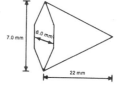

Base area:

$$B = 6(\frac{1}{2}bh)$$

$$= 6(\frac{1}{2})(3.5)(3.0)$$

$$= 31.5 \text{ mm}^2$$

Volume of sharpenings:

$$BH - \frac{1}{3}Bh$$

$$(31.5)(22) - \frac{1}{3}(31.5)(22)$$

$$462 \text{ mm}^3$$

b) Volume of pencil sharpener is Bh:
h is measured: 54 mm
B is approximated from an outline on graph paper (taking into account the "works" inside): 18,650 mm^2
$Bh = (54)(18,650)$
$= 1,007,100 \text{ mm}^3$
$$\frac{1007100}{462} = 2180$$

29

Section 1.6   Data in Graphs

*This section intro-
duces several basic
concepts of statistics.
Problems involving
data and statistics ap-
pear throughout the
text.*

Data is a word that means information. Nearly everybody collects and records, or **compiles**, data. Companies need to keep a record of sales, costs, profits, and supplies. Sports teams keep an inventory of equipment, season tickets, travel expenses, salaries, and team performance.

The word "data" is properly a plural word (the singular is "datum"), but many people will sometimes write "data is" and sometimes "data are."

Five students in Ms. Cataldo's class recorded data on "investments" of $200 each in the stock market. On the last class before their winter vacation, they made a **bar graph** to record their overall profits and losses.

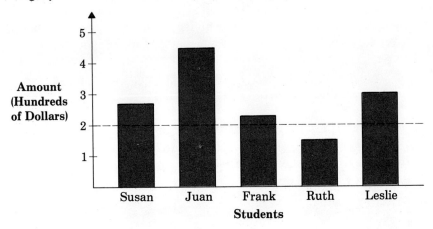

Their graph recorded the following amounts:

Susan	$260	Ruth	$150
Juan	$440	Leslie	$300
Frank	$225		

They added a dashed line at $200 so they could easily compare their own "statements" with their initial "investments."

Susan also used a **line graph** to record her "portfolio" for the last 10 trading days before her vacation. The line graph on the next page shows how the value of her stocks changed from day to day.

There are several vocabulary terms that are necessary for talking about graphed data. These two graphs have two **axes**, the horizontal axis, or **x-axis**, and the vertical axis, or **y-axis**. The ordered pair (0,0), which labels the point where the axes meet, is called the **origin**.

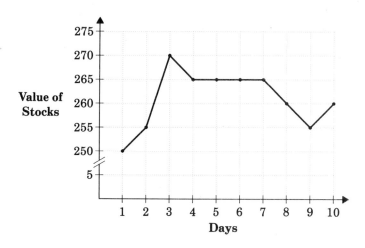

EXAMPLE

- In Susan's line graph, her stocks had their greatest value on day 3, when they were worth $270. The ordered pair for that point of the graph is (3,270).

Notice how Susan drew the vertical axis of her graph. Since there were no points that had a y-value less than 250, she "broke" the y-axis and only labeled values from 250 to 275.

Sample Problems

1   Make a line graph to record the midday temperatures (in degrees Celsius) for the 31 days of October in a New England town.

day	1	2	3	4	5	6	7	8	9	10	11	12	13	14	15
temp	15	16	14	11	7	6	5	6	11	16	19	23	18	14	16

day	16	17	18	19	20	21	22	23	24	25	26	27	28	29	30	31
temp	14	12	11	10	8	8	9	8	7	8	7	5	4	3	8	9

PROCEDURE   The x-axis must be labeled from 1 to 31, and the y-axis must be labeled from 3 to 23. Graph each (day, temperature) ordered pair, and connect the successive points with line segments.

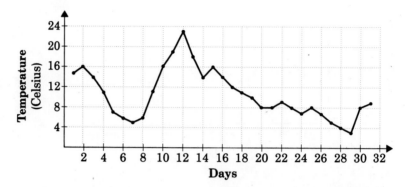

2   This graph shows the relationship between the Celsius and Fahrenheit temperature scales. Use it to find the equivalent temperatures for:

a $20°C$ b $-40°C$ c $50°F$ d $95°F$

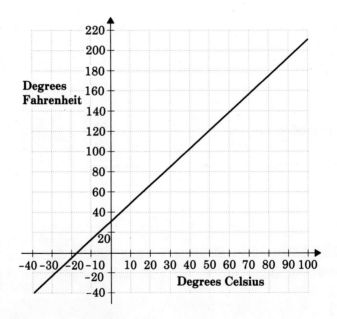

PROCEDURE

a   The graph goes through the point (20,68). Thus $20°C$ and $68°F$ represent the same temperature.

b The graph goes through the point $(-40,-40)$. If a Celsius thermometer reads $-40°$, then a Fahrenheit thermometer would also read $-40°$.

c The point $(10,50)$ is on the graph; thus the equivalent of $50°F$ is $10°C$.

d The point $(35,95)$ is on the graph. Thus $95°F$ and $35°C$ represent the same temperature.

Problem Set **A**

ASSIGNMENT GUIDE

Basic (1 day)
1–20

Average (1 day)
10–17, 20–23

Advanced (2 days)
(1) 11–14, 20–27
(2) 40: 10–24

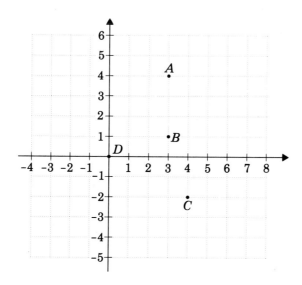

1 For this graph, the horizontal axis is called the __?__ and the vertical axis is called the __?__ .

x-axis, y-axis

2 On the graph, the ordered pair $(3,1)$ is labeled point __?__ and the ordered pair $(3,4)$ is labeled point __?__ .

B, A

3 On the graph, the coordinates of point C are $(\,?\,,\,?\,)$. Point D, which has coordinates $(0,0)$, is called the __?__ .

$(4, -2)$, origin

Use the graph of "Profit and Loss" for stores in the San Francisco Bay area to answer questions 4-9.

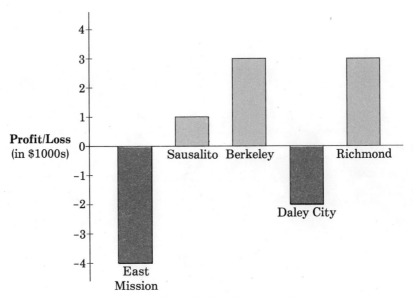

Stores in San Francisco Bay Area

4 Which store(s) lost the most money? What was that loss?

East Mission, $4000

5 Which store(s) made the most money? What was the profit?

Berkeley, Richmond, $3000

6 According to the graph, which store lost about $2,000?

Daley City

7 What was the approximate sum of the profits?

$7000

8 What was the approximate sum of the losses?

$6000

9 What was the overall profit or loss?

profit of $1000

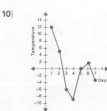

10)

10 The following data give the lowest Fahrenheit temperatures for a town in Michigan during the first week in January. Make a line graph to show these temperatures:

(1,12), (2,5), (3,−6), (4,−9), (5,0), (6,2), (7,−3)

The first member of each pair is the date; the second is the temperature in degrees Fahrenheit.

In a certain rectangle, the width is not changed but the length is increased. This graph shows how the perimeter of the rectangle changes as the length increases from 1 meter to 10 meters.

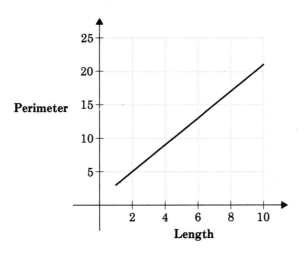

11 When the length is 3, what is the perimeter?
$p = 7m$

12 When the length is 8, what is the perimeter?
$p = 17m$

13 When the perimeter is 11, what is the length?
$\ell = 5m$

14 What is the width of the rectangle?
$w = \frac{1}{2}m$

In problems 15–19, find the value of each variable. (Review: Section 1.4)

Name a variable and:	The final result is:
15 divide it by 9	6
54	
16 add 48	98
50	
17 multiply it by 7	70
10	
18 subtract 3, then double the result	30
18	
19 divide it by 4, then add 13	15
8	

Problem Set **B**

The following data give the height above the ground for a ball thrown from a point 5 feet above the ground at 25 feet per second. The height was measured at intervals of two tenths of a second.

(0,5), (0.2,9.4), (0.4,12.5), (0.6,14.2), (0.8,14.8), (1,14), (1.2,12),

(1.4,8.6), (1.6,4)

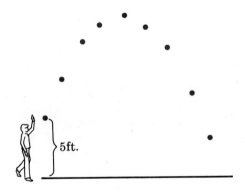

5ft.

20)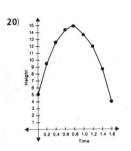

23)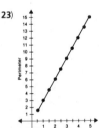

24)

25)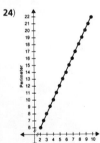

20 Make a line graph for the data.

21 Use the graph to estimate the maximum height reached by the ball. At what time, to the nearest tenth of a second, was that highest point reached?

   14.8 ft., 0.8 sec.

22 Use the graph to estimate how long the ball was in the air (to the nearest tenth of a second).

   1.6 seconds

23 Make a line graph showing how the perimeter changes for an **equilateral** triangle (all sides have the same length) as a side increases from 0.5 centimeters to 5.0 centimeters. (Graph the points at 0.5-centimeter intervals.)

24 Make a graph showing how the perimeter of a rectangle changes if the width remains 1 foot and the length increases, in 0.5-foot intervals, from 2 feet to 10 feet.

25 Make a line graph showing how the perimeter of an **isosceles** triangle changes (two sides have the same length) if the base remains 15 cm and the legs increase, in 2-cm increments, from 8 cm to 20 cm.

Problem Set C

26 The perimeter of a rectangular pen that is attached to the ends of a five-foot wall changes as the sides increase or decrease. (The ends stay five feet long, but the sides can be made longer or shorter.) Make a line graph showing how the perimeter changes with the length of the sides.

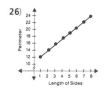

27 Graph the change in the circumference of a circle as the radius goes from 0.1 to 1.0 (use $\pi = 3.14$).

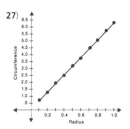

X tending the topic: **Organizing Data**

Data usually need to be organized. Suppose, for example, two fair dice were rolled 50 times. With each roll the total number of dots was counted, and the data were:

5, 7, 10, 2, 3, 5, 8, 6, 7, 11, 9, 4, 8, 10, 6, 7, 9, 5, 6, 3, 12, 8, 11, 4, 8,

7, 6, 7, 9, 4, 5, 7, 10, 9, 8, 7, 5, 9, 6, 7, 8, 7, 9, 6, 8, 5, 7, 6, 4, 8

Notice that all the sums from 2 to 12 are included. A table of the data can be made by listing the sums from 2 to 12 and using **tally marks**.

sum of dots	number of times the sum was rolled
2	I
3	II
4	IIII
5	⊬⊬ I
6	⊬⊬ II
7	⊬⊬ ⊬⊬
8	⊬⊬ III
9	⊬⊬ I
10	III
11	III
12	I

The sum of 10 dots was rolled 3 times, so the **frequency** of 10 is 3. The sum of 7 dots was rolled 10 times out of the 50 rolls, so the **relative frequency** of 7 is ten fiftieths:

$$\frac{10}{50} = \frac{1}{5}$$

Definitions

The number of times an item appears in a set of data is called the FREQUENCY of that item.

The RELATIVE FREQUENCY of an item is the fraction:

$$\frac{\text{the number of times an item appears}}{\text{the total number of data items}}$$

EXAMPLES

In the previous data, the frequency of the sum of 9 dots was 6, and the relative frequency of 9 dots was six fiftieths:

$$\frac{6}{50} = \frac{3}{25}$$

In computer talk, these statements can be written:

- FREQ (9) = 6
- RELFREQ (9) = $\frac{3}{25}$

Sample Problems

1   The Markemup Car Dealer kept track of the weekly sales on a board posted in the manager's office. One week, the board looked like this:

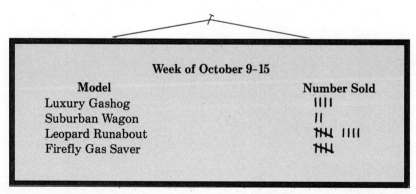

Week of October 9–15	
Model	**Number Sold**
Luxury Gashog	IIII
Suburban Wagon	II
Leopard Runabout	⊤⊢⊬⊣ IIII
Firefly Gas Saver	⊤⊢⊬⊣

a   How many cars were sold at Markemup from October 9–October 15?
PROCEDURE   Count the tally marks. A total of 20 cars was sold.
b   What is FREQ (Firefly Gas Saver)?
PROCEDURE   ⊤⊢⊬⊣ represents 5 cars sold. Thus FREQ (Firefly Gas Saver) = 5.
c   What is RELFREQ (Suburban Wagon)?
PROCEDURE   Two wagons were sold, so RELFREQ (Suburban Wagon) is two twentieths. This can be reduced to one tenth or written as 10%.

2   Here are some data:

  11, 14, 17, 12, 15, 11, 22, 23, 16, 14, 16, 18, 12, 17, 12, 16, 22,
  20, 15, 11, 12, 15, 22, 18

Make a relative frequency chart for the data. (First list the values from largest to smallest. Organize the data using tally marks, then write the frequency and relative frequency of each item.)

PROCEDURE

items	tally marks	frequency	relative frequency
23	|	1	$\frac{1}{24} \approx 4\%$
22	|||	3	$\frac{1}{8} \approx 13\%$
20	|	1	$\frac{1}{24} \approx 4\%$
18	||	2	$\frac{1}{12} \approx 8\%$
17	||	2	$\frac{1}{12} \approx 8\%$
16	|||	3	$\frac{1}{8} \approx 13\%$
15	|||	3	$\frac{1}{8} \approx 13\%$
14	||	2	$\frac{1}{12} \approx 8\%$
12	||||	4	$\frac{1}{6} \approx 17\%$
11	|||	3	$\frac{1}{8} \approx 13\%$

Problem Set X

Count the numbers of letters in these two sentences: *A flying saucer landed on the carrots in the garden. Its blue door opened and a little fat android popped out.*

1   What is FREQ (a)?
    (What is the frequency of the
    letter a ?)

    FREQ (a) = 9

2   What is RELFREQ (a)?

    RELFREQ (a) $= \frac{9}{88} \approx 10\%$

3   What is FREQ (e)?

    FREQ (e) = 10

4   What is RELFREQ (e)?

    RELFREQ (e) $= \frac{10}{88} \approx 11\%$

5   Find FREQ (o).

    FREQ (o) = 8

6   Find RELFREQ (o).

    RELFREQ (o) $= \frac{8}{88} \approx 9\%$

7   Find FREQ (s).

    FREQ (s) = 3

8   Find RELFREQ (s).

    RELFREQ (s) $= \frac{3}{88} \approx 3\%$

9   Find FREQ (k).

    FREQ (k) = 0

The spinner at the right was spun 100 times with the following results:

Color	Number of times the spinner landed there
Blue	ЖЖ III
Red	ЖЖЖЖЖЖ IIII
Green	ЖЖЖ III
Yellow	ЖЖЖ
Black	ЖЖЖ ЖЖ

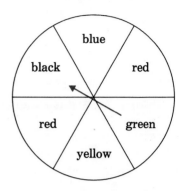

Find the following:

10 FREQ (Blue)

FREQ (Blue) = 13

11 FREQ (Red)

FREQ (Red) = 34

12 FREQ (Black or Yellow)
Hint: Add the frequencies of
black and yellow.

FREQ (Black or Yellow) = 35

13 FREQ (Red or Green)

FREQ (Red or Green) = 52

14 RELFREQ (Blue)

RELFREQ (Blue) = 13%

15 RELFREQ (Green)

RELFREQ (Green) = 18%

16 RELFREQ (Black or Yellow)

RELFREQ (Black or Yellow) = 35%

17 RELFREQ (Red or Green)

RELFREQ (Red or Green) = 52%

18 RELFREQ (Blue, Red, Green,
Yellow, or Black)

RELFREQ (Blue, Red, Green, Yellow or
Black) = 1

19 RELFREQ (not Red)

RELFREQ (not Red) = 66%

20 Is this a fair spinner?
(That means, does the spinner
select colors about the same
way you would expect?)

yes; the spinner lands in each
region about $\frac{1}{6}$ of the time

Roll two dice 144 times. Record the sum of the two dice each time.

21 List the frequency and relative frequency of each sum. (How many
entries will your chart need?)

answers will vary; the chart will need 11 entries (2 through 12)

22 For each sum, list all the ways possible to get that sum. (For example, 8
can be made with a 3 and 5, 5 and 3, 4 and 4, and so on.)

23 Can you explain why some sums have greater frequency than other
sums?

If there are more combinations to produce a sum, then that sum will have a greater frequency

24 What relative frequency would you **expect** for each sum of the two
dice? In 144 rolls, the expected RELFREQ for each sum would be:
2 4 times;   3 8 times;   4 12 times;   5 16 times;
6 20 times;   7 24 times;   8 20 times;   9 16 times;
10 12 times;   11 8 times;   12 4 times

22) 2 1+1   1 way
3 1+2, 2+1   2 ways
4 1+3, 3+1, 2+2   3 ways
5 1+4, 4+1,
2+3, 3+2   4 ways
6 1+5, 5+1,
2+4, 4+2, 3+3   5 ways
7 1+6, 6+1, 2+5,
5+2, 3+4, 4+3   6 ways
8 2+6, 6+2,
3+5, 5+3, 4+4   5 ways
9 3+6, 6+3,
4+5, 5+4   4 ways
10 4+6, 6+4, 5+5   3 ways
11 5+6, 6+5   2 ways
12 6+6   1 way

Chapter Study Guide

Vocabulary

ASSIGNMENT GUIDE

Basic (2 days)
(1) 44: 1–16
(2) 45: 17–30

Average (1 day)
44: 1–30

Advanced (1 day)
44: 1–30

As you study and review this chapter, be sure to learn the important mathematics vocabulary, including:

The Chapter Study Guide provides a summary of the vocabulary and skills of the chapter. The Guide could also be used as a list of objectives to introduce the chapter.

1   **Sequence**   A SEQUENCE is a list of numbers in a particular order. There is usually a pattern or rule to get from one number to the next.

-   3, 6, 9, 12, 15 is a sequence; 1 + 2 + 3 + 4 + 5 is not a sequence (because it represents the single number 15).

2   **Variable**   A VARIABLE is a symbol that may be replaced by any number or numbers from a specified set of numbers.

-   "In w weeks there are $7 \cdot w$ days." In that sentence, the letter w was used as a variable.

3   **Function**   A FUNCTION is a rule involving numbers and variables. The rule is applied to one number or variable and results in a single value.

-   The expression ADD 3 (8) can be interpreted as "start with 8. Add 3 to it." The result is 11.

-   The expression MULTIPLYBY 2 (x) can be interpreted as "start with x. Multiply it by 2." The result is $2x$.

ADD 3 (8) and MULTIPLYBY 2 (x) are used as functions.

Skills

Be sure you build the useful algebraic skills, including:

4   **Using formulas**   Use the distance formula $d = r \cdot t$ and find the value of d when $r = 55$ and $t = 4.2$.

PROCEDURE $d = r \cdot t$
$ = (55)(4.2)$
$ = 231$

5 **Finding a missing term in a sequence**   Find:
  a   the missing term in the sequence 4, 8, 12, x, 20.
  b   the fifth term in a sequence if the first term is 5 and the clue is MULTIPLYBY 3.
  c   the first term in a sequence if the clue is DIVIDEBY 2 and the third term is 5.

PROCEDURE

  a   The clue is ADD 4; the missing term is 16.
  b   The sequence is 5, 15, 45, 135, 405; the fifth term is 405.
  c   The sequence is 20, 10, 5; the first term is 20.

6 **Translating between verbal expressions and variable expressions**
  Translate:
  a   "a number more than 6" to a variable expression
  b   "$6 - q$" to a verbal expression
  c   "7 fewer than a number" to a variable expression
  d   "$\frac{1}{2}S + 3$" to a verbal expression
  e   "Name a variable. Then multiply it by 5. Then increase the result by 14."

PROCEDURE   The translations are:

  a $6 + x$
  b   a number fewer than six; six minus a number; six decreased by a number; etc.
  c $y - 7$
  d   one half of a number, increased by three; three more than one half of a number; etc.
  e $5t + 14$

7 **Evaluating variable expressions**
  Evaluate $6 \cdot x - 2 \cdot y$ if $x = 3$ and $y = 5$.

PROCEDURE

$$6 \cdot x - 2 \cdot y$$
$$6 \cdot 3 - 2 \cdot 5$$
$$18 - 10$$
$$8$$

8 Using "computer talk" expressions

Find the number represented by each expression:

a   ADD 7 (15)
b   SUBTRACT 5 (23)
c   MULTIPLYBY 6 (5)
d   DIVIDEBY 3 (15)

PROCEDURE

a $15 + 7 = 22$
b $23 - 5 = 18$
c $5 \cdot 6 = 30$
d $15 \div 3 = 5$

9 Locating ordered pairs on a graph

Construct a graph for these temperatures from midnight to noon on a mild winter morning:

time	Midnight	1	2	3	4	5	6	7	8	9	10	11	noon
temperature (°C)	5	5	6	4	4	4	5	6	8	10	9	9	8

PROCEDURE   Label the x-axis with the time and the y-axis with the temperature. The origin can represent the ordered pair (midnight, 0°C).

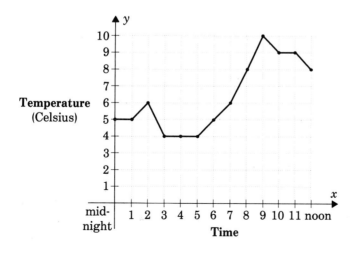

Chapter Test

Find the missing term in each sequence.

1 3, 9, 15, □, 27, 33
        21

2 2, 6, x, 54, 162
        18

3 40, 32, 24, __?__, 8
        16

4 20, 18, 17, 15, 14, __?__, __?__, 9
        12, 11

Fill in the blank.

5 If the first term in a sequence is 25 and the clue is SUBTRACT 4, then the fourth term is __?__.
        13

6 If the fourth term in a sequence is 81 and the clue is MULTIPLYBY 3, then the second term is __?__.
        9

7 If the fourth term in a sequence is 27 and the clue is ADD 7, then the first term is __?__.
        6

8 If the fifth term in a sequence is $\frac{1}{3}$ and the clue is DIVIDEBY 3, then the third term is __?__.
        3

Evaluate each expression if $a = 3$ and $b = 4$.

9 $2 \cdot a + 5$
        11

10 $b + a \cdot b$
        16

11 $0.4 \cdot a - 0.3 \cdot b$
        0

12 $\frac{5}{3} \cdot a - \frac{3}{4} \cdot b$
        2

13 Use the formula $A = lw$ and find the value of A when $l = 5$ and $w = 6$.
        30

14 Use the formula $p = 2l + 2w$ and find the value of p when $l = 7$ and $w = \frac{1}{2}$.
        15

15 Use the formula $F = \frac{9}{5}C + 32$ and find the value of F when $C = 10$.
        50

16 Use the formula $A = \frac{1}{2}hB + \frac{1}{2}hb$ and find the value of A when $h = 7, B = 10,$ and $b = 6$.
        56

In problems 17–22, match the verbal expression and the variable expression.

17 nine more than a number $_f$

a $9 \cdot n$

18 a number decreased by nine $_d$

b $9 - n$

19 the quotient of a number and nine $_c$

c $n \div 9$

20 the product of nine and a number $_a$

d $n - 9$

21 the difference between nine and a number $_b$

e $9 + 9n$

22 the sum of nine and the product of nine and a number $_e$

f $n + 9$

Translate each verbal expression to a variable expression.

23 Name a variable, divide it by four, and then add seven. $\frac{n}{4} + 7$

24 Name a variable, multiply it by one sixth, and then subtract the original number. $\frac{1}{6}n - n$

Choose the best verbal expression for each variable expression.

25 $6 - y$ $_c$

a a number decreased by six

b the difference between a number and six

c the difference between six and a number

26 $\frac{1}{2}x + 3$ $_c$

a half the product of a number and three

b half the sum of a number and three

c half a number increased by three

In problems 27–30, what is the value of the variable?

Name a variable and:	The final result is:
27 add 14	20 $_6$
28 multiply it by 7	1 $_{\frac{1}{7}}$
29 take half; then subtract 5	4 $_{18}$
30 subtract 5; then take half	4 $_{13}$

The Problem Sets that follow chapters 3, 7, 10, 12, and 14 are Cumulative Reviews; answers to the odd-numbered problems are at the end of the text.

No answers are provided for the other Problem Sets.

Problem Set: Grouping Data in Intervals

From the results of a 100-point algebra test, the teacher made the following table. In order to assign grades of A, B, C, D or F, she organized the scores into 5 intervals, or groups.

score	97	93	92	89	87	86	84	82	80
frequency	1	1	1	1	1	1	1	3	5

score	76	74	73	72	69	68	67	65	60
frequency	1	2	1	1	1	1	2	1	1

score	53	48	45	32
frequency	1	1	1	1

a List the intervals 0–59, 60–69, 70–79, etc. and make a frequency chart.

b List the intervals 1–60, 61–70, 71–80, etc. and make another frequency chart.

Chart a

Interval	Frequency
0–59	4
60–69	6
70–79	5
80–89	12
90–99	3

Chart b

Interval	Frequency
1– 60	5
61– 70	5
71– 80	10
81– 90	7
91–100	3

For each chart, the intervals all contain 10 numbers, but the frequency lists are quite different (except for the A grades). The teacher would have to choose which chart to use. Chart **a** would result in many B grades. Chart **b** would result in the grade of C being most frequent.

The following numbers are measurements:

> 55, 32, 86, 14, 2, 61, 75, 22, 83, 33, 41, 48, 53, 79, 11, 64, 36,
> 5, 24, 57

1 Make a frequency table, grouping the measurements into the intervals 0–30, 31–60, and 61–90. In the table, list the frequency of each and write the relative frequency as a percent for each interval.

The following list records the age of each U.S. President at his first inauguration:

> 57, 61, 57, 57, 58, 57, 61, 54, 68, 51, 49, 64, 50, 48, 65, 52, 56,
> 46, 54, 49, 50, 47, 55, 55, 54, 42, 51, 56, 55, 51, 54, 51, 60, 62,
> 43, 55, 56, 61, 52, 69

2 Find the maximum age and the minimum age.

3 Make a chart, grouping the ages into intervals 40–44, 45–49, 50–54, and so on. For each interval, list the frequency and express the relative frequency as a percent (to the nearest percent).

4 Make another chart, grouping the ages into the intervals 42–46, 47–51, 52–56, and so on. For each interval, list the frequency and express the relative frequency as a percent (to the nearest percent).

5 Make a chart using the intervals 41–50, 51–60, 61–70.

A researcher, testing an electrical circuit, recorded the following set of values for the current (in milliamperes):

> 3.28, 3.34, 3.43, 3.42, 3.38, 3.41, 3.42, 3.39, 3.42, 3.40, 3.44,
> 3.48, 3.50, 3.39, 3.38, 3.41, 3.35, 3.42, 3.42, 3.39, 3.44, 3.40

6 Find the maximum current and the minimum current.

7 Make a chart, grouping the values into the intervals 3.25–3.29, 3.30–3.34, 3.35–3.39, and so on. For each interval, list the frequency and express the relative frequency as a percent (to the nearest tenth of a percent).

8 Make another chart, grouping the values into the intervals 3.25–3.34, 3.35–3.44, etc., and find the relative frequencies.

1)

Interval	FREQ	RELFREQ
0–30	6	$\frac{6}{20} = 30\%$
31–60	8	$\frac{8}{20} = 40\%$
61–90	6	$\frac{6}{20} = 30\%$

2) maximum age: 69
minimum age: 42

3)

Interval	FREQ	RELFREQ
40–44	2	5%
45–49	5	13%
50–54	12	30%
55–59	12	30%
60–64	6	15%
65–69	3	8%

4)

Interval	FREQ	RELFREQ
42–46	3	8%
47–51	10	25%
52–56	13	33%
57–61	9	23%
62–66	3	8%
67–71	2	5%

5)

Interval	FREQ	RELFREQ
41–50	9	23%
51–60	23	58%
61–70	8	20%

6) maximum: 3.50
minimum: 3.28

7)

Interval	FREQ	RELFREQ
3.25–3.29	1	4.5%
3.30–3.34	1	4.5%
3.35–3.39	6	27.3%
3.40–3.44	12	54.5%
3.45–3.49	1	4.5%
3.50–3.54	1	4.5%

8)

Interval	FREQ	RELFREQ
3.25–3.34	2	9.1%
3.35–3.44	18	81.8%
3.45–3.54	2	9.1%

Chapter 2

SIGNED NUMBERS

CHAPTER SCHEDULE

Basic
Problem Sets   9 Days
Review   2 Days
Test   2 Days

Average
Problem Sets   8 Days
Review   1 Day
Test   2 Days

Advanced
Problem Sets   6 Days
Review   1 Day
Test   1 Day

This chapter develops techniques for adding and subtracting signed numbers and for solving equations involving addition and subtraction. Chapter 3 develops techniques for multiplying and dividing signed numbers.

Section 2.1   Sets of Numbers

When you use a scale or a ruler, you are using a **number line.** Every number line has a location for the **origin**, or zero. It also has a **positive direction**, a **negative direction**, and a **unit length.**

SECTION SCHEDULE

Basic (2 days)

Average (2 days)

Advanced (1 day)

Students could be asked to describe the necessary components of a number line: a location for the origin, a direction for positive (or negative) values, and a length for the unit.

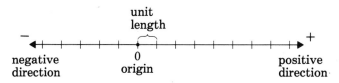

Labeling points on the number line can involve different sets of numbers. The numbers 1, 2, 3, 4, . . . are called the **NATURAL NUMBERS** or the **COUNTING NUMBERS.** (Three dots are read "and so on" or "et cetera." They indicate that the sequence of numbers continues.)

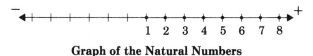

Graph of the Natural Numbers

The **WHOLE NUMBERS** are 0, 1, 2, 3, ... The set of whole numbers consists of the natural numbers along with zero.

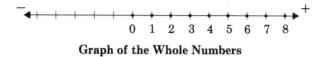

Graph of the Whole Numbers

The **INTEGERS** are . . . , −5, −4, −3, −2, −1, 0, 1, 2, ... The **positive integers** may be written with or without a positive sign, as +1, +2, +3, . . . or as 1, 2, 3, . . . , but the **negative integers** are always written with a negative sign, as . . . , −3, −2, −1.

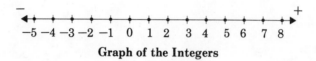

Graph of the Integers

The **RATIONAL NUMBERS** are used to label divisions between the integers. Rational numbers can be written as fractions, such as $\frac{1}{2}$, $-\frac{5}{3}$, or $2\frac{1}{4}$, or they can be written as decimals, such as 0.125 or −3.7. The name **rational** means that the number can be written as a **ratio**, or fraction, of two integers (examples: $1\frac{2}{3}$ can be written as $\frac{5}{3}$; −0.125 can be written as $\frac{-125}{1000}$).

There are also numbers that cannot be written as rational numbers. One such number is π (pi). Another example is .101001000100001 . . . (the pattern is "write one more zero than the last time"). These numbers are called the **IRRATIONAL NUMBERS.** The rational numbers and the irrational numbers together comprise the **REAL NUMBERS.** The graph of the real numbers includes every point on the number line.

The relationship among the sets of numbers is shown in the X section using a Venn diagram.

Solid dots or a thickened line indicate the graphed points on a number line. An open circle indicates that a point is not included. (See Sample Problem 1, p. 51.)

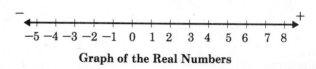

Graph of the Real Numbers

The **POSITIVE NUMBERS**, which are all the numbers greater than zero, are all those that are in the positive direction from the origin. The **NEGATIVE NUMBERS**, which are all less than zero, are all the numbers in the negative direction from the origin. The number zero is **neither** negative nor positive.

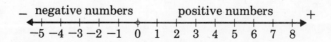

Sample Problems

1 Graph the following sets of numbers on a number line:
   a the first three whole numbers
   b the positive real numbers less than five

   PROCEDURE   Draw a separate number line for each part.
      a The whole numbers are 0, 1, 2, 3, 4, ... The first three whole numbers are 0, 1, and 2.

      b The graph should not include 0 (because zero is not a positive number) nor 5. Draw open circles at 0 and 5 (to indicate that 0 and 5 are not included). Shade the number line between 0 and 5.

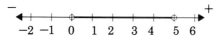

2 List the values that the variable y can represent under all three conditions:
     y is an integer $y < 9$ $y > 3$
                  ("y is less than 9")   ("y is greater than 3")
   PROCEDURE   The values that satisfy all three conditions are 4, 5, 6, 7, 8.

The order symbols are treated in Chapter 5.

Problem Set **A**

1 Is there a smallest natural number? If so, what is it?
   yes, 1

2 Is there a largest whole number? If so, what is it?
   no

3 Is there always a rational number between any two whole numbers?
   yes

4 Is there always a rational number between any two rational numbers?
   yes

5 Is there always a whole number between any two real numbers?
   no

6 Is there a smallest positive rational number?
   no

ASSIGNMENT GUIDE

Basic (2 days)
(1) 1–6, 8–22 (even)
(2) 23–33
   55: 7–11

Average (2 days)
(1) 8–26 (even)
(2) 28–37
   55: 2–11

Advanced (1 day)
28–44
55: 2–11

Students can research the mathematical terms density *and* successor *to pursue the ideas in problems 1–6.*

Problems 7–18 can be used as oral exercises (in addition to problems 1–6) by having students describe whether the graphs consist of points or lines.

In problems 7–18, graph each set of numbers on a separate number line.

7   1, 3, 5

8   −2, 0, 6

9   the first five natural numbers

10   the three smallest whole numbers

11   the real numbers between 2 and 4

12 $\frac{1}{2}$, $1\frac{1}{2}$, $3\frac{1}{2}$

13   0.5, 1.0, 2.5

14   −1.1, −2.2, −3.3

15 $\frac{1}{3}$, $\frac{2}{3}$, $\frac{7}{3}$

16   the positive real numbers less than 3

17   the negative integers greater than −4

18   the real numbers greater than 5

7)
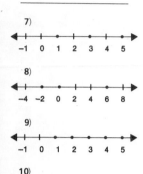

8)

9)

10)

11)

12)

13)

14)

15)

16)

17)

18)

For each of the following, list the value(s) that the variable can have.

19 w is a whole number; $w < 4$
0, 1, 2, 3

20 n is a natural number; $n < 6$
1, 2, 3, 4, 5

21 q is a rational number; q is the quotient formed by dividing 2 by 5
$\frac{2}{5}$

22 r is a real number; r is formed by writing a decimal point, then 7, then 1, then two 7's, then 1, then three 7's, then 1, and so on.
0.717717771 . . .

Evaluate each formula. (Review: Section 1.2)

23   Evaluate A in $A = \ell w$ if $\ell = 5$ and $w = 3$.
$A = 15$

24   Evaluate A in $A = \frac{1}{2} bh$ if $b = 3\frac{1}{2}$ and $h = 8$.
$A = 14$

25   Use the formula $p = 2\ell + 2w$ and find p to the **nearest whole number** if $\ell = 6\frac{13}{32}$ and $w = 4\frac{13}{16}$.
$p = 22$

26   Use the formula $F = \frac{9}{5}C + 32$ and find F if $C = 0$.
$F = 32$

27   Find the value of F in $F = \frac{9}{5}C + 32$ if $C = 25$.
$F = 77$

Problem Set **B**

In problems 28–33, the variables n, w, and r represent natural numbers, whole numbers, and real numbers, **respectively** (in that order). Graph each problem on a separate number line.

28 $w < 5$
　　(graph) solid dots at 0, 1, 2, 3, 4

29 $n < 4$
　　(graph) solid dots at 1, 2, 3

30 $n > 3$
　　(graph) solid dots at 4, 5, 6, . . .

31 $w > 0$
　　(graph) solid dots at 1, 2, 3, . . .

32 $r > 5$
　　(graph) open dot at 5, solid line in positive direction

33 $r < 4$
　　(graph) open dot at 4, solid line in negative direction

In problems 34–39, show that each number is a rational number.

34 1
　　$\frac{1}{1}, \frac{-7}{-7}$, etc.

35 0.2
　　$\frac{2}{10}$ or $\frac{1}{5}$

36 $3\frac{1}{7}$
　　$\frac{22}{7}$

37 $-11\frac{8}{13}$
　　$\frac{-151}{13}$

38 -4.327
　　$\frac{-4327}{1000}$

39 0
　　$\frac{0}{1}, \frac{0}{2}$, etc.

Problem Set **C**

Use a calculator to evaluate each formula:

40　Use the formula $A = \ell w$ and find A to the nearest natural number if $\ell = 5.643$ and $w = 11.708$.
　　66

41　Evaluate $A = \pi \cdot r \cdot r$ and express A as a rational number for $r = 7.13$ and $\pi = 3.14159$.
　　$A = 70.370158$

In problems 42–44, write the three numbers in order from smallest to largest.

42　0.55, 0.5, 0.555
　　0.5, 0.55, 0.555

43　2.333 . . . , 2.3, 2.33
　　2.3, 2.33, 2.333 . . .

44　5.27777 . . . , 5.272727 . . . , 5.27
　　5.27, 5.272727 . . . , 5.2777 . . .

Xtending the topic: "Nested Sets" of Numbers

Is −5 an integer? A rational number? A real number?

Is −5 a whole number? A natural number? An irrational number?

The answer is **yes** to the first three questions, and **no** to the second three questions.

The relationships among the sets of numbers can be shown using a Venn diagram. These diagrams were first used by Leonhard Euler (pronounced "oiler"), a Swiss mathematician, in the 18th century, and refined by John Venn, an English scholar, in the late 19th century.

The diagram uses "nested sets" to summarize the relationships among the sets of numbers. The diagram illustrates that every Natural number is also a Whole number, every Whole number is also an Integer, every Integer is also a Rational number, and every Rational number, and every Irrational number, is also a Real number.

The diagram also illustrates that a number cannot be both Rational and Irrational.

The diagram indicates that the Rationals and Irrationals are "mutually exclusive" sets. The diagram does not indicate another property: the two sets "exhaust" the Reals.

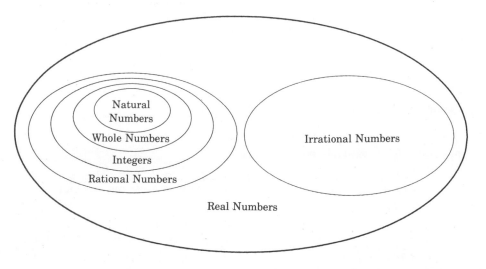

Sample Problem

1   Give examples, if possible, of the following:
    a a number that is a Rational number and an Integer.
    b a number that is a Rational number but is not an Integer.
    c a number that is an Integer but is not a Rational number.

PROCEDURE

    a $-3, -2, -1, 0, 1, 2, \ldots$; **every** Integer is an example of a Rational number and Integer.

    b $\frac{2}{3}, -1.5, 6\frac{1}{5}$ are examples of Rational numbers that are not Integers.

    c There is no number that is an Integer but not a Rational.

Problem Set X

1 Copy and complete this chart. Answers may vary. Reading across the chart, examples are: Natural Numbers: none, 5, none, none, none, none. Whole numbers: none, 5, none, none, none, none, 0. Integers: none, 5, none, none, -1, -1. Rational Numbers: none, 5, none, $\frac{2}{3}$, $\frac{2}{3}$, $\frac{2}{3}$. Irrational Numbers: none, none, π, π, π, π. Real Numbers: none, 5, π, π, π, π.

Give an example of a(n):   **That is not a(n):**

	Real Number	Irrational Number	Rational Number	Integer	Whole Number	Natural Number
Natural Number	none	5	none	none	none	none
Whole Number						
Integer						
Rational Number						
Irrational Number						
Real Number						

Name the "most nested" set of numbers that would be needed for each problem.

2 dates of a month
    Natural Numbers

3 mileage on a car odometer
    Real Numbers

4 attendance at a rock concert
    Whole Numbers (if no one attends) or Natural Numbers

5 cost for a movie ticket
    Rational Numbers

6 bank balances (in dollars and cents)
    Rational Numbers

7 football scores
    Whole Numbers

8 baseball batting averages
    Rational Numbers

9 television channels
    Natural Numbers

10 winter temperatures
    Rational Numbers

11 frequencies for FM radio stations
    Rational Numbers

Section 2.2   Graphing Signed Numbers

Many verbal phrases can be interpreted as **signed numbers,** or **directed numbers,** by using a positive sign or a negative sign. (A positive number can always be written without the "+" sign, but this section uses the positive sign for emphasis.)

EXAMPLES

■ positive		■ negative	
up 3	$+3$	down 4	-4
gain 6	$+6$	lose 6	-6
rise $1\frac{3}{8}$	$+1\frac{3}{8}$	fall $\frac{5}{8}$	$-\frac{5}{8}$
ahead 1 grade	$+1$	back 3 spaces	-3

A signed number can be shown on a number line as an arrow. For example, this graph shows two signed numbers, -4 and $+3$:

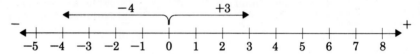

Both arrows start at the origin. The arrow points either in the negative direction (for -4) or in the positive direction (for $+3$).

A pair of signed numbers such as $+6$ and -6, or $-\frac{1}{2}$ and $+\frac{1}{2}$, are called **opposites.** On a number line, the arrows that represent a number and its opposite must have the same length.

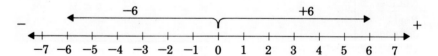

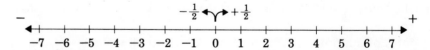

In computer talk, the expression OPP may be used to indicate the opposite of a number or variable.

EXAMPLES

- OPP $(3) = -3$
- OPP $(-8) = 8$
- OPP $(-6.2) = 6.2$

- OPP $(x) = -x$
- OPP $(-x) = x$

  The symbol "$-x$" should be read "the opposite of x".

Another term for the opposite is "additive inverse."

The Problem Set on page 91 provides a summary discussion of the three meanings of the "−" sign: negative numbers, opposite, and subtraction.

Students should realize that "$-x$" is a positive number whenever x is less than zero.

Sometimes it may be important to know the distance between a point and the origin, but the direction is not important. Consider this picture of one side of Main Street with a number line below it.

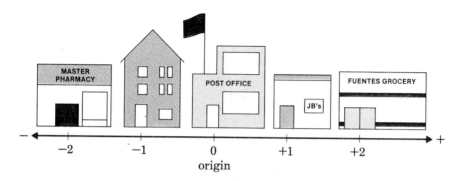

The pharmacy is at the point for −2, the Post Office is at the origin, and the grocery is at the point for +2. The distance between the points for the pharmacy and Post Office is two units, which is the same as the distance between the points for the Post Office and the grocery. For a number and its point on a number line, the distance between that point and the origin is called the **absolute value** of the number.

Definition

The ABSOLUTE VALUE of a number is the distance, on a number line, between the origin and the point for that number.

EXAMPLE

The absolute value of +3 is 3, and the absolute value of −3 is 3. In computer talk:

■   ABSVAL (+3) = 3   ABSVAL (−3) = 3

The sign, or notation, for absolute value is two vertical line segments. Thus |−4| is read, "The absolute value of negative 4."

Note that if two numbers are opposites, the numbers have the same absolute value. For example, −7 and +7 are opposites:

$$|-7| = 7$$

$$|+7| = 7$$

This can also be written without the "+" sign as |7| = 7. Thus |−7| = |7|. The variable x and the expression $-x$ are also opposites. Thus $|x| = |-x|$, even though the value of x may not be known.

This definition relates absolute value to distance on a number line. Another definition, more algebraic and formal, is:

$$|x| = \begin{cases} x \ \text{if } x \geq 0 \\ -x \ \text{if } x < 0 \end{cases}$$

Sample Problems

1   Write each phrase as a signed number and graph it on a number line.
    a   a surplus of 20 metric tons
    b   a loss of 8 pounds
    c   a decrease of 3.5 points

PROCEDURE   Label a number line appropriate for each signed number.

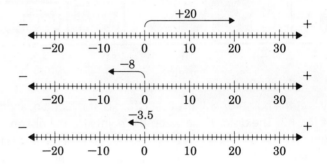

2   This graph records the temperature in Detroit for the first 10 days of January. Detroit's average temperature for this period is indicated by the dark line. Determine the number of degrees above or below average for each day and write the answer as a signed number.

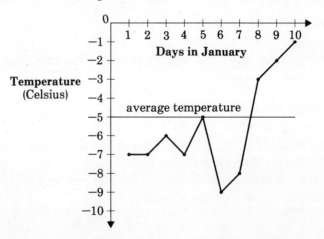

PROCEDURE   The average temperature is $-5°C$. On the first day, the temperature of $-7°$ is 2 degrees below the average (-2). On the tenth day, the temperature of $-1°$ is 4 degrees above the average ($+4$). The rest of the chart is filled in similarly:

Day	1	2	3	4	5	6	7	8	9	10
Temperature	$-7°$	$-7°$	$-6°$	$-7°$	$-5°$	$-9°$	$-8°$	$-3°$	$-2°$	$-1°$
Degrees above or below $-5°$	2 below	2 below	1 below	2 below	0	4 below	3 below	2 above	3 above	4 above
Signed Number	-2	-2	-1	-2	0	-4	-3	$+2$	$+3$	$+4$

3 An elevator begins on the ground floor. It is taken up to the fifth floor, down to the third floor, then down to the basement (one floor below the ground floor), and finally up two floors. Draw a picture to indicate the direction of each movement of the elevator.

PROCEDURE   Use vertical arrows to represent the movement of the elevator.

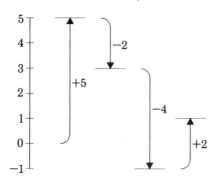

Problem Set A

ASSIGNMENT GUIDE

Basic (1 day)
11–22, 24–36 (even)

Average (1 day)
34–52

Advanced (1 day)
34–36, 43–64

1 A signed number can be used to indicate the amount and the __?__ of a measurement.
  direction

2 Two numbers such as -5 and $+5$ are called __?__ .
  opposites

3 What number is OPP (7)?   OPP (-5)?   OPP (0)?
  $-7, 5, 0$

4 For a number and its point on a number line, the distance between the point and the origin is called the __?__ of the number.
  absolute value

5 What is ABSVAL (5)?   ABSVAL $(-2\frac{1}{2})$?   ABSVAL (0)?
  $5, 2\frac{1}{2}, 0$

6 Which is greater, -7 or $|-7|$?
  $|-7|$ is greater than -7

Strictly speaking, zero does not have an opposite since zero is not a signed number. More informally, OPP (0) = 0.

In problems 7–10, graph each signed number as an arrow on a number line.

7 −3 arrow starts at origin, arrowhead at −3

8 +5 arrow starts at origin, arrowhead at +5

9 0 solid dot at origin

10 −3½ arrow starts at origin, arrowhead at −3½

Write each phrase as a signed number or zero.

11 deposit of $2.50
  +2.50

12 decrease of 8,000
  −8000

13 gain of 12 yards
  +12

14 rise of 5°F
  +5

15 7,990 feet above sea level
  +7,990

16 par golf
  0

17 loss of $15
  −15

18 $4 debt
  −4

19 5 kilometers per hour (km/h) over the speed limit
  +5

20 2 units in the negative direction
  −2

21 A large office building may have several sub-basements, or floors below the ground floor. An elevator begins at the ground floor and descends four floors to the bottom sub-basement. Then it ascends fourteen floors. Draw a picture to indicate the movement of the elevator. At what floor is it stopped? tenth floor

22 The temperature at noon was 67°. During the first hour after noon the temperature rose 2°. The next hour it rose 1°. Finally, during each of the next two hours the temperature dropped 3°. Draw a picture to show the change in temperature hour by hour since noon. What was the temperature at 4:00 p.m.? $67 + 2 + 1 - 3 - 3 = 64$

Find the following.

23 ABSVAL (−8)
  8

24 ABSVAL (−2)
  2

25 ABSVAL (14)
  14

26 ABSVAL (0)
  0

27 OPP (0)
  0

28 OPP (97)
  −97

29 OPP (−5)
  5

30 OPP (−932)
  932

Find the missing number in each sequence. (Review: Section 1.1)

31 9, 13, 17, x, 25, 29
21

32 53, 46, n, 32, 25, 18
39

33 0.02, 0.4, 0.78, r, 1.54
1.16

34 $4\frac{7}{8}$, $4\frac{1}{2}$, $4\frac{1}{8}$, $3\frac{3}{4}$, q, 3
$3\frac{3}{8}$

35 4, 3, 2, 1, 0, x
-1

36 10, 8, 6, 4, 2, 0, y
-2

Problem Set B

Six people are listed below with their actual weight and the normal weight (in pounds) for a person of their height and bone structure. Write how many pounds overweight (+) or underweight (−) each one is.

	Name	Actual Weight	Normal Weight
37	Healthy Helen	103	105
	−2		
38	Slim Freddy	102	135
	−33		
39	Fat Albert	253	149
	+104		
40	Macho Mike	132	130
	+2		
41	Hungry Hannah	176	153
	+23		
42	Slender Sue	95	110
	−15		

In problems 43–52, evaluate each expression:

43 OPP $(6 + 2 \cdot 3)$
−12

44 ABSVAL $(7 \cdot 3 - 15)$
6

45 OPP (x) if $x = 3$
−5

46 OPP (y) if $y = -5$
5

47 ABSVAL (r) if $r = 8$
8

48 ABSVAL (s) if $s = -2$
2

49 SUBTRACT 7 (OPP (-9.32))
2.32

50 HALF (ABSVAL $(9.3 - 7)$)
1.15

51 ADD 8 (OPP $(8 - 4 \cdot 2)$)
4.2

52 ADD 3 (OPP (x))
$3 - x$

Problem Set C

If 3.1415927 is taken as the value of π, use a signed number to compare these other approximations of π to it. Do not use more than 7 numbers after the decimal point when making comparisons.

53 3.14
      −0.0015927

54 $3\frac{1}{7}$
      +0.0012644

55 $3\frac{120}{847}$
      +0.0000838

56 $3\frac{297}{2100}$
      −0.0001642

57 Below is a graph of some of the winning times, in miles per hour, for the Indianapolis 500. Use a signed number to compare each time to that of Lee Wallard, who averaged 126.244 mph in 1951.

Gaston Chevrolet, −38.084; Billy Arnold, −25.764;
A. J. Foyt, +12.886; Al Unser, +35.119

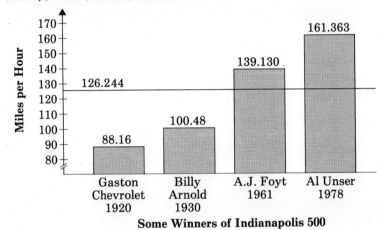

The break in the vertical axis indicates that the values 0 to 70 are not represented. Breaking an axis can distort the visual ratio of the heights on a bar graph.

Some Winners of Indianapolis 500

The latitude of Denver is $39\frac{3}{4}°$. Use a signed number to compare the latitude of each of the following cities to Denver.

58 Durham, NC $36°$
                    $-3\frac{3}{4}$

59 Houston $29\frac{3}{4}°$
                    -10

60 Detroit $42\frac{1}{3}°$
                    $+2\frac{7}{12}$

61 Omaha $41\frac{4}{15}°$
                    $+1\frac{31}{60}$

62 Juneau $58\frac{9}{30}°$
                    $+18\frac{11}{20}$

63 Miami $25\frac{47}{60}°$
                    $-13\frac{29}{30}$

64 One point in Death Valley is 282 feet below sea level, while the top of Mt. Rainier is 14,410 feet above sea level. What is the difference in elevation?
      14,692

Project: Two Versions of NIM

NIM-type games are for two players who take turns removing objects from a set. The game can vary in the number of objects at the start, the number that can be removed at each turn, and whether the player who takes the last object is the winner or the loser.

One simple NIM-type game starts with 21 objects. Each player can remove 1, 2, or 3 objects per turn, and the person who takes the last object is the winner.

1   If your opponent leaves you two objects, you can win by taking both of them. For what other numbers can you be a sure winner?

1)   A player is a sure winner if the opponent leaves 1, 2, or 3 items.

2   If your opponent leaves you six objects, how many should you take?

2)   If your opponent leaves six items, take two of them.

3   Use your answer to problem 2 and work backwards, one turn at a time: how many objects should you leave after your last turn? Your next-to-last turn? The turn before that?

3)   Always leave your opponent multiples of four items: 20, 16, 12, 8, 4, 0.

4   In the original game, would you want to go first or second?

4)   In a game that starts with 21 items, go first (and take 1 item).

Another version of NIM uses 16 objects. Players take turns removing any number of objects from any one row, and the player who takes the last object loses.

5   Develop an end-of-game strategy for the 3-2-1 arrangement. Do you want to leave 3-2-1 or do you want to take from 3-2-1?

5)   Leave 3-2-1.

6   Can you identify other "sure-win" patterns?

6)   Other "sure-win" patterns include 2-2, 3-3, 1-2-1-2, 1-3-1-3.

63

The X-section following Section 2.5 describes how to use absolute value to find the sum of signed numbers.

Section 2.3   Adding Signed Numbers

A football player gained 3 yards on one play, then lost 8 yards on the next play. The net result of the two plays was a loss of 5 yards.

The combination of the two plays can be shown on a number line as the sum of the directed numbers $+3$ and -8.

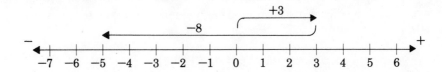

To represent $+3$, the first arrow points in the positive direction and is 3 units long. The first arrow starts at the origin.

The second arrow starts at the end of the first. To represent -8, the arrow points in the negative direction and is 8 units long. The second arrow ends at -5, which represents the net loss of 5 yards.

The number line diagram can be translated as adding signed numbers:

$$+3 + -8 = -5$$

Parentheses are usually used to avoid writing two signs together, so the addition should be written:

$$+3 + (-8) = -5$$

Sample Problems

1   Add $-4 + (-2)$

PROCEDURE   Start at the origin on a number line and draw an arrow for -4. From the arrowhead of -4, draw an arrow for -2. The result, -6, is below the second arrowhead.

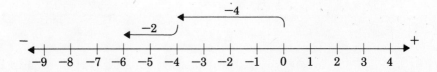

As an addition sentence, this problem can be written: $-4 + (-2) = -6$

2   Evaluate $x + y$ when $x = 5$ and $y = -3$.

   PROCEDURE   Substutite $x = 5$ and $y = -3$ into $x + y$.

   $x + y$

   $5 + (-3)$

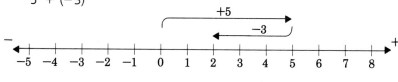

   $5 + (-3) = 2$

Problem Set A

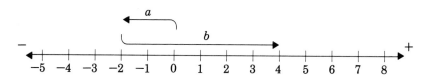

ASSIGNMENT GUIDE

Basic (1 day)
5–16, 18–28 (even),
29–40

Average (1 day)
36–56 (even)

Advanced (1 day)
46–60 (even)

1   On the number line, arrow a represents the signed number __?__. -2

2   Arrow b on the number line represents the signed number __?__. $+6$

3   The direction of an arrow indicates whether a signed number is __?__ or __?__.   positive or negative

4   To add signed numbers on a number line, the first arrow begins at the __?__ and the second arrow begins at the __?__ of the first arrow.   origin, end

Use a number line to find each sum.

5 $7 + (-2)$ **9** $-5 + 5$ **13** $-7 + 0$
   $+5$ 0 -7

6 $6 + (-3)$ **10** $-3 + 3$ **14** $-3 + 0$
   $+3$ 0 -3

7 $-2 + (-8)$ **11** $6 + (-6)$ **15** $0 + 2$
   -10 0 $+2$

8 $-3 + (-7)$ **12** $4 + (-4)$ **16** $0 + (-4)$
   -10 0 -4

Evaluate each variable expression in problems 17–28 if $a = 3$, $b = -2$, $x = -5$, and $y = -1$.

17 $x + y$
$-5 + (-1) = -6$

23 $a + y$
$3 + (-1) = 2$

18 $y + x$
$-1 + (-5) = -6$

24 $y + a$
$-1 + 3 = 2$

19 $a + b$
$3 + (-2) = 1$

25 $b + x$
$-2 + (-5) = -7$

20 $b + a$
$-2 + 3 = 1$

26 $x + b$
$-5 + (-2) = -7$

21 $x + a$
$-5 + 3 = -2$

27 $y + b$
$-1 + (-2) = -3$

22 $a + x$
$3 + (-5) = -2$

28 $b + y$
$-2 + (-1) = -3$

Evaluate each expression. (Review: Section 2.2)

29 ABSVAL (-2)
2

32 ABSVAL $(\,(-2) + (-3)\,)$
5

30 OPP (-3)
3

33 ABSVAL (-5) + ABSVAL (-1)
6

31 ABSVAL (-2) + ABSVAL (-3)
5

34 ABSVAL $(\,(-5) + (-1)\,)$
6

Problem Set **B**

Use the number line to find each sum.

35 $-7 + 2 + (-5)$
-10

38 $-2 + (-9) + 4$
-7

36 $-9 + 12 + (-6)$
-3

39 $-5 + (-3) + (-8)$
-16

37 $-4 + (-7) + 8$
-3

40 $-9 + (-5) + (-7)$
-21

Write each problem as a sum of signed numbers and find that sum.

41 The temperature at noon was 83°. During the next hour, the temperature dropped 5°. What was the temperature at 1:00 p.m.? 78°

42 An elevator started on the 11th floor. It went down 4 floors, up 2 floors, and then down 8 floors. Where did the elevator end?

43 Dwayne had $3 when he collected $4 from Mike. Then he spent $2 for lunch and 50¢ for a notebook. How much did Dwayne have left? $4.50

44 In playing a game, Yolanda lost 24 points on her first turn, gained 15 points on her second turn, then gained 23 and 19 points on her last two turns. What was her score after four turns? 33

Problem Set C

Use the number line to find each sum.

45 $3\frac{1}{4} + (-2\frac{1}{4})$ 1

46 $1\frac{1}{2} + (-5\frac{1}{4})$ $-3\frac{3}{4}$

47 $-\frac{5}{3} + \frac{3}{4}$ $-\frac{11}{12}$

48 $-2\frac{2}{3} + (-3\frac{7}{10})$ $-6\frac{11}{30}$

49 $-0.5 + 0.3$ -0.2

50 $2.7 + (-1.2)$ 1.5

51 $-0.01 + 0.03$ 0.02

Evaluate each expression.

52 ABSVAL [OPP (4) + ABSVAL [OPP (2)]]
   2

53 ABSVAL [OPP (4) + OPP (2)]
   6

54 ABSVAL [OPP (6)] + ABSVAL [OPP (3)]
   3

55 ABSVAL [OPP (6) + OPP (3)]
   9

56 ABSVAL [OPP (−7) − OPP (3)]
   10

57 ABSVAL [ABSVAL (−10) + OPP [ABSVAL (−10)]]
   0

58 OPP [ABSVAL (3 · 2⁴ − 3) + OPP (4² − 5²)]
   −54

59 OPP [ABSVAL (3 + 12 · 3²) + ABSVAL [OPP (5)]]
   −116

60 ABSVAL [OPP (7 − 9²) − OPP (9 − 7²)]
   34

61 ABSVAL [OPP (3 − 4 + 5) + OPP (6 − 7 + 8)]
   11

Section 2.4   Subtracting Signed Numbers

When signed numbers are used, there is a pattern between subtraction and addition:

Subtraction	**Addition**
$10 - (+9) = 1$	$10 + (-9) = 1$
$4 - (-2) = 6$	$4 + (+2) = 6$
$-3 - (+7) = -10$	$-3 + (-7) = -10$
$-6 - (-8) = 2$	$-6 + (+8) = 2$

Each pair of problems represents subtracting a signed number and adding the opposite of that signed number. In general, subtraction can always be changed to addition.

Property

If a and b are signed numbers, then: $a - b = a + (-b)$

In words, to subtract the signed number b from a, add the opposite of b to a.

EXAMPLES

- $15 - (-2)$ can be written as $15 + (+2)$:
  $15 - (-2) = 15 + (+2) = 17$

- $-12 - (+6)$ can be written as $-12 + (-6)$:
  $-12 - (+6) = -12 + (-6) = -18$

- $114 - (-45)$ can be written as $114 + (45)$:
  $114 - (-45) = 114 + 45 = 159$

In computer talk:

- $15 - (-2) = 15 + \text{OPP}(-2)$
  $\qquad\quad = 15 + (+2)$
  $\qquad\quad = 17$

- $-12 - (+6) = -12 + \text{OPP}(+6)$
  $\qquad\qquad\; = -12 + (-6)$
  $\qquad\qquad\; = -18$

- $144 - (-45) = 114 + \text{OPP}(-45)$
  $\qquad\qquad\;\; = 114 + 45$
  $\qquad\qquad\;\; = 159$

Brighter students may enjoy the challenge of interpreting subtraction on a number line:

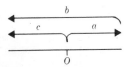

Since $a + b = c$, then $c - b = a$.

One description of $x - y$ is: Represent the signed number x. From the arrow for x, represent the opposite of the arrow for y. The result, $x - y$, is under the arrowhead for y.

Sample Problems

1 Rewrite as addition of signed numbers, and then add:
  a $5 - 12$
  b $5 - (-12)$
  c $-3 - 10$

PROCEDURE   Use the property that $a - b = a + \text{OPP}\,(b)$.
  a $5 - 12 = 5 + \text{OPP}\,(12)$
          $= 5 + (-12)$
          $= -7$
  b $5 - (-12) = 5 + \text{OPP}\,(-12)$
          $= 5 + 12$
          $= 17$
  c $-3 - 10 = -3 + \text{OPP}\,(10)$
          $= -3 + (-10)$
          $= -13$

2 Evaluate the expression $2x - y$ if $x = 7$ and $y = -3$.

PROCEDURE   Substitute the values for x and y into $2x - y$:
        $2x - y$
        $2\,(7) - (-3)$
        $2\,(7) + (+3)$
        $14 + 3$
        17

Problem Set A

ASSIGNMENT GUIDE

Basic (2 days)
(1) 5–29
(2) 72: 1–18

Average (1 day)
6–28 (even), 30–37
72: 2–18 (even)

Advanced (1 day)
6–28 (even), 30–38
72: 2–18 (even)

1 To subtract b from a, add __?__ to a.
    $-b$, OPP (b)

2 Adding the opposite of a number gives the same result as __?__ the number.
    subtracting

3 Subtracting a positive number gives the same result as adding a(n) __?__ number.
    negative

4 Subtracting a negative number gives the same result as adding a(n) __?__ number.
    positive

In problems 5–16, rewrite each subtraction problem as an addition problem. Then find the sum.

5 $9 - (+5)$
$9 + (-5) = 4$

6 $17 - (+13)$
$17 + (-13) = 4$

7 $8 - 6$
$8 + (-6) = 2$

8 $34 - 28$
$34 + (-28) = 6$

9 $(+3) - (+9)$
$(+3) + (-9) = -6$

10 $(+11) - (+14)$
$(+11) + (-14) = -3$

11 $5 - 7$
$5 + (-7) = -2$

12 $16 - 19$
$16 + (-19) = -3$

13 $-14 - (-6)$
$-14 + (+6) = -8$

14 From 6, subtract -6.
$6 - (-6) = 6 + 6 = 12$

15 From -2, subtract 8.
$-2 - 8 = -2 + (-8) = -10$

16 Subtract 2 from -7.
$-7 - 2 = -7 + (-2) = -9$

17 Evaluate $x - y$ for $x = -3$ and $y = 2$.
$-3 - 2 = -3 + (-2) = -5$

18 Evaluate $x - y$ for $x = 5$ and $y = 8$.
$5 - 8 = 5 + (-8) = -3$

19 If $y = \frac{1}{2}$ and $x = -2$, evaluate $4y - x$.
$4(\frac{1}{2}) - (-2) = 2 + (+2) = 4$

20 If $x = \frac{2}{3}$ and $y = -4$, evaluate $6x - y$.
$6(\frac{2}{3}) - (-4) = 4 + 4 = 8$

Translate to a variable expression. (Review: Section 1.3)

21 a variable n plus nine.
$n + 9$

22 eighteen added to a variable t
$t + 18$

23 five subtracted from a variable p
$p - 5$

24 eighteen more than x
$x + 18$

25 fourteen fewer than w
$w - 14$

In problems 26–29, write a verbal expression for each variable phrase. Start each expression with **Name a variable:** (Review: Section 1.4)

26–29) answers may vary

26 $2x - 9$

27 $y + 8$

28 $A \div 2 - 7$

29 $3k - 8 + k$

Problem Set **B**

In problems 30–37, rewrite each expression as a sum of signed numbers. Then find the sum.

30 $10 - 15 + 6 - 5$
-4

31 $+8 + (-3) + (-5) - 9$
-9

32 $75 - 55 - 100 - (-85)$
5

33 $-62 + 41 - (-38) + (-59)$
-42

34 $-2.8 + (-5.7) - 4.6 - 17$
-30.1

35 $5.28 - 6.7 - (-4.35) + 4$
6.93

36 $-5\frac{3}{8} + 2\frac{7}{8} - 1\frac{1}{8}$
$-3\frac{5}{8}$

37 $16\frac{4}{7} - 20 - (-8\frac{3}{7})$
5

Problem Set **C**

Below are two math cryptograms. Each letter represents only one digit and no digit can be assigned to more than one letter. Replace each letter by a digit so that the mathematical sentence is true.

38   FOUR − SEVEN = −THREE
(Hint: R = 2)
one solution is: $F = 7$, $O = 1$,
$U = 0$, $R = 2$, $T = 4$, $H = 9$,
$E = 6$, $S = 5$, $V = 3$, $N = 8$

39   HAIR − COMB = MESS
one solution is: $H = 9$, $A = 1$, $I = 6$,
$R = 0$, $C = 5$, $O = 7$, $M = 3$,
$B = 8$, $E = 4$, $S = 2$

*The cryptograms are
probably easier if they
are written as:*

FOUR	*COMB*
+ *THREE*	+ *MESS*
SEVEN	*HAIR*

*As additional hints,
students can start by
noticing restrictions
on pairs of letters: in
problem 38, if $R + E$
≤ 9, then $U = 0$;
$F + H \geq 9$, so that
$S = T + 1$.*

X tending the topic: **Using Absolute Value to Add Signed Numbers**

There is a general procedure for adding signed numbers. The procedure uses **absolute value,** which is always positive (or zero).

EXAMPLES

- To find the sum of two positive numbers, such as $5 + 3$, simply add them:

$$5 + 3 = 8$$

The sum of two positive numbers must be positive.

- To find the sum of two negative numbers, such as $-4 + (-3)$, find the sum of their absolute values:

$$|-4| + |-3| = 4 + 3 = 7$$

Write that sum with a negative sign:

$$-4 + (-3) = -7$$

The sum of two negative numbers must be negative.

- To find the sum of a positive number and a negative number, such as $-8 + 5$ or $7 + (-2)$, find the **difference** of their absolute values:

$$|-8| - |5| = 8 - 5 = 3$$
$$|7| - |-2| = 7 - 2 = 5$$

Write that difference with the sign of the number that has the greater absolute value:

$$-8 + 5 = -3$$
$$7 + (-2) = 5$$

The sum of two numbers with unlike signs may be positive or negative.

In all three examples, finding the sum is a two-step process: determine the sign of the sum after finding the absolute value of the sum.

Problem Set **X**

Add without using a number line.

1	$(+27) + (+33)$ 60	**7**	$17 + (-24)$ −7	**13**	$837 + 274$ 1111
2	$(+41) + (+26)$ 67	**8**	$26 + (-43)$ −17	**14**	$(-395) + (-492)$ −887
3	$-13 + (-18)$ −31	**9**	$-79 + 44$ −35	**15**	$(-835) + 244$ −591
4	$-29 + (-17)$ −46	**10**	$-63 + 58$ −5	**16**	$493 + (-278)$ 215
5	$28 + (-13)$ 15	**11**	$-27 + 44$ 17	**17**	$3 + (-6) + (-2)$ −5
6	$39 + (-25)$ 14	**12**	$-36 + 85$ 49	**18**	$-7 + 5 + (-4)$ −6

Section 2.5   Analyzing Phrases: Addition and Subtraction

SECTION SCHEDULE

Basic (1 day)

Average (1 day)

Advanced ($\frac{1}{2}$ day)

Sarah was making a shelf for her room and had a piece of wood that was 14 inches too long. It was not difficult to decide what to do—she sawed off the extra 14 inches.

This section introduces the concepts involved in solving equations. These concepts are extended and used in sections 2.6 and 2.7.

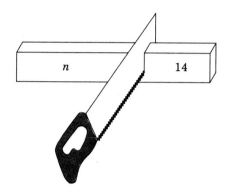

To get n from $n + 14$,   subtract 14.

To "isolate a variable" means to write it alone, with no numbers added to it or subtracted from it. If a number has been added to the variable, such as $n + 14$, subtract 14 to isolate the variable. If a number has been subtracted from the variable, such as $r - 10$,   add 10 to isolate the variable.

EXAMPLE

- To isolate the variable x in $x + 3$,   think of the **+3** as a "clue."
  Subtracting 3 from $x + 3$ will isolate x. Using computer talk:
      SUBTRACT 3 $(x + 3)$ is the same as x alone.

Sample Problems

1   Isolate a in the variable expression $a - 7$.

PROCEDURE   The "clue" says that 7 was subtracted from the variable. To isolate a, add 7 to $a - 7$:

    ADD 7 $(a - 7) = a$

2 For each verbal phrase, translate it to a variable expression and state how to isolate the variable.

    a twelve more than a number

    b 1.6 subtracted from a number

PROCEDURE

	translation	clue	to isolate the variable
a	$n + 12$	**+12**	SUBTRACT 12 $(n + 12)$
b	$r - 1.6$	**−1.6**	ADD 1.6 $(r - 1.6)$

3 Isolate the variable in variable expressions $4 + x$ and $-3 + y$.

Some students may have initial difficulty when the variable is not the first term in an expression.

PROCEDURE The "clues" are **4** and **−3**. To isolate the variables, use SUBTRACT 4 and ADD 3, respectively.

$$\text{SUBTRACT } 4\,(4 + x) = x$$
$$\text{ADD } 3\,(-3 + y) = y$$

ASSIGNMENT GUIDE

Basic (1 day)
1–20

Average (1 day)
1–28

Advanced ($\frac{1}{2}$ day)
See p. 79.

Problem Set **A**

For each variable expression, state the clue and tell how to isolate the variable.

1 $a - 24$
    −24, ADD 24 $(a - 24)$

2 $n - 19$
    −19, ADD 19 $(n - 19)$

3 $b + 13.2$
    +13.2, SUBTRACT 13.2 $(b + 13.2)$

4 $c + \frac{1}{2}$
    $+\frac{1}{2}$, SUBTRACT $\frac{1}{2}$ $(c + \frac{1}{2})$

5 $75 + e$
    +75, SUBTRACT 75 $(75 + e)$

6 $18 + t$
    +18 SUBTRACT 18 $(18 + t)$

7 $-14 + f$
    −14, ADD 14 (−14

8 $-12 + w$
    −12, ADD 12 (−12

9 $-2 + x$
    −2, ADD 2 (−2 + x

Find the value represented by each computer instruction. (Review: Section 1.5)

These review problems "preview" the kinds of problems students will see in the next section.

10 ADD 5 (19)
    24

11 SUBTRACT 7 (15)
    8

12 ADD 9 $(x - 9)$
    x

13 SUBTRACT 4 $(n + 4)$
    n

14 ADD 4 (−2)
    2

15 ADD 3 (−7)
    −4

16 SUBTRACT 2 (−9)
    −11

17 SUBTRACT 6 (−3)
    −9

Problem Set B

Translate each phrase into a variable expression. Then state the isolating process.

18 read five more books than Mary Ann did
$b + 5$, SUBTRACT 5 $(b + 5)$

19 ate three more goldfish than Eugene
$g + 3$, SUBTRACT 3 $(g + 3)$

20 temperature went up two point four degrees from last hour
$t + 2.4$, SUBTRACT 2.4 $(t + 2.4)$

21 lost five pounds from last week's weight
$w - 5$, ADD 5 $(w - 5)$

22 gained nine pounds from last month's weight
$p + 9$, SUBTRACT 9 $(p + 9)$

23 scored twelve more points than in the first half
$p + 12$, SUBTRACT 12 $(p + 12)$

24 shot three fewer baskets than in the third quarter
$s - 3$, ADD 3 $(s - 3)$

Problem Set C

To solve a verbal problem using algebra, it is necessary to use variables and write equations to represent the problems. An **equation** is a mathematical statement that two expressions have the same value. Later sections of this chapter show techniques to find values for the variables in an equation. Often a diagram is a useful help in translating a word problem into an equation. The diagram may be a number line or a sketch.

- Write an equation to represent this diagram:

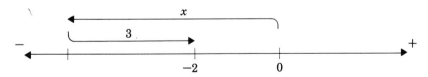

The diagram illustrates starting at the origin, then adding x (note that x must be a negative number), then adding $+3$, and ending at -2. The equation is:

$$0 + x + 3 = -2$$

It is usual to write this without the zero: $\quad x + 3 = -2$

■   Write an equation for the sentence: Five fewer than t is zero.

The variable phrase for "five fewer than t" is "$t - 5$." Since $t - 5$ is zero, the equation is: $t - 5 = 0$

In problems 25–28, select the equation that represents the verbal description or picture.

25   Name a variable and add 8. The result is -3. b

   a $n - 8 = -3$ **c** $n + (-3) = 8$

   b $n + 8 = -3$ **d** $8 + (-3) = n$

26   Name a variable and subtract 5. The result is 14. a

   a $n - 5 = 14$ **c** $n - 14 = -5$

   b $n + 5 = 14$ **d** $14 - 5 = n$

27

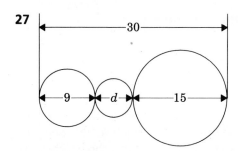

   a $24 + d = 30$

   b $24d = 30$

                       a

   c $24 \div d = 30$

   d $d - 24 = 30$

28

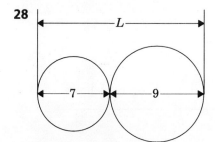

   a $7 + L = 9$

   b $9 + L = 7$

                       d

   c $9 - 7 = L$

   d $9 + 7 = L$

Write an equation that represents each problem. (Do not solve the equations.)

29   The sum of x and 7 is 4.

     $x + 7 = 4$

30   The sum of 5 and y is -3.

     $5 + y = -3$

31   Six fewer than y is fifteen.

     $y - 6 = 15$

32   Eight is n more than twelve.

     $8 = n + 12$

For problems 33–38, write a verbal problem that can be represented by the equation.

33 $n + 5 = 11$

36 $4 + t = 9$

34 $h - 10 = 12$

37 $y - 5 = -3$

35 $19 - x = 5$

38 $M = 5.9 - 3.2$

Section 2.6 Solving Equations: Addition and Subtraction

SECTION SCHEDULE

Basic (1 day)

Average (1 day)

Advanced ($\frac{1}{2}$ day)

These equations all have the same value for the variable x :

$$x + 7 = 17 \qquad x - 6 = 4 \qquad x + \tfrac{1}{2} = 10\tfrac{1}{2}$$

The solution to each of the equations is the value $x = 10$. A **solution** is usually written as an equation, with the variable isolated on one side of the equation.

Equations that have the same solution, such as the three equations above, are called **equivalent** equations.

Many texts take a set-theoretic approach to equations; a solution is a specified set of values. This text uses a language-oriented approach; a solution is the sentence, or equation, that has the variable isolated.

The set-theoretic definition is described in the X section following Section 5.1 because solution sets are more convenient for inequalities.

Definition

Two or more equations that have the same solution are called EQUIVALENT equations.

The process of finding the solution to an equation is called **solving** the equation.

The main purpose of the "computer talk" notation introduced in Chapter 1 is analyzing and solving equations. The notation, used throughout the text, is abbreviated starting in section 4.3, page 164.

EXAMPLE

- To find the solution to the equation $x - 9 = 13$, isolate the variable x. The "clue" is **−9**, so isolate the variable by adding 9.

The key to obtaining equivalent equations is to add or subtract the same number from both sides of the equation. (The next chapter will also use multiplication and division to obtain equivalent equations.)

$$x - 9 = 13$$
$$\text{ADD } 9 \, (x - 9) = \text{ADD } 9 \, (13)$$
$$x = 22$$

The equation $x - 9 = 13$ is now solved. The solution is $x = 22$.

Sample Problems

1   Solve and check: $t + 8 = 11$

PROCEDURE

The "clue" is **+ 8**, so subtract 8 from each side of the equation.

$$t + 8 = 11$$
$$\text{SUBTRACT } 8 \, (t + 8) = \text{SUBTRACT } 8 \, (11)$$
$$t = 3$$

To check, rewrite the original equation, substitute the value 3 for t, and evaluate each side of the equation separately.

$$t + 8 = 11$$
$$3 + 8 \overset{?}{=} 11$$
$$11 \overset{?}{=} 11 \checkmark$$

2   Solve and check: $y - 4 = 18$

PROCEDURE

Add or subtract the same number from each side of the equation.

$$y - 4 = 18$$
$$\text{ADD } 4 \, (y - 4) = \text{ADD } 4 \, (18)$$
$$y = 22$$

$$\textit{To check} \quad y - 4 = 18$$
$$22 - 4 \overset{?}{=} 18$$
$$18 \overset{?}{=} 18 \checkmark$$

3   Which of these equations has the solution $w = -6$?
  a $4 + w = -2$ **b** $-6 = w$ **c** $w - 1 = 5$

PROCEDURE   Check the solution $w = -6$ in each equation.

a $4 + w = -2$	**b** $-6 = w$	**c** $w - 1 = 5$
$4 + (-6) \overset{?}{=} -2$	$-6 \overset{?}{=} -6 \checkmark$	$(-6) - 1 \overset{?}{=} 5$
$-2 \overset{?}{=} -2 \checkmark$		$-7 \overset{?}{=} 5$ No

Equations **a** and **b** have the solution $w = -6$, but equation **c** does not.

Problem Set A

ASSIGNMENT GUIDE

Basic (1 day)
6–24 (even), 25–34

Average (1 day)
6–44 (even)

Advanced ($\frac{1}{2}$ day)
20–28 (even), 36–50
(even)
75: 18–38 (even)

1 What is the solution of the equation $t = 3$? $t = 3$

2 What is the solution of the equation $-4 = y$? $y = -4$

3 Two equations that have the same solution are called __?__. equivalent

4 Adding or subtracting the same number to both sides of an equation results in a(n) __?__ equation. equivalent

Solve and check.

5 $a + 5 = 9$
  $a = 4$

6 $B + 2 = 21$
  $B = 19$

7 $2 + y = 81$
  $y = 79$

8 $1 + h = -9$
  $h = -10$

9 $c - 8 = 14$
  $c = 22$

10 $x - 9 = -3$
  $x = 6$

11 $23 = R + 8$
  $15 = R$

12 $6 = A + 6$
  $0 = A$

13 $0 = \ell - 5$
  $\ell = 5$

14 $7 = t - 11$
  $t = 18$

15 $6 = D + 8$
  $D = -2$

16 $18 = -5 + u$
  $u = 23$

17 $a - 1 = -7$
  $a = -6$

18 $E - 12 = 3$
  $E = 15$

19 $61 + V = 43$
  $V = -18$

20 $6 = J + 11$
  $J = -5$

21 $-7 = m - 4$
  $m = -3$

22 $w - 3 = -3$
  $w = 0$

23 $14 = 2 + x$
  $x = 12$

24 $11 = y - 9$
  $y = 20$

Translate into an equation, solve the equation, and then check the solution.

25 Four plus V is equal to negative nine.
  $V = -13$

26 Seven subtracted from Q is the opposite of one.
  $Q = 6$

27 Three is equal to the sum of T and two.
  $T = 1$

28 Fourteen is equal to k minus one.
  $k = 15$

Translate to a variable expression. (Review: Section 1.3)

29 two more than N
$2 + N$

30 five less than y
$y - 5$

31 the sum of eight and t
$8 + t$

32 x decreased by one and nine tenths
$x - 1.9$

33 nineteen added to A
$19 + A$

34 eight subtracted from Q
$Q - 8$

Problem Set B

Solve and check.

35 $r + 0.02 = 1.95$
$r = 1.93$

36 $-3 + a = \frac{1}{2}$
$a = \frac{7}{2}$

37 $-\frac{3}{4} = t - 1\frac{3}{4}$
$t = 1$

38 $3.9 = A + 1.8$
$A = 2.1$

39 $h - 0.6 = -2.8$
$h = -2.2$

40 $j - \frac{3}{4} = 8\frac{1}{2}$
$j = \frac{37}{4}$

41 $2 + x = 1.4$
$x = -0.6$

42 $y + 3\frac{1}{3} = 5$
$y = \frac{5}{3}$

43 $6.18 = R + 2.89$
$R = 3.29$

44 $12 = w - 4.7$
$u = 16.7$

Problem Set C

Solve and check.

45 $x + 3 \cdot 3 = 2 \cdot 2 \cdot 2$
$x = -1$

46 $n + 2 = 2n$
$n = 2$

47 $m - 3 = 2m$
$m = -3$

48 $2x + 4 = x$
$x = -4$

49 $2y - 6 = y$
$y = 6$

50 $t + 3 = 2t - 4$
$t = 7$

51 $2w - 5 = w + 8$
$w = 13$

52 $2x + 1 = 5 + x$
$x = 4$

53 $3 - v = 5 - 2v$
$v = 2$

54 $2r - 11 = 1 - r$
$r = 4$

After-School Mathematics: Lemon Ice Vendor

During the summer Maria sells lemon ice from a push cart on the shopping mall downtown. She sells two sizes: a five-ounce lemon ice is fifty cents and a seven-ounce is seventy cents.

A friend of Maria's had been shopping all day, and she had only thirty cents left. She asked Maria if she could have a three-ounce lemon ice for the thirty cents. Maria agreed, but she had to think about how to measure three ounces since she didn't have a three-ounce cup.

This is how Maria solved the problem. First, she filled a five-ounce cup and poured the five ounces into a seven-ounce cup. Then she refilled the five-ounce cup and used it to fill up the seven-ounce cup. Since the seven-ounce cup had needed only two more ounces, she was left with three ounces in the five-ounce cup.

Maria was so pleased with herself for solving the problem that she spent an hour after work finding ways to get every amount between one ounce and twelve ounces.

Application: Left-Handed Desks

How many left-handed desks would be needed for all the classes of first-year algebra? Find the mean number of left-handed students per classroom, which is the total number of left-handed students divided by the number of classrooms.

Also find the maximum number of left-handed desks that would be needed per classroom so that every left-handed student could use one.

Section 2.7 Solving Problems: Addition and Subtraction

Solving problems, and then explaining the solution, requires organized work. Some steps that help organize the work are:

Step 1   Representing the problem as a question, using a variable and, if helpful, a diagram.

Step 2   Setting up and then solving an equation.

Step 3   Testing that the solution is reasonable, and then answering the original question.

Sample Problems

1   Maria is driving from Houston to Dallas, a distance of 225 miles. If she sees a sign saying "Dallas: 46 miles," how far has she driven?

PROCEDURE   To represent the problem, let d stand for the number of miles Maria has driven.

Set up and solve an equation:

$$d + 46 = 225$$
$$\text{SUBTRACT } 46 \ (d + 46) = \text{SUBTRACT } 46 \ (225)$$
$$d = 179$$

The solution seems reasonable. Maria has driven 179 miles so far.

2   For the following problem, which of the four equations represents a translation of the problem:

Fred has nine tropical fish. On his birthday, he was given eighteen more fish by his family and friends. How many fish did he have then?

A $9 + n = 18$ C $n + 9 = 18$
B $n + 18 = 9$ D $9 + 18 = n$

PROCEDURE   The correct translation is $9 + 18 = n$,   which is choice D.

Problem Set **A**

For each equation, select the sentence that the equation translates:

1 $n + 7 = 5$ *b*
   a The sum of a number and five is seven.
   b The sum of a number and seven is five.
   c Seven more than five is some number.
   d Seven is the result of increasing a number by five.

2 $10 = 7 - m$ *c*
   a The sum of ten and seven is some number.
   b The difference between ten and a number is seven.
   c Ten is the difference between seven and a number.
   d Ten is seven fewer than a number.

For each word problem, select the equation which is a correct translation.

3 Fourteen fewer than a number is nine. *a*
   a $N - 14 = 9$ c $N + 9 = 14$
   b $14 - 9 = N$ d $14 - N = 9$

4 The sum of a number and seventeen is five. *c*
   a $17 = 5$ c $n + 17 = 5$
   b $17 + 5 = n$ d $n + 5 = 17$

5 Willy needs to lose four pounds to be able to wrestle in the one hundred twenty-eight pound class. What is his current weight? *b*
   a $4 - 128 = W$ c $W = 4 - 128$
   b $W - 4 = 128$ d $4 - W = 128$

6 A plane cruising at nine thousand meters climbed to avoid a storm cloud and leveled off at eleven thousand five hundred meters. How high did it climb to avoid the storm? *a*
   a $9000 + C = 11500$ c $9000 = 11500 + C$
   b $11500 + C = 9000$ d $9000 = C + 11500$

7 In three years Melinda will be eighteen. How old is she now? *b*
   a $18 + y = 13$ c $3y = 18$
   b $y + 3 = 18$ d $y - 3 = 18$

ASSIGNMENT GUIDE

Basic (1 day)
8–25

Average (1 day)
8–16 (even), 26–34 (even)

Advanced (1 day)
26–44 (even)

As additional oral exercises, students could translate each of the choices in problems 1–7 to a variable or verbal expression.

For each problem, choose a variable, set up an equation, and find the answer. Remember to check your answers for reasonableness.

8 Name a variable and add forty-three. If the result is ninety-two, what is the value of the variable?

$x + 43 = 92, x = 49$

9 The sum of a number and twenty-four is fifty. What is the number?

$n + 24 = 50, n = 26$

10 A number decreased by eighteen is twenty. What is the number?

$s - 18 = 20, s = 38$

11 Pick a number and subtract thirty-eight. If the result is negative twenty, what is the original number?

$x - 38 = -20, x = 18$

12 The sum of two integers is negative twelve. If one integer is negative eight, what is the other?

$-8 + y = -12, y = -4$

13 The difference of two integers is thirteen. If the integer that was subtracted is negative four, what is the other integer?

$y - (-4) = 13, y = 9$

14 The 3 PM temperature of $46°F$ was $12°F$ more than the 8 AM temperature. What was the 8 AM temperature?

$m + 12 = 46, m = 34$

15 At the top of a ski-lift the temperature was $15°$ less than the temperature at the base of the mountain. If the temperature at the base was $29°$, what was the temperature at the top?

$29 - t = 15, t = 14$

16 Carlos said he was eighteen when he graduated from high school five years ago. How old is he now?

$c = 18 + 5, c = 23$

17 In six years, Joanne will be twenty-three years old. How old is she now?

$x + 6 = 23, x = 17$

Find the value of each function. (Review: Section 1.5)

18 MULTIPLYBY 2 (5)

10

19 DIVIDEBY 3 (24)

8

20 DIVIDEBY 3 ($3x$)

x

21 MULTIPLYBY 4 $\left(\dfrac{n}{4}\right)$

n

22 MULTIPLYBY 5 (3)

15

23 MULTIPLYBY 5 (2)

10

24 MULTIPLYBY 5 (1)

5

25 MULTIPLYBY 5 (0)

0

Problem Set B

26 Last Fall, the West High School marching band had eighty members. If twenty-eight members graduated since then and no new member joined, how many members are in the band this Fall?

52

27 Carol bought a pair of boots on sale for eighteen dollars. Last month they were selling for twenty-seven dollars. How much did she save?

$9

28 Heat and electricity together cost a company $850 for the month of January. If electricity alone cost $385, how much did the heat cost?

$465

29 The electric meter at a house read 78,244 kilowatt hours on June 1. One month later it read 80,138 kilowatt hours. How much electricity was used during that month?

1894 kWhrs

30 An auditorium has a seating capacity of one thousand two hundred. For one particular program, all the seats were filled with the exception of forty-eight at the back. How many seats were occupied?

1152

31 A car cost a used-car dealer $1,890, and was sold for $2,479. How much profit was made on the car?

$589

32 A student has grades of 65 and 76 on two exams. In order to maintain the average she desires, she must have accumulated 210 points after the third exam. What grade must she receive on her third exam so that the three scores will add up to 210?

69

33 A man owed $400 to his bank. He paid back $250 but later borrowed some more money. If he now owes $300, how much did he borrow?

$150

34 In September, E. J. Todd wrote checks for $47, $140, $86, $241, and $18. If her balance was $471 on September 30, and she made no deposits in September, how much did she start with on September 1?

$1003

35 A caterer charged four dollars a plate at a banquet for one hundred twenty-seven people. How much were her expenses if her profit was one hundred nineteen dollars?

$389

Problem Set C

36 If one fourth is added to a number, the sum is seven twelfths. What is the number?

$\frac{1}{3}$

37 The sum of two numbers is forty-two and three tenths. If one number is negative thirteen and eight tenths, what is the other?

56.1

38 If forty-two and sixty-three hundredths is subtracted from a number, the difference is twenty-nine and thirty-five hundredths. What is the number?

71.98

39 The difference of two fractions is three fourths. If the smaller fraction is one eighth, what is the other fraction?

$\frac{7}{8}$

40 Yu Wing's family was driving a car that held fourteen and four tenths gallons of fuel in its tank. When they stopped for gas, they filled up with thirteen and seven tenths gallons. How much had been left in the tank when they stopped?

0.7

41 One side of a record contains five songs. The times for the first four songs are $3\frac{1}{2}$, $5\frac{2}{3}$, $5\frac{1}{6}$, and $4\frac{1}{4}$ minutes. The whole side takes $24\frac{1}{3}$ minutes. How long is the fifth song?

$5\frac{3}{4}$ min.

42 A utility stock worth eighteen and seven eighths rose two and one half points one day. The following day, the stock closed at nineteen and five eighths. Did the stock go up or go down, and by how much?

$-1\frac{3}{4}$ (down)

43 Serena plans to sew a matching outfit of slacks, vest, and jacket. The entire outfit requires four and one half yards of fabric. If she already has the two and one half yards needed for the jacket, and three fourths yard for the vest, how much more should she buy for the slacks?

$1\frac{1}{4}$ yds.

44 In 1967, USSR Soyez I orbited the earth seventeen times before crashing. If the total time of the flight was twenty-six hours and forty minutes, how long did it take to fly one revolution?

94

45 In the first summer Olympic Games in Athens, two hundred eighty-five athletes participated. In the 1936 Olympics in Berlin, about eighteen times as many participated, and in Montreal, in 1976, nearly thirty-four times as many took part. About how many performed in those three Olympic games?

15, 105

Chapter Study Guide

ASSIGNMENT GUIDE

Basic (2 days)
(1) 90: 1–24
(2) 54: 11, 17
    71: 30–33
    79: 15–23 (odd)
    81: 1–7

Average (1 day)
90: 1–24
80: 35–43 (odd)
85: 31, 33, 35

Advanced (1 day)
90: 1–24
80: 51–54
86: 41, 43, 45

Vocabulary

As you study and review this chapter, be sure to learn the important mathematics vocabulary, including:

1   **Absolute Value**   For a number and its point on a number line, the ABSOLUTE VALUE of the number is the distance between the point and the origin.

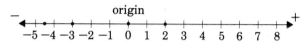

- The absolute value of −3 is 3.
- ABSVAL (2) = 2
- $|-4.5| = 4.5$

2   **Equivalent Equations**
Equations that have the same solution are called EQUIVALENT EQUATIONS.

- The following equations have the same solution, $y = -2$:

$$y + 5 = 3 \qquad\qquad -6 = y - 4 \qquad\qquad y - 2 = -4$$

Skills

Be sure you build the useful algebraic skills, including:

3   **Labeling points on a number line**
Label the points that represent $-4, -1\frac{1}{4}$, and 3.75.

PROCEDURE

Represent each number with a solid dot, and label the points:

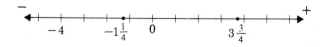

4 Using a number line to add signed numbers Find each sum:

a   3 + 2
b   −2 + 7
c   −3 + (−2)
d   5 + (−8)

PROCEDURE   Draw a separate number line for each sum.

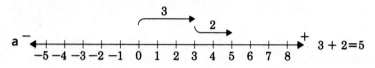

a $\quad 3 + 2 = 5$

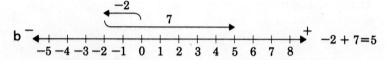

b $\quad -2 + 7 = 5$

c $\quad -3 + (-2) = -5$

d $\quad 5 + (-8) = -3$

5 Subtracting signed numbers Find each difference:

a   4 − (−6)
b   −3 − (−7)
c   −10 − 8

PROCEDURE   Use the subtraction property that $r - s = r + \text{OPP}(s)$.

a $\quad 4 - (-6) = 4 + \text{OPP}(-6)$
$\qquad\qquad\quad = 4 + 6$
$\qquad\qquad\quad = 10$

b $\quad -3 - (-7) = -3 + \text{OPP}(-7)$
$\qquad\qquad\qquad = -3 + 7$
$\qquad\qquad\qquad = 4$

c $\quad -10 - 8 = -10 + \text{OPP}(8)$
$\qquad\qquad\qquad = -10 + (-8)$
$\qquad\qquad\qquad = -18$

6 Solving equations

Solve each equation by isolating the variable, and check each solution:

a $\quad p + 5 = 12$

b $\quad q - 8 = -15$

c $\quad 17 = 8 + s$

PROCEDURE   Add or subtract a number from each side of the equation to isolate the variable:

a
$$p + 5 = 12$$
$$\text{SUBTRACT 5 } (p + 5) = \text{SUBTRACT 5 } (12)$$
$$p = 7$$

To check $\quad p + 5 = 12$
$$(7) + 5 \overset{?}{=} 12$$
$$12 \overset{?}{=} 12 \checkmark$$

b
$$q - 8 = -15$$
$$\text{ADD 8 } (q - 8) = \text{ADD 8 } (-15)$$
$$q = -7$$

To check $\quad q - 8 = -15$
$$(-7) - 8 \overset{?}{=} -15$$
$$-15 \overset{?}{=} -15 \checkmark$$

c
$$17 = 8 + s$$
$$\text{SUBTRACT 8 } (17) = \text{SUBTRACT 8 } (8 + s)$$
$$9 = s$$

To check $\quad 17 = 8 + s$
$$17 \overset{?}{=} 8 + (9)$$
$$17 \overset{?}{=} 17 \checkmark$$

7 Solving Problems
LeNay gained 6 pounds since the beginning of school. If she now weighs 91 pounds, what did she weigh at the start of school?

PROCEDURE   Use a variable and represent the problem as an equation. Let w represent LeNay's weight at the start of school. Then the equation is:

$$w + 6 = 91$$
$$\text{SUBTRACT 6 } (w + 6) = \text{SUBTRACT 6 } (91)$$
$$w = 85$$

LeNay weighed 85 pounds at the beginning of school.

Chapter Test

Graph each set of numbers on a separate number line.

1 the whole numbers < 4

    0, 1, 2, 3

3 the real numbers < 2

    open circle at 2, solid line in negative direction from 2

2 the natural numbers < 5

    1, 2, 3, 4

4 the integers > -4

    $-3, -2, -1, 0, 1, 2, \ldots$

5 Is $2\frac{1}{3}$ a positive number? a rational number? an integer?

    yes, yes, no

Use arrows on a number line to represent each sum.

6 $2 + (-7)$

    -5

7 $-5 + 3$

    -2

8 $-3 + (-4)$

    -7

Evaluate each expression.

9 OPP (18) + ABSVAL (-5)

    -13

12 ABSVAL (OPP (-2) + OPP (6))

    4

10 $-3 + 8$

    5

13 $17 + (-13) - (-4)$

    8

11 $-4 - (-12)$

    8

14 $-62 + 41 - (-38)$

    17

Evaluate $2x - y$ for the following values:

15 $x = 5$ and $y = -3$

    13

16 $x = \frac{1}{2}$ and $y = \frac{2}{3}$

    $\frac{1}{3}$

For each variable expression, tell how to isolate the variable.

17 $x + 8$

    SUBTRACT 8

19 $n + (-4)$

    ADD 4

18 $p - 3$

    ADD 3

20 $-9 + y$

    ADD 9

Solve and check each equation.

21 $x - 5 = -3$

    $x = 2$

22 $-8 = x + 16$

    $x = -24$

For each problem, choose a variable, set up an equation, and find the answer.

23 The sum of a number and twelve is negative three. What is the number?

    $x + 12 = -3, x = -15$

24 Kim is riding the new bicycle trail, which is 8 miles long. She sees a sign that says "Trail's End: 2.5 miles." How far has she ridden?

    $x + 2.5 = 8, x = 5.5$

Problem Set: Using the " – " Sign

The back of the text does not supply any answers for this Problem Set.

The negative sign has three different, but related, meanings in mathematics. It can be used in front of a single numeral to indicate a negative number.

Find each sum of signed numbers.

1 $63 + (-27)$
   36

2 $-738 + 472$
   -266

3 $-97 + (-127)$
   -224

4 $37 + (-3) + 8 + (-18)$
   24

5 $-4 + 10 + (-9) + (-2)$
   -5

6 $-\frac{2}{3} + (-\frac{1}{2}) + (-\frac{1}{12})$
   $-\frac{5}{4}$

When a negative sign is used between two numbers or expressions, it indicates the operation of subtraction.

Find each difference.

7 $-634 - (-973)$
   339

8 $-83 - (-83)$
   0

9 $52 - 18$
   34

10 $14 - (-12)$
   26

11 $52\frac{1}{4} - 45\frac{1}{2}$
   $6\frac{3}{4}$

12 $52\frac{1}{4} - (-45\frac{1}{2})$
   $97\frac{3}{4}$

When a negative sign is used before a variable or an expression, it means "the opposite of" that variable or expression.

Find each expression.

13 $-(8 + 3)$
   -11

14 $-(54 + 19 - 23)$
   -50

15 $-x$ if $x = 17$
   -17

16 $-y$ if $y = -12$
   12

For each negative sign, first indicate whether the sign means a negative number, subtraction, or "the opposite of." Then evaluate the expression.

17 $-3 - (6 + (-9))$
   neg, subt, neg; 0

18 $5 - 3(4) (-2)$
   subt, neg; 29

19 $4 - (-4)$
   subt, neg; 8

20 $(-t)^2 - t$ if $t = -4$
   opp, subt; 20

21 $-5 - (-y)$ if $y = -10$
   neg, subt, opp; -15

22 $-3 - (-17) + (-12)$
   neg, subt, neg, neg; 2

Chapter 3

CHAPTER SCHEDULE

Basic
Problem Sets	11 Days
Review	3 Days
Test	2 Days

Average
Problem Sets	10 Days
Review	2 Days
Test	2 Days

Advanced
Problem Sets	11 Days
Review	2 Days
Test	1 Day

OPERATIONS AND EQUATIONS

Chapter 3 extends the skills of solving equations to multiplication and division and to two-step equations.

Section 3.1 Using Natural Numbers as Exponents

SECTION SCHEDULE

Basic (1 day)

Average (2 days)

Advanced (2 days)

A certain radioactive isotope has a **half-life** of 1 day. This means that at the end of one day, only one half of the original amount of the isotope is still radioactive. After a second day, one half of the remaining amount is still radioactive, and so on.

- If a chemical starts with 1 gram of the radioactive isotope, then:

after 1 day	$\frac{1}{2}$ remains radioactive
after 2 days	$\frac{1}{2} \cdot \frac{1}{2}$ remains radioactive
after 3 days	$\frac{1}{2} \cdot \frac{1}{2} \cdot \frac{1}{2}$ remains radioactive
after 4 days	$\frac{1}{2} \cdot \frac{1}{2} \cdot \frac{1}{2} \cdot \frac{1}{2}$ remains radioactive

and so forth.

The product $\frac{1}{2} \cdot \frac{1}{2} \cdot \frac{1}{2} \cdot \frac{1}{2}$ can be written as $(\frac{1}{2})^4$, where $\frac{1}{2}$ is called the **base** and the natural number 4 is used as an **exponent**.

Definition

A natural number EXPONENT is a number that indicates how many times a BASE is used as a factor.

EXAMPLES

- $2^5 = 2 \cdot 2 \cdot 2 \cdot 2 \cdot 2 = 32$ "two raised to the fifth power;" or more simply, "two to the fifth"

- $(0.2)^2 = (0.2)(0.2) = 0.04$ "two tenths to the second power;" "two tenths squared"

- $a^3 = a \cdot a \cdot a$ "a to the third power;" "a cubed"

- $4^1 = 4,\ x^1 = x$ The exponent 1 means simply the base number; it is usual to omit the exponent 1.

In each case, the exponent is written just after the base and is written a half-line above the base. The entire expression of a base raised to an exponent is called a **power**.

Sample Problems

1   Write each expression using exponents:
   a $x \cdot x \cdot x \cdot x \cdot x$
   b $(4ab)(3a)(2b)(2b)$

   PROCEDURE   Count the number of times each base is used as a factor.
     a $x \cdot x \cdot x \cdot x \cdot x = x^5$
     b $(4ab)(3a)(2b)(2b) = (4 \cdot 3 \cdot 2 \cdot 2)(a \cdot a)(b \cdot b \cdot b)$
                  $= 48a^2b^3$

2   Rewrite each product without parentheses:
   a $(2a)^2$
   b $(5xy)^3$

   PROCEDURE   When an exponent follows a set of parentheses, then the base is the entire expression inside the parentheses:

a $(2a)^2 = (2a)(2a)$
$= (2 \cdot 2)(a \cdot a)$
$= 4a^2$

b $(5xy)^3 = (5xy)(5xy)(5xy)$
$= (5 \cdot 5 \cdot 5)(x \cdot x \cdot x)(y \cdot y \cdot y)$
$= 125x^3y^3$

In part **a**, note that $(2a)^2$ is **not** equal to $2a^2$. For the expression $(2a)^2$, the base is the entire expression inside the parentheses.

3 The number 4.13×10^5 represents $4.13 \times 10 \cdot 10 \cdot 10 \cdot 10 \cdot 10 = 413,000$. A number such as 4.13×10^5 is said to be in **scientific notation** when it is written as a product of a number between 1 and 10 (the number can be equal to 1 but must be less than 10) and a power of 10.

Students with calculators may need some explanation of the relation between scientific notation (e.g., 3.25×10^{64}) and calculator notation (e.g., $3.25 \quad 64$).

Write in scientific notation:

a 3,000,000   **b** 100   **c** 40,056.8

PROCEDURE   Write each number as the product of a number between 1 and 10 times a power of 10:

a $3,000,000 = 3 \times 1,000,000 = 3 \times 10^6$
b $100 = 1 \times 100 = 1 \times 10^2$ (or simply, 10^2)
c $40,056.8 = 4.00568 \times 10,000 = 4.00568 \times 10^4$

Problem Set A

ASSIGNMENT GUIDE

Basic (1 day)
6–40 (even)

Average (2 days)
(1) 20–40 (even), 54–60
(2) 64–68
99: 1–18

Advanced (2 days)
(1) 20–40 (even),
54–68 (even)
(2) 69–75
99: 1–18

1 In the expression 3^4, the natural number 4 is used as a(n) __?__. The base is __?__.
exponent, 3

2 The expression a^2 is read __?__; the expression $(3x)^5$ is read __?__.
a squared, a to the second power; the fifth power of $3x$

3 The expressions 4^1, y^1, and $(xt)^1$ are usually written __?__, __?__, and __?__, respectively.
4, y, xt

4 The expression 6.2×10^5 is written in __?__ __?__.
scientific notation

In problems 5–10, rewrite each expression as a product without using exponents.

5 a^5 $a \cdot a \cdot a \cdot a \cdot a$

7 $2x^4$ $2x \cdot x \cdot x \cdot x$

9 $4d^3k^2$ $4d \cdot d \cdot d \cdot k \cdot k$

6 b^7 $b \cdot b \cdot b \cdot b \cdot b \cdot b \cdot b$

8 $13n^6$ $13n \cdot n \cdot n \cdot n \cdot n \cdot n$

10 $11s^3t^5$ $11s \cdot s \cdot s \cdot t \cdot t \cdot t \cdot t \cdot t$

In problems 11–18, rewrite each expression using exponents.

11 $a \cdot a \cdot a$
a^3

15 $x \cdot x \cdot x \cdot y \cdot y$
$x^3 y^2$

12 $b \cdot b \cdot b \cdot b \cdot b \cdot b$
b^6

16 $a \cdot a \cdot b \cdot b$
$a^2 b^2$ or $(ab)^2$

13 $2 \cdot x \cdot x$
$2x^2$

17 $a \cdot b \cdot a \cdot b \cdot a \cdot a \cdot b$
$a^4 b^3$

14 $3 \cdot y \cdot y \cdot y \cdot y$
$3y^4$

18 $3 \cdot x \cdot y \cdot z \cdot y \cdot y \cdot x$
$3x^2 y^2 z$

In problems 19–28, express each number in scientific notation.

19 2345
2.345×10^3

24 six hundred
6.0×10^2

20 8103
8.103×10^3

25 four million
4.0×10^6

21 62,000
6.2×10^4

26 400
4.0×10^2

22 3,600,000,000
3.6×10^9

27 324.9
3.249×10^2

23 one googol (1 followed by 100 zeros)
1.0×10^{100}

28 36,001.72
3.600172×10^4

In problems 29–40, write each expression as a single real number.

29 5^2
25

33 $(\frac{1}{2})^2$
$\frac{1}{4}$

37 1.3×10^2
130

30 3^3
27

34 $(\frac{1}{3})^3$
$\frac{1}{27}$

38 2.1×10^7
21,000,000

31 4^2
16

35 10^5
100,000

39 3.27×10^5
327,000

32 2^5
32

36 10^8
100,000,000

40 8.032×10^6
8,032,000

In problems 41–50, find the sum or difference. (Review: Sections 2.3 and 2.4)

41 $5 - 9$
-4

46 $8 + (-11)$
-3

42 $5 + (-9)$
-4

47 $17 - (-4)$
21

43 $5 - (-9)$
14

48 $-3 + 19$
16

44 $-5 - 9$
-14

49 $25 - 3 + (-4)$
18

45 $-5 + (-9)$
-14

50 $-17 + 9 - 12 + (-3)$
-23

Problem Set B

In problems 51–60, evaluate each expression.

51 x^3 for $x = 5$
125

52 y^{17} for $y = 1$
1

53 $6x^2$ for $x = 4$
96

54 $7k^3$ for $k = 2$
56

55 $(2x)^2$ for $x = 3$
36

56 $(3v)^4$ for $v = 2$
1296

57 a^2b for $a = 6$ and $b = 8$
288

58 x^3y for $x = 3$ and $y = 4$
108

59 $(2t)^2w$ for $t = 5$ and $w = 12$
1200

60 $2t^2w$ for $t = 5$ and $w = 12$
600

In problems 61–68, express each as a power (that is, a base raised to an exponent).

61 8, base 2 (Solution: $8 = 2^3$)
2^3

62 9, base 3
3^2

63 81, base 3
3^4

64 625, base 5
5^4

65 625, base 25
25^2

66 $x^2 \cdot x^5$, base x
x^7

67 $y \cdot y^3 \cdot y^2$, base y
y^6

68 $x^2 \cdot y \cdot x^3 \cdot y^4$, base xy
$x^5 y^5$ or $(xy)^5$

Problem Set C

Problems 69–71 can be solved using a calculator with a y^x key.

69 Which is greater, 9^{10} or 10^9?
9^{10}

70 Which is greater, 5^{12} or 12^5?
5^{12}

71 Which is less, 10^{11} or 11^{10}?
11^{10}

72 Which is least, $(-5)^5$, -5^6, or $(-5)^6$?
-5^6

73 If $a \neq b$, is it ever true that $a^b = b^a$?
yes, $2^4 = 4^2$

74 Evaluate 3^{3^3}. (This means $3^{(3^3)}$.)
19,683

75 Evaluate $2^{2^{2^2}}$.
65,536

69) If $a > 2$ and $b > 2$,
$a^b > b^a$ when
$b > a$.

72) $(-5)^5 = -5^5$
$(-5)^6 = 5^6$
$-5^6 < -5^5 < 5^6$
$-5^6 < (-5)^5 < (-5)^6$

75) $2^{(2^{(2^2)})} = 2^{(2^4)} = 2^{16}$
$= 65536$

X tending the topic: **Properties of Exponents**

Several properties of natural number exponents follow from the definition. If m and n are natural numbers, then:

$$a^m = \underbrace{a \cdot a \cdot \ldots \cdot a}_{m \text{ factors}} \quad \text{and} \quad a^n = \underbrace{a \cdot a \cdot a \cdot \ldots \cdot a}_{n \text{ factors}}$$

Notice that

$$(a^m)(a^n) = \underbrace{(a \cdot a \cdot \ldots \cdot a)}_{m \text{ factors}} \underbrace{(a \cdot a \cdot a \cdot \ldots \cdot a)}_{n \text{ factors}}$$

$$= \underbrace{a \cdot a \cdot a \cdot a \cdot a \cdot \ldots \cdot a \cdot a \cdot a \cdot a}_{m + n \text{ factors}}$$

$$= a^{m+n}$$

$$(ab)^m = \underbrace{(ab)(ab) \cdot \ldots \cdot (ab)}_{m \text{ factors}}$$

$$= \underbrace{(a \cdot a \cdot \ldots \cdot a)}_{m \text{ factors}} \underbrace{(b \cdot b \cdot \ldots \cdot b)}_{m \text{ factors}}$$

$$= a^m b^m$$

$$(a^m)^n = \underbrace{(\underbrace{a \cdot a \cdot \ldots \cdot a}_{m \text{ factors}})^n}_{n \text{ factors}}$$

$$= \overbrace{(a \cdot a \cdot \ldots \cdot a)(a \cdot a \cdot \ldots \cdot a)(a \cdot a \cdot \ldots \cdot a) \ldots (a \cdot a \cdot \ldots \cdot a)}$$

$$= a^{mn}$$

Finally, note that
$$\frac{a^6}{a^4} = \frac{a \cdot a \cdot a \cdot a \cdot a \cdot a}{a \cdot a \cdot a \cdot a} = \frac{a \cdot a \cdot a \cdot a}{a \cdot a \cdot a \cdot a} \cdot \frac{a \cdot a}{1} = a^2$$

$$\frac{a^3}{a^5} = \frac{a \cdot a \cdot a}{a \cdot a \cdot a \cdot a \cdot a} = \frac{a \cdot a \cdot a}{a \cdot a \cdot a} \cdot \frac{1}{a \cdot a} = \frac{1}{a^2}$$

More generally:

$$\frac{a^m}{a^n} = \begin{cases} a^{m-n} & \text{if } m > n \\ 1 & \text{if } m = n \\ \dfrac{1}{a^{n-m}} & \text{if } m < n \end{cases}$$

To summarize, the following are four properties of natural number exponents:

Properties

If m and n are natural numbers, and a and b are bases, then:

$$a^m \cdot a^n = a^{m+n}$$
$$(ab)^m = a^m b^m$$
$$(a^m)^n = a^{mn}$$

$$\frac{a^m}{a^n} = \begin{cases} a^{m-n} & \text{if } m > n \\ 1 & \text{if } m = n \\ \dfrac{1}{a^{n-m}} & \text{if } m < n \end{cases}$$

Brighter students may be able to generate definitions for zero or integral exponents that would maintain these properties:

If $\dfrac{a^5}{a^5}$ is to be

$$a^{5-5} = a^0$$

then a^0 must be 1.

If $\dfrac{a^5}{a^7}$ is to be

$$a^{5-7} = a^{-2}$$

then a^{-2} must be

$$\dfrac{1}{a^2} \left(\text{or } a^{-n} = \dfrac{1}{a^n} \right)$$

Problem Set X

Use the properties of exponents to rewrite each expression:

1 $r^{20} \cdot r^{10}$

r^{30}

2 $r^5 \cdot r^m$

r^{m+5}

3 $q^t \cdot q^t$

q^{2t}

4 $(p \cdot q)^7$

$p^7 q^7$

5 $(3mn)^4$

$81 m^4 n^4$

6 $(2a^3 b)^4$

$16 a^{12} b^4$

7 $\dfrac{m^5}{m}$

m^4

8 $\dfrac{m^h}{m^q} \quad (h > q)$

m^{h-q}

9 $\dfrac{m^h}{m^q} \quad (h < q)$

$\dfrac{1}{m^{q-h}}$

Rewrite each expression using the given base. (Problem 10 is done as an example.)

10 9^4, base 3

Since $9 = 3^2$, rewrite 9^4 as $(3^2)^4 = 3^8$.

3^8

11 4^3, base 2

2^6

12 16^3, base 2

2^{12}

13 25^2, base 5

5^4

14 $(\tfrac{1}{8})^{10}$, base $\tfrac{1}{2}$

$\left(\dfrac{1}{2}\right)^{30}$

15 $(\tfrac{1}{4})^3$, base $\tfrac{1}{2}$

$\left(\dfrac{1}{2}\right)^6$

16 1000^{1000}, base 10

10^{3000}

17 $(0.01)^5$, base 0.1

$(0.1)^{10}$

18 $(0.49)^{15}$, base 0.7

$(0.7)^{30}$

Section 3.2 Multiplying Signed Numbers

Mr. Phillip Waters prepares the city pool for the swimming season.

- When filling the pool, water pours in at the rate of 30 gallons per minute. How many gallons flow into the pool in 3 minutes?
  Solution: $30 \cdot 3 = 90$

- How many fewer gallons were in the pool 3 minutes earlier? Using signed numbers, "3 minutes earlier" is -3, and there were 90 gallons fewer in the pool, or -90. In algebraic terms, the solution is: $30 \cdot (-3) = -90$

  In this example, a **positive factor** times a **negative factor** results in a **negative product**.

- When Mr. Waters drains the pool, the pool empties at the rate of 30 gallons per minute, or, as a signed number, -30. How many gallons have drained at the end of 3 minutes? Solution: $(-30) \cdot 3 = -90$

  In this case, a **negative factor** times a **positive factor** results in a **negative product**.

This example can be extended to talk about a negative factor times a negative factor.

- Suppose the pool is being drained. How many more gallons were in the pool 3 minutes ago?

rate:	-30	the pool is being drained
time:	-3	3 minutes ago
amount:	$+90$	there was more water in the pool 3 minutes ago

  The solution is: $(-30) \cdot (-3) = +90$. In this example, a **negative factor** times a **negative factor** results in a **positive product**.

These examples illustrate the general pattern for multiplying signed numbers:

Property

  a **The product of two positive numbers is positive.**

  b **The product of a negative number and a positive number is negative.**

  c **The product of two negative numbers is positive.**

Sample Problems

1   Multiply:
   a $(-2)(7)$
   b $(0)(-6)$
   c $(-5)(-6)$
   d $(-2)(-5)(7)$

> **PROCEDURE**   For each product, first find the absolute value of the product, and then determine whether the product is positive or negative.
>
> a   The absolute value of the product is 14, and the product must be negative:
> $$(-2)(7) = -14$$
> b   The product of any number times zero is zero:
> $$(0)(-6) = 0$$
> c   The absolute value of the product is 30, and the product must be positive:
> $$(-5)(-6) = 30$$
> d   The absolute value of the product is 70, and the product must be positive:
> $$(-2)(-5)(7) = 70$$
>
> In general, if no factor is zero, then an even number of negative factors results in a positive product, while an odd number of negative factors results in a negative product.

2   Evaluate each expression:
   a MULTIPLYBY 5 (-2)
   b MULTIPLYBY -4 $(7\frac{1}{2})$
   c MULTIPLYBY -4 (-3)
   d MULTIPLYBY $-\frac{1}{6}$ (-6)
   e MULTIPLYBY $-\frac{1}{2}$ (-2)

> **PROCEDURE**
>
> a   MULTIPLYBY 5 (-2) means $(-2)(5) = -10$
> b   MULTIPLYBY -4 $(7\frac{1}{2})$ means $(7\frac{1}{2})(-4) = -30$
> c   MULTIPLYBY -4 (-3) means $(-3)(-4) = 12$
> d   MULTIPLYBY $-\frac{1}{6}$ (-6) means $(-6)(-\frac{1}{6}) = 1$
> e   MULTIPLYBY $-\frac{1}{2}$ (-2) means $(-2)(-\frac{1}{2}) = 1$

ASSIGNMENT GUIDE

Basic (1½ days)

(1) 5–34
(2) See p. 108.

Average (1 day)
20–50 (even), 58–63

Advanced (1 day)
20–50 (even), 58–71

Problems 5–26 can be used as oral exercises by asking students to state the sign of the product.

Problem Set A

1 If two numbers have the same sign, then their product is ___?___.
positive

2 If two numbers have opposite signs, their product is ___?___.
negative

3 The product of a positive number times zero is ___?___.
zero

4 The product of a negative number times zero is ___?___.
zero

In problems 5–26, find each product.

5 $(\frac{1}{2})(-\frac{1}{2})$
$-\frac{1}{4}$

6 $(-1)(-1)$
1

7 $(-8)(6)$
-48

8 $(-12)(5)$
-60

9 $(-7)(+5)$
-35

10 $(-9)(+15)$
-135

11 $(3)(-9)$
-27

12 $(4)(-25)$
-100

13 $(2)(-17)$
-34

14 $(5)(-15)$
-75

15 $(-5)(+5)$
-25

16 $(-8)(+8)$
-64

17 $(7)(-7)$
-49

18 $(12)(-12)$
-144

19 $(-4)(-3)$
12

20 $(-20)(-40)$
800

21 $(-5)(-6)$
30

22 $(-10)(-35)$
350

23 $(-3)(0)$
0

24 $(-17)(0)$
0

25 $(0)(-5)$
0

26 $(0)(-23)$
0

In problems 27–34, evaluate each expression.

27 $4x$, for $x = -6$
-24

28 $8n$, for $n = -12$
-96

29 $-6y$, for $y = -2$
12

30 $-10t$, for $t = -5$
50

31 $3x - y$, for $x = -3, y = 5$
-14

32 $4m - n$, for $m = -7, n = 11$
-39

33 $-2s + t$, for $s = -3, t = -4$
2

34 $-5c - 2d$, for $c = 5, d = -2$
-21

In problems 35–43, write each power without an exponent.

35 $(-3)^2$ 9	**38** $(-5)^2$ 25	**41** $(-1)^5$ -1
36 -3^2 -9	**39** $(-3)^3$ -27	**42** $(-1)^{32}$ 1
37 $(-2)^2$ 4	**40** $(-4)^3$ -64	**43** $[(-2)(-3)]^3$ 216

In problems 44–47, evaluate each expression. (Review: Section 1.5)

These problems preview the concept of a reciprocal, which is presented in the next section.

44   **a**   DIVIDEBY 7 (21)   **b**   MULTIPLYBY $\frac{1}{7}$ (21)   *a* 3; *b* 3

45   **a**   MULTIPLYBY $\frac{1}{5}$ (2)   **b**   DIVIDEBY 5 (2)   *a* $\frac{2}{5}$; *b* $\frac{2}{5}$

46   **a**   DIVIDEBY $\frac{2}{3}$ (12)   **b**   MULTIPLYBY $\frac{3}{2}$ (12)   *a* 18; *b* 18

47   **a**   MULTIPLYBY 1 (27)   **b**   DIVIDEBY 1 (27)   *a* 27; *b* 27

Problem Set   **B**

In problems 48–57, write each product of signed numbers.

48 $(-3)(-7)(6)$ 126	**53** $(-8)(6)(-5)(7)$ 1680
49 $(-5)(11)(-2)$ 110	**54** $(3)(-6)(-5)(-10)$ -900
50 $(20)(-6)(5)$ -600	**55** $(-4)(-6)(-5)(-5)$ 600
51 $(-50)(-7)(2)$ 700	**56** $(36)(-2)(-6)(0)$ 0
52 $(2)(-3.4)(-5)$ 34	**57** $(-12)(8)(0)(-13)$ 0

Consider the function: $\text{RECIP}(x) = \dfrac{1}{x}$

Then RECIP (3) $= \dfrac{1}{3}$ and RECIP (10) $= \dfrac{1}{10}$. Evaluate these expressions:

58   RECIP (2) $\frac{1}{2}$

59   RECIP (5) $\frac{1}{5}$

60   RECIP $(\frac{1}{4})$ 4

61   RECIP $(\frac{2}{3})$ $\frac{3}{2}$

62   RECIP (1)   1

63   RECIP (y) $\frac{1}{y}$

Problem Set C

In problems 64–71, evaluate each expression.

64 $(-6)(3) + (-4)(3)$
-30

65 $-9 - (-5)(7)$
26

66 $3\frac{3}{4} + (-\frac{7}{2})(-\frac{1}{2})$
$5\frac{1}{2}$

67 $-\frac{3}{8} - (\frac{3}{4})(-\frac{5}{2})$
$1\frac{1}{2}$

68 $(-5.3)(-2.1) - (-.94)$
1207

69 $6 - (-5.2)(-8.7)$
-39.24

70 $325(-21) + 675(-21)$
$-21,000$

71 $42836 - (236)(-95)$
$65,256$

In problems 72 and 73, use the **convention** (the agreement) that rotation in the counterclockwise direction is considered positive and rotation in the clockwise direction is considered negative.

72) The ratio of 42 teeth clockwise (gear A) to 21 teeth counterclockwise (gear B) is $-2:1$. The ratio of revolutions of gear A to gear B is $-\frac{1}{2}:1$ or $-1:2$.

72 Gear A and gear B work together as suggested by the figure. Gear A has 42 teeth and gear B has 21 teeth.

  a If gear B makes 5 revolutions in one minute, how many revolutions does gear A make in two minutes?

  b If gear B makes 10 revolutions in one minute, how many revolutions does gear A make in two minutes?

  c If gear B makes r revolutions in one minute, how many revolutions does gear A make in two minutes?

$a \ -5$

$b \ -10$

$c \ -r$

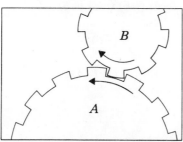

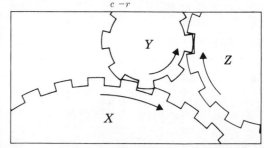

73) The ratio of 30 teeth clockwise (gear X) to 10 teeth counterclockwise (gear Y) to 20 teeth clockwise (gear Z) is $-3:1:-2$. The ratio of revolutions of gear X to gear Y to gear Z is $-\frac{1}{3}:1:-\frac{1}{2}$.

73 Gears X, Y, and Z work together as suggested by the figure. Gear X has thirty teeth, gear Y has ten teeth, and gear Z has twenty teeth. If gear Y revolves eight times per minute, how many revolutions do gears X and Z each make in one minute?

$X: -2\frac{2}{3}$ per minute, $Z: -4$ per minute

Section 3.3   Dividing Signed Numbers

SECTION SCHEDULE

Basic ($1\frac{1}{2}$ days)

Average (1 day)

Advanced (1 day)

The Wonders played at the Jackson Central High School Prom. The five musicians decided on equal shares of the $620 they earned. The drummer used her pencil and paper and divided:

$620 \div 5 = 124$

The guitarist used his calculator and multiplied:

$620 \cdot \frac{1}{5} = 124$

The two group members were using a general relationship between division and multiplication. For numbers a and b ($b \neq 0$), the following two expressions have the same value:

a divided by b $\qquad$ a times $\dfrac{1}{b}$

$$\frac{a}{b} \qquad\qquad a \cdot \frac{1}{b}$$

Property

If a and b are real numbers, $b \neq 0$, then $\dfrac{a}{b} = a \cdot \dfrac{1}{b}$.

EXAMPLES

- $\dfrac{8}{4} = 8 \cdot \dfrac{1}{4}$
- $\dfrac{100}{25} = 100 \cdot \dfrac{1}{25}$

Notice the products of the following pairs of numbers:

- $(5)\left(\dfrac{1}{5}\right) = 1$
- $(x)\left(\dfrac{1}{x}\right) = 1$

- $(-3)\left(-\dfrac{1}{3}\right) = 1$
- $(-t)\left(-\dfrac{1}{t}\right) = 1$

For each pair of numbers, the product of the two factors is 1. Such pairs of numbers are called **reciprocals**.

Definition

If $a \cdot b = 1$ for two real numbers a and b, then each number is the RECIPROCAL of the other number.

The term "multiplicative inverse" is often used for reciprocal.

EXAMPLES

- $\frac{1}{2} \cdot 2 = 1$, so $\frac{1}{2}$ and 2 are reciprocals

- $(-5)\left(-\frac{1}{5}\right) = 1$, so -5 and $-\frac{1}{5}$ are reciprocals

- $\left(\frac{2}{3}\right)\left(\frac{3}{2}\right) = 1$, so $\frac{2}{3}$ and $\frac{3}{2}$ are reciprocals

- $\left(-\frac{5}{7}\right)\left(-\frac{7}{5}\right) = 1$, so $-\frac{5}{7}$ and $-\frac{7}{5}$ are reciprocals

- $(a)\left(\frac{1}{a}\right) = 1$, $(-a)\left(-\frac{1}{a}\right) = 1$, so the pair a and $\frac{1}{a}$ are reciprocals, and the pair $(-a)$ and $\left(-\frac{1}{a}\right)$ are reciprocals (a cannot equal zero)

Note that there is no value for x so that $0 \cdot x = 1$. Therefore the number zero does not have a reciprocal.

A number and its reciprocal must have the same sign; that is, reciprocals are both positive or both negative. This property of reciprocals, along with the properties for multiplying signed numbers, can be used to illustrate properties for dividing signed numbers:

- If a positive number is divided by a negative number, the quotient is negative:

$$\frac{6}{-2} = (6)\left(-\frac{1}{2}\right) = -3$$

- If a negative number is divided by a positive number, the quotient is negative:

$$\frac{-8}{4} = (-8)\left(\frac{1}{4}\right) = -2$$

- If a negative number is divided by a negative number, the quotient is positive:

$$\frac{-24}{-3} = (-24)\left(-\frac{1}{3}\right) = 8$$

Property

a The quotient of two positive numbers is positive.

b The quotient of a positive number and a negative number is negative.

c The quotient of two negative numbers is positive.

Sample Problems

1   Divide:

a $\frac{-72}{6}$

b $\frac{-225}{-25}$

c $\frac{0}{-6}$

d $\frac{-\frac{5}{4}}{\frac{2}{3}}$

PROCEDURE   For each quotient, first find the absolute value of the quotient, and then determine whether it is positive or negative.

a   The absolute value of the quotient is 12 and the sign is negative:

$$\frac{-72}{6} = -12$$

b   The absolute value of the quotient is 9 and the quotient is positive:

$$\frac{-225}{-25} = 9$$

c   The numerator is zero, so the quotient must be zero:

$$\frac{0}{-6} = 0$$

d   Use the property that "x divided by y" is equal to "x times the reciprocal of y".

$$\frac{-\frac{5}{4}}{\frac{2}{3}} = \left(-\frac{5}{4}\right)\left(\frac{3}{2}\right) \quad \text{Note that } \frac{3}{2} \text{ and } \frac{2}{3} \text{ are reciprocals}$$

$$= -\frac{15}{8}$$

2   Evaluate each expression:
a   DIVIDEBY -8 (-40)
b   DIVIDEBY -10 (1000)

PROCEDURE

a   DIVIDEBY -8 (-40) means $\dfrac{-40}{-8} = 5$

b   DIVIDEBY -10 (1000) means $\dfrac{1000}{-10} = -100$

3   Evaluate $\dfrac{-12}{n}$ for $n = -3$.

PROCEDURE   Substitute -3 for n.

$$\frac{-12}{n} = \frac{-12}{-3} = 4$$

ASSIGNMENT GUIDE

Basic ($1\frac{1}{2}$ days)

(1) 7–28
   103: 35–47
(2) 29–46

Average (1 day)
8–48 (even)

Advanced (1 day)
37–41, 50–59
113: 5–13

Problem Set **A**

1 If two numbers are positive, their quotient is ___?___.
positive

2 If two numbers are negative, their quotient is ___?___.
positive

3 The quotient of a positive number and a negative number is ___?___.
negative

4 If the product of two numbers is $+1$, each number is the ___?___ of the other.
reciprocal

5 The reciprocal of a positive number is ___?___.
positive

6 The reciprocal of a negative number is ___?___.
negative

In problems 7–26, find each quotient of signed numbers.

7 $-10 \div 5$
-2

8 $-24 \div 6$
-4

9 $15 \div -3$
-5

10 $6 \div -2$
-3

11 $-12 \div -4$
3

12 $-35 \div -7$
5

13 $3 \div 4$
$\frac{3}{4}$

14 $4 \div 8$
$\frac{1}{2}$

15 $\frac{-8}{4}$
-2

16 $\frac{-18}{6}$
-3

17 $\frac{-9}{-3}$
3

18 $\frac{-51}{-17}$
3

19 $\frac{18}{-3}$
-6

20 $\frac{42}{-7}$
-6

21 $\frac{-4}{8}$
$-\frac{1}{2}$

22 $\frac{-6}{8}$
$-\frac{3}{4}$

23 $\frac{-5}{-10}$
$-\frac{1}{2}$

24 $\frac{-25}{-100}$
$-\frac{1}{4}$

25 $\frac{-3}{-9}$
3

26 $\frac{-25}{-30}$
$\frac{5}{6}$

27 Which of the following is a positive number?
  a $-\frac{1}{5}$ **b** $\frac{-1}{5}$ **c** $\frac{1}{-5}$ **d** $\frac{-1}{-5}$ *d*

28 Which of the following is a negative number?
  a $\frac{-7}{-3}$ **b** $(-7) \div (-3)$ **c** $-\frac{-7}{-3}$ **d** $\frac{7}{3}$ *c*

In problems 29–36, write the reciprocal of each number. Write "no reciprocal" if there is none.

29 $\frac{2}{7}$ $\frac{7}{2}$

30 $\frac{9}{4}$ $\frac{4}{9}$

31 $-\frac{3}{4}$ $-\frac{4}{3}$

32 $-\frac{2}{5}$ $-\frac{5}{2}$

33 $2\frac{1}{2}$

34 -8 $-\frac{1}{8}$

35 0 no reciprocal

36 -1 -1

Translate each of the following into a variable phrase and then evaluate it for $x = -2$, $y = -6$, $z = 12$. (Review: Section 1.3)

37 The quotient found by dividing y by x.　　3

38 The quotient found by dividing z by y.　　-2

39 The number z times the reciprocal of x.　　-6

40 The product of the reciprocal of z and y.　　$-\frac{1}{2}$

41 The number x divided by the sum of y and z.　　$-\frac{1}{3}$

Problem Set　**B**

In problems 42–49, evaluate each expression.

42 $\dfrac{x}{6}$　　for $x = -2$　　$-\frac{1}{3}$

43 $\dfrac{-10}{y}$　　for $y = -25$　　$\frac{2}{5}$

44 $\dfrac{x^2}{4}$　　for $x = -2$　　1

45 $\dfrac{t^3}{27}$　　for $t = -3$　　-1

46 $a + \dfrac{15}{-5}$　　for $a = -9$　　-12

47 $-7 + \dfrac{a}{6}$　　for $a = -12$　　-9

48 $y^2 - \dfrac{y}{3}$　　for $y = -9$　　84

49 $x^2y - \dfrac{x}{y}$　　for $x = -6$, $y = 2$　　75

Problem Set C

Evaluate each expression in problems 50–55.

50 $(-86.4) \div (-0.3)$

288

51 $(0.296) \div (-0.125)$

−2.368

52 the reciprocal of two tenths

5

53 the reciprocal of negative one and three tenths

$-\frac{10}{13}$

54 the reciprocal of one over x, $x = -1.21$

−1.21

55 the reciprocal of the opposite of a divided by b, $b = 8$, $a = 5$

ambiguous: $\dfrac{1}{-a} \div b = -\dfrac{1}{a \cdot b} = -\dfrac{1}{40}$, $\dfrac{1}{-a \div b} = -\dfrac{8}{5}$

56 The average of the numbers −96, 78, x, 82, and 79 is 86. Find the value of x.

287

57 In a test for a social studies class of thirty students, the average score for the top twenty grades was eighty-two percent. The average score for the bottom ten grades was sixty-four percent. What was the class average on the test?

76%

58 The average of four numbers is fifty-three. If a score of eighty-three is added, what is the new average of the five numbers?

59

59 A number is divided by two and gives a remainder of one. The quotient is then divided by seven and there is a remainder of four. Then the new quotient is divided by three and leaves a remainder of two. What is the smallest positive number that will work?

37

X tending the topic: Derivation of a Division Property

The previous section looked at a division property:

$$\frac{a}{b} = a \cdot \frac{1}{b}$$

This property can be **derived**, or shown to be a result of other mathematical properties. These other properties are:

---

57) The average for the 20 scores must be weighted twice that of the 10 scores:

$$\frac{2 \cdot 82 + 1 \cdot 64}{3} = \frac{164 + 64}{3}$$

$$= \frac{228}{3} = 76$$

58) $\dfrac{4 \cdot 53 + 83}{5} = \dfrac{212 + 83}{5}$

$$= \frac{295}{5} = 59$$

59) $\dfrac{N}{2} = Q_1$ plus rem. 1

$\dfrac{Q_1}{9} = Q_2$ plus rem. 4

$\dfrac{Q_2}{3} = Q_3$ plus rem. 2

To find the smallest positive value for N, work backwards:

$Q_2 = 2$: $\dfrac{2}{3} = 0 + $ rem. 2

$Q_1 = 18$: $\dfrac{18}{7} = 2 + $ rem. 4

$N = 37$: $\dfrac{39}{2} = 18 + $ rem. 1

The derivation is an algebraic proof that division is equivalent to multiplication by the reciprocal.

If a number is multiplied by 1, the result is the original number.

- $4 \cdot 1 = 4, \quad t \cdot 1 = t, \quad \dfrac{m}{n} \cdot 1 = \dfrac{m}{n}$

If a number is divided by 1, the result is the original number.

- $\dfrac{4}{1} = 4, \quad \dfrac{t}{1} = t, \quad \dfrac{\frac{m}{n}}{1} = \dfrac{m}{n}$

If a non-zero number is divided by itself, the result is 1.

- $\dfrac{4}{4} = 1, \quad \dfrac{t}{t} = 1, \quad \dfrac{\frac{m}{n}}{\frac{m}{n}} = 1$

Start with the expression $\dfrac{a}{b}$:

$$\dfrac{a}{b} = \dfrac{a}{b} \cdot \dfrac{\frac{1}{b}}{\frac{1}{b}} \qquad \text{since } \dfrac{\frac{1}{b}}{\frac{1}{b}} = 1$$

$$= \dfrac{a \cdot \frac{1}{b}}{b \cdot \frac{1}{b}} \qquad \text{multiply the two fractions}$$

$$= \dfrac{a \cdot \frac{1}{b}}{1} \qquad \text{since } b \cdot \dfrac{1}{b} = \dfrac{b}{b} = 1$$

$$= a \cdot \dfrac{1}{b}$$

This derivation shows that

$$\dfrac{a}{b} = a \cdot \dfrac{1}{b}$$

The value of b must be restricted so that $b \neq 0$, because division by zero is not defined.

One of the important results of this property is a shortcut for dividing fractions.

Let $\frac{m}{n}$ be a fraction. Then $\frac{n}{m}$ is its reciprocal.

$$\frac{m}{n} \cdot \frac{n}{m} = 1$$

$$\text{DIVIDEBY } \frac{m}{n} \left(\frac{m}{n} \cdot \frac{n}{m} \right) = \text{DIVIDEBY } \frac{m}{n} \ (1)$$

$$\frac{\frac{m}{n} \cdot \frac{n}{m}}{\frac{m}{n}} = \frac{1}{\frac{m}{n}}$$

$$\frac{n}{m} = \frac{1}{\frac{m}{n}}$$

Thus the reciprocal of $\frac{m}{n}$ can be written as $\frac{n}{m}$, and it can also be written as $\frac{1}{\frac{m}{n}}$.

To use the property that $\frac{a}{b} = a \cdot \frac{1}{b}$, suppose that a is the fraction $\frac{p}{q}$ and b is the fraction $\frac{m}{n}$. Substituting into $\frac{a}{b} = a \cdot \frac{1}{b}$ results in:

$$\frac{\frac{p}{q}}{\frac{m}{n}} = \frac{p}{q} \cdot \frac{1}{\frac{m}{n}}$$

$$= \frac{p}{q} \cdot \frac{n}{m}$$

The result is:

$$\frac{p}{q} \div \frac{m}{n} = \frac{p}{q} \cdot \frac{n}{m}$$

In words, the quotient of two fractions is the product of the first fraction times the reciprocal of the second fraction.

EXAMPLES

- $\dfrac{4}{3} \div \dfrac{1}{2} = \dfrac{4}{3} \cdot \dfrac{2}{1} = \dfrac{8}{3}$

- $\dfrac{\frac{1}{5}}{\frac{2}{7}} = \dfrac{1}{5} \cdot \dfrac{7}{2} = \dfrac{7}{10}$

Problem Set **X**

Divide the following:

1 $\frac{2}{3} \div \frac{5}{4}$ $\frac{8}{15}$

2 $\frac{13}{3} \div \frac{1}{2}$ $\frac{26}{3}$

3 $\dfrac{\frac{2}{5}}{\frac{2}{9}}$ $\frac{9}{5}$

4 $\dfrac{\frac{2}{9}}{\frac{2}{5}}$ $\frac{5}{9}$

5 $4\frac{1}{3} \div 3\frac{1}{2}$ $\frac{26}{21}$

6 $6\frac{2}{5} \div 1\frac{1}{2}$ $\frac{64}{15}$

7 $1 \div \frac{3}{4}$ $\frac{4}{3}$

8 $\dfrac{1}{\frac{5}{8}}$ $\frac{8}{5}$

9 $\dfrac{\frac{4}{9}}{\frac{2}{9}}$ 2

10 $\dfrac{3\frac{5}{8}}{7\frac{1}{4}}$ $\frac{1}{2}$

11 $\dfrac{a^2 b}{cd} \div \dfrac{cd^2}{ab}$ $\dfrac{a^3 b^2}{c^2 d^3}$

12 $\dfrac{\frac{x^2 y^3 z}{pq^2 r}}{\frac{x^2 yz^2}{p^2 qr^2}}$ $\dfrac{pry^2}{qz}$

13 $\dfrac{\frac{x^2 y^6}{a^4 b^2 c^2}}{\frac{(xy^3)^2}{(a^2 bc)^2}}$ 1

Section 3.4 **The Order of Operations**

SECTION SCHEDULE

Basic (1 day)

Average (1 day)

Advanced (1 day)

Which expression translates "double the sum of 5 and 7"?

    A $(2 \cdot 5) + 7$

    B $2 \cdot (5 + 7)$

The value of "double the sum of 5 and 7" is 24. Therefore, the translation cannot be choice **A**, because $(2 \cdot 5) + 7 = 17$. Choice **B** is correct:

    $2 \cdot (5 + 7) = 2 \cdot 12 = 24$

While the order of operations has been referred to earlier in the text, this section is the first explicit treatment.

Parentheses and other grouping symbols can be used to indicate the order in which to perform arithmetic operations.

    It is not necessary to use parentheses for every operation because mathematicians established certain conventions, or agreements, for evaluating expressions. First, calculate all powers. Then perform multiplication and division. Finally, perform addition and subtraction.

The Problem Set that follows Chapter 5 can provide a review of the order of operations in the context of ordering numbers.

- ▪ Evaluate the following expression: $\frac{24}{6} + 2 \cdot 3^2 - 5 \cdot 5$
      First, evaluate each power: $\frac{24}{6} + 2 \cdot 9 - 5 \cdot 5$
      Then, multiply and divide: $4 + 18 - 25$
      Then, add or subtract: -3
      Thus $\frac{24}{6} + 2 \cdot 3^2 - 5 \cdot 5 = -3$.

At the start of this section, the phrase "double the sum of 5 and 7" was translated as $2 \cdot (5 + 7)$. The parentheses were used to change the usual order of operations so that the addition, $5 + 7$, was done before multiplication. Parentheses are used to change the order of operations. Always work first within a set of parentheses. However, the operations inside the parentheses follow the regular order.

Convention

The order of performing arithmetic operations is the following:

a **First, perform the operations within a set of parentheses. If there is more than one set of parentheses, start with the innermost set.**

b **Next, calculate all powers.**

c **Then, perform all multiplications and divisions, working from left to right.**

d **Finally, perform all additions and subtractions, working from left to right.**

EXAMPLES

- $4 + 5^2 + 6 - 7^2 - \frac{8}{2} + 9$

  $4 + 25 + 6 - 49 - \frac{8}{2} + 9$

  $4 + 25 + 6 - 49 - 4 + 9$

  $44 - 53$

  -9

- $(4 + 5)^2 + (6 - 7)^2 - (\frac{8}{2} + 9)$

  $\quad 9^2 \quad + \quad (-1)^2 \; - (4 + 9)$

  $\quad 81 \quad + \quad 1 \quad - \quad 13$

  $\qquad\qquad 82 \quad - \quad 13$

  $\qquad\qquad\qquad 69$

Sample Problems

1 Evaluate $x(2 - y)^3$ for $x = 5$ and $y = 4$.

  PROCEDURE

  $\begin{aligned} x(2 - y)^3 &= 5\ (2 - 4)^3 \qquad &&\text{substitute 5 for } x \text{ and 4 for } y \\ &= 5\ (-2)^3 \qquad &&\text{simplify within parentheses} \\ &= 5\ (-8) \qquad &&\text{calculate powers} \\ &= -40 \qquad &&\text{multiply} \end{aligned}$

2 The formula for the area of an **annulus**, or ring, is $A = \pi(R^2 - r^2)$.
Find A for $\pi = 3.14$, $R = 5$, and $r = 3$.

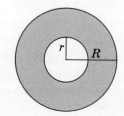

PROCEDURE

$$A = \pi \, (R^2 - r^2)$$
$$= 3.14 \, (5^2 - 3^2) \qquad \text{substitute}$$
$$= 3.14(25 - 9) \qquad \text{calculate powers within the ( )}$$
$$= 3.14 \, (16) \qquad \text{subtract within the ( )}$$
$$= 50.24 \qquad \text{multiply}$$

3   Translate from English to algebra:
"x-squared times the sum of y-cubed and five"

PROCEDURE

x-squared times the sum of y-cubed and five"

(x^2) (multiply)   (add) (y^3) (5)

$x^2 \, (y^3 + 5)$

The parentheses are needed in order to add y^3 and 5 before multiplying that by x^2.

Problem Set **A**

ASSIGNMENT GUIDE

Basic (1 day)
7–20, 22–34 (even)

Average (1 day)
22–32 (even), 34–43

Advanced (1 day)
21–30, 44–50

1   If there are no grouping symbols, which operation is performed first, addition or multiplication?
multiplication

2   If there are no grouping symbols, which operation is performed first, subtraction or multiplication?
multiplication

3   When adding and subtracting, in what order should the operations be done?
as they occur from left to right

4   When multiplying and dividing, in what order should the operations be done?
as they occur from left to right

5   If parentheses are "nested"—that is, if there are parentheses within parentheses—which operations are performed first?
innermost parentheses

"Nested sets" were also discussed in Section 2.1 X for subsets of the real number system.

6   If there are no grouping symbols, what is the order for performing the arithmetic operations?
powers, multiplication and division, addition and subtraction

Simplify the expressions in problems 7–20.

7 $-8 + 4 \cdot 7$
      20

8 $16 - 5 \cdot 3$
      1

9 $12 \div ((-4)(3))$
      -1

10 $42 \div (2)(-3)$
      -63

11 $-7(6 - 10)$
      28

12 $8(19 - 4)$
      120

13 $3^2 - 5^2$
      -16

14 $5^3 - 3^5$
      -118

15 $8(6 + 3(-2))$
      0

16 $5((-2) - (-4))$
      10

17 $2^3 + (-4)^2$
      24

18 $(-2)^4 - 2^4$
      0

19 $2^3 - 4^2$
      -8

20 $(-2)^3 - 2^3$
      -16

Evaluate the expressions in problems 21–30.

21 $x^2 - 9$ for $x = -3$
      0

22 $3(2x - 4)$ for $x = -5$
      -42

23 $6 - (6x^2 + 9)$ for $x = 2$
      -27

24 $5y + 2(y - 5)$ for $y = -3$
      -31

25 $(9 - 3x)^2$ for $x = 4$
      9

26 $\dfrac{x - 5}{11 - x}$ for $x = 14$
      -3

27 $\dfrac{3 - 5y}{2y + 2}$ for $y = 7$
      -2

28 $\dfrac{x^2 - x}{-3x}$ for $x = -2$
      1

29 $ab + 7(b + a)$ for $a = -8$ and $b = 3$
      -59

30 $a - 4b(8 - 5a)$ for $a = -1$ and $b = 4$
      -209

Translate each phrase into a variable phrase. Then state the process that will isolate the variable. (Review: Section 2.6)

These review problems preview the isolating process for multiplication and division in the next section.

31   ate three more figs than Mark did
      $3 + f$, ADD -3 $(3 + f)$

32   temperature went down nine degrees
      $t - 9$, ADD 9 $(t - 9)$

33   gained three kilograms since New Year's Day
      $w + 3$, ADD -3 $(w + 3)$

34   scored three fewer runs in the second inning
      $r - 3$, ADD 3 $(r - 3)$

Problem Set B

Simplify the expressions in problems 35–43.

35 $6 - 9 + 4^2$
13

38 $-16 \div 4^2$
-1

41 $2 - 3 \cdot (-5)^2$
-73

36 $5 - 3 \cdot 6^2$
-103

39 $-9 + 6 \div (-2)$
-12

42 $18 + 2(4 - 6)^3$
2

37 $\dfrac{3^3 \cdot 5}{-45}$
-3

40 $\dfrac{10 - 18}{-4}$
2

43 $\dfrac{(2 - 7)^2}{-9 - 16}$
-1

Problem Set C

In problems 44–47, evaluate each formula for the indicated variable. (Give answers correct to two decimal places.)

44 $\ell = a + (n - 1)d$ Find ℓ for $a = 0.6$, $n = 38$, and $d = -0.1$.
$\ell = -3.1$

45 $C = \frac{5}{9}(F - 32)$ Find C for $F = -5.3$.
$C = -20.72$

46 $A = \pi (R^2 - r^2)$ Find A for $\pi = \frac{22}{7}$, $R = 7$, and $r = 2\frac{1}{2}$.
$A = 134\frac{5}{14}$

47 $s = \dfrac{n}{2}(2a + (n - 1)d)$ Find s for $n = 18$, $a = -6$, and $d = 5$.
$s = 657.00$

48 Insert grouping symbols into the following expression so that when it is simplified the result is -7:

$$5 + 3 \cdot 4 + (-5) - 9$$

$5 + 3[4+(-5)] - 9$

49 Insert grouping symbols into the following expression so that when it is simplified the result is -12:

$$4 \cdot 2^3 - 5 \div (-6) + 5$$

$4(2^3-5)\div((-6)+5)$

50 Use four 4's and any operations or grouping symbols to form the numbers one through nine.

- The number 1 can be formed as:

$\frac{4 \cdot 4}{4 \cdot 4}$ or $\frac{4 \cdot 4}{4 \cdot 4}$ or $\frac{4}{4} + 4 - 4$.

50) answers may vary, some solutions are:

$\dfrac{4 \cdot 4}{4 + 4} = 2$

$4 - \left(\dfrac{4}{4}\right)^4 = 3$

$4 \cdot \left(\dfrac{4}{4}\right)^4 = 4$

$4 + \left(\dfrac{4}{4}\right)^4 = 5$

$4 + \dfrac{4 + 4}{4} = 6$

$4 + 4 - \dfrac{4}{4} = 7$

$(4+4) \cdot \dfrac{4}{4} = 8$

$4 + 4 + \dfrac{4}{4} = 9$

Project: Patterns and Guesses

Trace a few paths through the word **MATHEMATICS**.
a Start at any **M** along the main diagonal.
b Move down or right to **A**.
c Move down or right to **T**.
d Continue moving down or right, letter by letter, until you finish at the lower right corner with **S**.

										M
									M	A
								M	A	T
							M	A	T	H
						M	A	T	H	E
					M	A	T	H	E	M
				M	A	T	H	E	M	A
			M	A	T	H	E	M	A	T
		M	A	T	H	E	M	A	T	I
	M	A	T	H	E	M	A	T	I	C
M	A	T	H	E	M	A	T	I	C	S

1 After you trace several paths, write down your estimate of the number of different paths throughout the word **MATHEMATICS**.

2 Explain how you made your estimate. (For example, did you count the number of **M**'s in the diagonal, then the number of **A**'s, etc.?)

Often in mathematics (and in many problem situations) you can find a solution to a "large" problem by looking at similar problems that are "small." Consider paths through **TU**, **TRE**, and **FORE**:

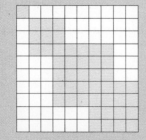

3 Trace all the paths through **TU**, **TRE**, and **FORE**. How many paths are in a 2 × 2 grid? in a 3 × 3 grid? in a 4 × 4 grid?

4 Do your answers to problem 3 suggest a pattern? Make a prediction for the number of paths in a 5 × 5 grid, and then test your guess. Then make another prediction for **MATHEMATICS**. How does this prediction compare with your answer to problem 1?

5 How many squares are there in a 10 × 10 grid?

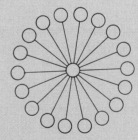

6 There are 19 circles. Write the numbers 1–19 in the circles so that any three numbers in a row will have the same sum.

---

1) answers will vary

2) answers will vary

3) 2×2: 2 paths
3×3: 4 paths
4×4: 8 paths

4) The pattern is that an $n \times n$ grid would have 2^{n-1} paths.
5×5: $2^{5-1} = 2^4 = 16$
11×11: $2^{11-1} = 2^{10}$
$= 1024$

5) Some "small" cases:
2×2: $4 + 1 = 5$
3×3: $9 + 4 + 1 = 14$
4×4:
$16 + 9 + 4 + 1 = 30$
5×5:
$25 + \ldots + 1 = 55$
The pattern is an $n \times n$ grid would have $1^2 + 2^2 + \ldots + n^2$ squares. For $n = 10$,
$1^2 + 2^2 + \ldots 10^2 = 385$.
A formula for the sum of the squares of the first n natural numbers is:
$$s_n = \frac{n(n+1)(2n+1)}{6}$$

6) The pattern is that the "middle number" (the median) takes the central circle and the outside pairs sum to twice the middle number.
Some "small" cases:

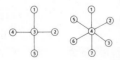

Section 3.5 Analyzing Phrases: Multiplication and Division

SECTION SCHEDULE

Basic (1 day)

Average (1 day)

Advanced (1 day)

Timothy needed a full basket of raspberries. After several minutes, he looked at the amount he had picked:

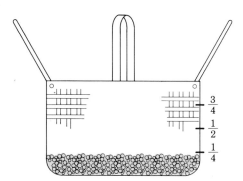

He had one fourth of a basket, so he knew that he needed four times as many berries. To get n from $\frac{1}{4} \cdot n$, multiply by 4. "To isolate a variable" means to write it alone, with a coefficient of 1. If the coefficient is not equal to 1, multiply by the reciprocal of the coefficient.

EXAMPLES

- Start with the variable phrase $3x$. To isolate the variable, multiply by the reciprocal of 3, which is $\frac{1}{3}$:

    MULTIPLYBY $\frac{1}{3}$ $(3x)$

    The result is $1 \cdot x$ or x.

- Start with $\frac{a}{2}$.

    MULTIPLYBY $2 \left(\frac{a}{2}\right)$

    The result is a.

- Start with the variable phrase $\frac{5}{2}y$. To isolate the variable, multiply by the reciprocal of $\frac{5}{2}$, which is $\frac{2}{5}$:

    MULTIPLYBY $\frac{2}{5}$ $(\frac{5}{2}y)$

    The result is $1 \cdot y$ or y.

The variable x could also be isolated by:
  DIVIDEBY 3 $(3x)$
However, some students might become confused, in Example 3, with:
  DIVIDEBY $\frac{5}{2}$ $(\frac{5}{2}y)$
Thus the text uses MULTIPLYBY and the reciprocal of the coefficient of the variable.

Sample Problems

1   Isolate the variable in each expression:

    a $7b$ **b** $\dfrac{t}{9}$ **c** $-\frac{1}{3}d$

    PROCEDURE   Multiply each expression by the number that leaves the variable with a coefficient of 1.

      a MULTIPLY BY $\frac{1}{7}$ $(7b)$ results in b

      b MULTIPLY BY 9 $\left(\dfrac{t}{9}\right)$ results in t

      c MULTIPLY BY -3 $(-\frac{1}{3}d)$ results in d

2   Translate each phrase to a variable expression, and then state how to isolate the variable:

    a triple a number
    b half of an amount
    c three fourths of a quantity

    PROCEDURE

      a The variable expression is $3 \cdot p$. To isolate the variable:

            MULTIPLY BY $\frac{1}{3}$ $(3 \cdot p)$ results in p.

      b The variable expression is $\dfrac{a}{2}$. To isolate the variable:

            MULTIPLY BY 2 $\left(\dfrac{a}{2}\right)$ results in a.

      c The variable expression is $\frac{3}{4}q$. To isolate the variable:

            MULTIPLY BY $\frac{4}{3}$ $(\frac{3}{4}q)$ results in q.

3   Which equation represents this problem: Reggie Jackson averaged one home run for every 16 times at bat for the New York Yankees in 1979. About how many times at bat did he need to hit 15 home runs?

    a $16n = 15$ **c** $\frac{1}{16} \cdot n = 15$

    b $15n = 16$ **d** $16 - 15 = n$

    PROCEDURE   If n represents the number of times at bat, then $\frac{1}{16} \cdot n$ gives the number of home runs. To hit 15 home runs, the equation would be $\frac{1}{16} \cdot n = 15$, which is choice **c**.

Problem Set A

ASSIGNMENT GUIDE

Basic (1 day)
6–40 (even)

Average (1 day)
16–48 (even)

Advanced (1 day)
16–48 (even), 50, 51

1 To "isolate a variable" means to write the variable with a coefficient of
____?____ .
1

2 The product of a number and its __?__ is 1.
reciprocal

3 If the coefficient of a variable is 6, then multiplying by __?__ will result
in a coefficient of 1.
$\frac{1}{6}$

4 If the coefficient of a variable is $-\frac{17}{21}$, multiplying by __?__ will result in a
coefficient of 1.
$-\frac{21}{17}$

In problems 5–14, state how to isolate the variable.

5 $8b$
MULTIPLY BY $\frac{1}{8}$

6 $17n$
MULTIPLY BY $\frac{1}{17}$

7 $\dfrac{x}{4}$ MULTIPLY BY 4

8 $\dfrac{y}{7}$ MULTIPLY BY 7

9 $(6.8)t$
MULTIPLY BY $\frac{1}{6.8}$

10 $(-3)s$
MULTIPLY BY $-\frac{1}{3}$

11 $\frac{1}{6}r$
MULTIPLY BY 6

12 $\frac{1}{8}w$
MULTIPLY BY 8

13 $\frac{3}{5}p$ MULTIPLY BY $\frac{5}{3}$

14 $\frac{5}{2}x$
MULTIPLY BY $\frac{2}{5}$

In problems 15–24, translate each phrase into a variable expression and state how
to isolate the variable.

15 double the quantity
$2x$, MULTIPLY BY $\frac{1}{2}$

16 three times as large
3ℓ, MULTIPLY BY $\frac{1}{3}$

17 divided into five parts
$\frac{n}{5}$, MULTIPLY BY 5

18 three fourths as much as last
year
$\frac{3}{4}y$, MULTIPLY BY $\frac{4}{3}$

19 seventy-five percent of the
students
$0.75 \cdot S$, MULTIPLY BY $\frac{1}{0.75}$

20 four percent of sales
$0.04S$, MULTIPLY BY $\frac{1}{0.04}$

21 at two thirds the speed
$\frac{2}{3}s$, MULTIPLY BY $\frac{3}{2}$

22 separated into seven parts
$\frac{P}{7}$, MULTIPLY BY 7

23 at only one quarter of the
cost
$\frac{1}{4}c$, MULTIPLY BY 4

24 sales are now two and a half
times what they were
$2.5S$, MULTIPLY BY $\frac{1}{2.5}$

Each of problems 25–27 is followed by four equations. Select the equation that represents the problem.

25 John is able to save $3.60 a week. How many weeks will it take him to save $28.80? *b*

a $3.60 = 28.80w$

c $3.60 + w = 28.80$

b $3.60 \cdot w = 28.80$

d $\dfrac{w}{3.60} = 28.80$

Some students may need a reminder to use a single unit for length.

26 Kim is building a wall with concrete blocks. If each block is 18 inches long, and the wall is to be 15 feet long, how many blocks long will the wall be? *b*

a $18 + 180 = \ell$

c $\dfrac{\ell}{18} = 180$

b $\dfrac{3}{2}\ell = 15$

d $\dfrac{\ell}{15} = \dfrac{3}{2}$

27 Amy is packing rubber balls that are $\frac{1}{2}$ inch in diameter into tubes that are 5 inches long. How many fit into each tube (without squeezing)? *a*

a $\dfrac{n}{2} = 5$

c $n \div \dfrac{1}{2} = 5$

b $2 \cdot n = 5$

d $5n = \dfrac{1}{2}$

Write an algebraic equation that expresses the relationship in each problem. (Do not solve the equations.)

28 The number v divided by five is seven. $\dfrac{v}{5} = 7$

29 The product of eight and k is thirty-four. $8k = 34$

30 The numbers twenty and x are the two factors of eighty. $20x = 80$

31 One third of n is nineteen. $\dfrac{1}{3}n = 19$

32–35) answers may vary Write a problem that can be represented by each equation.

32 $\dfrac{t}{6} = 20$

34 $10w = 250$

33 $5c = 300$

35 $\dfrac{m}{3} = 14$

Solve each equation. (Review: Section 2.6)

36 $r + 3 = 11$
  $r = 8$

37 $4 + h = 27$
  $h = 23$

38 $t - 3 = 19$
  $t = 22$

39 $17 = G + 6$
  $G = 11$

40 $0 = p - 2$
  $p = 2$

41 $3 = q + 7$
  $q = -4$

42 $d - 3 = -9$
  $d = -6$

43 $72 + X = 38$
  $X = -34$

44 $-5 = W - 3$
  $W = -2$

45 $22 = 5 + n$
  $n = 17$

Problem Set B

Write an equation that can represent each problem. (Do not solve the problem.)

46 Nancy puts fifty cents into a sock under her bed every night. How much did she save in the month of September? $0.50(30) = n$

47 Nobu has stacked the ninety-six fish he caught into three equal piles. How many fish are in each pile? $\frac{96}{3} = f$

48 Sally counted seventeen freckles on her face before she went to the beach. When she came back from the beach, she counted twenty-four freckles. How many freckles did she get at the beach? $17 + f = 24$

49 Jules is three times as old as Jim. If Jim is thirteen, how old is Jules? $3 \cdot 13 = J$

Problem Set C

50 A large rectangular picture puzzle has over two thousand five hundred pieces, according to the box. The bottom border is finished first, and is sixty-one pieces long. How many pieces will probably be along one of the puzzle's sides? about 41 pieces

51 The round base of a cylindrical cannister holds between one hundred thirty-five and one hundred sixty-five beans, and the beans can be piled between forty-five and fifty-five beans high. What is the range for the number of jelly beans in the cannister? between 6075 and 9075

Section 3.6   Solving Equations: Multiplication and Division

Many students can solve one-step problems easily, without using algebraic techniques. However, the need for the techniques will be apparent for the next section on two-step equations.

In Chapter 2, the phrase **solve an equation** was established to mean find an equivalent equation with the variable isolated. The key in this section is to produce equivalent equations by multiplying (or dividing) both sides of an equation by the same number.

EXAMPLE

- To solve the equation $7x = 56$, multiply both sides of the equation by $\frac{1}{7}$, the reciprocal of 7:

$$7x = 56$$
$$\text{MULTIPLYBY } \tfrac{1}{7}\,(7x) = \text{MULTIPLYBY } \tfrac{1}{7}\,(56)$$
$$x = 8$$

The equations $7x = 56$ and $x = 8$ are equivalent because they have the same value for the variable.

Sample Problems

1   Solve and check: $\frac{1}{4}y = 12$

PROCEDURE   If both sides are multiplied by the same number, the new equation will be equivalent to the old equation. Multiply both sides by 4, because that will give 1 as the coefficient of the variable.

$$\tfrac{1}{4}y = 12$$
$$\text{MULTIPLYBY } 4\,(\tfrac{1}{4}y) = \text{MULTIPLYBY } 4\,(12)$$
$$y = 48$$

To check, rewrite the original equation, substitute the value 48 for y, and evaluate each side of the equation separately:

$$\tfrac{1}{4}y = 12$$
$$\tfrac{1}{4}\,(48) \stackrel{?}{=} 12$$
$$12 \stackrel{?}{=} 12 \checkmark$$

2   Solve: $\dfrac{3}{4} = \dfrac{t}{7}$

PROCEDURE   The coefficient of the variable is $\frac{1}{7}$, so multiply both sides by 7:

$$\frac{3}{4} = \frac{t}{7}$$

$$\text{MULTIPLY BY } 7\left(\frac{3}{4}\right) = \text{MULTIPLY BY } 7\left(\frac{t}{7}\right)$$

$$\frac{21}{4} = t$$

The technique of using the cross-product to solve a proportion is presented in Section 8.2.

Problem Set A

ASSIGNMENT GUIDE

Basic (2 days)
(1) 1–20
(2) 21–32

Average (1 day)
6–42 (even)

Advanced (1 day)
21–28, 44–62 (even)

1   If both sides of an equation are multiplied by the same number, the two equations are ___?___.   equivalent

2   In the equation $\frac{4}{3}p = 10$, the coefficient of the variable is ___?___. $\frac{4}{3}$

3   To isolate the variable in the equation $\frac{4}{3}p = 10$, multiply both sides by ___?___. $\frac{3}{4}$

4   In the equation $1\frac{3}{4}q = 6$, the coefficient of q is ___?___ and the reciprocal of that coefficient is ___?___. $1\frac{3}{4}, \frac{4}{7}$

In problems 5–28, solve and check each equation.

5 $4n = 40$
$n = 10$

6 $-7x = 63$
$x = -9$

7 $\dfrac{m}{5} = 8$
$m = 4$

8 $\dfrac{k}{9} = -2$
$k = -18$

9 $2y = 11$
$y = \frac{11}{2}$

10 $3m = 17$
$m = \frac{17}{3}$

11 $\dfrac{y}{10} = -10$
$y = -100$

12 $\dfrac{g}{11} = 12$
$g = 132$

13 $6a = 3$
$a = \frac{1}{2}$

14 $5x = 4$
$x = \frac{4}{5}$

15 $\frac{1}{2}w = 5$
$w = 10$

16 $\frac{1}{3}x = 7$
$x = 21$

17 $3 = -\dfrac{w}{5}$
$w = -15$

18 $16 = \dfrac{b}{8}$
$b = 125$

19 $14 = 7x$
$x = 2$

20 $-24 = 5y$
$y = -\frac{24}{5}$

21 $\dfrac{k}{17} = 2$
$k = 34$

22 $\dfrac{k}{17} = 0$
$k = 0$

23 $1 = \dfrac{k}{-17}$
$k = -17$

24 $5y = 0$
$y = 0$

25 $1.3 = \dfrac{k}{4}$
$k = 5.2$

26 $\dfrac{d}{12} = 1.2$
$d = 14.4$

27 $\frac{3}{7}x = 21$
$x = 49$

28 $\frac{2}{3}t = 10$
$t = 15$

In problems 29–32, write an equation for each problem and solve it. (Review: Section 2.7)

29 Pick a number and add seventeen. If the result is thirty-nine, what is the original number?

$n = 22$

30 A number decreased by eleven is fifteen. What is the number?

$d = 26$

31 The sum of two integers is negative sixteen. If one integer is negative eleven, what is the other?

$i = -5$

32 The 2 P.M. temperature of 31°C was 5° more than the temperature at 7 A.M. What was the 7 A.M. temperature?

$C = 26$

Problem Set **B**

In problems 33–42, translate each sentence into an equation and solve it.

33 Five times n is equal to fifty.

$n = 10$

34 The number x divided by three is equal to seventeen.

$x = 51$

35 The number ℓ divided by eight is equal to two.

$\ell = 16$

36 Two times t is the same as thirteen.

$t = \dfrac{13}{2}$

37 The product of a and four is negative twenty.

$a = -5$

38 The product of w and four is two.

$w = \dfrac{1}{2}$

39 Twenty-four is the quotient of v divided by six.

$v = 144$

40 Six is the opposite of the quotient of x divided by seven.

$x = -42$

41 Eighteen and the product of nine and y are the same number.

$y = 2$

42 Negative twelve and the product of three and n are the same number.

$n = -4$

Problem Set C

In problems 43–62, write an equation and solve it.

43 The product of a number and five is sixty. What is the number?

  $n = 12$

44 Three times some number is negative thirty-nine. What is the number?

  $s = -13$

45 One fourth of a number is negative thirteen. What is the number?

  $x = -52$

46 When a number is divided by negative thirty-six the quotient is negative two. What is the number?

  $m = 72$

47 In order to buy a shirt, Otis needs to save thirteen dollars and fifty cents. If he saves all of his allowance, a dollar and a half per week, in how many weeks will he have enough money?

  $m = 9$

48 The sum of the measures of the angles of a triangle is one hundred eighty degrees. If all the angles are the same measure, what is the measure of one angle?

  $a = 60$

49 Exactly three tenths of the freshman class at Central High are honor roll students. If the honor roll has one hundred twenty names on it, how many freshmen are there?

  $h = 400$

50 Ms. Clementi has an annual salary of sixteen thousand four hundred forty dollars. How much does she earn in one month?

  $s = 1370$

51 Julie's baseball team has one hundred fourteen hits so far, and the season is only one third through. What is a good guess for the number of hits they will get by the end of the season?

  $y = 342$

52 If you charge $2.50 for mowing a lawn, how many jobs would you have to get to earn $39.95 needed to buy a portable cassette player? (If you round off $39.95 to $40.00, will it make any difference in your answer?)

  $m = 15.98$ or 16, no

53 One-liter returnable bottles of fruit punch are priced at three for one dollar and nine cents. What would you expect to pay for one bottle?

  $x = 37$

54 A shipment of one hundred twenty sale dresses, each the same price, costs a department store two thousand two hundred eighty dollars. At what price must each dress sell in order for the store to break even?

  $d = 19$

55 If the U.S. population in 1970 was twenty-three sevenths of the U.S. population in 1890, and in 1970 that population was two hundred seven million persons, what was the U.S. population in 1890?

$p = 63,000,000$

56 How many hours will it take you to go four hundred twenty-five miles at an average speed of fifty-three miles per hour?

k = about 8 hours (8.0188679)

57 The entrance price to an amusement park is nine and half dollars per person. No extra fees are charged for the various rides. If there are forty different rides in the park, what is the actual cost per ride? If Daren only has time to go on eleven rides, what is his cost per ride?

$r = 86\frac{4}{11}$

58 The average person uses twenty gallons of water per day for showers, which is thirty-seven percent of the total household water per person per day. What is the average amount of water used per person per day in an average household?

w = 54.054 gallons per day per person

59 A town agrees to pay one fourth of the cost of installing curbing in front of a house. The owner of the house is assessed eight hundred dollars for the curbing. What did the town claim was the total cost of the curbing?

$x = 1066.67$

60) The answer assumes that she didn't travel east to another time zone. In that case:

$$\frac{300 \text{ mi.}}{4\frac{1}{2} \text{ hrs.}} = 67 \text{ mph}$$

60 A businesswoman drove off at 3 p.m. on a trip of three hundred miles. When she arrived in her hotel room at 8:30 p.m., she called her son at home to see how things were going. He claimed she must have been speeding. Was he right?

s = 54.5 miles per hour. She probably was not speeding.

61 A spectacular example of the homing instinct in birds was provided by a Manx Shearwater that was taken from its nesting burrow in an island off the Welsh Coast of Britain, banded, and flown across the Atlantic. It returned to its burrow off the Welsh Coast thirteen days after its release in Boston, Massachusetts, having crossed more than three thousand miles of sea. What was the Manx Shearwater's average speed?

s = 230.77 miles/day (9.6 miles per hour)

62 The relative humidity (R) is the ratio of the amount of water vapor (V) actually in the air to the amount (v) which the air could hold if saturated at the same temperature.

    a   Write a formula for relative humidity.

    b   If the relative humidity is eighty-five hundredths and the amount of water vapor at the saturation point is forty grams, how much water vapor is actually present?

a $R = \dfrac{V}{v}$ b V = 34 grams

After-School Mathematics: Travel Planner

Judson is an assistant at a travel agency. The agency is planning a "caravan" for a group trip from Chicago to Orlando, with stops at Cincinnati, Knoxville, Atlanta, and Jacksonville. For each leg of the trip, the vacationers could take major expressways, state highways, or country roads. The agency recommended several routes for each leg:

There were 5 routes from Chicago to Cincinnati: $294 \rightarrow 65 \rightarrow 74$, $94 \rightarrow 41 \rightarrow 52 \rightarrow 65 \rightarrow 50$, $94 \rightarrow 30 \rightarrow 27$, $294 \rightarrow 421 \rightarrow 231 \rightarrow 45 \rightarrow 46 \rightarrow 74$, $94 \rightarrow 41 \rightarrow 50$.

There were 4 routes from Cincinnati to Knoxville: 75, $127 \rightarrow 40$, $27 \rightarrow 63 \rightarrow 75$, $52 \rightarrow 23 \rightarrow 11$.

There were 4 routes from Knoxville to Atlanta: $40 \rightarrow 26$, $129 \rightarrow 28 \rightarrow 23$, 75, $40 \rightarrow 77$.

There were 3 routes from Atlanta to Jacksonville: $75 \rightarrow 10$, $19 \rightarrow 82 \rightarrow 1 \rightarrow 301$, $75 \rightarrow 16 \rightarrow 441 \rightarrow 10$.

There were 3 routes from Jacksonville to Orlando: $95 \rightarrow 4$, $17 \rightarrow 4$, $301 \rightarrow 40 \rightarrow 95 \rightarrow 4$.

Judson's boss asked him to draw a map for every route between Chicago and Orlando. He started drawing them, but soon he realized that it would be a big job—there were 720 different routes!

The total number of routes is the product of the numbers of choices:

$5 \cdot 4 \cdot 4 \cdot 3 \cdot 3 = 720$

*The Application in Chapter 12 (p. 499) involves this same counting principle: If there are **a** and **b** options, respectively, to make two independent choices, then there are **a·b** different options in total.*

Application: Staggered Start

On a curved racing track, the outside lanes are longer than the inside lanes. Thus the racers take a staggered start so that they run equal distances.

Suppose three racers are running four hundred meters on a five-hundred meter circular track. What is the length x? What is the length y?

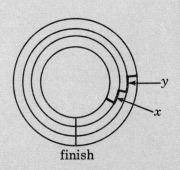

finish

The measurement of the lane width is needed.

Assume the lane width is one meter. Then the extra distance around the entire track is:

$2\pi(r+1) - 2\pi r$
$= 2\pi = 6.28$ m

For only four fifths of the distance around the track, the starts should be staggered by:

$\frac{4}{5}(6.28) = 5.024$

or about 5 meters.

Section 3.7 Solving Two-Step Equations

*For many students,
solving two-step equa-
tions is the first time
they see the usefulness
of algebraic tech-
niques. The key for
students is that they
perform the two steps
in the correct order.*

Mary said, "I'm thinking of a number. If you triple it and then add fifteen, the result is nine. What's the number?"

Carlotta let n represent the number, so "triple it and add fifteen" was translated as $3n + 15$. "The result is nine" gave her the equation: $3n + 15 = 9$.

To solve an equation means to find an equivalent equation with the variable isolated. To isolate the variable in a two-step equation such as $3n + 15 = 9$, reverse the order of how the variable expression was built. The phrase $3n + 15$ means:

First, multiply by 3.
Second, add 15.

To isolate the variable in $3n + 15$:

First, subtract 15.
Second, multiply by $\frac{1}{3}$.

Isolate the variable by reversing the two steps of the variable expression. Carlotta explained: "It's like tying two knots in a rope and then untying them. You must untie the outside knot before you can untie the inside knot."

The solution of the equation $3n + 15$ looks like:

$$3n + 15 = 9$$
$$\text{SUBTRACT 15 } (3n + 15) = \text{SUBTRACT 15 } (9)$$
$$3n = -6$$
$$\text{MULTIPLY BY } \tfrac{1}{3} (3n) = \text{MULTIPLY BY } \tfrac{1}{3} (-6)$$
$$n = -2$$

Sample Problems

1 Solve and check: $\frac{2}{3}b - 9 = 15$

PROCEDURE   The variable phrase $\frac{2}{3}b - 9$ means that first, b was multiplied by $\frac{2}{3}$, and second, 9 was subtracted. To isolate the variable b, reverse the steps:

$$\tfrac{2}{3}b - 9 = 15$$
$$\text{ADD 9 } (\tfrac{2}{3}b - 9) = \text{ADD 9 } (15)$$
$$\tfrac{2}{3}b = 24$$
$$\text{MULTIPLY BY } \tfrac{3}{2} (\tfrac{2}{3}b) = \text{MULTIPLY BY } \tfrac{3}{2} (24)$$
$$b = \tfrac{3 \cdot 24}{2} = 3 \cdot \tfrac{24}{2} = 3 \cdot 12 = 36$$

To check
$$\tfrac{2}{3}b - 9 = 15$$
$$\tfrac{2}{3}(36) - 9 \overset{?}{=} 15$$
$$24 - 9 \overset{?}{=} 15$$
$$15 \overset{?}{=} 15 \checkmark$$

2 Solve and check: $-3 = 41 - 4x$

PROCEDURE The variable phrase $41 - 4x$ means that first, x was multiplied by -4 and then, 41 was added. To isolate the variable, reverse the steps:

$$-3 = 41 - 4x$$
$$\text{SUBTRACT } 41\,(-3) = \text{SUBTRACT } 41\,(41 - 4x)$$
$$-44 = -4x$$
$$\text{MULTIPLYBY } -\tfrac{1}{4}(-44) = \text{MULTIPLYBY } -\tfrac{1}{4}(-4x)$$
$$\frac{-44}{-4} = \frac{-4x}{-4}$$
$$11 = x$$

To check
$$-3 = 41 - 4x$$
$$-3 \overset{?}{=} 41 - 4(11)$$
$$-3 \overset{?}{=} 41 - 44$$
$$-3 \overset{?}{=} -3 \checkmark$$

Problem Set A

ASSIGNMENT GUIDE

Basic (2 days)
(1) 1–20
(2) 26–39

Average (2 days)
(1) 16–38 (even)
(2) 40–54

Advanced (3 days)
(1) 40–54
(2) 58–76 (even)
(3) 77–80
   138: 2–14 (even),
   16–19

Indicate the two operations that must be performed, in the correct order, to isolate the variable.

1 $3y - 7$
ADD 7, MULTBY $\tfrac{1}{3}$

2 $\dfrac{f}{2} + 8$
ADD -8, MULTBY 2

3 $-5 + 8u$
ADD 5, MULTBY $\tfrac{1}{8}$

4 $\tfrac{3}{5}t - \tfrac{12}{27}$
ADD $\tfrac{12}{27}$, MULTBY $\tfrac{5}{3}$

5 $4j + 5$
ADD -5, MULTBY $\tfrac{1}{4}$

6 $9b - 6$
ADD 6, MULTBY $\tfrac{1}{9}$

7 $\dfrac{a}{3} - 10$
ADD 10, MULTBY 3

8 $\tfrac{1}{5}C + 12$
ADD -12, MULTBY 5

9 $6 + 7m$
ADD -6, MULTBY $\tfrac{1}{7}$

10 $-5 + \dfrac{r}{3}$
ADD 5, MULTBY 3

11 $\dfrac{d}{7} - \dfrac{4}{19}$
ADD $\tfrac{4}{19}$, MULTBY 7

12 $-8y + 20$
ADD -20, MULTBY $-\tfrac{1}{8}$

13 $\tfrac{3}{4}t + 11$
ADD -11, MULTBY $\tfrac{4}{3}$

14 $-\tfrac{2}{3}x - 7$
ADD 7, MULTBY $-\tfrac{3}{2}$

Problems 15–34 can be used as additional oral exercises by having students name the two operations that will isolate the variable.

Solve each equation, indicating the steps involved.

15 $3x + 5 = 20$
ADD −5, MULTBY $\frac{1}{3}$, $x = 5$

16 $2n − 7 = 19$
ADD 7, MULTBY $\frac{1}{2}$, $n = 13$

17 $15 = 6r − 9$
ADD 9, MULTBY $\frac{1}{6}$, $r = 4$

18 $18 = 4w + 6$
ADD −6, MULTBY $\frac{1}{4}$, $w = 3$

19 $3x + 11 = 2$
ADD −11, MULTBY $\frac{1}{3}$, $x = -3$

20 $12 + 4z = 32$
ADD −12, MULTBY $\frac{1}{4}$, $z = 5$

21 $3b − 23 = 4$
ADD 23, MULTBY $\frac{1}{3}$, $b = 9$

22 $21 = 8r − 11$
ADD 11, MULTBY $\frac{1}{8}$, $r = 4$

23 $2x + 4 = 11$
ADD −4, MULTBY $\frac{1}{2}$, $x = \frac{7}{2}$

24 $4x + 19 = 7$
ADD −19, MULTBY $\frac{1}{4}$, $x = -3$

25 $24 + 5r = 39$
ADD −24, MULTBY $\frac{1}{5}$, $r = 3$

26 $37 + 4n = 73$
ADD −37, MULTBY $\frac{1}{4}$, $n = 9$

27 $13 = 2x − 7$
ADD 7, MULTBY $\frac{1}{2}$, $x = 10$

28 $6x − 8 = −56$
ADD 8, MULTBY $\frac{1}{6}$, $x = -8$

29 $18 − 3x = 12$
ADD −18, MULTBY $-\frac{1}{3}$, $x = 2$

30 $26 − 3x = 2$
ADD −26, MULTBY $-\frac{1}{3}$, $x = 8$

31 $34 − 7x = 20$
ADD −34, MULTBY $-\frac{1}{7}$, $x = 2$

32 $7t + 29 = 1$
ADD −29, MULTBY $\frac{1}{7}$, $t = -4$

33 $−2x − 5 = −19$
ADD 5, MULTBY $-\frac{1}{2}$, $x = 7$

34 $−3x − 9 = 18$
ADD 9, MULTBY $-\frac{1}{3}$, $x = -9$

Write an equation and solve each problem. (Review: Sections 2.7 and 3.6)

35 The sum of the measures of the angles of a pentagon is five hundred forty degrees. If a pentagon has five equal angles, what is the measure of any one of them?
108°

36 At the floor of a cave, the temperature was 18°*F* lower than it was at the mouth of the cave. If the temperature at the floor was 50°*F*, what was the temperature at the mouth?
68°

37 A bricklayer submitted a total bill of $296.08 for a job. The bill included costs for materials ($65.50), labor ($158.40), insurance ($22.18), and an overhead cost that was illegible. What was the overhead cost?
$50

38 Serena bought a dress at the Thrift Shoppe that cost only one twentieth of its original price. If Serena paid two dollars and fifty cents, what was the original price?
$50

39 Suppose a baseball pitcher allowed ten runs in fifteen innings. At this rate, what was the pitcher's ERA, or the number of runs allowed in nine innnings?
6.00

Problem Set B

Translate each sentence to an equation, and solve the equation.

40 Three fewer than five times a number is seventeen.

$5n - 3 = 17, n = 4$

41 Four times a number, plus five, is twenty-nine.

$4n + 5 = 29, n = 6$

42 Three times a number, subtracted from fifty-three, is thirty-two.

$53 - 3x = 32, x = 7$

43 The sum of twice a number and fifteen is negative thirteen.

$2x + 15 = -13, x = -14$

44 Four hundred thirty-eight is forty-seven more than the product of a
number and twenty-three.

$438 = 47 + 23y, y = 17$

45 The difference between five and half a number is negative ten.

$5 - \frac{m}{2} = -10, m = 30$

Solve each equation:

46 $18 + 3x = 22$

$x = \frac{4}{3}$

47 $26 - 3x = 51$

$x = -\frac{25}{3}$

48 $\frac{5x}{2} - 10 = 30$

$x = 16$

49 $1.5x + 4 = 22$

$x = 12$

50 $7x - 8 = 8.1$

$x = 2.3$

51 $\frac{t}{5} - 1 = 1$

$t = 10$

52 $7t + 1.7 = 1.8$

$t = \frac{1}{70}$

53 $\frac{n}{-6} - 4 = 7$

$n = -66$

54 $\frac{2}{3}x + 5 = -13$

$x = -27$

Problem Set C

Biologists have found that the number of chirps per minute made by crickets of a
certain species is related to the temperature. This relationship may be stated alge-
braically:

$$F = \frac{c}{4} + 37$$

In the equation, c is the number of cricket chirps per minute and F is the Fahrenheit
temperature.

55 If the temperature is $80°F$, how many chirps can you expect to hear in
a minute?

172 chirps

56 If you only count chirps for fifteen seconds, how can you quickly estimate the temperature?

use formula and multiply by 4 or add 37 to the
number you count

Equations for prob-
lems 57–76 are:

Solve each problem.

57) $100 = 16 + 2j$

57 Ramón has sixteen more than twice as many trading cards as his brother Jaime. Ramón has one hundred cards. How many has Jaime?

42 cards

58) $2x + 3 = 7$

58 Elvira is three years older than twice her sister's age. If Elvira is seven, how old is her sister?

2 years

59) $2c - 1 = 19$

59 The number of Libras in an algebra class is one less than twice the number of Capricorns. If there are nineteen Libras, how many Capricorns are there?

10 Capricorns

60) $10x + 45.31 = 82.81$

60 Ms. Asnien is a mechanic who charges $10 an hour plus the cost of the parts. If the total charge for a tune-up is $82.81 and parts were $45.31, how long did she work on the car?

3.75 hours

61) $50x + 144 + 37 = 681$

61 Mr. Lee is a consultant who charges $50 an hour plus expenses. If his bill is for $681, and his expenses were a $144 plane ticket and $37 in local transporation, how many hours did he charge for?

10 hours

62) $60 + 0.40x = 150$

62 Dennis has a job that pays him sixty dollars a week plus a forty percent commission on his sales. How much must he sell to make a total of one hundred fifty dollars per week?

$225 in sales

63) $5000 + 0.1x = 20,000$

63 Eloise got a five thousand dollar research grant from her publisher plus a royalty of ten percent on sales of her book. How much (in dollars) must the book sell for Eloise to make twenty thousand dollars on the book?

$150,000

64) $\frac{1}{6}x - 50 = 986$

64 Sesu bought a used car for fifty dollars less than one sixth of its original cost. Find the original cost if Sesu paid nine hundred eighty-six dollars for it.

$6216

65) $\frac{3}{4}x - 250 = 5282$

65 As an employee of the plant, Gerta could buy a car for three fourths of its sticker price. When she did, she was pleasantly surprised to get a two hundred fifty dollar rebate as well as the employee discount. If the car cost Gerta five thousand two hundred eighty-two dollars in all (counting the rebate), what was the sticker price?

$6709.33

66) $4 + 3x = 37$

66 The number of girls in the freshman class of Miss Master's School is four more than three times the number of boys. If there are thirty-seven girls in the class, how many boys are there?

11 boys

67 The value of my money is forty-eight cents more than four times the value of the nickels I have. If I have two dollars and sixty-eight cents, how many nickels do I have?

    11 nickels

67) $0.48 + 4(0.05)x = 2.68$

68 Katy has only quarters and pennies in her purse, for a total of one dollar and eighty-one cents. If she has six pennies, how many quarters does she have?

    7 quarters

68) $0.06 + 0.25x = 1.81$

69 For a chemistry experiment, Nadine had to determine a temperature in Celsius, but all she had was a Fahrenheit thermometer. If her reading was $200°F$ and if the only formula she could remember was $F = \frac{9}{5}C + 32$, what was the Celsius temperature (to the nearest tenth of a degree)?

    $93.33°C$

69) $200 = \frac{9}{5}C + 32$

70 For a science report, Leslie needed to find out the Celsius equivalent of $14°F$. Use the formula $F = \frac{9}{5}C + 32$ to find the Celsius reading.

    $10°C$

70) $14 = \frac{9}{5}C + 32$

71 Mr. Green weighs one hundred fifty-eight pounds. This is sixteen pounds less than three times his child's weight. What is his child's weight?

    58 pounds

71) $3x - 16 = 158$

72 In five years, Edna gained enough to weigh five pounds more than twice her previous weight. If she now weighs one hundred eleven pounds, what did she weigh five years ago?

    53 pounds

72) $2x + 5 = 111$

73 Three eighths of a certain rational number when increased by the number five sixths is equal to the number one. What is the rational number?

    $\frac{4}{9}$

73) $\frac{3}{8}x + \frac{5}{6} = 1$

74 An isosceles triangle has at least two sides of equal length, called the legs. The third side is called the base. If an isosceles triangle has base thirteen cm and perimeter forty-six cm, what is the length of one leg?

    16.5 cm

74) $2x + 13 = 46$

75 Ilsa has $700 of principal ($p$) to invest in a savings account for one year. Her bank tells her she will get back the amount (A) of $743.75 at the end of one year (t). What is the rate of interest (r) her bank is offering? Assume simple interest and use the formula $A = p + prt$.

    6.25%

75) $743.45 = 700 + 700r$

76 A wasp walks carefully around the edge of a window, trying to find a way out. When she is back at her starting point, she has walked eighty-six inches. If the window pane is eighteen inches wide, how tall is the pane? Use $p = 2\ell + 2w$.

    25 inches

76) $86 = 2\ell + 36$

The winners of the U.S. Women's Open Golf Tournament from 1959–1980 had the following scores:

year		score	year		score
1959	Mickey Wright	287	1970	Donna Caponi	287
1960	Besty Rawls	291	1971	JoAnne Carner	288
1961	Mickey Wright	293	1972	Susie Berning	299
1962	Murle Lindstrom	301	1973	Susie Berning	290
1963	Mary Mills	289	1974	Sandra Haynie	295
1964	Mickey Wright	290	1975	Sandra Palmer	295
1965	Carol Mann	290	1976	JoAnne Carner	292
1966	Sandra Spuzich	297	1977	Hollis Stacy	292
1967	Catherine LaCoste	294	1978	Hollis Stacy	289
1968	Susie Berning	289	1979	Jerilyn Britz	284
1969	Donna Caponi	294	1980	Amy Alcott	280

77 Find the average of these scores.

78 Find the frequency of each score.

79 Find the relative frequency of each score, expressed as a fraction, then as a percent.

80 If you include recent winners, how much do problems 77 and 79 change?

The Grey Streak Bus Line needs a time schedule for a daily run from San Francisco to Sacramento, a distance of 80 miles. For one week, the bus left San Francisco at 1:25 P.M. each day. Arrival times in Sacramento for the five days were:

Monday, 2:45 P.M.   Thursday, 3:05 P.M.
Tuesday, 2:55 P.M.   Friday, 2:50 P.M.
Wednesday, 2:50 P.M.

81 Find the average time for the run.

82 If the bus is scheduled to leave San Francisco each weekday at 1:25 P.M., what time would the bus be expected in Sacramento?

A laboratory tested two brands of light bulbs for burning times. The bulbs that were tested were random samples of each brand.

	Burning life (hours)			
Brand X:	1025	1100	1300	1075
Brand Y:	900	1225	1400	1075

77) 291.18
78) 280, 1; 284, 1; 287, 2; 288, 1; 289, 3; 290, 3; 291, 1; 292, 2; 293, 1; 294, 2; 295, 2; 297, 1; 299, 1; 301, 1
79) 280: $\frac{1}{22}$, 4.5%; 284: $\frac{1}{22}$, 4.5%; 287: $\frac{1}{11}$, 9%; 288: $\frac{1}{22}$, 4.5%; 289: $\frac{3}{22}$, 13.6%; 290: $\frac{3}{22}$, 13.6%; 291: $\frac{1}{22}$, 4.5%; 292: $\frac{1}{11}$, 9%; 293: $\frac{1}{22}$, 4.5%; 294: $\frac{1}{11}$, 9%; 295: $\frac{1}{11}$, 9%; 297: $\frac{1}{22}$, 4.5%; 299: $\frac{1}{22}$, 4.5%; 301: $\frac{1}{22}$, 4.5%
80) Some recent winners are:
1981 Pat Bradley   279
1982 Janet Alex   283
81) 1 hour, 28 minutes
82) 2:53 PM

83 What was the longest burning life? What was the shortest?

longest, BRAND Y, 1400; shortest, BRAND Y, 900

84 Compute the mean (average) life for each brand.

BRAND X, mean 1125 hrs, BRAND Y, mean 1150 hrs.

85 Which brand has the greater mean burning life?

BRAND Y

86 Which brand exhibits a more uniform burning life (that is, a smaller range)?

BRAND X

X tending the topic: Two-Step Function Machines

The format of the nonsense names for the function machines is similar to function notation, which is introduced at the end of the text in Chapter 13.

Chapter 1 used "function machines" to introduce computer expressions:

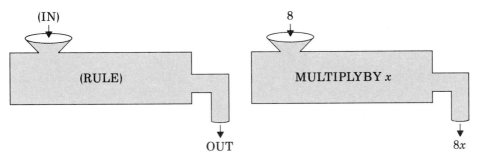

Sometimes the rule is known only by the output. Consider the two functions DUB $(x) = 2x - 5$ and   MAS $(x) = 3x + 6$. These functions can be represented as:

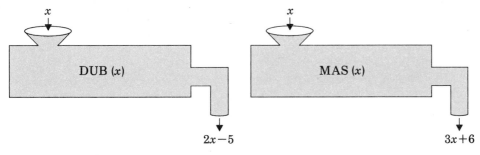

Put 6 into the DUB (x) machine:

$$\text{DUB } (x) = 2x - 5$$
$$\text{DUB } (6) = 2(6) - 5$$
$$= 12 - 5$$
$$= 7$$

Put -2 into the MAS (x) machine:

$$\text{MAS } (x) = 3x + 6$$
$$\text{MAS } (-2) = 3(-2) + 6$$
$$= -6 + 6$$
$$= 0$$

Problem Set X

Here are some functions and their meanings, without the machine drawings:

$$DIAN(x) = \frac{x}{4} + 5 \qquad\qquad DIUN(x) = \frac{x}{4} - 1$$

$SQAV(x) = x^2 + x \qquad\qquad SQUV(x) = x^2 - x$

$MAV(x) = 3x + x \qquad\qquad CAV(x) = x^3 + x$

$MUV(x) = 8x - x \qquad\qquad CUT(x) = x^3 - 10$

$SQUR(x) = x^2 - 4 \qquad\qquad CUAN(x) = x^3 + 9$

$SQAF(x) = x^2 + 5$

If $x = 4$, find the value of each function:

1   DUB (x)
    3

2   DUB $(x - 4)$
    −5

3   MAS (x)
    18

4   DUB $(x) - 4$
    −1

5   DIAN (x)
    6

6   DIUN (x)
    0

7   MAV (x)
    16

8   MUV (x)
    28

9   SQUR (x)
    12

10   SQAF (x)
    21

11   SQAV (x)
    20

12   SQUV (x)
    12

13   CAV (x)
    68

14   CUT (x)
    54

15   CUAN (x)
    73

16   CUAN $(x - 2)$
    17

Make up a function name for each of the following. Then evaluate it for $x = 5$.

17   __?__ $(x) = 5x - 7$
    18

18   __?__ $(x) = 2x^2 + 3$
    53

19   __?__ $(x) =$ __?__
    (Make up your own function)
    Answers will vary

Section 3.8 Literal Equations

SECTION SCHEDULE

Basic (1 day)

Average (1 day)

Advanced (1 day)

A formula such as the distance formula, $r \cdot t = d$, is called a **literal equation** (literal means "expressed by letters"). The steps for isolating a variable in an equation can be used to isolate a variable in a literal equation.

- Isolate r in the distance formula:

$$d = rt$$

$$\text{MULTIPLY BY } \frac{1}{t} (d) = \text{MULTIPLY BY } \frac{1}{t} (rt)$$

$$\frac{d}{t} = rt \cdot \frac{1}{t} = r$$

Thus $r = \dfrac{d}{t}$. Isolating a variable in a literal equation is called **solving** the equation for that variable.

Definition

To SOLVE A LITERAL EQUATION for a variable means to find an equivalent equation with that variable isolated on one side of the equation.

EXAMPLES

- Solve for t:

$$A = prt$$

$$\text{MULTIPLY BY } \frac{1}{p} (A) = \text{MULTIPLY BY } \frac{1}{p} (prt)$$

$$\frac{A}{p} = rt$$

$$\text{MULTIPLY BY } \frac{1}{r} \left(\frac{A}{p} \right) = \text{MULTIPLY BY } \frac{1}{r} (rt)$$

$$\frac{A}{rp} = t$$

- Solve for C:

$$F = \tfrac{9}{5}C + 32$$

$$\text{SUBTRACT 32 } (F) = \text{SUBTRACT 32 } (\tfrac{9}{5}C + 32)$$

$$F - 32 = \tfrac{9}{5}C$$

$$\text{MULTIPLY BY } \tfrac{5}{9} (F - 32) = \text{MULTIPLY BY } \tfrac{5}{9} (\tfrac{9}{5}C)$$

$$\tfrac{5}{9} (F - 32) = C$$

Sample Problems

1   Solve for D in $A = \frac{1}{2}Dd$ (the area of a square in terms of its diagonals):

PROCEDURE

$$A = \tfrac{1}{2}Dd$$
$$\text{MULTIPLYBY } 2\,(A) = \text{MULTIPLYBY } 2\,(\tfrac{1}{2}Dd)$$
$$2A = Dd$$
$$\text{MULTIPLYBY } \frac{1}{d}(2A) = \text{MULTIPLYBY } \frac{1}{d}\,(Dd)$$
$$\frac{2A}{d} = D$$

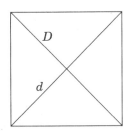

2   Solve for N in $P = CN + T$.

PROCEDURE

$$P = CN + T$$
$$\text{SUBTRACT } T\,(P) = \text{SUBTRACT } T\,(CN + T)$$
$$P - T = CN$$
$$\text{MULTIPLYBY } \frac{1}{C}\,(P - T) = \text{MULTIPLYBY } \frac{1}{C}\,(CN)$$
$$\frac{P - T}{C} = N$$

Problem Set   **A**

ASSIGNMENT GUIDE

Basic (1 day)
2–32 (even)

Average (1 day)
14–44 (even)

Advanced (1 day)
40–58

State the result of each algebraic operation:

1   MULTIPLYBY $1(p)$
$$p$$

2   MULTIPLYBY $\frac{1}{2}\,(3K - R)$
$$\frac{3K - R}{2}$$

3   SUBTRACT $t\,(d)$
$$d - t$$

4   ADD $c\,(x)$
$$x + c$$

5   MULTIPLYBY $p\,(r)$
$$pr$$

6   DIVIDEBY $h\,(k)$
$$\frac{k}{h}$$

7   ADD $b\,(a)$
$$a + b$$

8   SUBTRACT $m\,(n)$
$$n - m$$

9   DIVIDEBY $w\,(z)$
$$\frac{z}{w}$$

10   MULTIPLYBY $x\,(y)$
$$xy$$

11   DIVIDEBY $3\,(4a + b)$
$$\frac{4a + b}{3}$$

12   SUBTRACT $v\,\left(\dfrac{M}{r}\right)$
$$\frac{M}{r} - v$$

Solve each equation for the indicated variable.

13 $d = rt$ for t
$$t = \frac{d}{r}$$

14 $C = \pi d$ for d
$$d = \frac{c}{\pi}$$

15 $s = c + e$ for c
$$c = s - e$$

16 $M = r + t$ for r
$$r = M - t$$

17 $C = B - A$ for B
$$B = C + A$$

18 $f = a - b$ for a
$$a = f + b$$

19 $x = w - z$ for z
$$z = w - x$$

20 $H = y - d$ for d
$$d = y - H$$

21 $C = Bh$ for B
$$B = \frac{C}{h}$$

22 $p = 4s$ for s
$$s = \frac{p}{4}$$

23 $i = prt$ for p
$$p = \frac{i}{rt}$$

24 $i = prt$ for t
$$t = \frac{i}{pr}$$

Solve each problem. (Review: Chapter 3)

25 Write 403,900 in scientific notation.
4.039×10^5

26 Evaluate $5m - 3n$ for $m = -4, n = -7$.
1

27 Evaluate $\dfrac{-6x}{y}$ for $x = 8, y = 3$.
-16

28 Evaluate $t(3 - t) + 5t$ for $t = 9$.
-9

29 Translate the following into algebra and tell how to isolate the variable: divided among four people.
$\frac{n}{4}$ MULTBY 4

30 Translate the following into an equation and solve: Twenty-four and the product of x and twelve are the same number.
2

31 The sum of the measures of the interior angles of any hexagon is seven hundred twenty. Use an equation to determine the measure of one interior angle of a regular hexagon (all six angles have the same measure).
$120°$

32 Translate the following into an equation and solve: The sum of three times a number and seven is twenty-two.
5

33 Paul bought a used boat for forty dollars less than one third its original cost. Find the original cost if Paul paid three thousand sixty dollars for the boat.
$9300

Problem Set B

Indicate the operations that must be done, in the correct order, to isolate the indicated variable.

34 $2\ell + h$ isolate ℓ
ADD $-h$, MULTBY $\frac{1}{2}$

37 $2f + 3y$ isolate f
ADD $-3y$, MULTBY $\frac{1}{2}$

35 $\dfrac{Bh}{3}$ isolate B
MULTBY 3, MULTBY $\frac{1}{h}$

38 $\dfrac{3 + r}{5}$ isolate r
MULTBY 5, ADD -3

36 $\dfrac{x + y + z}{4}$ isolate x
MULTBY 4, ADD $-y$, ADD $-z$

39 $r - atx^2$ isolate t
ADD $-r$, MULTBY $-\frac{1}{ax^2}$

Solve each equation for the indicated variable.

40 $A = \dfrac{bh}{2}$ for h $h = \frac{2A}{b}$

43 $A = \dfrac{ap}{2}$ for a $a = \frac{2A}{P}$

41 $V = \pi r^2 h$ for h $h = \frac{v}{\pi r^2}$

44 $P = \dfrac{d^2 n}{2.5}$ for n $n = \frac{2.5D}{d^2}$

42 $A = \frac{1}{2}Dd$ for d $d = \frac{2A}{D}$

Problem Set C

Solve each equation for the indicated variable.

45 $P = b + 2\ell$ for ℓ $\ell = \frac{P-b}{2}$

52 $A = \frac{1}{2}bh$ for h $h = \frac{2A}{b}$

54) Multiply both sides by $f \cdot a \cdot b$:
$(f \cdot a \cdot b)\left(\frac{1}{f}\right) = \left(\frac{1}{a} + \frac{1}{b}\right)(f \cdot a \cdot b)$
$ab = fb + fa$
$ab = f(b + a)$
$\frac{ab}{a + b} = f$

46 $F = \frac{9}{5}C + 32$ for C $C = \frac{5}{9}(F - 32)$

53 $SA = 2\pi r^2 + 2\pi rh$ for h $h = \frac{SA - 2\pi r}{2\pi r}$

47 $P = 2\ell + 2w$ for w $w = \frac{P - 2\ell}{2}$

54 $\dfrac{1}{f} = \dfrac{1}{a} + \dfrac{1}{b}$ for f $f = \frac{ab}{a + b}$

48 $S = 180n - 360$ for n $n = \frac{(S + 360)}{180}$

55 $\dfrac{1}{f} = \dfrac{1}{a} + \dfrac{1}{b}$ for a $a = \frac{bf}{b - f}$

58) First, remove parentheses:
$l = a + (n - 1)d$
$l = a + nd - d$
$l - a + d = nd$
$\frac{l - a + d}{d} = n$

49 $A = \frac{1}{2}h(B + b)$ for h $h = \frac{2A}{B + b}$

56 $Ax + By = C$ for y $y = \frac{C - Ax}{B}$

50 $A = \frac{1}{2}h(B + b)$ for B $B = \frac{2A}{h} - b$

57 $\dfrac{y - s}{x - r} = m$ for y $y = m(x - r)$

51 $A = \frac{1}{2}h(B + b)$ for b $b = \frac{2A}{h} - B$

58 $\ell = a + (n - 1)d$ for n $n = \frac{(\ell - a + d)}{d}$

Chapter Study Guide

ASSIGNMENT GUIDE

Basic (3 days)
(1) 146: 1–27
(2) 126: 33–38
     133: 21–25
(3) 147: 8–46 (even)

Average (2 days)
(1) 132: 25–39 (odd)
     146: 1–27
(2) 147: 8–12, 18–30
     (even), 40–47

Advanced (2 days)
(1) 134: 57–65 (odd),
     81, 82
     146: 1–27
(2) 143: 24–36, 40–49

Vocabulary

As you study and review this chapter, be sure that you learn the important mathematics vocabulary, including:

1   Exponent, Base   A natural number EXPONENT is a number that indicates how many times a BASE is used as a factor.

- The product $6 \cdot 6 \cdot 6$ can be written 6^3. The power 6^3 indicates that the base 6 has been raised to the exponent 3.

2   Reciprocal   If $a \cdot b = 1$ for two real numbers a and b, then each number is the RECIPROCAL of the other.

- The pair of numbers 2 and $\frac{1}{2}$ are reciprocals because $(2)\left(\frac{1}{2}\right) = 1$.

- Each pair of numbers 6 and $\frac{1}{6}$, -4 and $-\frac{1}{4}$, $\frac{2}{3}$ and $\frac{3}{2}$ are reciprocals because the product of each pair is 1.

Skills

Be sure you build the useful algebraic skills, including:

3   Using natural numbers as exponents
Write each product without parentheses:
a $(4)^3 \cdot (5)^2$
b $(n)^1$
c $(2xy)^3 \cdot 2xy^3$

PROCEDURE

a $(4)^3 \cdot (5)^2 = 4 \cdot 4 \cdot 4 \cdot 5 \cdot 5 = 64 \cdot 25 = 1600$
b $(n)^1$ means the same as n
c $(2xy)^3 \cdot 2xy^3 = (2xy)(2xy)(2xy) \cdot 2xy^3$
$$= 2 \cdot 2 \cdot 2 \cdot 2 \cdot x \cdot x \cdot x \cdot x \cdot y \cdot y \cdot y \cdot y \cdot y \cdot y$$
$$= 16x^4 \cdot y^6$$

4   **Multiplying signed numbers**   Find each product:

a $(15)(-3)$ c $(-15)(-3)$

b $(-15)(3)$ d $(-5)(-4)(3)$

PROCEDURE   In general, if two numbers have the same sign, their product is positive. If two numbers have opposite signs, their product is negative.

a $(15)(-3) = -45$ c $(-15)(-3) = 45$
b $(-15)(3) = -45$ d $(-5)(-4)(3) = (20)(3) = 60$

5   **Dividing signed numbers**   Find each quotient:

a $\frac{15}{-3}$ c $\frac{-15}{-3}$

b $\frac{-15}{3}$ d $\frac{15}{3}$

PROCEDURE   In general, if two numbers have the same sign, their quotient is positive. If two numbers have opposite signs, their quotient is negative.

a $\frac{15}{-3} = -5$ c $\frac{-15}{-3} = 5$
b $\frac{-15}{3} = -5$ d $\frac{15}{3} = 5$

6   **Following the conventional order of operations**
Calculate the value of each expression:

a $3 \cdot 4 + 5$

b $6 \cdot 5 + 4^3 \div 2 - 1$

c $(6 - 5)^2 - (4 + 2) \cdot 6 + 8 \div 2$

PROCEDURE   For any expression, the order of operations is:

exponentiation
multiplication and division
addition and subtraction

However, if parentheses are used in the expression, the calculations inside the parentheses are performed first.

a $3 \cdot 4 + 5 = 12 + 5 = 17$

b $6 \cdot 5 + 4^3 \div 2 - 1 = 6 \cdot 5 + 64 \div 2 - 1$
$$= 30 + 32 - 1$$
$$= 61$$

c $(6 - 5)^2 - (4 + 2) \cdot 6 + 8 \div 2 = (1)^2 - (6) \cdot 6 + 8 \div 2$
$$= 1 - 36 + 4$$
$$= -31$$

7 Solving two-step equations

Solve the equation $3p - 17 = 31$ for the variable p.

PROCEDURE

$$3p - 17 = 31$$
$$\text{ADD } 17\ (3p - 17) = \text{ADD } 17\ (31)$$
$$3p = 48$$
$$\text{MULTIPLY BY } \tfrac{1}{3}\ (3p) = \text{MULTIPLY BY } \tfrac{1}{3}\ (48)$$
$$p = 16$$

$$\textit{To check} \qquad 3p - 17 = 31$$
$$3(16) - 17 \overset{?}{=} 31$$
$$48 - 17 \overset{?}{=} 31$$
$$31 \overset{?}{=} 31 \checkmark$$

8 Solving literal equations Solve for q: $n = pq + t$

PROCEDURE

$$\text{ADD } -t\ (n) = \text{ADD } -t\ (pq + t)$$
$$n - t = pq$$
$$\text{MULTIPLY BY } \frac{1}{p}\ (n - t) = \text{MULTIPLY BY } \frac{1}{p}\ (pq)$$
$$\frac{n - t}{p} = q$$

9 Solving problems The honor roll at Adelphi High School contains one tenth of the students in the school, plus five students more. If there are one hundred twenty-seven students on the honor roll, how many students are there in the school?

PROCEDURE Let t represent the total number of students in the high school. The honor roll has one tenth of the students, plus five more students, so the equation is:

$$\tfrac{1}{10}t + 5 = 127$$
$$\text{SUBTRACT } 5\ (\tfrac{1}{10}t + 5) = \text{SUBTRACT } 5\ (127)$$
$$\tfrac{1}{10}t = 122$$
$$\text{MULTIPLY BY } 10\ (\tfrac{1}{10}t) = \text{MULTIPLY BY } 10\ (122)$$
$$t = 1220$$

There are 1220 students in the school.

Chapter Test

Perform the indicated operations.

1 $3(-3)$
-9

4 $(-2)(-6)$
12

7 $-6 \div (-2) + 5 \cdot 3^2$
48

2 $-10 \div 5$
-2

5 $(-4) \div (\frac{1}{2})$
-2

8 $5 - 2(3 - 7)^2$
-27

3 $(-\frac{1}{2})^3$
$-\frac{1}{8}$

6 $(-5)(3)(-3)$
45

9 $3(9 - 2^2)^2 - 4$
71

10 Write 64,000 in scientific notation.
6.4×10^4

Evaluate each expression for $x = 3$ and $y = -2$.

11 $-2x - y$
-4

12 $\dfrac{3 - 2x}{2y + 3}$
1

13 $(2x^2 + 4y)^2$
100

Write the reciprocal of each number.

14 $\dfrac{3}{2}$
$\frac{2}{3}$

15 $\dfrac{a}{b}$
$\frac{b}{a}$

16 $-y$
$-\frac{1}{y}$

State how to isolate x in each variable expression.

17 $\dfrac{2}{5}x$
MULTIPLY BY $\frac{5}{2}$

18 $-6x$
MULTIPLY BY $-\frac{1}{6}$

19 $\dfrac{ax}{3b}$
MULTIPLY BY $\frac{3b}{a}$

Solve each equation for x.

20 $-8 = 2x$
$x = -4$

22 $-\frac{2}{3}x = 10$
$x = -15$

24 $\dfrac{x}{3} - 7 = 2$
$x = 27$

21 $\dfrac{x}{4} = \dfrac{5}{8}$
$x = \frac{5}{2}$

23 $m^2 = px$
$x = \frac{m^2}{p}$

25 $2x + 5 = 17$
$x = 6$

In problems 26–27, write an equation and solve it.

26 A video-game store purchased thirty video-cassettes at a cost of $750. To break even, what should be the average charge for each game?
$25

27 Rolf spent $3.50 at a school dance. If admission was $1.50 and he bought 5 cans of pop, what did each drink cost?
$0.40

Problem Set: Cumulative Review 1–3

Problem Set A

Fill in the blanks.

1 A list of numbers in a particular order is a(n) __?__.
   sequence

2 A number that can be written as a ratio of two integers is called a(n) __?__ number.
   rational

3 To add signed numbers on a number line, the first arrow starts at the __?__. The second arrow starts at the __?__ of the first arrow.
   origin; end

4 Equivalent equations are equations that have the same __?__.
   solution

5 In the expression $5x^2$, the variable is __?__, the 5 is a(n) __?__, and the 2 is a(n) __?__.
   x; coefficient; exponent

6 When two numbers have the same sign, their product is __?__. When they have opposite signs, their product is __?__.
   positive; negative

7 When two numbers have the same sign, their quotient is __?__. When they have opposite signs, their quotient is __?__.
   positive; negative

Multiple Choice

8 The formula for the perimeter of a rectangle is $p = 2l + 2w$. If $l = 5$ and $w = 8$, the perimeter is: _b_
   a 40   c 13
   b 26   d 80

9 Which of the following is not a translation of $3 + n$: _c_
   a the sum of a number and three
   b a number increased by three
   c the product of three and a number
   d three more than a number

10 The sum $7 + (-2)$ is: _b_
   a −5   c +9
   b +5   d −9

11 To isolate the variable in $r - \frac{1}{3}$, perform the operation: _a_

    a ADD $\frac{1}{3}$
    c MULTIPLYBY $\frac{1}{3}$
    b ADD $-\frac{1}{3}$
    d OPP $\frac{1}{3}$

12 A translation of *the sum of a number and twelve is negative five* is: _b_

    a $(-5) + y = 12$
    c $12 + (-5) = y$
    b $y + 12 = -5$
    d $y + (-5) = 12$

13 The value of $-7c + 2d$ when $c = -1$ and $d = -5$ is: _d_

    a -18
    c 3
    b -17
    d -3

14 The expression $6((-3) - (-9))$ can be written without parentheses as: _b_

    a -72
    c -9
    b 36
    d -27

15 The variable expression that represents the phrase *twice as much* is: _d_

    a $2 + x$
    c $x \div 2$
    b $x - 2$
    d $2x$

16 Solve for w: $-8w = 44$ _d_

    a $w = -352$
    c $w = 36$
    b $w = 52$
    d $w = -5\frac{1}{2}$

17 Solve for z: $-8 = 2 + 5z$ _a_

    a $z = -2$
    c $-\frac{5}{6}$
    b $z = -\frac{6}{5}$
    d $z = -50$

Perform the indicated operation(s).

18 $14 + (-8) + 3$
    9

19 $16 + (-16)$
    0

20 $(+11) + (-6)$
    5

21 $(-9)(12)$
    -108

22 $(-42) \div (-6)$
    7

23 $(-81) \div (9) + (18)(2)$
    27

24 $3\frac{1}{4} + 2\frac{1}{2}$
    $5\frac{3}{4}$

25 $6\frac{8}{9} - 5\frac{1}{6}$
    $1\frac{13}{18}$

26 $3\frac{1}{3} + 8\frac{2}{9} + 6\frac{5}{6}$
    $18\frac{7}{18}$

27 $4\frac{1}{5} - 3\frac{1}{2} + 5\frac{3}{10}$
    6

28 $-0.172 + 1.535 - 0.021$
    1.342

29 $(-0.43)(-0.11)$
    0.0473

Problem Set B

Represent each inequality on a number line.

30 $w < 5$; w is a whole number
    solid dots at 0, 1, 2, 3, 4

32 $r < -4$; r is a real number
    heavy line in the negative direction from an open dot at −4

31 $n > 3$; n is a natural number
    solid dots at 4, 5, 6, 7, . . .

33 $i > 0$; i is an integer
    solid dots at 1, 2, 3, 4, . . .

Evaluate each expression.

34 ADD 16 (OPP (3))
    13

37 RECIP $\left(\frac{5}{6}\right)$ $\frac{6}{5}$

35 SUBTRACT 16 (9)
    −7

38 $(5 - 8)^2 \div (-8 - 10)$ $-\frac{1}{2}$

36 OPP (19) + ABSVAL (−12)
    −7

39 $(3 - 7)^3 \div (-4)$
    16

Solve each equation.

40 $\dfrac{n - 3}{2} = 3$
    $n = 9$

43 $\dfrac{x}{7} = -3$
    $x = -21$

41 $1 + m = -6$
    $m = -7$

44 $r \div 17 = -5$
    $r = -85$

42 $12 + 6y = 19$
    $y = \dfrac{7}{6}$

45 $7t - 13 = 1$
    $t = 2$

Problem Set C

46 The sum of two integers is negative one hundred seventy-four. If one integer is negative ninety-seven, what is the other integer?
    −77

47 The sum of two equal numbers is thirty-seven. What is the product of the numbers?
    $\dfrac{1369}{4}$

48 A rectangle four meters wide has a perimeter that is twenty-four meters. Find the length of the rectangle.
    $\ell = 8$

49 *Old mathematicians never die; they just reduce to lowest terms.*
    a Find FREQ (m).   **d** Find FREQ (a).   **g** Find RELFREQ (e).
    b Find FREQ (e).   **e** Find FREQ (g).   **h** Find RELFREQ (y).
    c Find FREQ (y).   **f** Find RELFREQ (m).   **i** Find RELFREQ (a).

    a 3 b 9 c 1 d 3 e 0 f $\frac{3}{52}$; 6% g $\frac{9}{52}$; 17% h $\frac{1}{52}$; 2% i $\frac{3}{52}$; 6%

Chapter 4

CHAPTER SCHEDULE

Basic
Problem Sets 12 Days
Review 2 Days
Test 2 Days

Average
Problem Sets 10 Days
Review 1 Day
Test 2 Days

Advanced
Problem Sets 10 Days
Review 1 Day
Test 1 Day

THE DISTRIBUTIVE PROPERTY

Section 4.1   Multiplying Monomials

SECTION SCHEDULE

Basic (2 days)

Average (2 days)

Advanced (2 days)

The area of a rectangle is the product of the length and width of the rectangle:

$$A = \ell \cdot w$$
$$= (2y)\,(y^3)$$
$$= 2y^4$$

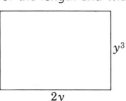

y^3

$2y$

In this problem, $2y$, y^3, and $2y^4$ is each a **monomial** (mō nō′ mē əl).

Definition

> A MONOMIAL is a single term that is a constant, or a variable, or a product of constants and variables.

EXAMPLES

- Each expression xy, $10K$, 5, r, x^2y, and $6w^5z^3$ is a monomial.

- The following expressions are **not** monomials: $\dfrac{6}{x}$ $\dfrac{4s^2}{r}$

  Each involves division by a variable.

Brighter students may also appreciate the following distinction: while $3 + d$ is a binomial, $(3+d)$ is often considered to be a monomial.

The expressions $3 + d$, $2c - 4$, and $5x + 2y - 3$ are not monomials because each involves addition and/or subtraction.

In the monomial $6w^5z^3$, the constant factor 6 is called the **numerical coefficient** (kō′ə fish′ənt) of the variable term w^5z^3.

Definition

The NUMERICAL COEFFICIENT (or simply COEFFICIENT) of a monomial is the constant factor in the term.

EXAMPLES

monomial: $-6m$ $\dfrac{x}{8}$ $5x^2y$ a $-b^3c^2$

- coefficient: -6 $\dfrac{1}{8}$ 5 1 -1

The coefficient of a term must be expressed as a simple factor. For example, in the term $2y \cdot 8z$ the coefficient is 16.

Sample Problems

1 Express each product as a monomial. What is the coefficient of each term?

  a $(4x^2)(x^3)$ **b** $(-2a^2b)(3a^6)$ **c** $(6x^2)^4$

PROCEDURE

  a $(4x^2)(x^3) = (4 \cdot x \cdot x)(x \cdot x \cdot x)$
  $\qquad = 4x^5$

  The coefficient of the monomial is 4.

  b $(-2a^2b)(3a^6) = (-2)(3)(a \cdot a \cdot b)(a \cdot a \cdot a \cdot a \cdot a \cdot a)$
  $\qquad\qquad = -6a^8b$

  The coefficient of the monomial is -6.

  c $(6x^2)^4 = (6x^2)(6x^2)(6x^2)(6x^2)$
  $\qquad = (6 \cdot x \cdot x)(6 \cdot x \cdot x)(6 \cdot x \cdot x)(6 \cdot x \cdot x)$
  $\qquad = 6 \cdot 6 \cdot 6 \cdot 6 \cdot x^8$
  $\qquad = 1296x^8$

  The coefficient is 1296.

2 Express the product $(2 \cdot 10^3)(7 \cdot 10^4)$ in scientific notation.

PROCEDURE

$$(2 \cdot 10^3)(7 \cdot 10^4) = (2 \cdot 10 \cdot 10 \cdot 10)(7 \cdot 10 \cdot 10 \cdot 10 \cdot 10)$$
$$= (2 \cdot 7)(10^7)$$
$$= 14 \times 10^7$$
$$= (1.4)(10) \times 10^7$$
$$= 1.4 \times 10^8$$

1.4×10^8 is in scientific notation.

Problem Set A

ASSIGNMENT GUIDE

Basic (2 days)
(1) 7–24
(2) 25–32
   157: 1–12

Average (2 days)
(1) 21–42
(2) 43–48
   157: 1–12

Advanced (2 days)
(1) 21–44
(2) 49–54
   157: 1–12, 16

1 Is m^2n a monomial? Why or why not?

    yes, product of (constants and) variables

2 Is $y - 4z^2$ a monomial? Why or why not?

    no, operation of subtraction

3 Is $\dfrac{v}{3}$ a monomial? Why or why not?

    yes, product of a constant ($\frac{1}{3}$) and a variable (v)

4 Is $\dfrac{-9}{m}$ a monomial? Why or why not?

    no, division by a variable

5 What is a numerical coefficient?

    a factor that is a constant

6 Does every monomial have a coefficient? Explain.

    yes, if no constant stated, 1 is the coefficient

Express each product as a single monomial and then state the coefficient of each.

7 $3x^2 \cdot x$
    $3x^3$, 3

8 $-5x^3 \cdot x^2$
    $-5x^5$, -5

9 $n \cdot 5n$
    $5n^2$, 5

10 $a^2 \cdot 7a$
    $7a^3$, 7

11 $6x^2 \cdot 3x^5$
    $18x^7$, 18

12 $-5x^2 \cdot 9x^4$
    $-45x^6$, -45

13 $(-2x^2)(-3x^2)$
    $6x^4$, 6

14 $-8x^3 \cdot \frac{1}{2}x^3$
    $-4x^6$, -4

15 $y^2 \cdot y^6$
    y^8, 1

16 $x^3 \cdot x$
    x^4, 1

17 $4n^2 \cdot 5p$
    $20n^2p$, 20

18 $-3k^3(-2a^2)$
    $6a^2k^3$, 6

19 $(-w^4)(w^3)$
    $-w^7$, -1

20 $x^4 \cdot (-x^3) \cdot x^2$
    $-x^9$, -1

21 $(5x)^2$
    $25x^2$, 25

22 $(-3y)^2$
    $9y^2$, 9

23 $(2x^2y)^3$
    $8x^6y^3$, 8

24 $(-1xy^2)^4$
    x^4y^8, 1

Translate each verbal phrase into a variable expression.

25 the product of three and x-squared

$3x^2$

26 the quotient of x to the fourth power and six

$\dfrac{x^4}{6}$

Translate each sentence into a variable expression and then write each expression as a monomial.

27 Multiply four y-squared by two y-cubed.

$4y^2 \cdot 2y^3 = 8y^5$

28 Find the product of x to the fourth power, negative nine, and eight x-cubed.

$x^4 \cdot (-9) \cdot 8x^3 = -72x^7$

Let $x = 3$ and $y = 4$. Evaluate the expressions in column A and column B. (Review: Section 1.2)

These review problems preview the Distributive Property.

A	**B**
29 $xy + 4y$	$(x + 4)y$
28, 28	
30 $2x + 12$	$2(x + 6)$
18, 18	
31 $-3x + 6y$	$-3(x - 2y)$
15, 15	
32 $x^2 - xy$	$x(x - y)$
$-3, -3$	

Problem Set **B**

In problems 33–42, express each product as a monomial.

33 $2x^2 \cdot 9xy^2$

$18x^3y^2$

34 $-3x^4y \cdot 2x^2$

$-6x^6y$

35 $(16a^2b) \left(\frac{1}{4}a^3b\right)$

$4a^5b^2$

36 $\left(\frac{2}{5}a^3c^2\right)(10c^5)$

$4a^3c^7$

37 $(-6y^2)^2 (5y^3)$

$180y^7$

38 $(4x^3)(2x)^3$

$32x^6$

39 $(2 \cdot 10^3)(4 \cdot 10^2)$

$8 \cdot 10^5$

40 $(-7 \cdot 10^5)(6 \cdot 10^4)$

$-42 \cdot 10^9$

41 $2 \cdot 3 \cdot 2^3 \cdot 3^2$

432

42 $5 \cdot 7 \cdot 2^2 \cdot 5^3 \cdot 7 \cdot 2^2$

$490{,}000$

43 Find the area of a rectangle with a length of $4x^2$ and a width of $9x^3$.

$36x^5$

44 Find the area of a rectangle with dimensions $8xy^3z$ by $6x^2y^2z$.

$48x^3y^5z^2$

In problems 45–48, express each number in scientific notation.

45 123,000

1.23×10^5

46 4050

4.05×10^3

47 853.4085

8.534085×10^2

48 3.14159

3.14159×10^0

Problem Set C

Rewrite each pair of numbers in scientific notation, find their product, and then express that product in scientific notation.

- 5,000,000,000; 3,000

   PROCEDURE

   $5,000,000,000 = 5 \times 10^9$
   $3,000 = 3 \times 10^3$

   $(5 \cdot 10^9)(3 \cdot 10^3) = 15 \times 10^{12}$
   $= (1.5 \times 10) \times 10^{12}$
   $= 1.5 \times 10^{13}$

49 4,286,000,000; 15,230

6.527578×10^{13}

50 two hundred thirty million; sixty-five thousand

1.495×10^{13}

51 eight hundred seventeen billion; four hundred ninety-three million

4.02781×10^{20}

52 the product of sixty-five million and thirteen million

8.45×10^{14}

53 the quotient of one hundred seventy-five billion and twenty-five million

7.0×10^3

54 A farm grows sod in a field with dimensions $11x^2$ feet by x^3 feet. If $x = 9.86$, find the area of the field to the nearest whole number of square feet, and express that number in scientific notation.

1.025126×10^6

X tending the topic: Prime Numbers

For any natural number greater than one, it is always possible to express that number as a product of positive factors. For example:

$$35 = 1 \cdot 35 \qquad 36 = 1 \cdot 36 \quad 36 = 4 \cdot 9 \qquad 37 = 1 \cdot 37$$
$$35 = 5 \cdot 7 \qquad 36 = 2 \cdot 18 \quad 36 = 6 \cdot 6$$
$$36 = 3 \cdot 12$$

Some numbers, such as 35 or 36, can be factored more than one way. A number such as 37, however, can be factored only as 1 times itself. Such a number is called a **prime**.

Definition

> A PRIME NUMBER is a natural number greater than 1 that can be expressed as a product of natural numbers in only one way—itself times 1.

EXAMPLES

- The first 10 primes are 2,3,5,7,11,13,17,19,23,29. (Natural numbers greater than 1 that are not primes, such as 4,6,8,9, are called **composite** numbers.)

Sample Problems

1   Find the prime factors of $80x^3y^2$.

PROCEDURE   Use the convention that a variable with an exponent of 1 is considered to be a prime. Thus x^3y^2 is factored as $x \cdot x \cdot x \cdot y \cdot y$. For the factors of the coefficient, use a "factor tree:"

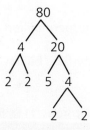

The prime factors of $80x^3y^2$ are 2, 5, x, and y.

2 The **prime factorization** of the number 36 is $2^2 \cdot 3^2$. The number is written as a product of primes, each prime with its exponent. Write the prime factorization of:

a 210   b $80x^3y^2$ c 12,600

Prime factorization is used in Section 4.7X (p. 188) to find the GCF of two expressions.

PROCEDURE

a $210 = 2^1 \cdot 3^1 \cdot 5^1 \cdot 7^1 = 2 \cdot 3 \cdot 5 \cdot 7$

b $80x^3y^2 = 2^4 \cdot 5^1 \cdot x^3 \cdot y^2$

c

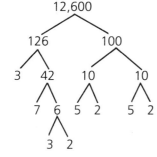

$12,600 = 2^3 \cdot 3^2 \cdot 5^2 \cdot 7$

Problem Set **X**

Write a "factor tree" for each number.

1   24
    $2^3 \cdot 3$

2   392
    $2^3 \cdot 7^2$

3 $450x^2y^5$
    $2 \cdot 3^2 \cdot 5^2 \cdot x^2 \cdot y^3$

4 $495a^3$
    $3^2 \cdot 5 \cdot 11$

5   1,000,000
    $2^6 \cdot 5^6$

6   30031
    prime

Write the prime factorization of each number.

7   24
    $2^3 \cdot 3$

8   392
    $2^3 \cdot 7^2$

9 $450x^2y^5$
    $2 \cdot 3^2 \cdot 5^2 \cdot x^2 \cdot y^5$

10 $495a^3$
    $3^2 \cdot 5 \cdot 11 \cdot a^3$

11   1,000,000
    $2^6 \cdot 5^6$

12   30031
    $1 \cdot 300031$

13   18,225
    $3^6 \cdot 5^2$

14   2880
    $2^6 \cdot 3^2 \cdot 5$

15   1001
    $7 \cdot 11 \cdot 13$

16   Take any 3-digit number, and write it twice (eg. 417,417). Divide the new 6-digit number by 13. (The remainder will be zero!) Divide the quotient by 7. (The remainder will be zero.) Then divide that quotient by 11. (Again, zero remainder!) What is the last quotient? Why does this "trick" work?

    The original number. Multiplication is by $1001 = 13 \cdot 7 \cdot 11$.

Section 4.2 Adding and Subtracting Like Monomials

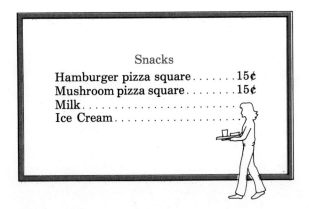

Suppose that yesterday you bought 3 hamburger pizza squares, and today you bought 2 mushroom pizza squares. How much did you spend on pizza in the past two days?

There are two ways to find the total. One way uses the fact that all the pizza squares were the same price:

$(3 + 2) \cdot 15$

Another way is to calculate what was spent each day:

$3 \cdot 15 + 2 \cdot 15$

Each method results in the same total amount:

$$(3 + 2) \cdot 15 = 5 \cdot 15 = 75$$
$$3 \cdot 15 + 2 \cdot 15 = 45 + 30 = 75$$

At any price for pizza squares, the two methods will give the same result. Let p represent the price, in cents, of one square. Then the cost of 3 hamburger squares and 2 mushroom squares can be calculated as $(3 + 2)p$ or $3p + 2p$:

$$(3 + 2)p = 3p + 2p$$

Notice how each side would translate to a verbal phrase. The left-hand side is, "First add 3 and 2, and then multiply that sum by a variable." The right-hand side is, "First multiply a variable by 3, and the variable by 2, and then add the two products." The equal sign indicates that "the results have the same value."

This example is an illustration of the **Distributive Property**, which is a general relationship between addition and multiplication (or subtraction and multiplication).

Property

If a, b, and c represent any numbers, then the following two expressions always have the same value:

$$a(b + c)$$
$$a \cdot b + a \cdot c$$

This relationship is called the **DISTRIBUTIVE PROPERTY**.

The Distributive Property is usually written in the form of an equation, $a(b + c) = a \cdot b + a \cdot c$, but it can be written in different forms. This section applies two forms of the Distributive Property:

$$ba + ca = (b + c)a$$
$$ba - ca = (b - c)a$$

One use of the Distributive Property is to explain addition or subtraction of monomials, such as $7x^2 + 11x^2$ or $7x^2 - 11x^2$. Monomials such as $7x^2$ and $11x^2$ are called **like terms**.

Definition

If monomials have the same variable(s), and corresponding variables have the same exponents, then the monomials are **LIKE TERMS**.

EXAMPLES

- $7x^2$, $11x^2$

    Each has a variable x with an exponent 2.

- $3p$, $2p$

    Each has a variable p (with an exponent 1).

- $-6xy^2$, $8xy^2$, $13xy^2$

    Each has a variable x with exponent 1, and a variable y with exponent 2.

- $3(x + y)$, $-2(x + y)$

    The variable is $(x + y)$.

- $3t^4$, t^4, $3t^4$

    Each has a variable t with exponent 4 (the coefficient of t^4 is 1).

In general, like terms may differ only in their coefficients.

Sample Problems

1   Use the Distributive Property to explain each addition or subtraction:
   a $7x^2 + 11x^2$
   b $7x^2 - 11x^2$

PROCEDURE

   a   The Distributive Property states that the following expressions have the same value:

$$ba + ca$$
$$(b + c)a$$

Replace b by 7, c by 11, and a by x^2:

$$7x^2 + 11x^2$$
$$(7 + 11)x^2$$
$$18x^2$$

Thus $7x^2 + 11x^2 = 18x^2$.

   b   The following expressions have the same value:

$$ba - ca$$
$$(b - c)a$$

Let $b = 7$, $a = x^2$, and $c = 11$:

$$7x^2 - 11x^2$$
$$(7 - 11)x^2$$
$$- 4x^2$$

Thus $7x^2 - 11x^2 = -4x^2$.

2   Combine the like terms in the following:

$$-5p + 3q - q + 7p.$$

PROCEDURE $-5p$ and $7p$ are like terms, as are $3q$ and $-q$:

$$-5p + 3q - q + 7p$$
$$-5p + 7p + 3q - q$$
$$(-5 + 7)p + (3 - 1)q$$
$$2p + 2q$$

Thus $-5p + 3q - q + 7p = 2p + 2q$.

Problem Set A

ASSIGNMENT GUIDE

Basic (1 day)
5–24, 26, 28, 30

Average (1 day)
22–30 (even), 31–44

Advanced (1 day)
31–49

1 When are monomials considered **like terms**?

same variable, corresponding variables have same exponents

2 Can monomials with the same coefficient be **like terms**? Give examples.

yes, $4y$ and $4y$ (answers may vary)

3 The Distributive Property shows a relationship between which operations?

multiplication and addition (or multiplication and subtraction)

4 State one use of the Distributive Property.

combining like terms

Copy the following equations and replace each __?__ with the correct expression.

5 $5x + 3x = (5 + \underline{\ ?\ })x$
$\qquad = \underline{\ ?\ }\ x$

3, 8

6 $2y - 5y = (2 - \underline{\ ?\ })y$
$\qquad = \underline{\ ?\ }\ y$

5, −3

7 $6a + a = (6 + \underline{\ ?\ })a$
$\qquad = \underline{\ ?\ }$

1, 7a

8 $b^2 - 8b^2 = (\underline{\ ?\ } - 8)\ \underline{\ ?\ }$
$\qquad = \underline{\ ?\ }$

1, b^2, $-7b^2$

9 $7x - 5x + 11x = (7 - 5 + 11)\ \underline{\ ?\ }$
$\qquad = \underline{\ ?\ }$

x, $13x$

10 $-6y^2 + 4y^2 - \underline{\ ?\ }\ y^2 = (-6 + \underline{\ ?\ } - 7)y^2$
$\qquad = \underline{\ ?\ }\ y^2$

7, 4, 9

Add or subtract the like terms.

11 $4x + 9x$

13x

12 $2a - 3a$

−a

13 $5b^2 - 3b^2$

$2b^2$

14 $-9xy + 12xy$

3xy

15 $8y - y$

7y

16 $x^2 - 4x^2$

$-3x^2$

17 $5n - 6n + 8n$

7n

18 $-9x^2 - x^2 - 5x^2$

$-15x^2$

19 $2x + 3x - 5x$

0

20 $-6y - 2y + 8y$

0

In problems 21–24, find the perimeter of each figure.

21

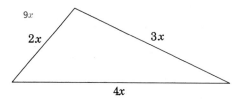

9x

2x　　　　　3x

4x

22　a square, each side of length 5y
20y

23　a pentagon (5 sides) with three sides of length 7x and the other two sides of length 2x
25x

24　a rectangle with length 4x and width x
10x

Solve each equation. (Review: Section 3.7)

25　$3x + 7 = 13$
$x = 2$

28　$\frac{1}{2}x - 4 = -7$
$x = -6$

26　$-2x - 5 = 11$
$x = -8$

29　$-3 + x = 8$
$x = 11$

27　$-x + 13 = 4$
$x = 9$

30　$5 - 2x = 9$
$x = -2$

Problem Set　**B**

Add or subtract the like terms.

31　$9a + 3b + 2a$
$11a + 3b$

37　$4x^2 - 3x + 2x - x^2$
$3x^2 - x$

32　$4y + 5x - 2y$
$5x + 2y$

38　$-2y^2 + 5y^2 + 4x - 3$
$4x + 3y^2 - 3$

33　$7 + 8x + 9$
$8x + 16$

39　$3x^2 + 9x - 7x - 6$
$3x^2 + 2x - 6$

34　$-3 + 5 - x^2$
$-x^2 + 2$

40　$4a^2 + 2a - 10a + 1$
$4a^2 - 8a + 1$

35　$6x - 7 + 2 - 3x$
$3x - 5$

41　$x^2 + 3x - 3x - 9$
$x^2 - 9$

36　$4xy + 9 - 6xy - 5$
$2xy + 4$

42　$4x^2 - 10x + 10x - 25$
$4x^2 - 25$

43 Mr. Dolatowski's car has a gas tank that holds eight more liters of gas than his neighbor's car.

  a If the neighbor's car holds x liters of gas, write an expression for the number of liters of gas Mr. Dolatowski's car holds.

  b Write an expression for the total number of liters of gas that can be pumped into both cars.

  a $x + 8$ b $2x + 8$

44 Jae Kim jogged a certain distance one week. The following three weeks of the month she increased her run by five miles each week.

  a If m is the number of miles jogged the first week, express the number of miles jogged the second week.

  b Write an expression for the number of miles jogged the third week.

  c Write an expression for the number of miles jogged the fourth week.

  d What is the total number of miles jogged during the month by Ms. Kim?

  a $m + 5$ b $m + 10$ c $m + 15$ d $4m + 30$

Problem Set C

45 Write a formula for the area of the figure. The width of the rectangle and the height of the triangle is each s units.

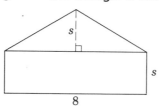

45) Area of triangle $= \frac{1}{2} b \cdot h$
$\quad = \frac{1}{2} \cdot 8 \cdot s$
$\quad = 4s$
Area of rectangle $= b \cdot h$
$\quad = 8s$
Total area $= 12s$

The **surface area** of a three dimensional figure is the sum of the areas of the sides, top, and bottom. In problems 46–49, write a formula for the surface area, S, of each figure. Combine like terms where you can.

46 a closed cereal box

$S = 2h\ell + 2\ell w + 2wh$

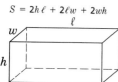

48 a closed cube

$S = 6e^2$

48) Since each of the six faces has an area of e^2, the total area is $6e^2$.

47 a box with no lid

$S = 2h\ell + 2wh + \ell w$

49 a cube with no top

$S = 5e^2$

Section 4.3 Solving Equations with Like Monomials

Consecutive integers are numbers such as 2 and 3, or -9 and -8, or 1029 and 1030. If n is any integer, then n and $n + 1$ are consecutive integers.

Puzzles about consecutive integers can be solved using algebra. The puzzles often translate into equations such as:

$$3n + 4n = 14$$
$$2p - 3 + 6p = 21$$
$$3q + 5 = q + 11$$

Solving such equations requires skill in combining like monomials.

*This section intro-
duces equations with
the variable on both
sides of the equation.*

Sample Problems

1 Solve each equation:
  a $3n + 4n = 14$
  b $2p - 3 + 6p = 21$

  PROCEDURE Solve each equation by finding an equivalent equation that has the variable isolated.

  a
$$3n + 4n = 14$$
$$(3 + 4)n = 14$$
$$7n = 14$$
$$\text{MULTIPLYBY } \tfrac{1}{7} (7n) = \text{MULTIPLYBY } \tfrac{1}{7} (14)$$
$$n = 2$$

  b From now on, the text will use an abbreviated form of "computer talk":

*Some students may
need an explicit state-
ment that the abbrevi-
ated form still
applies to both sides of
an equation.*

$$2p - 3 + 6p = 21$$
$$2p + 6p - 3 = 21$$
$$(2 + 6)p - 3 = 21$$
$$8p - 3 = 21$$

  ADD 3: $\quad 8p = 24$
  MULTBY $\tfrac{1}{8}$: $\quad p = 3$

2 Solve and check: $14t + 12 = 11t - 3$

PROCEDURE

$$14t + 12 = 11t - 3$$

SUBT 11t: $3t + 12 = -3$

SUBT 12: $3t = -15$

MULTBY $\frac{1}{3}$: $t = -5$

To check $14t + 12 = 11t - 3$

$$14(-5) + 12 \overset{?}{=} 11(-5) - 3$$
$$-70 + 12 \overset{?}{=} -55 - 3$$
$$-58 \overset{?}{=} -55 - 3$$
$$-58 \overset{?}{=} -58 \checkmark$$

3   The sum of 3 consecutive odd integers is 3. Find the integers.

PROCEDURE   Let n represent the first odd integer. The next odd integer is $n + 2$, and the third consecutive odd integer is $n + 4$. The equation is:

$$n + n + 2 + n + 4 = 3$$
$$3n + 6 = 3$$

SUBT 6: $3n = -3$

MULTBY $\frac{1}{3}$: $n = -1$

The first odd integer is -1. The other two odd integers must be $+1$ and $+3$.

To check   Is the sum of the three integers equal to 3?

$$(-1) + (1) + (3) \overset{?}{=} 3$$
$$0 + 3 \overset{?}{=} 3$$
$$3 \overset{?}{=} 3 \checkmark$$

Problem Set **A**

ASSIGNMENT GUIDE

Basic (2 days)
(1) 1–15
(2) 16–28

Average (1 day)
15–22, 27–41

Advanced (1 day)
6, 7, 16, 18, 22, 31–39, 42, 44

1   How is the Distributive Property used to combine the like terms in the equation $3x + 4x = 21$?

$3x + 4x$, $(3+4)x$, $7x$

2   Explain what steps you would use to solve $3x + 4x = 21$.

$(3+4)x$, $7x = 21$, MULTBY $\frac{1}{7}$

3   Name four consecutive even integers beginning with 12; beginning with x.

12, 14, 16, 18; x, $x + 2$, $x + 4$, $x + 6$

4   When will $n + 2$ be an odd integer?

n is odd

Solve and check.

5 $4n - 3n = 6$
  $n = 6$

6 $2x - x = -5$
  $x = -5$

7 $2n + 3n = 20$
  $n = 4$

8 $n + n = 24$
  $n = 12$

9 $2x + 3 = x + 5$
  $x = 2$

10 $3x + 2 = 2x + 7$
  $x = 5$

11 $5n + 3 = 4n + 14$
  $n = 11$

12 $2x + 4 = x + 3$
  $x = -1$

13 $3n + 2 = n + 10$
  $n = 4$

14 $3x + 17 = x + 9$
  $x = -4$

15 $5w + 8 = 3w + 18$
  $w = 5$

16 $5b + 2 = 2b + 10$
  $b = \dfrac{8}{3}$

17 $7x - 4 = 5x + 11$
  $x = \dfrac{15}{2}$

18 $5n - 2 = n + 18$
  $n = 5$

19 $5n - 3 = 2n - 9$
  $n = -2$

20 $3b - 2 = b - 10$
  $b = -4$

21 $6x - 5 = 3x - 8$
  $x = -1$

22 $8n - 7 = 5n - 13$
  $n = -2$

23 Find two consecutive integers whose sum is ninety-three.

46, 47

24 Find three consecutive integers whose sum is one hundred thirty-five.

44, 45, 46

25 A path twenty-four meters long has three wooden blocks followed by one slate block as its pattern. Each block is one meter long. How many of each block are in the path?

18 wood, 6 slate

26 A necklace of one hundred twenty-five beads has a pattern of four yellow beads for each red one. How many of each color are there?

100 yellow, 25 red

For each problem, evaluate and compare the expressions in columns A and B. Let $a = 5$ and $b = -2$. (Review: Section 1.2)

A	**B**
27 $2(a + 4)$	$2a + 8$
18, 18 same	
28 $-3(b - a)$	$-3b + 3a$
21, 21 same	
29 $a(b + 5)$	$ab + 5a$
15, 15 same	
30 $a(2b - a)$	$2ab - a^2$
-45, -45 same	

Problem Set B

Solve and check:

31 $2n + 2n + 2 = 14$
  $n = 3$

35 $n + n + 12 = 3n - 4n$
  $n = -4$

32 $x + 4 + x + 2 + x = 42$
  $x = 12$

36 $4x + x = 5x - 2x + 10$
  $x = 5$

33 $2p - 6 + 3p = 4p - 1$
  $p = 5$

37 $6x + 3 - x = 3x + 10 - x$
  $x = -\frac{7}{3}$

34 $7d + 3 - 2d = 4d + 10$
  $d = 7$

38 $6k - 4k - 1 = k + 10 - 2k$
  $k = \frac{11}{3}$

39 Find two consecutive odd integers whose sum is one hundred seventy-six. [87, 89]

40 Jason has forty centimeters of wire. With it he wants to make a rectangle that is four centimeters longer than it is wide. What should be the dimensions of the rectangle?
  $w = 8$ cm, $\ell = 12$ cm

40) $2x + 2(x + 4) = 40$

41 Sue wants to build a pen that is nine feet narrower than it is long. She has sixty-eight feet of fencing. Draw a sketch and find the dimensions of the pen.
  $\ell = 21\frac{1}{2}$ ft, $w = 12\frac{1}{2}$ ft

41) $2x + 2(x + 9) = 68$

Problem Set C

42 Georgette wants to tile a five-foot by twelve-foot hall with one-foot-square tiles. The pattern she will use needs two blue tiles for each red tile. How many tiles of each kind should she buy?
  40 blue, 20 red

42) $2x + x = 60$

43 Mack is tiling a room with eight-inch-square tiles. The floor is eight feet long and six feet wide. He is going to use a pattern that calls for five blue tiles for each green tile. How many tiles of each color does he want?
  18 green, 90 blue

43) $\dfrac{\text{area of floor}}{\text{area of 1 tile}} = \dfrac{6912}{64}$
  $= 108$
  Thus there are 108 tiles.
  $5x + x = 108;\ x = 18$

44 Joan is going to build a patio and fence it in completely. She wants a square region at one end that would be paved and a planting area four feet wide along one side of the square where she can have a flower garden. A roll of fencing is fifty feet long. If she uses the whole roll, how many square feet will be paved?
  110.25 sq. ft.

44)

$4x + 8 = 50;\ x = 10\frac{1}{2}$

The area of the paved square is 110.25 square feet.

Project: Two Model Players

The spinner and the program are called Monte Carlo methods because they generate probabilistic approximations as a solution. The empirical values generated by Monte Carlo methods should be close to values generated by computing theoretical probabilities. The theoretical probabilities are:

2) Prob. of at least 8 out of ten is the sum of the probabilities of 8, 9, and 10:

$$\binom{10}{8}(.6)^8(.4)^2$$
$$+ \binom{10}{9}(.6)^9(.4)^1$$
$$+ \binom{10}{10}(.6)^{10}(.4)^0$$

which is 0.1673.

3) Prob. of at least 5 out of 10 is the sum of the probabilities of 5 through 10:

$$\binom{10}{5}(.875)^5(.125)^5$$
$$+ \binom{10}{6}(.875)^6(.125)^4$$
$$+ \ldots + \binom{10}{10}(.875)^{10}(.125)^0$$

The sum is 0.9995. The probability of at least 9 out of 10 is 0.6389.

4) The exact results can be repeated if the computer always generates the same sequence of random numbers.

5) For a player who shoots 87.5%:
    50 FOR J = 1 to 1000
    60 $X =$
        $INT(RND(1)*1000)$
    70 IF $X < 875$ THEN C
        $= C + 1$
For 5 out of 10 (similar for 9 out of 10):
    90 IF $C > = 5$ THEN S
        $= S + 1$
    130 PRINT "LEAST 5
        BASKETS IS"; P

During the basketball season, Belinda has made 60% of her free throws. What is the probability that she will make at least eight out of the next ten?

1 Use a spinner as a **simulation** or **model**. Spin the arrow ten times. If the arrow indicates **basket** eight or more times, record a **success**; if the arrow records **basket** fewer than eight times (out of ten), record a **failure**. Repeat this process, recording **success** or **failure**, 100 times.

Miss (40%)

Basket (60%)

2 Out of the hundred sets of trials, how many times were recorded **success**? What is the estimated probability that Belinda will make at least 8 out of the next 10 baskets?

3 Make another spinner for Mel, who shoots 0.875 from the foul line. What is the probability that she will hit at least 5 of the next 10? What about at least 9 of the next 10?

This computer program uses random numbers to simulate a 60% free throw shooter. Statement 60 generates 100 random numbers from 0 through 99. The numbers 0–59 represent baskets and 60–99 represent missed shots.

```
10   PRINT "HOW MANY TRIALS?"
20   INPUT N
30   FOR I = 1 TO N
40   C = 0
50   FOR J = 1 TO 100
60   X = INT(RND(1)*100)
70   IF X < 60 THEN C = C + 1
80   NEXT J
90   IF C >= 8 THEN S = S + 1
100  NEXT I
110  P = S/N
120  PRINT "THE PROBABILITY OF AT ";
130  PRINT "LEAST 8 BASKETS IS "; P
140  END
```

4 Do you always get exactly the same results when you run this program?

5 How can the program be revised for a player who shoots 0.875? How can the program be revised to estimate the probability of making at least 5 out of 10? at least 9 out of 10?

Section 4.4   Removing Parentheses

SECTION SCHEDULE

Basic (1 day)

Average (1 day)

Advanced ($1\frac{1}{2}$ days)

The Distributive Property can be used to explain how to remove parentheses in a variable expression such as $8(x + 3)$. This section applies four forms of the Distributive Property for numbers a, b, c:

$$a(b + c) = ab + ac \qquad (b + c)a = ba + ca$$
$$a(b - c) = ab - ac \qquad (b - c)a = ba - ca$$

Sample Problems

1   Use the Distributive Property to explain how to remove the parentheses in $(2x - 9) \cdot 4x$.

PROCEDURE   These two expressions must have the same value:

$$(b - c)a$$
$$ba - ca$$

Substitute $2x$ for b, 9 for c, and $4x$ for a:

$$(2x - 9) \cdot 4x$$
$$2x \cdot 4x - 9 \cdot 4x$$
$$8x^2 - 36x$$

Thus $(2x - 9) \cdot 4x = 8x^2 - 36x$.

2   Remove the parentheses and then combine the like terms in $-5(n - 3p) + 6n$.

PROCEDURE

The expressions $a(b - c)$ and $ab - ac$ must have the same value.

$$-5(n - 3p) + 6n$$
$$-5n - (-5)(3p) + 6n$$
$$-5n - (-15p) + 6n$$
$$-5n + 15p + 6n$$
$$-5n + 6n + 15p$$
$$(-5 + 6)n + 15p$$
$$1n + 15p$$
$$n + 15p$$

ASSIGNMENT GUIDE

Basic (1 day)
10–30

Average (1 day)
13–34

Advanced (1$\frac{1}{2}$ days)
(1) 17–20, 29–40
(2) See p. 174.

Problem Set **A**

1 Name two uses of the Distributive Property.
combining like terms, removing parentheses

2 Explain how the Distributive Property can be used to remove the parentheses in $3 + (4y + 2)$.
$3+(4y +2) = 3+1(4y +2) = 3+4y +2 = 4y +5$

Copy the following exercises and replace each $\underline{\quad?\quad}$ with the correct expression.

3 $5(x + 3) = 5x + 5 \cdot \underline{\quad?\quad}$
3

4 $6(y - 2) = 6y - 6 \cdot \underline{\quad?\quad}$
2

5 $x(y + 7) = xy + \underline{\quad?\quad}$
7x

6 $(b + c) \cdot a = ba + c \cdot \underline{\quad?\quad}$
a

7 $(4 + m)(-3) = -12 - 3 \cdot \underline{\quad?\quad}$
m

8 $\underline{\quad?\quad} (y + 8) = xy + 8x$
x

9 $\underline{\quad?\quad} (2x - 5) = 6x^2 - 15x$
3x

10 $2(\underline{\quad?\quad} + 7) = 6x + 14$
3x

11 $5(x + \underline{\quad?\quad}) = 5x + 5$
1

12 $\underline{\quad?\quad}(3x^2 + 2x) = 3x^2 + 2x$
1

Use the Distributive Property to remove the parentheses.

13 $6(x + 3)$
$6x + 18$

14 $-5(3x + 2)$
$-15x - 10$

15 $8(x^2 + 3x - 2)$
$8x^2 + 24x - 16$

16 $-(4x^2 - 5x + 1)$
$-4x^2 + 5x - 1$

Translate the verbal phrases into variable expressions containing parentheses. Then distribute to remove the parentheses.

17 The product of $4x$ and the difference $2x$ minus $5y$.
$4x(2x -5y) = 8x^2 - 20xy$

18 The sum $-3x$ plus $2x^2$; that sum multiplied by x.
$(-3x +2x^2)x = -3x^2 + 2x^3$

19 5 added to $11x$ and then that sum multiplied by $3x$.
$(5+11x)3x = 15x + 33x^2$

20 $2m$ subtracted from $7a$ and that difference multiplied by $-5am$.
$(7a -2m)(-5am) = -35a^2m + 10am^2$

Rewrite each of the following subtraction problems as a sum. (Review: Section 2.4)

21 $12x - 30$
$12x + (-30)$

22 $91 - 215y$
$91 + (-215y)$

23 $5x^2 - 12x$
$5x^2 + (-12x)$

24 $-7 - ab$
$-7 + (-ab)$

Problem Set B

In problems 25–32, remove the parentheses and then combine the like terms.

25 $2(x + 9) + 7x$

$9x + 18$

26 $6 + 4(2x - 8)$

$8x - 26$

27 $-(2x + 5) + 3x$

$x - 5$

28 $-(5x^2 + 2x) - 4x$

$-5x^2 - 6x$

29 $8x(2x + 10) - 16x^2$

$80x$

30 $6x^2 + 5(12x^2 - 3x)$

$66x^2 - 15x$

31 $-3(2x + 9) + 2(4x + 7)$

$2x - 3$

32 $4(5x^2 - 2x + 1) + 6(9 - 3x)$

$20x^2 - 26x + 58$

Problem Set C

Remove the parentheses, combine the like terms, and then evaluate the expression for the given value of x.

33 $2x(3x - 5) + 6(2x^2 - 5x)$ $x = 6$

408

34 $6x^3 + 5x(x^2 - 3x + 2) - 7x^2$ $x = 5$

875

35 $-(4x^3 - 5x^2 - 2x - 6) + 2(x^2 - 5x)$ $x = -2$

82

36 $-3x^2(2x - 5) + 7x^2 + (4x^3 - 5x)$ $x = 3$

129

When using a calculator to evaluate expressions such as those in problems 33–36, a memory key is not necessary.

- In problem 33, after the first two steps, the problem becomes $18x^2 - 40x = (18x - 40)x$. To evaluate for $x = 6$, enter:

    18 $\boxed{\times}$ 6 $\boxed{=}$ $\boxed{-}$ 40 $\boxed{=}$ $\boxed{\times}$ 6 $\boxed{=}$

    The result is 408.

For many calculators, some of the $\boxed{=}$ keystokes can be eliminated.

- Problem 34 simplifies to $11x^3 - 22x^2 + 10x = ((11x - 22)x + 10)x$. To evaluate for $x = 5$, enter:

    11 $\boxed{\times}$ 5 $\boxed{=}$ $\boxed{-}$ 22 $\boxed{=}$ $\boxed{\times}$ 5 $\boxed{=}$ $\boxed{+}$ 10 $\boxed{=}$ $\boxed{\times}$ 5 $\boxed{=}$

    The result is 875.

37) $-4x^3 + 7x^2 - 8x + 6$
   $= ((-4x + 7)x - 8)x + ($

For $x = -2$, the value is 82.

38) $-2x^3 + 22x^2 - 5x$
   $= ((-2x + 22)x - 5)x$

For $x = 3$, the value is 129.

37 Use this method to evaluate problem 35.
   82

38 Use this method to evaluate problem 36.
   129

39 Find the perimeter of a regular octagon (8 sides) if each side
   is $3x - 2$ inches.
   $24x - 16$

40 Find the area of a rectangle with base $2x - 5$ centimeters and
   height $4x$ centimeters.
   $(8x^2 - 20x)$ sq cm

$\mathbf{X}$ tending the topic: Computer Programs to Evaluate Expressions

Problems 33–36 in Section 4.4 asked to evaluate an expresssion for one value of a variable. When an expression must be evaluated for several values of the variable, a computer program will save time. The following BASIC program evaluates the expression $2x(3x^2 - 6)$ for the eleven integral values of x from -5 to 5:

```
10 PRINT "X",  "2*X*(3*X^2  -  6)"
20 X = -5
30 PRINT X,  2*X*(3*X^2 -6)
40 IF X = 5 THEN 70
50 X = X + 1
60 GO TO 30
70 END
```

For a shorter program, re-place lines 20, 40, 50, and 60 with:
   25 FOR $X = -5$ TO 5
   35 NEXT X

Note: A shorter program can be written with the use of a FOR . . . NEXT statement.

Problem Set $\mathbf{X}$

The programs should use the following expressions in lines 10 and 30:
1) $4*x*(x - 3)$
2) $-5*x \wedge 2*(2*x + 1)$
3) $0.6*(x \wedge 3 -0.7*x + -5)$

Write a program that will evaluate the given expression for integral values of x from -10 to 10.   programs may vary

1 $4x(x - 3)$ **2** $-5x^2(2x + 1)$ **3** $.6(x^3 - .7x - 5)$

Section 4.5 Solving Equations With Parentheses

SECTION SCHEDULE

Basic (2 days)

Average (2 days)

Advanced ($1\frac{1}{2}$ days)

In solving equations such as $25t = 15(t + 2)$ or $n - 3(n - 2) = n - 9$, the first step is to remove the parentheses. The next steps are to combine the like terms and then isolate the variable.

Sample Problems

1   Remove the parentheses in each phrase:

   a $-5(4n + 2)$ c $-7(-t - 8)$

   b $-3(5m - 6)$ d $-(2q + 3)$

PROCEDURE

Use the following form of the Distributive Property:

$$a(b + c) = ab + ac$$

This form expresses the Distributive Property as a sum. Each negative sign is considered as part of one of the terms.

a $-5(4n + 2)$

      $(-5)(4n) + (-5)(2)$

      $(-20n) + (-10)$

        $-20n - 10$

c $-7(-t - 8)$

      $(-7)((-t) + (-8))$

      $(-7)(-t) + (-7)(-8)$

        $(7t) + (56)$

         $7t + 56$

b $-3(5m - 6)$

      $(-3)(5m + (-6))$

      $(-3)(5m) + (-3)(-6)$

      $(-15m) + (18)$

        $-15m + 18$

d $-(2q + 3)$

      $(-1)(2q + 3)$

      $(-1)(2q) + (-1)(3)$

      $(-2q) + (-3)$

        $-2q - 3$

2   Solve and check:

   a $25t = 15(t + 2)$ b $n - 3(n - 2) = n - 9$

PROCEDURE

a   equation: $25t = 15(t + 2)$ *To check* $25t = 15(t + 2)$

      distribute: $25t = 15t + 30$ $25(3) \stackrel{?}{=} 15(3 + 2)$

      ADD $-15t$: $10t = 30$ $75 \stackrel{?}{=} 15(5)$

      MULTBY $\frac{1}{10}$: $t = 3$ $75 \stackrel{?}{=} 75 \checkmark$

b   equation: $n - 3(n - 2) = n - 9$

        distribute: $n + (-3)(n + (-2)) = n - 9$

                $n + (-3)(n) + (-3)(-2) = n - 9$

                $n - 3n + 6 = n - 9$

combine like terms: $-2n + 6 = n - 9$

SUBT n: $-3n + 6 = -9$

SUBT 6: $-3n = -15$

MULTBY $-\frac{1}{3}$: $n = 5$

To check $n - 3(n - 2) = n - 9$

$(5) - 3(5 - 2) \overset{?}{=} 5 - 9$

$5 - 3(3) \overset{?}{=} -4$

$5 - 9 \overset{?}{=} -4$

$-4 \overset{?}{=} -4 \checkmark$

ASSIGNMENT GUIDE

Basic (2 days)
(1) 3–10, 25–28
(2) 15–24

Average (2 days)
(1) 5, 12, 16, 29–33
(2) 25–28, 35–39
    167: 36–41

Advanced (1½ days)
(1) 5, 12, 16, 25–33
(2) 34, 35, 40–45
    172: 1–3

Problem Set **A**

1 What are the uses of the Distributive Property in solving the equation $5n = 3(n - 4)$?

removing parentheses, combining like terms

2 Why is it necessary to remove the parentheses to solve the equation $5n = 3(n - 4)$?

to combine $5n$ and $3n$

In problems 3–20, solve and check.

3 $3(n - 2) = 12$
$n = 6$

4 $-2(x + 5) = 20$
$x = -15$

5 $45t = 30(t + 3)$
$t = 6$

6 $50t = 25(t + 6)$
$t = 6$

7 $3(n + 2) = 2n + 9$
$n = 3$

8 $5(x - 3) = 4x + 20$
$x = 35$

9 $6(v - 3) = 4v + 12$
$v = 15$

10 $5(w - 2) = 2w + 14$
$w = 8$

11 $3(2 + w) - 2w = 13$
$w = 7$

12 $2b - (b + 2) = 18$
$b = 20$

13 $4(r + 3) - 4 = 20$
$r = 3$

14 $3t - (t + 5) = 11$
$t = 8$

15 $x - 2(x + 7) = 8$
$x = -22$

16 $3n - 4(n - 5) = n - 6$
$n = 13$

17 $2p - 5(p + 1) = 7p + 9$
$p = -\frac{7}{5}$

18 $2z - 3 = 5z - 2(z - 4)$
$z = -11$

19 $2(d + 1) - d = 13$
$d = 11$

20 $4 - 2(x + 3) = 2x - 10 - x$
$x = \frac{8}{3}$

21 Find two consecutive integers if twice the second equals the first.

$-2, -1$

22 Find two consecutive integers such that three times the second minus the first is seven.

$2, 3$

23 Find two consecutive odd integers such that five times the first plus three times the second is forty-six.

$5, 7$

24 Find two consecutive odd integers such that the second minus three times the first is zero.

$1, 3$

Translate each verbal phrase into a variable expression that uses parentheses. Then use the Distributive Property to remove the parentheses. (Review: Section 3.4)

25 twice the sum of three times x and seven

$2(3x + 7) = 6x + 14$

26 one half the difference of eight y and twelve

$\frac{1}{2}(8y - 12) = 4y - 6$

27 five times the sum of Mary's age (m) and Hector's age (h)

$5(m + h) = 5m + 5h$

28 the sum of one integer (k) and three times the next larger integer

$k + 3(k + 1) = k + 3k + 3 = 4k + 3$

Problem Set B

Solve each equation.

29 $14 - (x - 3) = 3x - (x - 11)$

$x = 2$

30 $17 - (2w - 5) = 11 - (3w + 4)$

$w = -15$

31 $7 - 5(5 - 2x) = x - 4(3x - 6)$

$x = 2$

32 $2 + 3(4x - 2) = 8 + (x - 1)$

$x = 1$

33 $9(x - 5) + 2x = 5(2x - 3) - 4$

$x = 26$

34 $-3(2x + 7) - 4x = 2(7 - 3x) + 1$

$x = -9$

35 $(3x - 1) - (6x + 8) = -(5x - 7)$

$x = 8$

Translate each equation into an English sentence.   answers may vary

36 $2(x - 7) = 19$

37 $4x - 10 = 3(2x + 5)$

38) $3x + 5 = 2(x + 7)$;
$x = 9$

38 Three times a number plus five is equal to twice the sum of the number and seven. What is the number?
9

39) $25 - 2(x + 1)$
$= 4x - 1$; $x = 4$

39 Find two consecutive integers such that when twice the second is subtracted from twenty-five the difference is equal to one less than four times the first.
4, 5

Problem Set C

40) $2x + 2(x + 2) = 60$;
$x = 14$

40 Harold is going to build a fenced-in patio. He will have a square patio with a two-foot border inside the fence at one end for growing tomatoes. A roll of fencing is sixty feet long. If he uses the whole roll, what will be the width of the patio?
14 ft

41) $2(13 - x) - 4x = 11$
$x = \dfrac{5}{2}$

41 The sum of two numbers is thirteen. Twice the larger number minus four times the smaller number is eleven. What is the smaller number?
$2\dfrac{1}{2}$

42) Any pair of values x and $x + 5$, $x > 0$, will satisfy the problem. Calvin's score can be any even positive integer ≥ 10.

42 Calvin scored five more field goals than free throws in a recent basketball game. If it had been reversed (five more free throws than field goals), he would have scored five fewer points. How many points did he score?
10, 12, 14, . . .

43) $0.5x + (75 - x) = 55$
$x = 40$
40 tickets at 50¢
35 tickets at $1.00

43 For a school Halloween dance, seventy-five tickets were sold. It cost fifty cents per ticket if you wore a costume and one dollar otherwise. If fifty-five dollars was received for ticket sales how many tickets were sold at each price?
35 at $1, 40 at 50¢

44) Six rows can be planted along the ten-foot dimension, five rows along the eight-foot dimension.
$x + 2x = 30$;
$x = 10$

44 Mario is planning a small garden. He wants to plant twice as many tomato plants as pepper plants. The garden is ten feet long and eight feet wide. He is going to space the plants two feet apart in each direction. How many of each kind of plant should he buy?
20 tomatoes, 10 peppers

45) Eleven rows of nine

$x + 2x = 99$;
$x = 33$

45 How many plants will fit in a garden that has twice Mario's dimensions?
66 tomatoes, 33 peppers

After-School Mathematics: Painting

Randi was tired of the way her room looked, so she wanted to redecorate. She decided that new curtains and a new coat of paint would fix up the room.

To find the total wall area of her room, Randi made a "flattened" diagram of the room:

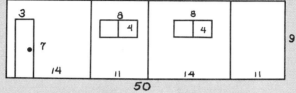

The wall area was 450 square feet, less 64 square feet (for the two windows) and less 21 square feet (for the door), or 365 square feet.

According to the salesperson at the paint store, Randi needed about $3\frac{1}{2}$ quarts of paint. Each quart cost $4.50 so the total cost would be $18.00. The salesperson pointed out to her that she could buy a gallon of paint for only $14.00.

Randi thought that the gallon price was a real bargain until she realized that she was planning to cover the old dark blue paint with off-white paint. Therefore, she would need to give the walls two coats of paint! That would be two gallons of paint, or $28.00. Even without new curtains, her redecorating scheme was more expensive than she thought it would be.

Application: Magnification

A compound microscope has an eyepiece lens that magnifies an object by ten times (10X). It also has three objective lenses: 4X, 10X, and 40X.

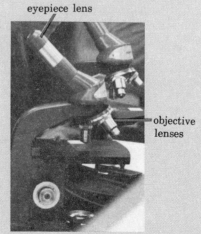

eyepiece lens

objective lenses

1   Suppose an object on a slide is eight ten-thousandths of an inch in diameter. How large can it appear to the viewer?

2   Suppose an object has an area of 0.003 square millimeters. What will the area appear to be, using each objective lens?

1) The products of 0.0008 and 40, 100, and 400, respectively: 0.032 in., 0.08 in., 0.32 in.

2) The products of 0.003 and 40, 100, and 400, respectively: 0.12 mm², 0.3 mm², 1.2 mm²

Section 4.6 Adding and Subtracting Polynomials

To express the perimeter p of this figure, write the sum of the lengths of the four sides:

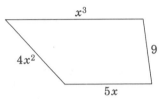

$$p = x^3 + 4x^2 + 5x + 9$$

Each of the terms x^3, $4x^2$, $5x$, and 9 is a monomial. The expression $p = x^3 + 4x^2 + 5x + 9$ is called a **polynomial** (päl'i nō'mē əl).

Definition

A POLYNOMIAL is an indicated sum or difference of monomials.

EXAMPLES

- Each of the following is a polynomial:

  $n^2 - 3n + 5$

  $4t^5 + 16t^4 + 12$

  $3p^2q^2 + 10pq^2 - 5q^2 + 3q - 1$

  $-4m^5$

  14

  The last two examples are polynomials of one term, which are also called monomials. Polynomials with two terms are called **binomials**, and polynomials with three terms are called **trinomials**.

- $r^2 - 1$ is a binomial

  $ab^2c + abcd^3$ is a binomial

- $r^2 - 2r - 5$ is a trinomial

  $x^2yz + xy^2z + xyz^2$ is a trinomial

The Distributive Property can be used to explain how to add or subtract pairs of polynomials.

Sample Problems

1 Add the two trinomials $3x^2 - 5x + 2$ and $7x^2 - 9x + 3$.

PROCEDURE Write the sum and then use the Distributive Property to combine the like terms:

$$3x^2 - 5x + 2 + 7x^2 - 9x + 3$$
$$3x^2 + 7x^2 - 5x - 9x + 2 + 3$$
$$(3 + 7)x^2 + (-5 - 9)x + 5$$
$$10x^2 \qquad + (-14)x \qquad + 5$$
$$10x^2 \qquad - 14x \qquad + 5$$

2 Subtract the binomial $3y - 2$ from the binomial $5y - 4$.

PROCEDURE Write the difference and then use the Distributive Property to remove the parentheses.

$$5y - 4 - (3y - 2)$$
$$5y - 4 + (-1)(3y - 2)$$
$$5y - 4 + (-1)((3y) + (-2))$$
$$5y - 4 + (-1)(3y) + (-1)(-2)$$
$$5y - 4 + (-3y) + (2)$$
$$5y - 4 - 3y + 2$$
$$5y - 3y - 4 + 2$$
$$2y - 2$$

Many students will be able to combine some of these steps.

3 Simplify the expression $m(3m^2 + 6m - 1) - 2m^2(5 - 4m)$ by removing the parentheses and then combining like terms.

PROCEDURE

The Distributive Property can be used for a sum of many terms:

$$a(b + c + d + e) = ab + ac + ad + ae$$

Use the Distributive Property, then combine the like terms.

$$m(3m^2 + 6m - 1) - 2m^2(5 - 4m)$$
$$(m)(3m^2 + 6m + (-1)) + (-2m^2)(5 + (-4m))$$
$$(m)(3m^2) + (m)(6m) + (m)(-1) + (-2m^2)(5) + (-2m^2)(-4m)$$
$$(3m^3) + (6m^2) + (-m) + (-10m^2) + (8m^3)$$
$$3m^3 + 8m^3 + 6m^2 - 10m^2 - m$$
$$11m^3 - 4m^2 - m$$

ASSIGNMENT GUIDE

Basic (2 days)
(1) 1–12, 17–20
(2) 13–16
    182: 1–9

Average ($1\frac{1}{2}$ days)
(1) 6–20 (even), 21–28
(2) See p. 184.

Advanced ($1\frac{1}{2}$ days)
(1) 10–20 (even), 21–28
    182: 1–9
(2) See p. 184.

Problem Set A

1 In a polynomial, different terms are separated by ___?___ signs or ___?___ signs.

    plus, minus

2 A polynomial with three terms is called a(n) ___?___ .

    trinomial

3 A binomial is a polynomial with ___?___ terms.

    two

4 If a polynomial is multiplied by the number ___?___ , then the sign of every term is changed.

    −1

Simplify each expression by removing parentheses and combining like terms.

5 $(4y + 8) - (2y + 5)$

    $2y + 3$

6 $(6y^2 - 5y) - (7y - 4y^2)$

    $10y^2 - 12y$

7 $3x^2 + 4x - 8 + 7 - 4x + 11x^2 - 6$

    $14x^2 - 7$

8 $5xy^2 + 9x^2y - 7xy^2 + 2x^2 - 11x^2y$

    $2x^2 - 2x^2y - 2xy^2$

9 $(9n^2 + 5n) + (6n^2 - 2n)$

    $15n^2 + 3n$

10 $(11 - 8y) + (10y + 4)$

    $2y + 15$

11 $(x^2 + 3x + 5) - (2x^2 + 4x - 3)$

    $-x^2 - x + 8$

12 $(6x^2 - 5x + 7) - (5x^2 + 8x - 9)$

    $x^2 - 13x + 16$

13 $(4x^2 + 7x^3 + 5x + 10) + (8x + 6x^3 - 4x^2 + 7)$

    $13x^2 + 13x + 17$

14 $(15n^2 - 6n - 8n^4 - 5) + (7n^3 - 21n^2 + 8n)$

    $-8n^4 + 7n^3 - 6n^2 + 2n - 5$

15 $9x + (6 - 8x) + (4 + x)$

    $2x + 10$

16 $x^2 + (2x^2 - x + 7) + (-3x^2 + 6x - 8)$

    $5x - 1$

Solve each equation. (Review: Section 4.3)

17 $2x + 6 = x + 7$

    $x = 1$

18 $3w - 12 = 2w + 2$

    $w = 14$

19 $4n - 11 = 6n + 6$

    $n = -\frac{17}{2}$

20 $5y + 2 - 3y = -10$

    $y = -6$

Problem Set B

21 Add $(8x + 7)$ and $(4x - 8)$.

$12x - 1$

22 Find the sum of $(-7x^2 + 6x - 4)$ and $(3x^2 - 5x + 1)$.

$-4x^2 + x - 3$

23 Subtract $(-6x + 5)$ from $(4x^2 + 6x - 7)$.

$4x^2 + 12x - 12$

24 From $(4y^2 - 3y)$, subtract $(2y + 7y^2)$.

$-3y^2 - 5y$

25 Write the product of $2x$ and $(3x^2 + 5x - 7)$.

$6x^3 + 10x^2 - 14x$

26 Write the product of 6, $-3a$, and $(2a - 4)$.

$-36a^2 + 72a$

Find the unmarked measurement.

27

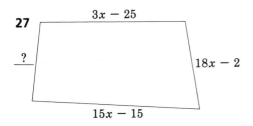

perimeter $= 42x - 36$

$6x + 6$

28

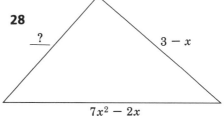

perimeter $= 4x^2 - 5x + 12$

$-3x^2 - 2x + 9$

Problem Set C

Suppose you deposit $1000 in a savings account on your birthday every year, and make no withdrawals. At the end of every year, all the money in your account is to be multiplied by r. That amount will be added to what is already in your account. Write a simplified expression (no parentheses) that represents the amount in your savings account after:

29 one year

$1000 + 1000r$

30 two years

$1000 + 2000r + 1000r^2$

31 three years

$1000 + 3000r + 3000r^2 + 1000r^3$

32 four years

$1000 + 4000r + 6000r^2 + 4000r^3 + 1000r^4$

33 If $r = 0.0975$, find the value of each expression in problems 29–32.

$1097.50, $1204.51, $1321.95, $1450.84

30) $(1000 + 1000r)$
   $+ (1000 + 1000r)r$
   $= 1000 + 2000r$
   $+ 1000r^2$

31) $1000 + 2000r + 1000r^2$
   $+ (1000 + 2000r$
   $+ 1000r^2)r$
   $= 1000 + 3000r$
   $+ 3000r^2 + 1000r^3$

32) $1000 + 3000r + 3000r^2$
   $+ 1000r^3$
   $+(1000 + 3000r$
   $+ 3000r^2 + 1000r^3)r$
   $= 1000 + 4000r$
   $+ 6000r^2 + 4000r^3$
   $+ 1000r^4$

X tending the topic: The Degree of a Polynomial

The term **degree** can refer to the exponents of a monomial. If a monomial has one variable, then the degree of that monomial is simply the exponent:

EXAMPLES

- monomial: $5y^9$ $3x^2$ $2z$ 14 0
- degree: 9 2 1 0 none

The expression 0 is the only monomial with undefined degree.

If a monomial has several variables, the degree of that monomial is the sum of the exponents of the variables.

EXAMPLES

- monomial: $2x^4y^3$ $15r^2s^2t^5$ $4p^2q$ $3^2x^3y^5$ $(5xy)^2$
- degree: 7 9 3 8 4

The coefficient of $3^2x^3y^5$ is 9; it does not affect the degree of the term. The monomial $(5xy)^2$ is equal to $25x^2y^2$, so its degree is 4.

The **degree of a polynomial** is the highest degree of its terms; the degree of $6x^3y + 2xy^2 - 1$ is 4. The degree of $5 - 2rs + 3r^2s + 6r^2s^2 - 9r^3s^3$ is 6.

Equations can be classified according to their degree. When a first-degree equation (e.g., $y = 3x + 7$) is graphed, the graph is a line. The graphs of some second-degree equations are circles, ellipses (ovals), or open curves called parabolas (par ah' bō las) or hyperbolas (hī per' bō las).

Problem Set X

State the degree of each polynomial.

1 $7x^3$
  3

2 $-12xy^2z$
  4

3 89
  0

4 $-3x + 9$
  1

5 $5x^3 - 9x^2 + 4y^2x^2$
  4

6 $3 + 3q - 5q^2 + 6q^3$
  3

7 $5t + (5t)^2 + (5t)^3$
  3

8 $5st + (5st)^2 + (5st)^3$
  6

9 $6y^2z^2 + 5y^3z - 3yz^3$
  4

Section 4.7 Finding Greatest Common Factors

SECTION SCHEDULE

Basic (2 days)

Average ($1\frac{1}{2}$ days)

Advanced ($1\frac{1}{2}$ days)

The two integers 12 and 16 have several positive factors that are the same:

    factors of 12:   1,2,3,4,6,12

    factors of 16:   1,2,4,8,16

The factors 1, 2, and 4 are **common** to both 12 and 16. The factor 4 is **greatest**, or largest, of the common factors. The **Greatest Common Factor** (**GCF**) of two or more integers is the greatest integer that is a factor of each.

EXAMPLES

- The GCF of 10 and 25 is 5.

- The GCF of 45 and 30 is 15.

- The GCF of 7 and 28 is 7.

The greatest common factor of two or more monomials is the product of the factors common to the monomials. For example, consider the factors of the following two monomials:

    $24x^2y$

    $16x^3y^3$

For the coefficients 24 and 16, 8 is the GCF.
For the factors x^2 and x^3, x^2 is the GCF.
For the factors y and y^3, y is the GCF.
    The product, $8x^2y$, is the greatest common factor of the two monomials $24x^2y$ and $16x^3y^3$.

There are several ways to find the GCF of two expressions. Prime factorizations are used in Section 4.7X (p. 188). Other methods are to use intersections of Venn diagrams or draw circles around common factors.
    For example, to find the GCF of $12x^2y$ and $10x^3y^3$:

- Factors   Factors
  of   of
  $12x^2y$ $10x^3y^3$

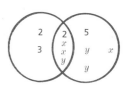

- $12x^2y$
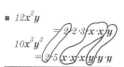
$10x^3y^3$

Sample Problems

1   Find the GCF of 45 and 81.

    PROCEDURE   Factor each integer:

        $45 = 3 \cdot 3 \cdot 5$
        $81 = 3 \cdot 3 \cdot 3 \cdot 3$

    The product $3 \cdot 3$ is common to both integers. The GCF of 45 and 81 is 9.

2 Find the GCF of the monomials $18a^3b^4$ and $30a^2b^3c$.

PROCEDURE

For the coefficients 18 and 30, the GCF is 6.
For the factors a^3 and a^2, the GCF is a^2.
For the factors b^4 and b^3, the GCF is b^3.
The factor c is **not** common to both monomials. Therefore the GCF of $18a^3b^4$ and $30a^2b^3c$ is $6a^2b^3$.

3 Factor each polynomial by writing it as a product of a monomial times another polynomial.

a $5x^3 + 21x^2$ **b** $2x^2 + 6xy - 8xy^2$

PROCEDURE   For each polynomial, find the GCF of its terms. Then use the Distributive Property to rewrite the polynomial as a product.

    a The GCF of $5x^3$ and $21x^2$ is x^2.

$$5x^3 + 21x^2$$
$$(x^2)(5x) + (x^2)(21)$$
$$(x^2)(5x + 21)$$

    b The GCF of $2x^2$, $6xy$, and $-8xy^2$ is $2x$.

$$2x^2 + 6xy - 8xy^2$$
$$(2x)(x) + (2x)(3y) + (2x)(-4y^2)$$
$$(2x)(x + 3y - 4y^2)$$

This procedure of rewriting a polynomial as a monomial times another polynomial is called "taking out a common factor."

ASSIGNMENT GUIDE

Basic (2 days)
(1) 1–18, 31–38
(2) 19–30, 39–42

Average (1½ days)
(1) 20–30 (even), 40–56 (even)
(2) 182: 1–9
    188: 5–11

Advanced (1½ days)
(1) 39–46, 48–66 (even)
(2) 181: 29–34
    188: 5–12

Problem Set **A**

1 Describe the GCF of two integers.

    The GCF is the greatest integer that is a factor of each integer

2 If the GCF of two integers is 6, list 4 positive integers that are factors of the two integers.

    1, 2, 3, 6

3 The GCF of the two monomials a^2b^2 and ab^2 is ___?___.

    ab^2

4 The trinomial $4x + 4x^2 + 4x^3$ can be written as (___?___) $(1 + x + x^2)$.

    $4x$

Multiple Choice   Determine the GCF of each pair of numbers or expressions.

5   6 and 12   *c*
   a 3   **b** 2   **c** 6   **d** 12

6   13 and 39   *a*
   a 13   **b** 1   **c** 3   **d** 39

7   42 and 48   *b*
   a 8   **b** 6   **c** 42   **d** 48

8   55 and 88   *c*
   a 5   **b** 1   **c** 11   **d** 20

9 $2x$ and x^2 *a*
   a x **b** $2x$ **c** x^2 **d** $2x^2$

10 $17t^3$ and $7t^2$ *c*
   a $7t^2$ **b** 1   **c** t^2 **d** t^3

11 $3t^2$ and $15t$ *b*
   a $5t$ **b** $3t$ **c** $3t^2$ **d** $15t^3$

12 $32r^4$ and $20r^3$ *d*
   a $2r^3$ **b** $4r$ **c** $16r^4$ **d** $4r^3$

13 xy^2 and x^2y *a*
   a xy **b** x^3y^3 **c** xy^2 **d** y^2x^2

14 xy^2 and x^2 *c*
   a xy **b** x^2 **c** x **d** y^2

15 $4mn$ and $18m^2n$ *a*
   a $2mn$ **b** $9m^2n$ **c** $4mn$ **d** $18m$

16 $10abc$ and $15a^2c^2$ *d*
   a $5abc$ **b** $5a^2bc^2$ **c** $150a^3bc^3$ **d** $5ac$

17 $11a^2$ and $30b^3$ *a*
   a 1   **b** $2ab$ **c** $11a^2$ **d** $30b^3$

18 $8ab$ and $15xy$ *c*
   a 4   **b** $abxy$ **c** 1   **d** $5abxy$

Write the following as a product of a monomial (the GCF) and a polynomial.

19 $2x + 6$
$2(x+3)$

24 $5a - 5b$
$5(a-b)$

20 $3y - 9$
$3(y-3)$

25 $8x^2 - 20x$
$4x(2x-5)$

21 $28x - 7x^2$
$7x(4-x)$

26 $30y^3 + 24y^2$
$6y^2(5y+4)$

22 $12y + 6y^3$
$6y(2+y^2)$

27 $7x^4 + 5x^3$
$x^3(7x+5)$

23 $4x + 4$
$4(x+1)$

28 $3x^2y^3 - 8xy^4$
$xy^3(3x-8y)$

29 The area of a rectangle is $(18x^2 - 3x)$ and its width is $3x$. What is its length?
$6x - 1$

30 The perimeter of a square is $(12x + 8)$. Find the length of one of its sides.
$3x + 2$

Use the Distributive Property to remove the parentheses. (Review: Section 4.4)

31 $2x(x + 3)$
$2x^2 + 6x$

35 $(-x + 2)x$
$-x^2 + 2x$

32 $3x(x - 5)$
$3x^2 - 15x$

36 $(-x - 3)x$
$-x^2 - 3x$

33 $(2x - 7)x$
$2x^2 - 7x$

37 $-8(5x - 1)$
$-40x + 8$

34 $(4x - 5)x$
$4x^2 - 5x$

38 $-7(2x + 9)$
$-14x - 63$

Problem Set **B**

Find the GCF for each triple.

39 6, 12, 18
6

43 $2xy^2, 3x^2y, 4xy$
xy

40 22, 11, 33
11

44 $10pq, 21pr, 11rq$
1

41 6, 12, 15
3

45 $20a^2b^3, 28ab^2, 16b$
$4b$

42 24, 30, 36
6

46 $4a^3b^2, 6a^2b, 8a^4b^2$
$2a^2b$

Use the Distributive Property to write the following as a product of a monomial (the GCF) and a polynomial.

47 $2x + 2y - 2z$

$2(x + y - z)$

48 $4x^2 - 8x + 12$

$4(x^2 - 2x + 3)$

49 $18a^2 + 9a - 3$

$3(6a^2 + 3a - 1)$

50 $5 - 15x + 10x^2$

$5(1 - 3x + 2x^2)$

51 $a^2b - ab^2$

$ab(a - b)$

52 $t^2 - t$

$t(t - 1)$

53 $12x^4 - 4x^3 + 8x^2$

$4x^2(3x^2 - x + 3)$

54 $6x^3 - 12x^2 + 24x^5$

$6x^2(x - 2 + 4x^3)$

55 $21y^2 - 14y + 35y^3$

$7y(3y - 2 + 5y^2)$

56 $20x^2y^2 - 26xy^2 - 14x^2y$

$2xy(10xy - 13y - 7x)$

Problem Set C

Determine the GCF and write each expression as a product of the GCF and a polynomial.

57 $200x^3y^4 - 140x^2y^5$

$20x^2y^4(10x - 7y)$

58 $324a^2b^2c^2 + 378ab^3c^2$

$54ab^2c^2(6a + 7b)$

59 $70x^2 - 98x^7 - 560x^4$

$14x^2(5 - 7x^5 - 40x^2)$

60 $165a^3x^3 - 770a^4x^4 + 1265a^2x^5$

$55a^2x^3(3a - 14a^2x + 23x^2)$

61 $105r^2s + 147rs^2$

$21rs(5r + 7s)$

62 $72m^3n^2 - 108m^2n^3 - 18mn^3 + 36m^2n^2$

$18mn^2(4m^2 - 6mn - n + 2m)$

63 $ax^2 + ax + a$

$a(x^2 + x + 1)$

64 $cdx^3 + 3cdx^2 + 3cdx$

$cdx(x^2 + 3x + 3)$

65 $\dfrac{1}{24}p^2 - \dfrac{1}{8}p^3 + \dfrac{1}{48}p^4$

$\frac{1}{8}p^2(\frac{1}{3} - p + \frac{1}{6}p^2)$

66 $mn + 3m - 4n$

$1(mn + 3m - 4n)$

67 $\dfrac{a^2}{b^2}x^5 - \dfrac{a}{b^2}x^3 + \dfrac{a^2}{b}x$

$\frac{a}{b}x(\frac{a}{b}x^4 - \frac{1}{b}x^2 + a)$

$\mathbf{X}$ tending the topic: Prime Factorization and the GCF

Another method for finding the GCF of two numbers is to use the prime factorization of each number.

Sample Problem

1   Find the GCF of 504 and 3780.

> PROCEDURE
> First, use a factor tree or any other method to write the prime factorizations:
>
> $$504 = 2^3 \cdot 3^2 \cdot 7$$
> $$3780 = 2^2 \cdot 3^3 \cdot 5 \cdot 7$$
>
> The GCF is the product of the common factors 2, 3, and 7, each with an exponent. The exponent is the highest power common to both. Thus the GCF is:
>
> $$2^2 \cdot 3^2 \cdot 7^1 = 4 \cdot 9 \cdot 7 = 252$$
>
> The GCF of 504 and 3780 is 252.

Problem Set $\mathbf{X}$

Use prime factorizations to find the GCF of each pair of expressions.

1   48 and 120
       24

2   36 and 45
       9

3   700 and 1575
       175

4   1000 and 72
       8

5    $90x^3y$ and $225x^2y^2$
       $45x^2y$

6    $\frac{1}{36}x^5y^5z^7$ and $\frac{1}{24}x^4y^6z^3$
       $\frac{1}{12}x^4y^5z^3$

7   72 and 108
       36

8   72 and 18
       18

9   108 and 18
       18

10   36 and 108
       36

11   $98x^3z^2$ and $28x^5z^3$
       $14x^3z^2$

12   $(75ab)^2$ and $45ab^2$
       $15ab^2$

Chapter Study Guide

ASSIGNMENT GUIDE

Basic (2 days)
(1) 192: 1–22
(2) 174: 11–14
    181: 22–26 (even)
    187: 47–49

Average (1 day)
180: 11–17 (odd)
187: 47–53 (odd)
192: 1–22

Advanced (1 day)
176: 36–39
187: 57–67 (odd)
192: 1–22

Vocabulary

As you study and review this chapter, be sure to learn the important mathematics vocabulary, including:

1   **Monomial**   A MONOMIAL is a single term that is a constant, a variable, or a product of constants and variables.

- Each of the following terms is a monomial: y 6 $-\dfrac{2x^2y}{5}$

   The following expressions are **not** monomials: $\dfrac{10}{k}$ $2x + 4$

   The first expression includes division by the variable and the second is not a single term.

2   **Numerical Coefficient**   The NUMERICAL COEFFICIENT (or simply COEFFICIENT) of a monomial is the constant factor in the term.

- The coefficients of $4xy^2$, $\frac{1}{2}bcd$, and $-q$ are 4, $\frac{1}{2}$, and -1, respectively.

3   **Like Terms**   If monomials have the same variable(s), and corresponding variables have the same exponents, then the monomials are LIKE TERMS.

- The pair of monomials $7x^2$ and $5x^2$, and the pair $-3ab$ and ab are like terms. The pair of monomials $7r^2s$ and $5rs^2$ are **not** like terms, because corresponding variables have different exponents.

4   **Polynomial**
A POLYNOMIAL is an indicated sum or difference of monomials.

- Each of the following expressions is a polynomial:

   $9x^2 - 3x + 1$
   $2z^3 - 14$
   $3npq$

Skills

Be sure you build the useful algebraic skills, including:

5   **Multiplying monomials**   Find the product $(5x^2)(-3x^4)$.

PROCEDURE
Multiply the coefficients and then determine the exponent for the variable:

$$(5x^2)(-3x^4)$$
$$(5)(-3)(x^2)(x^4)$$
$$(-15)(x \cdot x)(x \cdot x \cdot x \cdot x)$$
$$-15x^6$$

6   **Using the Distributive Property**
Explain how to perform the following:
a   subtract: $4t - 9t$
b   remove the parentheses in $7z(z^2 + 5)$

PROCEDURE   The Distributive Property states that the following pairs
of expressions have the same value:

$$ab - ac \qquad\qquad a(b + c)$$
$$a(b - c) \qquad\qquad ab + ac$$

a $4t - 9t$ **b** $7z(z^2 + 5)$
   $t(4 - 9)$ $(7z)(z^2) + (7z)(5)$
   $t(-5)$ $7z^3 + 35z$
   $-5t$

7   **Adding or subtracting polynomials**
Find the difference: $(5y^2 + 3y - 2) - (8y^2 - 6y + 1)$

PROCEDURE   Rewrite the subtraction problem as an addition problem, distribute to remove the parentheses, and then combine the like terms:

$$(5y^2 + \quad 3y \quad - 2) \quad\quad - \quad\quad (8y^2 - \quad 6y \quad + \quad 1)$$
$$(1)[5y^2 + \quad 3y \quad + (-2)] + (-1)[8y^2 + \quad (-6y) \quad + \quad 1]$$
$$(1)(5y^2) + (1)(3y) + (1)(-2) + (-1)(8y^2) + (-1)(-6y) + (-1)(1)$$
$$5y^2 + \quad 3y \quad - \quad 2 \quad - \quad 8y^2 \quad + \quad 6y \quad - \quad 1$$
$$5y^2 - 8y^2 \quad + 3y + 6y \quad - 2 - 1$$
$$-3y^2 \qquad\quad + 9y \qquad\quad - 3$$

8 Finding the Greatest Common Factor   Find the GCF of $8x^2y^3$ and $12xy^5$

PROCEDURE

For the coefficients 8 and 12, the GCF is 4.
For the factors x^2 and x, the GCF is x.
For the factors y^3 and y^5, the GCF is y^3.
Therefore the GCF of $8x^2y^3$ and $12xy^5$ is $4xy^3$.

9 Solving equations containing parentheses
Solve for p and check: $7(p - 6) = 5p - 12$

PROCEDURE

$$7(p - 6) = 5p - 12$$

distribute: $7p - 42 = 5p - 12$
ADD $-5p$: $2p - 42 = -12$
ADD 42: $2p = 30$
MULTBY $\frac{1}{2}$: $p = 15$

$To\ check$
$$7(p - 6) = 5p - 12$$
$$7(15 - 6) \stackrel{?}{=} 5(15) - 12$$
$$7(9) \stackrel{?}{=} 75 - 12$$
$$63 \stackrel{?}{=} 63 \checkmark$$

Math History: Descartes and Fermat

In the seventeenth century, two French amateur mathematicians, René Descartes and Pierre de Fermat, independently developed coordinate geometry. Fermat was first, and was also more modern and thorough, but his work was not published until after his death. Consequently, the coordinate system was named the Cartesian plane, after Descartes.

Descartes thought of himself as a scientist and philosopher, but he enjoyed solving problems in geometry. In the process of solving such problems, he used a coordinate system as a tool. When Descartes published his major work on the scientific method, he illustrated the method with three appendices at the back of the book. One appendix showed techniques for applying the ideas of algebra to solve problems of geometry. These techniques developed into the branch of mathematics called coordinate geometry.

Chapter Test

State the coefficient of each term.

1 $-6x^2y$
   -6

2 y^3
   1

3 $(-3x)^2$
   9

4 $3a^2(-2b)^2$
   12

5 $(27b^2c)(\tfrac{1}{3}bc)^2$
   3

6 $(2 \cdot 10^2)(3 \cdot 10)(10x)$
   $60,000$

Add or subtract the like terms.

7 $4x + 6x$
   $10x$

8 $6a - 7a$
   $-a$

9 $xy - 3yx + xy^2 - 2y^2x$
   $-2xy - xy^2$

10 $5y^2 + 4y - 3y^2 - y$
   $2y^2 + 3y$

Remove the parentheses and then combine like terms.

11 $6(-3x + 2)$
   $-18x + 12$

12 $(2m - 3) - (5m + 1)$
   $-3m - 4$

13 $(9y^2 + 9 - 3y) + (8 + 2y - y^2)$
   $8y^2 - y + 17$

14 $6x - 3(7x - 1)$
   $-15x + 3$

Solve and check.

15 $4x + 3 = 3x - 7$
   $x = -10$

16 $9y - 1 = 5y + 31$
   $y = 8$

17 $5(p - 3) = 2p - 3$
   $p = 4$

18 $4 - (r + 5) = 2(5r - 4) - 4r$
   $r = 1$

True or false:

19 The polynomial $3x^2 + 2x - 4$ is called a binomial.
   false

20 The GCF of 24 and 84 is 4.
   true

Write an equation for each problem, and solve it. Be sure to answer the original question.

21 Find two consecutive integers whose sum is one hundred twenty-one.
   $x + x + 1 = 121$; 60, 61

22 A rectangle has a length eight centimeters longer than its width. The perimeter of the rectangle is forty centimeters. Find the length and width.
   $2w + 2(w + 8) = 40$; 6, 14

Problem Set: Solving Uniform Motion Problems

Problems that involve an average speed or a steady rate are called **uniform motion** problems. The formula $r \cdot t = d$ represents the relationship between rate r, time t, and distance d.

Three steps for organizing work and solving problems were presented in Section 2.7. These steps can be restated as:

Step 1   Use variables and a diagram, if helpful, to list expressions for r, t, and d for each object or person in the problem.

Step 2   Identify two quantities that are equal. Sometimes two rates are equal, or two times are equal, or two distances are equal. Set up an equation and then solve it.

Step 3   Answer the question in the problem, and check the solution.

The second step often requires using the Distributive Property to solve the equation.

■   J. C. and three of her friends left the Dew Drop Inn in a hot air balloon and flew for an hour and a half before landing in a field. Sue picked them up in her truck and then drove back to the Dew Drop Inn at a rate eighteen miles per hour faster than the rate of the balloon. The truck ride took only thirty minutes. The distance covered by the balloon in flight and truck was the same. What was the average rate of the balloon?

Let r represent the rate of the balloon, and list expressions for r, t, and d:

	balloon	truck
r:	r	$r + 18$
t:	$\frac{3}{2}$	$\frac{1}{2}$ (both in hours)
d:	$\frac{3}{2}r$	$\frac{1}{2}(r + 18)$

Since the distances traveled were equal, the equation is:

$$\tfrac{3}{2}r = \tfrac{1}{2}(r + 18)$$

distribute: $\tfrac{3}{2}r = \tfrac{1}{2}r + 9$

SUBT $\tfrac{1}{2}r$: $r = 9$

The average rate of the balloon was 9 mph.

To check   The balloon traveled at 9 mph for an hour and a half, or 13.5 miles. The truck traveled at 27 mph for half an hour, or 13.5 miles.

In problems 1–16, use variables to represent r, t, and d. Set up and solve an equation, and then answer the original question.

1   Miguel can take an express bus to work that travels 50 km/h (kilometers per hour), but on nice days he leaves an hour earlier and rides his 10-speed bicycle to work at a rate of 30 km/h. Either way, he arrives at the same time. How far does Miguel have to travel to work?

$50t = 30(t+1)$; $t = 75$

2   Two airplanes leave O'Hare Airport at the same time. They fly in opposite directions at 400 mph and 550 mph, respectively. In how many hours will they be 3800 miles apart?

$400t + 550t = 3800$; $t = 4$

3   Juan walked home from school at 3 mph. It took him the same time to then bike over to Carlos' house at 7 mph. If Juan walked and biked a total of 6 miles, how long did it take him to walk home from school?

$3t + 7t = 6$; $t = \dfrac{3}{5}$

4   Mr. Wexler left the office at 9:00 A.M. and drove 5 hours to a regional sales meeting. His boss, Ms. Markwell, left the same office at 11:00 A.M. and drove at an average rate of 10 mph faster than Mr. Wexler. If Ms. Markwell arrived one hour later, what was her average speed?

$5r = 4(r+10)$; $r = 50$

5   Juanita jogged for one hour and then returned by walking along the same route. The return trip took two hours at a rate three miles per hour slower than her jogging rate. How far did Juanita jog?

$r = 2(r-3)$; $r = 6$

6   Bobby drove one hundred laps (two hundred miles) to win the Dunlevy Road Classic. The race took him eighty minutes to complete. Twenty of those minutes were driven under the yellow caution flag. Under the yellow flag, he had to slow down his rate by two miles per minute. How many laps were run under the caution flag?

$20(r-2) + 60r = 200$; $r = 3$ (10 laps)

7   Marvella rode her horse at 9 km/h until it threw a shoe. She walked her horse back at 3 km/h. If the round trip took 4 hours, how long did it take Marvella to walk her horse back?

$9(4-t) = 3t$; $t = 3$

8   Mr. Chang had a flat tire on a desolate road in Alaska. He knew he had just filled his gas tank several miles back down the road. Since his spare was also flat, he walked toward the gas station for help. His walking rate was 3 mph whereas his driving rate had been 45 mph. It took him 4 hours from the time he got gas to return to the station. How long did it take Mr. Chang to walk to the station?

$45(4-t) = 3t$; $t = 3\frac{3}{4}$

9 At 12 o'clock noon two boats are 162 nautical miles apart speeding toward each other. One boat is traveling at 30 knots and the other at 24 knots. At what time will they pass each other? (30 knots = 30 nautical miles/hour)

$30t + 24t = 162$; $t = 3$ (3 P.M.)

10 Ms. Wilson left Marshfield driving a scenic route parallel to the railroad tracks at 60 km/h. A train left Marshfield two hours later traveling at 110 km/h. How far did the train travel before overtaking Ms. Wilson's car?

$60t = 110(t-2)$; $t = \frac{22}{5}$ (264 km)

11 Todd rode his Big Wheel bike to the park at 4 mph. Melanie left 3 minutes later and rode her 5-speed bike to the park at 10 mph. If the park is one half mile from where they each started, did Melanie pass Todd before reaching the park?

$4t = 10(t - \frac{1}{20})$; $t = \frac{1}{12}$ ($\frac{1}{3}$ mile)

12 Batman and Robin were in pursuit of the Joker. Although the Joker had a one-hour headstart, the Batmobile was averaging 25 km/h more than the Joker's car. It took 3 hours for the Dynamic Duo to overtake the Joker. How many kilometers did the chase cover?

$3(r+25) = 4r$; $r = 75$ (300 km)

13 Pam Newell was driven at 25 mph to inspect the new building construction site west of town. After her visit she was flown back in the company's helicopter at 75 mph. The total travel time was 7 hours. How many miles is the round trip?

$25t = 75(7-t)$; $t = 1\frac{3}{4}$ (262.5 mi)

14 The starship Skyruler passed space station Alpha One. Seven minutes later starship Solar Queen flew by the same station traveling __?__ /min faster than the Skyruler. Four minutes later the Solar Queen was only __?__ away from the other ship. How far beyond station Alpha One was the Skyruler? (Make up your own problem.)

answers may vary

15 Andy and Dee crawled along a sidewalk. They found a breadcrumb and carried it toward their hill. Their crawling rate was slowed by five inches per minute by this load. Still, they continued to transport the crumb to the hill. They spent the same amount of time with the breadcrumb, two hours, as without it but they crawled three times farther without it. How far did they carry the breadcrumb?

$2r = 3(2(r-5))$; $r = 7\frac{1}{2}$ (300 in.)

16 Two stoplights each take three minutes to go from red to green. Sam had found that if he leaves the first stoplight as it turns green and travels fifty miles per hour, he will reach the second just as it is turning red. But if he travels forty miles per hour, he reaches the second just as it turns green. How far apart are the stoplights?

$\frac{5}{2}$ miles

16) Insufficient information is given. With the additional information that the second light takes 45 seconds to turn from green to red, either rate can be used to find the distance:

$(\frac{5}{6})(3) = \frac{15}{6} = \frac{5}{2}$

$(\frac{4}{6})(3\frac{3}{4}) = (\frac{4}{6})(\frac{15}{4}) = \frac{15}{6} = \frac{5}{2}$

	Search End of Data	Load Format	Change Format	Di Fo
n to	Search Content	Search Seq C	Search Record N	E o J

Chapter 5

INEQUALITIES

CHAPTER SCHEDULE

Basic
Problem Sets   6 Days
Review   2 Days
Test   2 Days

Average
Problem Sets   7 Days
Review   1 Day
Test   2 Days

Advanced
Problem Sets   9 Days
Review   1 Day
Test   1 Day

Set notation is convenient for indicating solutions of inequalities. Section 5.1X introduces the language of solution sets, which may then be used throughout the chapter.

Section 5.1 Using the Order Symbols $<$ and $>$

SECTION SCHEDULE

Basic (1 day)

Average (1 day)

Advanced (2 days)

To **order** two numbers means to state which number is less and which number is greater. For the numbers 2 and 5, the two order sentences that can be written are:

    2 is less than 5
    5 is greater than 2

Using the symbol $<$ for "is less than" and the symbol $>$ for "is greater than," the two sentences can be rewritten:

    $2 < 5$
    $5 > 2$

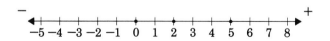

For all of the number lines in this chapter, the positive direction is to the right. In later chapters, which will have vertical number lines, "up" will also be the positive direction.

If two positive numbers are represented on a number line, the point that is "more positive," or further in the positive direction, represents the greater number. Notice that the point for 5 is "more positive" than the point for 2. This description applies to any pair of numbers on a number line. The point that is more positive represents the number that is greater.

EXAMPLES

- $2 > 0$

- $5 > -3$

- $-3 > -79$ -3 is more positive than -79

- $-80 > -81$ -80 is more positive than -81

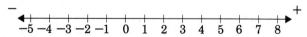

Some students may need an explicit description that the number that is "more negative" is the smaller number.

Each of these sentences can be rewritten using the $<$ symbol:

$$0 < 2$$
$$-3 < 5$$
$$-79 < -3$$
$$-81 < -80$$

Mathematical sentences that use order symbols are called **inequalities**.

Sample Problems

1   Replace each <u>?</u> with $<$ or $>$.
    a -5 <u>?</u> 3
    b 3 <u>?</u> -3
    c $(-1) + (-2)$ <u>?</u> -5
    d 4 <u>?</u> $2 + 3$

PROCEDURE

    a $-5 < 3$
    b $3 > -3$
    c $(-1) + (-2)$ <u>?</u> -5
                   -3 <u>?</u> -5
                   -3 $>$ -5
     Thus $(-1) + (-2)$ $>$ -5
    d 4 <u>?</u> $2 + 3$
           4 <u>?</u> 5
           4 $<$ 5
     Thus 4 $<$ $2 + 3$

2 If n can only represent nonnegative integers, find the solution to the inequality $n < 4$.

PROCEDURE   The nonnegative integers are 0,1,2,3,4,5,6, ... To satisfy the sentence $n < 4$, n can take on the values 0,1,2, or 3. Thus the solution is $n = 0$, $n = 1$, $n = 2$, or $n = 3$.

3 On a number line, graph the values for n if n is a real number and $n > -3$.

PROCEDURE   For $n > -3$, values of n are all the real numbers greater than -3, but not the number -3.

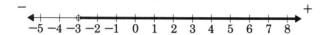

Use an open circle at -3 to indicate that n cannot equal -3, and use a thick line to represent all the real numbers greater than -3.
    The graph represents the sentences $n > -3$ and $-3 < n$.

The conventions of "open circle" and "closed dot" are used throughout the text.

Problem Set A

ASSIGNMENT GUIDE

Basic (1 day)
2–30 (even) ⨯

Average (1 day)
2, 4, 6, 14, 16, 18, 32–44 (even)

Advanced (2 days)
(1) 31–36, 46–52 (even),
    54–57
(2) 203: 1–11

In problems 1–6, translate each inequality into words.

1 $9 > 5$
1   nine is greater than five

2 $-2 < 4$
2   negative two is less than four

3 $5 > 0$
3   five is greater than zero

4 $-8 > -14$
4   negative eight is greater
       than negative fourteen

5 $-20 < -7$
5   negative twenty is less than
       negative seven

6 $12 > -12$
6   twelve is greater than
       negative twelve

In problems 7–12, replace each question mark with $<$ or $>$.

7 $13 \underline{\ \ ?\ \ } -18$
7      $13 > -18$

8 $-13 \underline{\ \ ?\ \ } 18$
8      $-13 < 18$

9 $-18 \underline{\ \ ?\ \ } -13$
9      $-18 < -13$

10 $-9 \underline{\ \ ?\ \ } -13$
10      $-9 > -13$

11 $9 \underline{\ \ ?\ \ } -13$
11      $9 > -13$

12 $13 \underline{\ \ ?\ \ } -9$
12      $13 > -9$

In problems 13–18, write each sentence in symbols. Replace the question mark with < or >.

13 Ten is greater than two.
  $10 > 2$

14 Negative ten is less than negative three.
  $-10 < -3$

15 Negative twelve is __?__ than negative fifteen.
  $-12 > -15$

16 Nine is __?__ than eleven.
  $9 < 11$

17 Fourteen is __?__ than negative thirteen.
  $14 > -13$

18 Negative fourteen is __?__ than thirteen.
  $-14 < 13$

Problems 19–26 reinforce the concept that $x < a$ and $a > x$ are equivalent expressions.

In problems 19–26, use the > symbol and the < symbol to write two sentences that represent each graph.

19 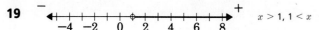 $x > 1, 1 < x$

20 $x < 3, 3 > x$

21 $x < -3, -3 > x$

22 $x > -4, -4 < x$

23 $x > 0, 0 < x$

24 $x < -5, -5 > x$

25 $x < 5, 5 > x$

26 $x < 0, 0 > x$

For each expression, list all values for the variable. (Review: Section 2.1)

27 $x < 10$; x is a natural number
  $1, 2, 3, \ldots, 9$

28 $x < 5$; x is a whole number
  $0, 1, 2, 3, 4$

29 x is between -3.5 and 4.5; x is a positive integer
  $1, 2, 3, 4$

30 x is between -3.5 and 4.5; x is a negative integer
  $-3, -2, -1$

Problem Set B

In problems 31–36, replace each __?__ with <, >, or =.

31   8 __?__ 4 + 3

$8 > 4 + 3$

32   7 __?__ 27 ÷ 3

$7 < 27 \div 3$

33   −12 __?__ (2) (−10)

$-12 > (2)(-10)$

34   (−7) + (−3) __?__ −10

$(-7)+(-3) = -10$

35   −8 __?__ 0 − 9

$-8 > 0 - 9$

36   −15 ÷ 3 __?__ −2

$-15 \div 3 < -2$

In problems 37–45, draw the graph that each sentence represents.

37 $a > 3$
    arrow in positive direction
    from an open dot at 3

38 $b < 1$
    arrow in negative direction
    from an open dot at 1

39 $c > -6$
    arrow in positive direction
    from an open dot at −6

40 $d < -2$
    arrow in negative direction
    from open dot at −2

41 $5 > x$
    arrow in negative direction
    from open dot at 5

42 $15 < y$
    arrow in positive direction
    from open dot at 15

43 $z = -2$ closed dot at −2

44 $w < -2$ arrow in negative direction
                 from open dot at −2

45 $r > -2$
    arrow in positive direction
    from open dot at −2

Problem Set C

In problems 46–54, graph each solution on a number line.

46 $x + 12 = 15$; x is a real number
    closed dot at 3

47 $n < 6$; n is a positive integer
    closed dots at 1, 2, 3, 4, 5

48 $n > -7$; n is a nonpositive integer
    closed dots at −6, −5, −4, −3, −2, −1, 0

49 $n > 2$; n is a positive one-digit integer
    closed dots at 3, 4, 5, 6, 7, 8, 9

50 $n < 8$; n is a nonnegative integer
    closed dots at 0, 1, 2, 3, 4, 5, 6, 7

51 $m + 3 > 8$; m is a real number
    arrow in positive direction from an open dot at 5

52 $m + 3 > -8$; m is a nonpositive integer
    closed dots at −10, −9, −8, . . . , −2, −1, 0

53 $m + 3 > -8$; m is a nonnegative integer
    closed dots at 0, 1, 2, 3, 4, ...

54 $m + 3 > -8$; m is an odd integer
    closed dots at −9, −7, −5, −3, −1, 1, etc.

55 The letters $m, n, p,$ and q represent numbers on the following number line. Use $<$ or $>$ to replace each question mark.

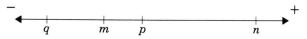

a m ___?___ n $m < n$ **c** q ___?___ p $q < p$ **e** p ___?___ q $p > q$

b n ___?___ p $n > p$ **d** p ___?___ m $p > m$ **f** q ___?___ n $q < n$

56 Draw a number line and represent two positive real numbers x and y such that $y > x$. Locate $-x$ and $-y$ on the number line. Then use $<$, $=$, or $>$ to replace each question mark:

a $-x$ ___?___ $-y$ $-x > -y$ **d** $-y$ ___?___ x $-y < x$

b $-x$ ___?___ x $-x < x$ **e** $-(-x)$ ___?___ x $-(-x) = x$

c y ___?___ $-x$ $y > -x$ **f** $-x$ ___?___ y $-x < y$

57 The symbol $\neq$ means "is not equal to." Draw a number line and graph the values of n if $n \neq 2$.

arrows in negative and positive directions from an open dot at 2

$\mathbf{X}$tending the topic: Solution Sets for Inequalities

In this text, a "solution" is an equation that has an isolated variable. As an example, the solution for the sentence $2x + 5 = 9$ is the equation $x = 2$.

Another way to think about a solution is as a set of values. For the sentence $2x + 5 = 9$, where x is a real number, the solution is the **set** that consists of one **element**, the number 2. In notation, the solution to $2x + 5 = 9$ is $\{2\}$ ("the set whose only element is 2"). This approach does not change the methods for solving equations or inequalities, but it does affect how to think about, and present, the results. This notation can be very useful for inequalities, where a solution often consists of more than one value.

Sample Problems

1 Find the solution set for $n < 4$, if n is a nonnegative integer.

PROCEDURE
The values that n can take are 0,1,2, and 3. Thus the solution set is $\{0,1,2,3\}$.

2 Graph the solution set for the sentence $n > -3$, where n is a real number, and write the solution set.

PROCEDURE

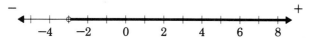

The solution set consists of all the real numbers greater than -3 (the open dot at -3 indicates that the number -3 is not included). The solution set is written $\{n : n > -3\}$ ("the set of numbers n such that n is greater than negative three").

Problem Set **X**

Write the solution set for each equality or inequality.

1 $x + 12 < 15$; x is a positive integer

{1,2}

2 $2y - 5 = 7$; y is an even integer

{6}

3 $z < 6$; z is an even, nonnegative integer

{0,2,4}

4 $w > 2$; w is a one-digit integer

{3,4,5,6,7,8,9}

Graph the solution set for each sentence, and write the solution set.

5 all positive numbers greater than two and less than six

line from open dot at 2 to open dot at 6; $\{x : 2 < x < 6\}$

6 all numbers that are three units from zero

dots at -3 and 3; $\{-3,3\}$

7 all numbers that are two units or less from the number five

line from closed dot at 3 to closed dot at 7; $\{x : 3 \leq x \leq 7\}$

8 all integers that are six units or less from negative three and five tenths

$\{-9,-8,-7,\ldots,0,1,2\}$

9 all positive numbers greater than thirteen and less than one half of thirty-seven

line from open dot at 13 to closed dot at $18\frac{1}{2}$; $\{x : 13 < x < 18\frac{1}{2}\}$

10 all integers between three and eight, inclusive

{3,4,5,6,7,8}

11 all integers between five halves and seventeen halves

{3,4,5,6,7,8}

Section 5.2   Compound Inequalities

In common language, "or" is often used in the exclusive sense: "A or B but not both." The mathematical use is always in the inclusive sense: "A or B or both."

The word **or** is an important word in mathematics:

> A shipping department has a handling charge of $1.22 for any package it sends out that weighs 500 grams or more.

If g represents the weight, and if $g = 500$ *or* if $g > 500$, then the handling charge is $1.22. These values for g can be represented on a number line:

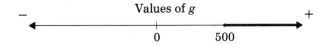

The heavy dot represents $g = 500$, and the thick arrow represents $g > 500$. The sentence, $g = 500$ *or* $g > 500$,   can be rewritten as a single inequality, $g \geq 500$ ("g is greater than or equal to 500").

The symbol $\geq$ is called a **compound order symbol** because it combines more than one symbol. A sentence that uses such a symbol, like $g \geq 500$,   is called a **compound inequality**.

The word **or** is also used another way in mathematics:

> Another shipping department has a 75¢ weighing fee for any package that is 10 pounds or under *or* that is 25 pounds or over.

If p represents the weight, then the weighing fee is charged if $p \leq 10$ ("p is less than or equal to 10") *or* if $p \geq 25$ ("p is greater than or equal to 25"). These values for p can be shown on a number line:

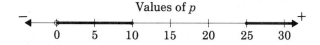

A package can't weigh zero pounds, so zero (and all the negative numbers) are not possible values of p.

The word **and** is also an important word in mathematics:

> A beverage shipper has a handling charge of $1.50 for amounts 3 liters or more, *and* has a measuring charge of $2 for amounts 10 liters or less. An amount of 7 liters will be charged $1.50 *and* $2.

If q represents the amount, then there is a handling charge when $q \geq 3$ *and* there is a measuring charge when $q \leq 10$. These values for q can be shown on a number line:

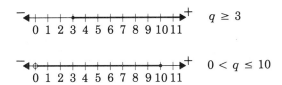

$q \geq 3$

$0 < q \leq 10$

The values for q when $q \geq 3$ *and* $q \leq 10$ are:

$3 \leq q \leq 10$

The sentences $q \geq 3$ *and* $q \leq 10$ can be written as a single sentence, $3 \leq q \leq 10$ ("q is greater than or equal to 3 *and* q is less than or equal to 10").

Sample Problems

1 Graph each inequality on a number line:

   a $x \leq -3$

   b $y < 7$

   c $z \geq 4$

   d $w > -2$

   PROCEDURE Use a solid dot for $\leq$ or $\geq$, and use an open circle for $<$ or $>$.

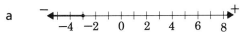

a $x \leq -3$

b $y < 7$

c $z \geq 4$

d $w > -2$

2   Graph each inequality on a number line:

    a $x > 3 \ or \ x < -1$

    b $y = 5 \ or \ y \geq 7$

    c $z \geq -1 \ or \ z \leq 4$

PROCEDURE   Graph each pair of conditions on the same number line. For *or* sentences, values of the variable are those that satisfy either sentence (or both).

a

$x > 3 \quad or \quad x < -1$

b

$y = 5 \quad or \quad y \geq 7$

c

$z \geq -1 \quad or \quad z \leq 4$

The graphs in Sample Problem 2 can be interpreted as the union of two sets; the graphs in Sample Problem 3, as the intersection of two sets.

Notice that z can be any real number.

3   Graph each inequality on a number line:

    a $-2 < x \ and \ x < 7$

    b $y \leq 3 \quad and \quad 0 \leq y$

    c $z < -2 \ and \ 3 < z$

PROCEDURE   Graph each pair of conditions and then graph the values that satisfy both conditions. For *and* sentences, values of the variable must satisfy *both* conditions.

a
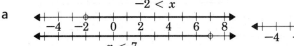
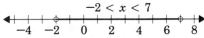

b
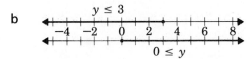
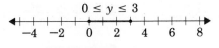

c
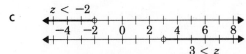
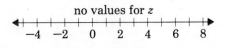

In part **c**, there are no values for z that satisfy both conditions.

Problem Set **A**

ASSIGNMENT GUIDE

Basic (1 day)
2–26 (even), 27–30

Average (2 days)
(1) 2–28 (even), 30–38
(2) 40–52 (even), 54–58

Advanced (2 days)
(1) 31–38, 40–52 (even),
    54–58
(2) 60–70 (even), 72–75

Translate each compound inequality into words.

1 $n \le 4$
  n is less than or equal to four

2 $n \le 0$
  n is less than or equal to zero

3 $n \ge -2$
  n is greater than or equal to
  negative two

4 $n \ge 6$
  n is greater than or equal to
  six

5 $-1 \le n$
  n is greater than or equal to
  negative one

6 $0 \le n$
  n is greater than or equal
  to zero

For problems **7–12,** graph each compound inequality in problems 1–6.

13 On a number line, represent all the negative integers greater than or equal to -5.

14 On a number line, represent all the positive integers less than or equal to 11.

7) arrow in negative direction from a closed dot at 4

8) arrow in negative direction from a closed dot at 0

9) arrow in positive direction from a closed dot at -2

10) arrow in positive direction from a closed dot at 6

11) arrow in positive direction from a closed dot at -1

12) arrow in positive direction from a closed dot at 0

13) closed dots at -5, $-4, -3, -2, -1$

14) closed dots at 1, 2, 3, 4, . . . , 10, 11

In problems 15–26, state the inequality represented by each graph. (Use x as the variable.)

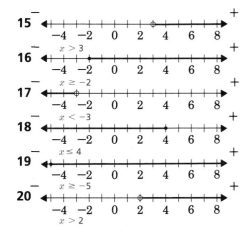

15 $x > 3$

16 $x \ge -2$

17 $x < -3$

18 $x \le 4$

19 $x \ge -5$

20 $x > 2$

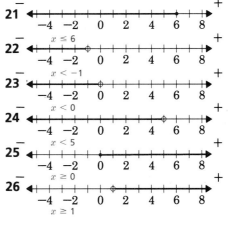

21 $x \le 6$

22 $x < -1$

23 $x < 0$

24 $x < 5$

25 $x \ge 0$

26 $x \ge 1$

Solve each equation. (Review: Section 2.7)

27 $x + 7 = 3$
   $x = -4$

28 $y - 12 = 20$
   $y = 32$

29 $5 - z = 6$
   $z = -1$

30 $w + \frac{2}{5} = 6$
   $w = \frac{28}{5}$

Problem Set **B**

Match each graph with the compound inequality that represents it.

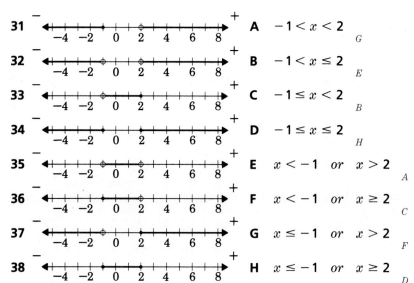

31   A $-1 < x < 2$
                                          G

32   B $-1 < x \le 2$
                                          E

33   C $-1 \le x < 2$
                                          B

34   D $-1 \le x \le 2$
                                          H

35   E $x < -1$ *or* $x > 2$
                                          A

36   F $x < -1$ *or* $x \ge 2$
                                          C

37   G $x \le -1$ *or* $x > 2$
                                          F

38   H $x \le -1$ *or* $x \ge 2$
                                          D

In problems 39–46, translate each sentence into algebraic symbols.

39 x is greater than one *or* less than negative two.

  $x > 1 \; or \; x < -2$

40 y is greater than negative two *and* less than one.

  $-2 < y < 1$

41 z is between one and four, including one.

  $1 \le z < 4$

42 m is less than or equal to negative three *or* greater than three.

  $m \le -3 \; or \; m > 3$

43 n is greater than or equal to two *or* less than one.

  $n \ge 2 \; or \; n < 1$

44 p is between negative one and negative four, inclusive of negative four.

  $-4 \le p < -1$

45 q is greater than negative three *and* less than or equal to zero.

  $-3 < q \le 0$

46 r is greater than or equal to negative two *and* less than or equal to positive two.

  $-2 \le r \le 2$

For problems **47–54**, draw the graph represented by each sentence in problems 39–46.

47) arrow in −direction from open dot at −2, arrow in +direction from open dot at 1

48) heavy line from open dot at −2 to open dot at 1

49) heavy line from closed dot at 1 to open dot at 4

50) arrow in −direction from solid dot at −3, arrow in +direction from open dot at 3

51) arrow in −direction from open dot at 1, arrow in +direction from closed dot at 2

52) heavy line from closed dot at −4 to open dot at −1

53) heavy line from open dot at −3 to closed dot at −3

54) heavy line from closed dot at −2 to closed dot at 2

In problems 55–58, x can only have integer values. Find the value(s) of x for each problem.

55 $\quad 3.1 < x < 4.2$
$\quad\quad x = 4$

57 $\quad 0 \le x < \frac{3}{4}$
$\quad\quad x = 0$

56 $\quad -5.3 < x \le -2$
$\quad\quad x = -5, -4, -3, -2$

58 $\quad -20 < x < -19$
$\quad\quad$ no values

Problem Set C

In problems 59–72, draw a graph for each compound inequality.

59 $\quad n < 2 \quad and \quad n = 1$
$\quad\quad$ closed dot at 1

66 $\quad -3 \le r \le 2$
$\quad\quad$ heavy line from closed dots
$\quad\quad$ at -3 and 2

60 $\quad n > 1 \quad and \quad n \le -2$
$\quad\quad$ no values

67 $\quad -1 < s < 1$
$\quad\quad$ heavy line from open dots at
$\quad\quad -1$ and 1

61 $\quad n < 3 \quad and \quad n = 3$
$\quad\quad$ no values

68 $\quad 0 \le t < 4$
$\quad\quad$ heavy line from closed dot at
$\quad\quad$ 0 to open dot at 4

62 $\quad n < 2 \quad or \quad n > -1$
$\quad\quad$ any real number

69 $\quad -3 < u \le 0$
$\quad\quad$ heavy line from open dot at
$\quad\quad -3$ to closed dot at 0

63 $\quad n < -3 \quad or \quad n > 2$
$\quad\quad -$ from open dot at 3,
$\quad\quad +$ from open dot at 2

70 $\quad 4 > v > 1$
$\quad\quad$ heavy line from open dots at
$\quad\quad$ 1 and 4

64 $\quad n > 4 \quad and \quad n < 7$
$\quad\quad$ heavy line from open
$\quad\quad$ dot at 4 to open dot at 7

71 $\quad -5 > w \ge -8$
$\quad\quad$ heavy line from closed dot
$\quad\quad$ at -8 to open dot at -5

65 $\quad n \le 6 \quad and \quad n \ge 6$
$\quad\quad$ closed dot at 6

72 $\quad -1.5 \le x \le 2.5$
$\quad\quad$ heavy line from closed dots
$\quad\quad$ at -1.5 to 2.5

73 An expressway has a speed limit of fifty-five mph and a minimum of forty mph. Write an inequality showing the speed, s, of a car:
a traveling within the limits,
b speeding,
c traveling too slowly.

$\quad$ a $40 \le S \le 55$ $\quad$ b $S > 55$ $\quad$ c $g < 40$

74 Two sides of a triangle have lengths six cm and ten cm. Write the compound inequality that tells what the measure of the third side may be.
$\quad\quad 4 < \ell < 16$

75 The Children's Hospital refers infants younger than six months old to the Neonatal Center, and refers adolescents older than twelve to the General Hospital. Write the compound inequality that tells the age range for patients in the Children's Hospital. $\frac{1}{2} \le c \le 12$

The property that the sum of the lengths of two sides of a triangle is greater than the length of the third side is often called the triangle inequality. It is equivalent to the statement that the shortest distance between two points is along a segment.

Section 5.3   Solving Inequalities Using Addition

Annette is older than her brother Bobby. If Annette's age and Bobby's age are represented by a and b, respectively, then: $a > b$

Three years ago, Annette was older: $a - 3 > b - 3$

In five years, Annette will still be older: $a + 5 > b + 5$

In general for an inequality, if the same positive or negative number is added to both sides of the inequality, the order symbol does not change.

Property

The ADDITION PROPERTY OF INEQUALITY is that the order of an inequality does not change if a number is added to both sides. In symbols, let a, b, and c represent real numbers:

$$\text{If } a < b, \quad \text{then} \quad a + c < b + c$$
$$\text{If } a > b, \quad \text{then} \quad a + c > b + c$$

EXAMPLES

- $$50 < 70$$
  ADD 30: $80 < 100$

- $$50 > 30$$
  ADD -75: $-25 > -45$

Examples with a variable illustrate how to solve certain inequalities:

- $$x + 7 > 12$$
  ADD -7: $x > 5$

- $$x - 3 > 1$$
  ADD 3: $x > 4$

The solution to the inequality $x + 7 > 12$ is the sentence $x > 5$. The solution to $x - 3 > 1$ is $x > 4$.

Sample Problems

1   Solve for m : $m + 12 \geq 7$

PROCEDURE   The compound inequality $m + 12 \geq 7$ means:

$$m + 12 > 7 \quad or \quad m + 12 = 7$$

The inequality and the equation are solved the same way:

$$m + 12 > 7 \qquad\qquad m + 12 = 7$$
$$\text{ADD} -12: \qquad m > -5 \qquad \text{ADD} -12: \qquad m = -5$$

The solution is $m > -5$ or $m = -5$. These mathematical sentences can be written as a single solution: $m \geq -5$

For many compound inequalities, both parts can be solved together:

$$m + 12 \geq 7$$
$$\text{ADD} -12: \qquad m \geq -5$$

2   Solve for each variable:

a $7n + 10 > 6n - 8$ **b** $3p + 5 \leq 2p - 1$

PROCEDURE   Isolate the variable in each inequality:

a $7n + 10 > 6n - 8$

    ADD -10: $7n > 6n - 18$

    ADD $-6n$: $n > -18$

b $3p + 5 \leq 2p - 1$

    ADD -5: $3p \leq 2p - 6$

    ADD $-2p$: $p \leq -6$

Problem Set A

Suppose Annette weighs x kilograms, and her friend Freeda, who is heavier, weighs y kilograms.

1   What inequality shows the relation between x and y?

    $x < y, y > x$

2   If they each gain 4 kg, what inequality would show the relation between the new weights?

    $x + 4 < y + 4, y + 4 > x + 4$

3   If they each gain k kg, what inequality would show the relation between the new weights?

    $x + k < y + k$

In problems 4–6, start with the inequality $5 > -3$ and apply the instruction to each side. Write the resulting sentence.

4   ADD 10   **5**   ADD (-5) **6**   ADD 3

    $15 > 7$ $0 > -8$ $8 > 0$

If students obtain inequalities like $18 > -n$ (or $6 \leq -p$), they will have to go through the steps that justify the Multiplication Property of Inequality (Section 5.4):

$$18 > -n$$
ADD n: $n + 18 > 0$
ADD -18: $n > -18$

ASSIGNMENT GUIDE

Basic (1 day)
2–20 (even), 22–26

Average (1 day)
28–44 (even), 46–50

Advanced (1 day)
28–44 (even), 46–50, 52, 54

Solve each inequality.

7 $x + 3 < 8$
  $x < 5$

8 $y + 4 < -6$
  $y < -10$

9 $a + 5 > 10$
  $a > 5$

10 $b + 6 > -3$
  $b > -9$

11 $a - 5.2 < 10$
  $a < 15.2$

12 $b - 3.6 < 4$
  $b < 7.6$

13 $c - 6 > 2$
  $c > 8$

14 $-\dfrac{17}{5} > x - \dfrac{12}{5}$
  $-1 > x$

15 $5 < x + 7$
  $-2 < x$

16 $5 > 7 + x$
  $-2 > x$

17 $-8 < 3 + y$
  $-11 < y$

18 $-10 < y + 12$
  $-22 < y$

19 $9.1 < x - 19.8$
  $28.9 < x$

20 $19.2 > x - 8.6$
  $27.8 > x$

21 $d - 2 > -5$
  $d > -3$

22 $-\dfrac{18}{7} < x - \dfrac{20}{7}$
  $\frac{2}{7} < x$

Solve each equation. (Review: Section 3.6)

23 $3x = 17$
  $x = \frac{17}{3}$

24 $\dfrac{y}{12} = -4$
  $y = -48$

25 $4w = w$
  $w = 0$

26 $-\dfrac{3}{5}z = -\dfrac{2}{5}$
  $z = \frac{2}{3}$

Problem Set B

Solve each inequality.

27 $x - 3 \le 5$
  $x \le 8$

28 $x - 3 \ge -7$
  $x \ge -4$

29 $x + 2 \ge 8$
  $x \ge 6$

Solve each inequality.

30 $x + 2 \le -5$
  $x \le -7$

31 $x - 6.4 \ge -2.3$
  $x \ge 4.1$

32 $x - \dfrac{12}{5} \le -\dfrac{3}{5}$ $x \le \frac{9}{5}$

33 $2x - 2 > x + 3$
  $x > 5$

34 $2x + 5 > x + 1$
  $x > -4$

35 $x + 1 < 2x + 3$
  $-2 < x$

36 $2x + 1 < 3x - 2$
  $3 < x$

37 $4x + 7 \ge 2 + 3x$
  $x \ge -5$

38 $4 + x \le 2x - 3$
  $7 \le x$

Solve each inequality.

39 $3(x + 1) > 2x - 5$
$x > -8$

40 $2(x + 2) < x + 3$
$x < -1$

41 $3(x - 2) \geq 2(x + 1)$
$x \geq 8$

42 $4(x + 1) \leq 3(x - 2)$
$x \leq -10$

43 $x + 3 \leq 2$ or $x - 2 \geq -1$
$x \leq -1$ or $x \geq 1$

44 $x + 3 \geq 8$ or $x - 1 \leq 2$
$x \geq 5$ or $x \leq 3$

45 $x + 1 \geq 2$ and $x - 1 \leq 2$
$x \geq 1$ and $x \leq 3, 1 \leq x \leq 3$

46 $x + 2 > -5$ and $x + 4 < 3$
$x > -7$ and $x < -1, -7 < x < 1$

In problems 47–50, state an inequality that describes the problem. Then solve the inequality and answer the original question.

47 A number increased by eight is greater than or equal to twenty. What is the number?
$n + 8 \geq 20, n \geq 12$

48 A number decreased by four is less than or equal to fifteen. What is the number?
$n - 4 \leq 15, n \leq 19$

49 Guillio plans to work no more than ten hours at the supermarket next weekend. If he is scheduled to work six hours on Saturday, how many hours can he work on Sunday?
$w + 6 \leq 10, w \leq 4$

50 Meredith and her family planned to spend at most five hundred dollars on their vacation trip. If the transportation costs one hundred seventy-five dollars, what could they plan to spend on other expenses?
$v + 175 \leq 500, v \leq 325, \$325$ or less

Problem Set C

Solve each compound inequality and use a number line to graph the values of the variable.

51 $x + 3 \leq 2(x + 1)$ and $2(x - 1) \geq 3x - 5$
$1 \leq x \leq 3$

52 $3(x + 1) \leq 2(x + 1)$ or $3x + 2 \geq 2(x + 2)$
$x \leq 1$ or $x \geq 2$

53 $x + 1 = 0$ or $x + 2 = 0$ or $2(x - 3) \geq x - 5$
$x = -1$ or $x = -2$ or $x \geq 1$

54 $(x - 1 \geq 0$ or $x + 1 \leq 0)$ and $(x \leq 2$ or $x \geq -3)$
$x \geq 1$ or $x \leq -1$

Project: The Cost of Money

A large loan for a new automobile or a home is usually paid off over a period of years. The following program calculates the monthly payment and total amount paid for a long term loan. A is the amount borrowed, i is the annual interest rate, t is the term of the loan in years, and P is the monthly payment.

```
10   PRINT "ENTER AMOUNT BORROWED, INTEREST RATE, NUMBER OF YEARS"
20   INPUT A, I, T
30   E = (1 + I/12)^(12*T)
40   P = (INT(100*A*I*E/(12*(E-1))) + 1)/100
50   PRINT "MONTHLY PAYMENT IS $"; P
60   PRINT "TOTAL AMOUNT PAID IS $"; 12*T*P
70   PRINT "AGAIN?  IF YES, ENTER 1. IF NO, ENTER 0."
80   INPUT X
90   IF X = 1 THEN 10
100  END
```

1 Use the program (or a calculator) to compute the monthly payment and total repaid for different amounts borrowed at 15 percent for 20 years.

Amount borrowed	10,000	20,000	30,000	50,000	80,000
Monthly Payment	?	?	?	?	?
Total Repaid	?	?	?	?	?

2 A family needs a $50,000 mortgage for 20 years. Use the program (or a calculator) to look at the effects of several different interest rates.

Annual Interest Rate	12%	14%	15%	16%	17%	18%
Monthly Payment	?	?	?	?	?	?
Total Repaid	?	?	?	?	?	?

3 Another family can get a $50,000 mortgage at an interest rate of 15 percent. How will the length of the loan affect their monthly payments and total amount repaid?

Years of the loan	10	15	20	25	30	40
Monthly Payment	?	?	?	?	?	?
Total Repaid	?	?	?	?	?	?

1) $10,000: 131.67;
   31,600.80
   $20,000: 263.36;
   63,206.40
   $30,000: 395.04;
   94,809.60
   $50,000: 658.39;
   158,013.60
   $80,000: 1053.44;
   252,825.60

2) 12%: 550.55;
   132,132.00
   14%: 621.77;
   149,224.80
   15%: 658.39;
   158,013.60
   16%: 695.63;
   166,951.20
   17%: 733.41;
   176,018.40
   18%: 771.66;
   185,198.40

3) 10: 806.68;
   96,801.60
   15: 699.80;
   125,964.00
   20: 658.40;
   158,016.00
   25: 640.42;
   192,126.00
   30: 632.23;
   227,602.80
   40: 626.62;
   300,777.60

Section 5.4 Solving Inequalities Using Multiplication

SECTION SCHEDULE

Basic (1$\frac{1}{2}$ days)

Average (1$\frac{1}{2}$ days)

Advanced (1$\frac{1}{2}$ days)

When both sides of an inequality are multiplied by a positive number, the resulting inequality has the same order symbol.

EXAMPLES

- Start with $8 > 2$

  MULTBY 3: $24 > 6$
  MULTBY 2: $16 > 4$
  MULTBY 10: $80 > 20$
  MULTBY 100: $800 > 200$
  MULTBY $\frac{1}{2}$: $4 > 1$
  MULTBY $\frac{1}{8}$: $1 > \frac{1}{4}$

- Start with $5 < 7$

  MULTBY 3: $15 < 21$
  MULTBY 2: $10 < 14$
  MULTBY 10: $50 < 70$
  MULTBY $\frac{1}{5}$: $1 < \frac{7}{5}$

When both sides of an inequality are multiplied by a negative number, notice that the result is an inequality with the order symbol reversed.

EXAMPLES

- $$\begin{array}{rcc} & 8 & > & 2 \\ \text{MULTBY} -2: & -16 & \underline{?} & -4 \\ & -16 & < & -4 \end{array}$$

- $$\begin{array}{rcc} & -3 & > & -10 \\ \text{MULTBY} -4: & 12 & \underline{?} & 40 \\ & 12 & < & 40 \end{array}$$

- $$\begin{array}{rcc} & 5 & < & 7 \\ \text{MULTBY} -10: & -50 & \underline{?} & -70 \\ & -50 & > & -70 \end{array}$$

- $$\begin{array}{rcc} & -7 & < & 3 \\ \text{MULTBY} -4: & 28 & \underline{?} & -12 \\ & 28 & > & -12 \end{array}$$

Reversing the order symbol is sometimes referred to as **changing the direction**, or **changing the sense**, of the order symbol.

Property

The **MULTIPLICATION PROPERTY OF INEQUALITY** is that the sense of an inequality is not changed when both sides are multiplied by a positive number, and the sense of an inequality is changed when both sides are multiplied by a negative number. In symbols, let a, b, and k represent real numbers:

If $a < b$ and $k > 0$,   then $ak < bk$
If $a < b$ and $k < 0$,   then $ak > bk$

Sample Problems

1 Solve for the variable:

    a $\dfrac{x}{4} > 5$ **b** $-\tfrac{1}{3}y > 2$ **c** $-4z < 12$

PROCEDURE

   a $\dfrac{x}{4} > 5$

     MULTBY 4: $x > 20$ Both sides of the inequality were multiplied by a positive number; the order was not changed.

   b $-\tfrac{1}{3}y > 2$

     MULTBY -3: $y < -6$ Both sides of the inequality were multiplied by a negative number; the order was reversed.

   c $-4z < 12$

     MULTBY $-\tfrac{1}{4}$: $z > -3$ The order was reversed.

2 Solve for the variable: $\dfrac{y}{-2} \le -5$

  PROCEDURE   The compound inequality means:

$$\dfrac{y}{-2} < -5 \quad or \qquad\qquad\qquad \dfrac{y}{-2} = -5$$

   MULTBY -2: $y > 10$ MULTBY -2: $y = 10$

The solution, $y \ge 10$,   could be obtained in one step: $\dfrac{y}{-2} \le -5$

                                      MULTBY -2: $y \ge 10$

ASSIGNMENT GUIDE

Basic (1½ days)
(1) 1–18
(2) See p. 222.

Average (1½ days)
(1) 1–8, 10, 12, 14, 31–40
(2) See p. 222.

Advanced (1½ days)
(1) 32–54 (even)
(2) See p. 222.

Problem Set **A**

Start with the inequality $-12 < -3 < 6$. Write an inequality for all three of the numbers after performing each operation on all the numbers.

1 **MULTBY 3**   **3** **MULTBY $-\tfrac{1}{3}$**
     $-36 < -9 < 18$ $4 > 1 > -2$

2 **MULTBY -3**   **4** **MULTBY $\tfrac{1}{3}$**
     $36 > 9 > -18$ $-4 < -1 < 2$

In problems 5–8, start with the inequality $p < q$. Write the inequality that results from each instruction.

5 MULTBY $\frac{1}{10}$

$$\frac{p}{10} < \frac{q}{10}$$

7 MULTBY -10

$$-10p > -10q$$

6 ADD $\frac{1}{10}$

$$p + \frac{1}{10} < q + \frac{1}{10}$$

8 ADD -10

$$p - \frac{1}{10} < q - \frac{1}{10}$$

Find each solution.

9 $3x > 12$
$x > 4$

15 $5x < -15$
$x < -3$

21 $-7x \geq 77$
$x \leq -1$

10 $2x < 20$
$x < 10$

16 $3x > -9$
$x > -3$

22 $-6x \leq 54$
$x \geq -9$

11 $-2x > 6$
$x < -3$

17 $-\frac{1}{3}x < 3$
$x > -9$

23 $\frac{x}{-10} \leq -5$
$x \geq 50$

12 $-5x < 10$
$x > -2$

18 $-\frac{1}{2}x > 2$
$x < -4$

24 $\frac{x}{9} \geq -8$
$x \geq -72$

13 $\frac{1}{2}x > 4$
$x > 8$

19 $-20x > 10$
$x < -\frac{1}{2}$

25 $-8x \leq -96$
$x \geq 12$

14 $\frac{1}{3}x < 2$
$x < 6$

20 $-10x < -5$
$x > \frac{1}{2}$

26 $-15x \leq 135$
$x \geq -9$

Solve each equation. (Review: Section 3.7)

27 $4x - 3 = 11$
$x = \frac{7}{2}$

29 $\frac{2}{5}z - 1 = 0$
$z = \frac{5}{2}$

28 $\frac{y}{3} + 7 = 13$
$y = 18$

30 $4 - \frac{8}{3}w = 12$
$w = -3$

These two-step equations preview the two-step inequalities in Section 5.5.

Problem Set **B**

Find each solution.

31 $-6x < \frac{2}{3}$
$x > -\frac{1}{9}$

34 $200 \geq \frac{-1}{20}x$
$x \geq -4000$

37 $x \div 5 \geq -12$
$x \geq -60$

32 $\frac{x}{9} < \frac{2}{3}$
$x > 6$

35 $\frac{1}{3} \leq \frac{2}{3}x$
$x \geq \frac{1}{2}$

38 $20 \leq -2x$
$x \leq -10$

33 $3 \geq \frac{x}{3}$
$x \leq 9$

36 $20x < \frac{4}{5}$
$x < \frac{1}{25}$

39 $-4x \leq -3$
$x \geq \frac{3}{4}$

40 $-5x \geq 3$
$x \leq -\frac{3}{5}$

For each problem, state an inequality and solve it.

41 Six times a number decreased by four times the number is less than twenty-eight.

$x < 14$

42 One half of a number increased by one third of the number is greater than or equal to twenty.

$x \geq 24$

43 The Daily Herald pays Christine five cents for each paper she delivers. If she earns at least three dollars per day, how many does she deliver?

$x \geq 60$

44 The village of Indian Hill permits a resident to plant a garden in a section of public-owned land. Each plot must be a rectangle and have an area of at most one hundred two square meters. If every plot is six meters wide, what can be the values for its length?

$\ell \leq 17$

Problem Set **C**

Find each solution.

45 $\frac{1}{6} \geq -2x + x$

$x \geq -\frac{1}{6}$

47 $\frac{1}{3}x - \frac{2}{5}x \leq 4$

$x \geq -60$

46 $-\frac{3}{4} \leq 8x - 20x$

$x \leq \frac{1}{16}$

48 $-\frac{1}{2}x - \frac{1}{4}x \geq -19$

$x \leq \frac{76}{3}$

Solve each inequality and use a number line to represent the solution.

49 $-\frac{3}{4}x \geq \frac{3}{2}$ *and* $\frac{x}{-4} < 1$

$-4 < x \leq -2$

50 $-100x + 30x \geq 35$ *or* $-5x < -3$

$x \leq -\frac{1}{2}$ or $x > \frac{3}{5}$

51 $\frac{5}{2}x > \frac{35}{2}$ *and* $x - 7 < 2$

$7 < x < 9$

52 $3 + y < 6 + 2y$ *and* $7y + 5 > 33$

$y > -3$ and $y > 4$

53 $5x + 2 = 17$ *or* $4x - 2 > 10$

$x \geq 3$

54 $3x - 1 \leq -7$ *and* $3(x - 3) \geq -15$

$x \leq -2$ and $x \geq -2, x = -2$

55 $-7x - 12 < 30$ *and* $-3x + 15 \leq -3$

$x \geq 6$

X tending the topic: Properties of Inequalities

The basic property of inequalities is called the **Trichotomy** (trī kät′ ə mē) **Property**. The prefix "tri-" indicates "three."

Trichotomy Property

If a and b are any real numbers, then one of the following is true:

$$a < b \qquad a = b \qquad a > b$$

Sections 5.3 and 5.4 presented two other properties of inequalities. The Addition Property of Inequality states that adding a real number to both sides of an inequality does not affect the **sense** of the inequality. In symbols, let a, b, and c represent any real numbers.

If $a > b$, then $a + c > b + c$.

If $a < b$, then $a + c < b + c$.

The Multiplication Property of Inequality states that multiplying both sides of an inequality by a negative number reverses the sense of the inequality:

If $a > b$, then $ac < bc$ if $c < 0$.

If $a < b$, then $ac > bc$ if $c < 0$.

The sense of the inequality is not changed if both sides are multiplied by a positive number:

If $a > b$, then $ac > bc$ if $c > 0$.

If $a < b$, then $ac < bc$ if $c > 0$.

When general results and mathematical techniques are explained, derived, and/or justified, mathematical properties are part of that presentation.

Problem Set X

Result A

If a and b are positive numbers, and if $a > b$, then $a - b$ must be positive.

Result A is derived on p. 220.

EXAMPLES

- $8 > 5$

  $8 - 5 > 0$

- $75 > 74$

  $75 - 74 > 0$

Does *Result A* still hold in problems 1–3 where one or both numbers are non-positive?

1 $a = 5, b = -3$

yes

2 $a = 0, b = -3$

yes

3 $a = -10, b =$ __?__ (Fill in a value of b such that $a > b$)

yes

Result B

The justification for Result B starts on the bottom of this page.

If two different numbers are positive, then their average must be between them.

EXAMPLES

- The average of 10 and 20 is 15, and $10 < 15 < 20$.
- The average of 66 and 72 is 69, and $66 < 69 < 72$.

Does *Result B* hold in problems 4–7 where one or both numbers are nonpositive?

4 $a = 5, b = -3$ **6** $a = -10, b = -4$

yes   yes

5 $a = 0, b = -3$ **7** $a = -10, b = -14$

yes   yes

The addition and multiplication properties of inequality can be used to show that both results hold for all real values of the variables.

Result A Suppose a and b are any real numbers such that $a > b$. The Addition Property of Inequality states that the sense of the inequality does not change if the same number is added to each side.

$$a > b$$
$$\text{ADD } -b: \quad a - b > b - b$$
$$a - b > 0$$

Result B Again, suppose a and b are any real numbers such that:

$$a < b$$
$$\text{Then: } a + a < b + a \quad \text{(add } a \text{ to both sides)}$$
$$2a < b + a$$
$$\frac{2a}{2} < \frac{b + a}{2} \quad \text{(multilpying both sides by } \tfrac{1}{2}, \text{ a positive number, does not change the sense of the inequality)}$$
$$a < \frac{b + a}{2}$$

Start again with the original inequality: $a < b$

Then: $b + a < b + b$ (add b to both sides)

$b + a < 2b$

$$\dfrac{b + a}{2} < \dfrac{2b}{2}$$ (Multiplication Property of Inequality)

$$\dfrac{b + a}{2} < b$$

Combining $a < \dfrac{b + a}{2}$ and $\dfrac{b + a}{2} < b$ results in $a < \dfrac{b + a}{2} < b$

In words, the average of two different numbers must be between them.

Section 5.5   Solving Inequalities Using More Than One Operation

SECTION SCHEDULE

Basic ($1\frac{1}{2}$ days)

Average ($1\frac{1}{2}$ days)

Advanced ($2\frac{1}{2}$ days)

Many inequalities can be solved by combining the methods of the two previous sections. This section provides practice solving inequalities that involve both addition and multiplication.

Sample Problems

1   Solve for x: $4 - 5x > 19$

PROCEDURE

$$4 - 5x > 19$$

ADD -4: $-5x > 15$

MULTBY $-\frac{1}{5}$: $x < -3$

2   Solve for y: $2y + 3 \geq 5y + 8$

PROCEDURE

$$2y + 3 \geq 5y + 8$$

ADD -3: $2y \geq 5y + 5$

ADD $-5y$: $-3y \geq 5$

MULTBY $-\frac{1}{3}$: $y \leq -\frac{5}{3}$

ASSIGNMENT GUIDE

Basic ($1\frac{1}{2}$ days)
(1) 1–10
(2) 11–16
    217: 23–30

Average ($1\frac{1}{2}$ days)
(1) 8–12, 17–22
(2) 24, 26, 28–32
    218: 41–44

Advanced ($2\frac{1}{2}$ days)
(1) 18–36 (even)
(2) 37–44
    220: 1–7
(3) 225: 11–20

Problem Set **A**

Solve each inequality for x.

1 $2x + 3 > 11$
$x > 4$

2 $3x - 1 < 14$
$x < 5$

3 $-2x + 1 \le 13$
$x \ge -6$

4 $-3x + 2 \ge 17$
$x \le -5$

5 $-\frac{1}{2}x - 2 > 5$
$x < -14$

6 $-\frac{1}{3}x + 1 < 5$
$x > -12$

7 $3x + 1 > x + 9$
$x > 4$

8 $7x - 1 < 4x - 7$
$x < -2$

9 $4x - 2 > x - 5$
$x > -1$

10 $5x - 3 < 3x + 2$
$x < \frac{5}{2}$

11 $2x + 5 < 4x + 2$
$x > \frac{3}{2}$

12 $x + 3 > 3x + 7$
$x < -2$

Solve each inequality. (Review: Sections 5.2 and 5.3)

13 $x - 7 \le 12$
$x \le 19$

14 $y + 2 > -6$
$y > -8$

15 $-3z \ge 7$
$z \le -\frac{7}{3}$

16 $-\frac{4}{5}w < 10$
$w > -\frac{25}{2}$

Problem Set **B**

Solve for x.

17 $2(x + 4) > x + 10$
$x > 2$

18 $3(x + 6) > 2x + 11$
$x > -7$

19 $5x - 3(x + 1) < 9$
$x < 6$

20 $10x - 15 < 9x - 30$
$x < -15$

21 $6x - 2(x + 1) > 7$
$x > \frac{9}{4}$

22 $3x - 4(x - 2) < 5$
$x > 3$

23 $2x - (3 - 5x) < 6$
$x < \frac{9}{7}$

24 $x - (2 - 3x) > 5$
$x > \frac{7}{4}$

25 $5(x - 3) \ge 3(x + 3)$
$x \ge 2$

26 $6(x + 5) \le 2(x + 3)$
$x \le -6$

27 $-3(x + 2) + 4(x + 1) \le 7$
$x \le 9$

28 $6(x^2 + x) - 6x^2 + 5 \ge 2$
$x \ge -\frac{1}{2}$

State an inequality for each problem and then solve it.

29 Twice a certain number decreased by five is at most thirteen. What is the number?

$2x - 5 \leq 13,\ x \leq 9$

30 If each side s of a square is increased by three cm, the perimeter will be more than thirty-nine cm. What is the length of one side?

$4(s + 3) > 39,\ s > \dfrac{27}{4}$

Solve each inequality, and represent the inequality on a number line.

31 $2x + 4 \leq 6 \quad or \quad x \geq 2x - 4$

$x \leq 4$

32 $x - 2 \leq 2x + 3 \quad and \quad -3x - 6 > 2x - 5$

$x \geq -5$ and $x < -\dfrac{1}{5},\ -5 \leq x < -\dfrac{1}{5}$

Problem Set C

Find each solution.

33 $5x - (x - 1) \geq x - (2 - x)$

$x \geq -\dfrac{3}{2}$

34 $2(x + 3) + x \leq 3 - (3 - x)$

$x \leq -3$

35 $2x + 3(1 - x) < x - (2x + 1)$

no values for x

36 $3(x - 1) - x \geq 4(x - 2) - 2x$

all real values of x

Solve each inequality and graph the solution.

37 $-3 - x < 2x < 3 + x$

$-1 < x < 3$

38 $x - 1 < 2x + 3 < x + 4$

$-4 < x < 1$

39 $2x - 3 \geq 3x - 1 \geq 2x + 4$

$-2 \geq x \geq 5$

40 $3x + 3 \leq 4x - 8 \leq 7 + 3x$

$11 \leq x \leq 15$

41 $4x - 20 < 5x - 3 < 4(x + 2) - 3$

$-17 < x < 8$

42 $7 \leq 2(x + 6) - 3 < 15$

$-1 \leq x \leq 3$

State an inequality for each problem and then solve it.

43 The base of a certain triangle is five times the height of the triangle. If the base is decreased by four cm, and the height increased by eleven is doubled, the sum of the new dimensions is less than two hundred seven cm. Find the number of centimeters in the base of the triangle.

43) $(5h - 4) + 2(h + 11)$ < 207

$5h - 4 + 2(h + 11) < 207,\ h < 27$, base < 135

44 The sum of two numbers is forty-eight. The difference of three times the larger and four times the smaller exceeds five times the smaller by at least twelve. Find the smaller number.

44) $3(48 - s) - 4s > 5s$ $+ 12$

$3x - 4(48 - x) > 5(48 - x) + 12,\ x \geq 11$,
The smaller number is at least 11

5.5 More than One Operation   **223**

X tending the topic: **Using Absolute Value in Inequalities**

There are two approaches to interpreting the inequality $|x - 5| < 2$ ("The absolute value of x minus 5 is less than 2"). One interpretation is on a number line. The symbol $|x - 5|$ can be interpreted as the distance between the points for x and for 5. Thus $|x - 5| < 2$ represents x values such that the distance between x and 5 is less than 2.

The values for x that satisfy this condition are $3 < x < 7$.

Another interpretation of $|x - 5| < 2$ is that the difference between x and 5 must be less than 2 *and* it must be greater than -2:

$$x - 5 < 2 \quad and \quad x - 5 > -2$$

ADD 5: $\qquad x < 7 \quad and \qquad x > 3$

These two inequalities, $x < 7$ and $x > 3$, can be written as $3 < x < 7$. Thus both interpretations give the same result.

Sample Problems

1 Use a number line to find the values for the variable:

    a $|y - 1| \geq 3$ **b** $|z + 5| < 12$

PROCEDURE

    a "The distance between y and 1 is greater than or equal to 3"

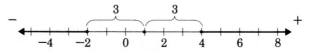

Thus $y \leq -2 \ or \ y \geq 4$

    b $|z + 5| < 12$ can be rewritten $|z - (-5)| < 12$ ("The distance between z and -5 is less than 12").

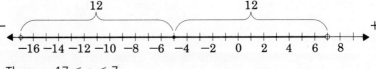

Thus $-17 < z < 7$

2 Find the values for the variables:

    a $|p + 1| > 6$ **b** $|q - 1| < 5$ **c** $|2r - 3| \geq 4$

PROCEDURE

    a $p + 1 > 6 \quad or \quad p + 1 < -6$

      ADD -1: $p > 5 \quad or \qquad p < -7$

    b $q - 1 < 5 \quad and \quad q - 1 > -5$

      ADD 1: $q < 6 \quad and \qquad q > -4$

                   $-4 < q < 6$

    c $2r - 3 \geq 4 \quad or \quad 2r - 3 \leq -4$

      ADD 3: $2r \geq 7 \quad or \qquad 2r \leq -1$

      MULTBY $\frac{1}{2}$: $r \geq \frac{7}{2} \quad or \qquad r \leq -\frac{1}{2}$

Problem Set X

In problems 1–10, use a number line to find values for each variable.

1 $|x| = 5$
    $x = 5 \ or \ x = -5$

2 $|y| = 10$
    $y = 10 \ or \ y = -10$

3 $|z| > 5$
    $z > 5 \ or \ z < -5$

4 $|p| \leq 7$
    $-7 \leq p \leq 7$

5 $|q - 3| \leq 4$
    $-1 \leq q \leq 7$

6 $|m - 2| < 1$
    $1 < m < 3$

7 $|n + 1| < 2$
    $-3 < n < 1$

8 $|r + 3| \geq 3$
    $r \leq -6 \ and \ r \geq 0$

9 $|s - 2| \geq 1$
    $s \leq 1 \ or \ s \geq 3$

10 $|2 - t| \leq 1$
    $1 \leq t \leq 3$

In problems 11– 20, find the values for each variable.

11 $|5 - x| \leq 2$
    $3 \leq x \leq 7$

12 $|2y - 8| \geq 6$
    $y \leq 1 \ or \ y \geq 7$

13 $|6 - 3p| \geq 6$
    $p \leq 0 \ or \ p \geq 4$

14 $|4 - 3q| = 0$
    $q = \frac{4}{3}$

15 $|10 - 2r| < 12$
    $-1 < r < 11$

16 $|s + 2.5| \geq 4$
    $s \leq -6.5 \ or \ s \geq 1.5$

17 $|3t - .8| = 5$
    $t = -1.4 \ or \ t = 1.9\overline{3}$

18 $|3 + 3v| \leq 1.7$
    $-\frac{1.3}{3} \geq v \geq -\frac{4.7}{3}$

19 $|2x - 1| \leq 2.2$
    $-0.6 \leq x \leq 1.6$

20 $|2x - 1| \geq 2.2$
    $x \leq 0.6 \ or \ x \geq 1.6$

After-School Mathematics: Buying on Time

Jerry works as a busboy at a local restaurant on weekends, and he commutes to work on his rather old undependable bicycle. As he was walking his bike to the service station to fill the tires with air, he passed the bike shop. He noticed a sign in the window.

SALE!   Lightweight 10-speed Bikes $300!
Use our easy monthly payment plan!

Although Jerry wanted to buy one on the spot, he didn't have the money. He inquired about the monthly payment plan. If he used the plan, he would have to pay $75 down and pay the balance in twelve monthly installments of $22.50 each.

Jerry calculated the total price: 75 + (12) (22.50) = $345.00. The salesperson said that the interest was only $45 on $300, or 15 percent. Jerry realized, however, that since he would have to pay $75 down, the store was really charging $45 on $225, or 20 percent.

At the service station, Jerry noticed that his chain was rusty, four spokes were missing, and a spring was about to come through the seat. On the way home, he stopped at the bike shop again.

A: 7.3%	N: 7.8
B: 0.9	O: 7.4
C: 3.0	P: 2.7
D: 4.4	Q: 0.3
E: 13	R: 7.7
F: 2.8	S: 6.3
G: 1.6	T: 9.3
H: 3.5	U: 2.7
I: 7.4	V: 1.3
J: 0.2	W: 1.6
K: 0.3	X: 0.5
L: 3.5	Y: 1.9
M: 2.5	Z: 0.1

From these percentages, the index fingers would type 42.2% of the letters, the ring fingers would type 19.3% of the letters (disregarding the semicolon).
(Sinkov, Abraham. Elementary Cryptanalysis: A Mathematical Approach. New York: Random House, 1968, p. 177.)

Application: QWERTY

A typewriter keyboard is sometimes referred to as QWERTY, after the six keys in the top row of letters. The keys of a manual typewriter can jam if two keys from the same side of the typewriter are hit at the same time. The QWERTY keyboard was designed so that common letter pairs, like *q* and *u*, or like *t* and *h*, are not both on the same side.

A trained typist uses the index fingers for the letters *R, T, Y, U, F, G, H, J, V, B, N,* and *M* and uses the ring fingers for *W, S, X, O, L,* and semicolon.

Take a passage of about one hundred words from a novel or a short story. What percent of the letters was typed with index fingers? What percent was typed with ring fingers? Do your results change very much for different passages?

Chapter Study Guide

ASSIGNMENT GUIDE

Basic (2 days)
(1) 230: 1–29
(2) 201: 32–44 (even)
    212: 27–30
    217: 19–22

Average (1 day)
222: 23, 25, 27
230: 1–29

Advanced (1 day)
208: 39, 41, 47, 49
223: 33, 35
230: 1–29

Skills

As you study and review this chapter, be sure you build the useful algebraic skills, including:

1 Stating inequalities   Write an inequality for each pair of numbers:

  a   10 and 5

  b -6 and 7

  c -15 and -30

  d -4.5 and -4.4

PROCEDURE

On a number line, the greater number is the number that is "more positive."

a $5 < 10$; $10 > 5$

b $-6 < 7$; $7 > -6$

c $-30 < -15$; $-15 > -30$

d $-4.5 < -4.4$;
    $-4.4 > -4.5$

2 Graphing compound inequalities

Match each graph with the compound inequality it represents:

A $3 < x < 7$

B $-5 < x < 2$

C $-4 \le x \le 3$

D $-4 < x < 3$

E $x < -2 \text{ or } x > 4$

F $x \le -2 \text{ or } x \ge 4$

PROCEDURE

Notice that "open dots" indicate $<$ or $>$ and "closed dots" indicate $\leq$ or $\geq$.

a $x \leq -2 \ or \ x \geq 4$; choice **F**
b $-5 < x < 2$; choice **B**
c $-4 < x < 3$; choice **D**
d $3 < x < 7$; choice **A**
e $-4 \leq x \leq 3$; choice **C**
f $x < -2 \ or \ x > 4$; choice **E**

3 **Using the Addition Property of Inequality** Solve each inequality:

a $x + 3 < 5$ c $z - 2 \leq 1$
b $y - 7 > -3$ d $w + 7 \geq -5$

PROCEDURE

a $\qquad x + 3 < 5$ c $\qquad z - 2 \leq 1$
ADD -3: $\quad x < 2$ ADD 2: $\quad z \leq 3$

b $\qquad y - 7 > -3$ d $\qquad w + 7 \geq -5$
ADD 7: $\quad y > 4$ ADD -7: $\quad w \geq -12$

4 **Using the Multiplication Property of Inequality** Solve each inequality:

a $3x < 5$ c $\dfrac{2}{3}z \leq 1$

b $-\dfrac{y}{7} > -3$ d $-\dfrac{7}{5}w \geq 2$

PROCEDURE

a $\qquad 3x < 5$ c $\qquad \dfrac{2}{3}z \leq 1$
MULTBY $\frac{1}{3}$: $x < \dfrac{5}{3}$ MULTBY $\frac{3}{2}$: $z \leq \dfrac{3}{2}$

b $\qquad -\dfrac{y}{7} > -3$ d $\qquad -\dfrac{7}{5}w \geq 2$
MULTBY -7: $y < 21$ MULTBY $-\frac{5}{7}$: $w \leq \dfrac{-10}{7}$

5 **Solving inequalities that involve more than one operation**

Solve each inequality:

a $2x - 3 < 9$ b $-5 - 3y \geq 7$ c $2(z - 3) \geq -5(z + 1)$

PROCEDURE

a
$$2x - 3 < 9$$
ADD 3: $\quad 2x < 12$
MULTBY $\frac{1}{2}$: $\quad x < 6$

b
$$-5 - 3y \geq 7$$
ADD 5: $\quad -3y \geq 12$
MULTBY $-\frac{1}{3}$: $\quad y \leq -4$

c
$$2(z - 3) \geq -5(z + 1)$$
distribute: $\quad 2z - 6 \geq -5z - 5$
ADD 6: $\quad 2z \geq -5z + 1$
ADD $5z$: $\quad 7z \geq 1$
MULTBY $\frac{1}{7}$: $\quad z \geq \frac{1}{7}$

Math History: *Squaring the Circle*

In the fifth century B.C. an early scientist named Anaxagoras was imprisoned for suggesting that the sun was larger than Greece and that the moon only reflected light from the sun. While in prison, he worked on a problem that was to baffle mathematicians for over 2000 years. That problem is to use only an unmarked straightedge and a compass to construct a square that has the same area as a given circle.

Over the centuries, attempts at "circle-squaring" came to be a fashionable pastime. Many people thought they had solved the problem, but there were always errors in the methods. By 1775, circle-squaring was so popular that the Academy of Paris resolved not to look at any new "solutions." A century later, Augustus De Morgan made a hobby out of collecting the incorrect solutions to the problems.

Finally in 1882, C. L. F. Lindemann showed that it is impossible to square the circle with only an unmarked straightedge and a compass. He showed that a line segment of length π was necessary for any solution. Then he used algebra to show that the two tools were not enough to construct such a line segment.

Chapter Test

Replace each ___?___ with $<$, $>$, or $=$.

1 $\quad 4 \underline{\ \ ?\ \ } -2$
    $>$

4 $\quad -5 \underline{\ \ ?\ \ } 0$
    $<$

7 $\quad -8 \underline{\ \ ?\ \ } 8 \cdot \left(-\frac{1}{4}\right)$
      $<$

2 $\quad -3 \underline{\ \ ?\ \ } -6$
    $>$

5 $\quad -8.1 \underline{\ \ ?\ \ } -8.2$
     $>$

8 $\quad -6 \underline{\ \ ?\ \ } (3)(-2)$
     $=$

3 $\quad \frac{3}{4} \underline{\ \ ?\ \ } -\frac{1}{2}$
    $>$

6 $\quad \frac{10}{3} \underline{\ \ ?\ \ } 3\frac{1}{3}$
     $=$

9 $\quad \frac{9}{10} \underline{\ \ ?\ \ } \frac{10}{11}$
     $<$

Translate each inequality into words.

10 $\quad 10 \geq -3$
Ten is greater than or equal to negative three.

12 $\quad -3 < x < 2$
x is greater than negative three and x is less than two

14 $\quad -5 < x \leq 2$
x is greater than negative five and less than or equal to two.

11 $\quad -9 < 4$
Negative nine is less than four.

13 $\quad 0 \leq x \leq 1$
x is greater than or equal to zero and less than or equal to nine.

15 $\quad -5 \leq x < 2$
x is greater than or equal to negative five and less than two.

Graph each inequality on a number line.

16 $\quad x \geq 1$
solid dot at 1, solid line in the positive direction from 1

17 $\quad y < -2$
open circle at -2, solid line in the negative direction from -2

18 $\quad z \leq 0$
solid dot at 0, solid line in the negative direction from 0

19 $\quad x \leq -4 \quad or \quad x = 2$
solid dot at -4, solid line in the negative direction from -4, solid dot at 2

20 $\quad x \leq -4 \quad or \quad x \geq 2$ solid dot at -4, solid line in the negative direction from -4; solid dot at 2, solid line in the positive direction from 2

21 $\quad x \geq -4 \quad and \quad x \leq 2$
solid line between a solid dot at -4 and a solid dot at 2

Solve for each variable.

22 $\quad 3x > -18$
$\quad\quad x > -6$

23 $\quad (x + 12) \div 2 < 7$
$\quad\quad x < 2$

24 $\quad -\frac{1}{2}x + 12 < 7$
$\quad\quad x > 10$

25 $\quad 3y + 5 \geq y - 7$
$\quad\quad y \geq -6$

26 $\quad 2(-y + 3) \leq (y - 4)$
$\quad\quad y \geq \frac{10}{3}$

27 $\quad y - 1 \leq 3y + 1 \leq 7 + y$
$\quad\quad -1 \leq y \leq 3$

28   Ron has at most three dollars to spend for lunch. If he buys a milkshake for seventy cents and fries for fifty-five cents, how many eighty-cent hamburgers can he buy?
$\quad$ 2

29   Rona walks her dog two or three times each day, and each walk lasts between fifteen and twenty-five minutes. Write a compound inequality that represents the time Rona spends each day walking her dog.
$\quad 30 \leq x \leq 75$

Problem Set: The Order of Operations

The order for performing operations in mathematics is: parentheses, exponentiation, multiplication and division (left to right), and addition and subtraction (left to right). Fill in each blank with $<$, $=$, or $>$.

1 $-8 + 9 \cdot 10 \div 5$ __?__ 10

     $10 = 10$

2 $-(8 + 9 \cdot 10 \div 5)$ __?__ -20

     $-26 < -20$

3 $3 \cdot 12 \div 6 - 10 + 2$ __?__ 0

     $-2 < 0$

4 $3 \cdot (12 \div 6) - 10 + 2$ __?__ -2

     $-2 = -2$

5 $4 - 7^2 + 5 \cdot 8 - 24$ __?__ -15

     $-29 < -15$

6 $(4 - 7)^2 + 5 \cdot (8 - 24)$ __?__ 89

     $-71 < 89$

7 $15 \div 3 \cdot 8 - 5 + 7 \cdot 2$ __?__ 45

     $49 > 45$

8 $15 \div 3 \cdot (8 - 5 + 7) \cdot 2$ __?__ 75

     $100 > 75$

9 $15 - 10 + 3^2 \cdot 14 \div 7$ __?__ 33

     $23 < 33$

10 $(15 - 10 + 3^2 \cdot 14) \div 7$ __?__ 15

     $18\frac{5}{7} > 15$

11 $(-8 + 9 \cdot 10) \div 5$ __?__ 16

     $16\frac{2}{5} > 16$

12 $(-8 + 9) \cdot 10 \div 5$ __?__ 2

     $2 = 2$

13 $3 \cdot (12 \div 6 - 10) + 2$ __?__ -18

     $-22 < -18$

14 $3 \cdot 12 \div (6 - 10) + 2$ __?__ 10

     $-7 < 10$

15 $4 - 7^2 + 5 \cdot (8 - 24)$ __?__ -30

     $-125 < -30$

16 $((4 - 7)^2 + 5) \cdot 8 - 24$ __?__ 100

     $88 < 100$

17 $15 \div 3 \cdot (8 - 5) + 7 \cdot 2$ __?__ 25

     $29 > 25$

18 $15 \div (3 \cdot 8) - (5 + 7) \cdot 2$ __?__ -24

     $-23\frac{3}{8} > -24$

19 $(15 - 10 + 3)^2 \cdot 14 \div 7$ __?__ 128

     $128 = 128$

20 $15 - (10 + 3)^2 \cdot 14 \div 7$ __?__ 210

     $-323 < 210$

In problems 21–26, $a = 7$ and $b = -3$. Evaluate each expression.

21 $3a - (6 \div 2) + b$

     15

22 $(3a - 6) \div 2 + b$

     $4\frac{1}{2}$

23 $3a - 6 \div (2 + b)$

     27

24 $(b - 9) \div (a + 2b)$

     -12

25 $(b - (9 \div a)) + 2b$

     $-10\frac{2}{7}$

26 $b - (9 \div (a + 2b))$

     -12

Use parentheses and operation symbols to express the given number. (Problem 27 is done.)

27   Use 1, 2, 8, 12, 20;   make 4.

     ▪ $1 + 2 + (20 - 12) \div 8 = 4$

28   Use 6, 9, 10, 18, 20;   make 8.

     $6 \cdot (-9 + 10) - (18 - 20)$

29   Use 4, 4, 8, 10, 19;   make 17.

     $4 \div 4 \cdot (8 - 10) + 19$

30   Use 3, 5, 10, 12, 16;   make 14.

     $3 + 5 + 10 + (12 - 16)$

31   Use 2, 7, 9, 16, 19;   make 2.

     $2 \cdot 7 - 9 + (16 - 19)$

Chapter 6

POLYNOMIALS

CHAPTER SCHEDULE

Basic
Problem Sets   10 Days
Review   4 Days
Test   2 Days

Average
Problem Sets   9 Days
Review   1 Day
Test   2 Days

Advanced
Problem Sets   9 Days
Review   1 Day
Test   1 Day

The chapter schedule assumes that Basic courses will have the midyear review following Chapter 6.

Section 6.1   Multiplying Binomials

SECTION SCHEDULE

Basic (1 day)

Average ($1\frac{1}{2}$ days)

Advanced (1 day)

The length of this rectangle is $(a + b)$ and the width is $(c + d)$. One way to calculate the area of the large rectangle is to multiply its length and its width. Another way is to add the areas of the four small rectangles.

Area is: $(a + b)\,(c + d)$

Area is: $ac + ad + bc + bd$

Both expressions represent the same area, so the expressions are equal:

$(a + b)\,(c + d) = ac + ad + bc + bd$

In algebraic terms, the left-hand side is a product of two binomials, and the right-hand side is a sum of four monomials.

The Distributive Property provides a way to find the product of two binomials.

Some students may need a review of the Distributive Property and of the terms monomial and binomial.

Sample Problems

1   Use the Distributive Property to multiply $(2x + 7)(x + 5)$.

PROCEDURE   The Distributive Property states that $(b + c)a = ba + ca$.
Let $(b + c)$ be $(2x + 7)$ and let a represent $(x + 5)$:

$$
\begin{aligned}
(b + c)\,(a) &= ba &&+ ca \\
(2x + 7)(x + 5) &= 2x(x + 5) + 7(x + 5) \\
&= 2x^2 + 10x + 7x + 35 \\
&= 2x^2 + 17x + 35
\end{aligned}
$$

*Replacing the mono-
mial **a** with the ex-
pression (**x** + 5) may
cause some students
initial difficulty.*

Notice that the product $2x^2 + 17x + 35$ is written so that it is in
descending powers of the variable x. When a variable expression has one
variable, it is usual to write the terms in descending powers.

2   Use the **vertical form** to multiply $(2x + 7)(x + 5)$.

*Students should be
able to show that the
two algebraic methods
of the Distributive
Property and its verti-
cal form, and the geo-
metric method on
p. 233, all give the
same result.*

PROCEDURE

$$
\begin{array}{r}
2x + 7 \\
x + 5 \\
\hline
\end{array}
$$

*The text first finds the
product of **x** and
(**2x** + 7) so that the
order of terms is the
same as the order for
the **FOIL** pattern,
p. 239.*

multiply x and $(2x + 7)$: $2x^2 + 7x$
multiply 5 and $(2x + 7)$: $ 10x + 35$
add: $2x^2 + 17x + 35$

Notice that like terms are lined up vertically. The vertical form gives the
same four terms as "partial products" and the same final result as in Sample
Problem 1.

3   Multiply $(2r - 5s)(x - 2y)$.

PROCEDURE

$$
\begin{array}{l}
2r - 5s \\
\underline{x - 2y} \\
2rx - 5sx \\
\underline{\; - 4ry + 10sy} \\
2rx - 5sx - 4ry + 10sy
\end{array}
$$

There are no like terms, so no terms are aligned vertically.

Problem Set A

ASSIGNMENT GUIDE

Basic (1 day)
4–32 (even), 37, 38
Average ($1\frac{1}{2}$ days)
(1) 4–32 (even), 43–47
(2) See p. 240.

Advanced (1 day)
33–49
238: 2–8 (even)

1   When 2 binomials are multiplied, how many terms are in the product before combining like terms?

   four

2   What property justifies the vertical form for multiplying binomials?

   distributive property

In problems 3–16, use the vertical form to multiply each pair of binomials. Write the answer in descending powers of the variable.

3 $(a + 6)(a + 3)$

   $a^2 + 9a + 18$

4 $(x + 4)(x + 5)$

   $x^2 + 9x + 20$

5 $(x + 7)(x - 3)$

   $x^2 + 4x - 21$

6 $(m + 6)(m - 5)$

   $m^2 + m - 30$

7 $(a - 7)(a - 2)$

   $a^2 - 9a + 14$

8 $(p - 8)(p - 1)$

   $p^2 - 9p + 8$

9 $(2x + 1)(x + 3)$

   $2x^2 + 7x + 3$

10 $(n + 4)(3n + 2)$

   $3n^2 + 14n + 8$

11 $(2a - 8)(3x + 4)$

   $2ax + 8a - 24x - 32$

12 $(16b + 3)(3n - 4)$

   $48bn - 64b + 9n - 12$

13 $(12 - 7x)(10 - 5x)$

   $35x^2 - 130x + 120$

14 $(10m - 5)(10m - 5)$

   $100m^2 - 100m + 25$

15 $(4 + a)(4 - a)$

   $16 - a^2$

16 $(2 - x)(2 + x)$

   $4 - x^2$

Problems 14–20 involve perfect-square trinomials and differences of two squares. These are discussed on pages 248 and 250, respectively.

17   Find the product of $(10a - 11)$ and $(10a + 11)$.

   $100a^2 - 121$

18   Multiply $(12x + 5)$ and $(12x - 5)$.

   $144x^2 - 25$

19   Square $(5x + 2)$.

   $25x^2 + 20x + 4$

20   Multiply $(2x - 3)$ by itself.

   $4x^2 - 12x + 9$

In problems 21–24, write the expression that should replace ___?___.

21 $(x + 2)(x + 3) = $ ___?___ $ + 3x + 2x + 6$

   x^2

22 $(2x - 1)(x + 7) = $ ___?___ $ + 14x - 1x - 7$

   $2x^2$

23 $(n + 6)(n + 3) = n^2 + 3n + 6n + $ ___?___

   18

24 $(3y + 1)(2y - 3) = 6y^2 - 9y + 2y - $ ___?___

   3

Multiply each pair of monomials. (Review: Section 4.1)

25 $5y \cdot 3y^2$

$15y^3$

26 $(12x^2)(-3x^5)$

$-36x^7$

27 $3a^2b \cdot ab^2c$

$3a^3b^3c$

28 $(15m^2n^3)(-6m^3n)$

$-90m^5n^4$

29 $(-x^2y^2z)(-xy^2z^5)$

$x^3y^4z^6$

30 $(-3a^2c^2)(17b^2d^2)$

$-51a^2b^2c^2d^2$

31 $ax^2y \cdot a^2xy^2$

$a^3x^3y^3$

32 $r^2t^3 \cdot rt^3$

r^3t^6

Problem Set **B**

In problems 33–42, use the vertical form to find each product.

33 $(x - 2y)(3x + 7y)$

$3x^2 + xy - 14y^2$

34 $(5x + 4y)(x - y)$

$5x^2 - xy - 4y^2$

35 $(4 + ab)(4 - ab)$

$16 - a^2b^2$

36 $(x^2 - 5)(x^2 + 5)$

$x^4 - 25$

37 $(x + 1)(x^2 + 3x + 1)$

$x^3 + 4x^2 + 4x + 1$

38 $(x + 2)(x^2 - 3x + 4)$

$x^3 - x^2 - 2x + 8$

39 $(y + 6)(2y^2 - 5y - 4)$

$2y^3 + 7y^2 - 34y - 24$

40 $(c - 1)(c^2 + 2c - 1)$

$c^3 + c^2 - 3c + 1$

41 $(y - x)(2x + 3y + 8)$

$-2x^2 - 8x - xy + 8y + 3y$

42 $(5a - 3b + 9)(b + 4a)$

$20a^2 + 36a - 7ab + 9b - 3b^2$

43 Find an expression for the area of a rectangle with base $(3x + 5)$ inches and height $(4x - 8)$ inches.

$12x^2 - 4x - 40$

44 Find an expression for the area of a triangle which has base $(2x + 4)$ and height $(x - 1)$.

$x^2 + x - 2$

45 Bella wants to build a pen that is twelve feet narrower than it is long. She has one hundred feet of fencing. Draw and label a sketch, and find the length and width of the pen.

$w = 19, \ell = 31$

46 Find two consecutive integers such that the sum of the first and twice the second is eighty-three.

27, 28

47 Find two consecutive even integers such that the sum of the first and three times the second is thirty.

6, 8

Problem Set **C**

48 The area of this rectangle is the product $(x + y)(a + b + c)$. The area can also be found by adding the areas of each small rectangle. What is the area of the large rectangle? How many terms are in the answer?

$ax + bx + cx + ay + by + cy$; 6 terms

49 Multiply $(2x + y)$ by $(4a^2 + 2b - c)$.

$8a^2x + 4bx - 2cx + 4a^2y + 2by - cy$

50 A student calculated the product $(y^2 - 5y + 3)(2y^2 + 7y - 4)$ to be $2y^4 - 3y^3 - 33y^2 + 41y - 12$. She wanted to test her answer.

There is one test that will usually show whether an error has been made. Replace the variable by a number in each of the factors and in the product. For example, replacing y by 1, the two given polynomials have the values -1 and 5, and their product is $(-1)(5) = -5$. Replacing the variable y by 1 in the product results in $2 - 3 - 33 + 41 - 12 = -5$. If this result was not -5, the product would have been incorrect.

Explain why this test works. Will it always work?

50) If the two values are not the same, the multiplication was not correct. However, incorrect multiplication may not result in different values:

$(x + 3)(x + 2)$
$\neq x^2 + 6x + 5$

But for $x = 1$:

$(1 + 3)(1 + 2) \overset{?}{=} 1^2 + 6 \cdot 1 + 5$
$4 \cdot 3 \overset{?}{=} 1 + 6 + 5$
$12 \overset{?}{=} 12$ ✓

In problems 51–55, find the products and test them. Use the value 2 as the replacement for the variable.

51 $(3x^2 + 7x - 5)^2$

$9x^4 + 42x^3 + 19x^2 - 70x + 25$; 441

52 $(2y^2 - 3y + 1)(5y^2 + 6y - 3)$

$10x^4 - 3y^3 - 19y^2 + 15y - 3$; 87

53 $(z^3 + z^2 + 3z - 1)(2z^2 - 3z + 1)$

$2z^5 - z^4 + 4z^3 - 10z^2 + 6z - 1$; 51

54 $(a^2 - 3a - 3)(a^2 - 3a + 3)$

$a^4 - 6a^3 + 9a^2 - 9$; -5

55 $(2x^3 - 3x + 1)(3x^2 + x - 2)$

$6x^5 + 2x^4 - 13x^3 + 7x - 2$; 132

X tending the topic: **Multiplying Polynomials**

The vertical form of the Distributive Property can be used to multiply any two polynomials.

Sample Problems

1   Multiply: $(3x^3 + 5x^2 - 7x - 10)(x^3 - 2x^2 + 3x - 4)$

PROCEDURE
$$
\begin{array}{r}
3x^3 + 5x^2 - 7x - 10 \\
x^3 - 2x^2 + 3x - 4 \\
\hline
3x^6 + 5x^5 - 7x^4 - 10x^3 \\
- 6x^5 - 10x^4 + 14x^3 + 20x^2 \\
9x^4 + 15x^3 - 21x^2 - 30x \\
- 12x^3 - 20x^2 + 28x + 40 \\
\hline
3x^6 - x^5 - 8x^4 + 7x^3 - 21x^2 - 2x + 40
\end{array}
$$

2   Multiply: $(2y^3 - 6y^2 + 3y - 5)(5y^4 - 3y^2 + 1)$

PROCEDURE
$$
\begin{array}{r}
2y^3 - 6y^2 + 3y - 5 \\
5y^4 - 3y^2 + 1 \\
\hline
10y^7 - 30y^6 + 15y^5 - 25y^4 \\
- 6y^5 + 18y^4 - 9y^3 + 15y^2 \\
2y^3 - 6y^2 + 3y - 5 \\
\hline
10y^7 - 30y^6 + 9y^5 - 7y^4 - 7y^3 + 9y^2 + 3y - 5
\end{array}
$$

Problem Set X

Find each product.

1   $(x^2 + 3x + 1)(x + 5)$
$x^3 + 8x^2 + 16x + 5$

2   $(y^2 - y + 6)(2y - 3)$
$2y^3 - 5y^2 + 15y - 18$

3   $(4z^3 - 3z^2 + 2z - 5)(z - 1)$
$4z^4 - 7z^3 + 5z^2 - 7z + 5$

4   $(r^2 - 2r + 1)(r^2 - 2r + 1)$
$r^4 + 4r^3 + 6r^2 - 4r + 1$

5   $(2s^2 + s - 5)^2$
$4s^4 + 4s^3 - 19s^3 - 10s + 25$

6   $(1 + 2t - 3t^2 + 7t^3)^2$
$49t^6 - 42t^5 + 37t^4 + 2t^3 - 2t^2 + 4t + 1$

7   $(v - 1)^4$
$v^4 - 4v^3 - 6v^2 - 4v + 1$

8   $(2w^2 + 3w + 4)^3$
$8w^6 + 36w^5 + 102w^4 + 171w^3 + 204w^2 + 144w +$

Section 6.2   Using the FOIL Pattern

SECTION SCHEDULE

Basic (2 days)

Average ($1\frac{1}{2}$ days)

Advanced (1 day)

The product of two binomials is the sum of four monomials:

$$(x + a)(x + b) = x^2 + bx + ax + ab$$

The steps in finding the four monomials can be summarized by the **FOIL** pattern:

$$
\begin{aligned}
(x + a)(x + b) = \quad & x^2 && \text{(the product of the \textbf{F}irst terms, } x \text{ and } x) \\
+ \, & bx && \text{(the product of the \textbf{O}uter terms, } x \text{ and } b) \\
+ \, & ax && \text{(the product of the \textbf{I}nner terms, } a \text{ and } x) \\
+ \, & ab && \text{(the product of the \textbf{L}ast terms, } a \text{ and } b)
\end{aligned}
$$

The FOIL pattern can be used to find the product of any two binomials.

Sample Problems

1   Use the FOIL pattern to calculate each product.
   a $(2x + 5)(3x + 4)$ **b** $(a - 7)(2a + 3)$

PROCEDURE

a

$$
\begin{aligned}
& \qquad\quad \text{F} \quad\ \text{O} \quad\ \text{I} \quad\ \text{L} \\
(2x + 5)(3x + 4) &= 2x \cdot 3x + 2x \cdot 4 + 5 \cdot 3x + 5 \cdot 4 \\
&= 6x^2 \quad\ + 8x \quad + 15x \quad + 20 \\
&= 6x^2 + 23x + 20
\end{aligned}
$$

b

$$
\begin{aligned}
& \qquad\quad\ \text{F} \quad\ \text{O} \quad\ \text{I} \quad\ \text{L} \\
(a - 7)(2a + 3) &= a \cdot 2a + a \cdot 3 + (-7)(2a) + (-7)(3) \\
&= 2a^2 \quad + 3a \ - 14a \qquad - 21 \\
&= 2a^2 - 11a - 21
\end{aligned}
$$

The sum of the Outer term plus the Inner term is called the **middle term** of the trinomial.

2   Use the FOIL pattern to multiply $(4b + 3)(2b - 5)$.

PROCEDURE   Find the middle term first:

$$
\begin{aligned}
& \qquad\quad \text{O} \qquad\quad \text{I} \\
& (4b)(-5) + (3)(2b) \\
& \quad -20b \quad + \quad 6b \\
& \qquad\quad -14b
\end{aligned}
$$

Then write the complete multiplication sentence:

$$(4b + 3)(2b - 5) = 8b^2 - 14b - 15$$

3   Find the product $(2x - 5)(2x + 5)$.

*The term **conjugate** is
introduced on p. 250.*

PROCEDURE

$$\mathbf{O+I} \text{ is:} \quad (2x)(5) + (-5)(2x)$$
$$(10x) + (-10x)$$
$$0$$

$$(2x - 5)(2x + 5) = 4x^2 + 0 - 25$$
$$= 4x^2 - 25$$

In this example, since $\mathbf{O+I}$ is zero, the product has no middle term.

ASSIGNMENT GUIDE

Basic (2 days)
(1) 5–16, 35–40
(2) 17–34

Average ($1\frac{1}{2}$ days)
(1) 17–34
(2) 41–52
    238: 2–8 (even)

Advanced (1 day)
22–28 (even), 42–60
(even)

Problem Set A

1   Name three methods for multiplying two binomials.
    Distributive Property, Vertical Form, FOIL

2   What do the letters in FOIL stand for?
    First(product of first terms) Outer(product of outer terms)
    Inner(product of inner terms), Last(product of last terms)

3   Can FOIL be used to multiply a binomial and a trinomial? Explain.
    No, FOIL is not a property, just a summary of the pattern for multiplying binomials

4   Is it possible to multiply two binomials and have a binomial for an
    answer? Support your answer with an example.
    Yes, $(a - 4)(a + 4) = a^2 - 16$

Supply the middle term in each product. (Be sure to include the sign.)

5 $(x + 5)(x + 6) = x^2 \underline{\ \ ?\ \ } + 30$
    $+11x$

6 $(b + 5)(b + 5) = b^2 \underline{\ \ ?\ \ } + 25$
    $+10b$

7 $(x - 3)(x - 4) = x^2 \underline{\ \ ?\ \ } + 12$
    $-7x$

8 $(y - 8)(y - 1) = y^2 \underline{\ \ ?\ \ } + 8$
    $-9y$

9 $(x + 7)(x - 3) = x^2 \underline{\ \ ?\ \ } - 21$
    $+4x$

10 $(c - 6)(c + 5) = c^2 \underline{\ \ ?\ \ } - 30$
    $-c$

11 $(2x + 1)(x + 3) = 2x^2 \underline{\ \ ?\ \ } + 3$
    $+7x$

12 $(2y + 10)(3y + 4) = 6y^2 \underline{\ \ ?\ \ } + 40$
    $+38y$

13 $(2a - 1)(3a + 4) = 6a^2 \underline{} - 4$
$+5a$

14 $(5x + 2)(3x - 6) = 15x^2 \underline{} - 12$
$-24x$

15 $(x - 2)(x + 2) = x^2 \underline{} - 4$
$+0x$

16 $(4y + 3)(4y - 3) = 16y^2 \underline{} - 9$
$+0y$

Use the FOIL pattern to write the product of each pair of binomials:

17 $(x + 5)(x + 7)$
$x^2 + 12x + 35$

18 $(x + 2)(x + 4)$
$x^2 + 6x + 8$

19 $(y - 9)(y - 2)$
$y^2 - 11y + 18$

20 $(c - 5)(c - 1)$
$c^2 - 6c + 6$

21 $(x + 9)(x - 3)$
$x^2 + 6x - 27$

22 $(y - 3)(y + 4)$
$y^2 + y - 12$

23 $(2x + 3)(5x + 6)$
$10x^2 + 27x + 18$

24 $(3y + 7)(4y + 1)$
$12y^2 + 31y + 7$

25 $(7y - 5)(2y - 3)$
$14y^2 - 31y + 15$

26 $(2x - 5)(3x - 4)$
$6x^2 - 23x + 20$

27 $(11y + 9)(3y - 2)$
$33y^2 + 5y - 18$

28 $(2x - 7)(5x + 6)$
$10x^2 - 23x - 42$

29 $(3y - 1)(3y - 1)$
$9y^2 - 6y + 1$

30 $(4t + 3)(4t + 3)$
$16t^2 + 24t + 9$

31 $(5r - 1)(5r + 1)$
$25r^2 - 1$

32 $(2r + 1)(3r + 1)$
$6r^2 + 5r + 1$

33 $(8n - 3)(n - 8)$
$8n^2 - 67n + 24$

34 $(3n + 1)(n + 3)$
$3n^2 + 10n + 3$

Replace each $\underline{}$ with the correct expression. (Review: Section 6.1)

These problems preview the following section on factoring trinomials.

35 $(x + \underline{})(x + 7) = x^2 + 12x + 35$
5

36 $(x - \underline{})(x - 7) = x^2 - 14x + 49$
7

37 $(x + \underline{})(x - 10) = x^2 - 6x - 40$
4

38 $(x - \underline{})(x + 5) = x^2 + 2x - 15$
3

39 $(x + \underline{})(x + \underline{}) = x^2 + 11x + 28$
$7, 4$

40 $(x + \underline{})(x - \underline{}) = x^2 + 3x - 10$
$5, 2$

Problem Set B

Find each product.

41 $(2x + 3y)(x + y)$

$2x^2 + 5xy + 3y^2$

42 $(4a - 2b)(2a - 4b)$

$8a^2 - 20ab + 8b^2$

43 $(5 - x)(3 + x)$

$15 + 2x - x^2$

44 $(6 + 5x)(7 - 2x)$

$42 + 23x - 10x^2$

45 $(2x - 4y)(2x + 4y)$

$4x^2 - 16y^2$

46 $(x^2 + 7y)(x^2 - 7y)$

$x^2 - 49y^2$

47 $(8y - 1)^2$

$64y^2 - 16y + 1$

48 $(x + 2y)^2$

$x^2 + 4xy + 4y^2$

49 the square of $(9 + 10y)$

$81 + 180y + 100y^2$

50 $(4 - 3x)$ multiplied by itself

$16 - 24x + 9x^2$

Problem Set C

Notice the pattern of the products $(x + c)^2$ and $(x - c)^2$:

$$(x + c)^2 \qquad\qquad (x - c)^2$$
$$(x + c)(x + c) \qquad\qquad (x - c)(x - c)$$
$$x^2 + cx + cx + c^2 \qquad\qquad x^2 - cx - cx + c^2$$
$$x^2 + 2cx + c^2 \qquad\qquad x^2 - 2cx + c^2$$

Each trinomial, because it is the square of a binomial, is called a **perfect-square trinomial**. The first term and the third term are always positive. The middle term may be positive or negative.

Use the patterns for perfect-square trinomials to write each product:

51 $(x + 1)^2$

$x^2 + 2x + 1$

52 $(a + 5)^2$

$a^2 + 10a + 25$

53 $(x - 2)^2$

$x^2 - 4x + 4$

54 $(x - 8)^2$

$x^2 - 16x + 64$

55 $(2a + 1)^2$

$4a^2 + 4a + 1$

56 $(5y + 6)^2$

$25y^2 + 60y + 36$

57 $(7a - 5)^2$

$49a^2 - 70a + 25$

58 $(x - 3y)^2$

$x^2 - 6xy + 9y^2$

Use the pattern for a perfect-square trinomial to perform each calculation mentally.

Other mental multiplication techniques are presented in the Project on p. 274.

59 $(22)^2$

Hint: $22^2 = (20 + 2)^2$

484

60 $(41)^2$

1681

61 $(79)^2$

6241

Project: The "Rule of 78"

The previous chapter (page 226) described a store that charged $45 interest on $225 for one year. The monthly payment was $(225 + 45) \div 12$ or $22.50.

    Suppose a buyer has already made six monthly payments, and now wants to pay the balance of the account. Is the buyer entitled to a refund of some of the interest charges? If so, how much of a refund?

    Many stores use the following calculation, called the "Rule of 78," to determine the percentage of interest that is refunded. If the original loan was for T payments, and if R payments remain, then the percentage is the ratio:

$$\frac{1 + 2 + 3 + \ldots + R}{1 + 2 + 3 + 4 + \ldots + T}$$

- After 6 monthly payments (out of 12), the percentage is:

$$\frac{1 + 2 + 3 + 4 + 5 + 6}{1 + 2 + 3 + 4 + 5 + 6 + 7 + 8 + 9 + 10 + 11 + 12} = \frac{21}{78}$$

The total amount of interest was $45:

$$\frac{21}{78} \cdot 45 = 12.11538$$

The refund would be $12.11.

1 If the $45 interest charge was divided equally among the twelve payments, how much interest would have been paid after six months?

2 The interest on a two-year loan (24 payments) is $500. Use the "Rule of 78" to calculate the amount of refund if the loan is paid off after:
a 6 months	**c** 12 months	**e** 18 months
b 9 months	**d** 15 months	**f** 21 months

3 After several monthly payments, a loan is paid in full and about half of the interest is refunded. How many monthly payments had been made, if the term of the loan was:
a 12 months	**c** 36 months	**e** 120 months
b 24 months	**d** 48 months	**f** 240 months

4 For a 12-month loan, what is the percentage of refund after 10 months? after 11 months?

5 Can you guess why the "Rule of 78" was given its name?

---

1) $\dfrac{6}{12} \cdot 45 = 22.50$

2a) $\dfrac{1 + 2 + \ldots + 18}{1 + 2 + 3 + \ldots + 24}$

$\dfrac{171}{300} \cdot 500 = 285 \qquad = \dfrac{171}{300}$

b) $\dfrac{1 + 2 + \ldots + 15}{1 + 2 + 3 + \ldots + 24}$

$\dfrac{120}{300} \cdot 500 = 200 \qquad = \dfrac{120}{300}$

c) $\dfrac{1 + 2 + \ldots + 12}{1 + 2 + 3 + \ldots + 24}$

$\dfrac{78}{300} \cdot 500 = 130 \qquad = \dfrac{78}{300}$

d) $\dfrac{1 + 2 + \ldots + 9}{1 + 2 + 3 + \ldots + 24}$

$\dfrac{45}{300} \cdot 500 = 75 \qquad = \dfrac{45}{300}$

e) $\dfrac{1 + 2 + \ldots + 6}{1 + 2 + 3 + \ldots + 24}$

$\dfrac{21}{300} \cdot 500 = 35 \qquad = \dfrac{21}{300}$

f) $\dfrac{1 + 2 + 3}{1 + 2 + 3 + \ldots + 24}$

$\dfrac{6}{300} \cdot 500 = 10 \qquad = \dfrac{6}{300}$

3a) After 3 payments:
$\dfrac{1 + 2 + \ldots + 9}{78} = 0.58$

After 4 payments:
$\dfrac{1 + 2 + \ldots + 8}{78} = 0.46$

b) After 7 payments:
$\dfrac{1 + 2 + \ldots + 17}{1 + 2 + 3 + \ldots + 24}$
$= 0.51$

c) After 10 payments:
$\dfrac{1 + 2 + \ldots + 26}{1 + 2 + 3 + \ldots + 36}$
$= 0.52$

d) After 14 payments:
$\dfrac{1 + 2 + \ldots + 34}{1 + 2 + 3 + \ldots + 48}$
$= 0.51$

e) After 35 payments:
$\dfrac{1 + 2 + \ldots + 85}{1 + 2 + 3 + \ldots + 120}$
$= 0.50$

f) After 70 payments:
$\dfrac{1 + 2 + \ldots + 170}{1 + 2 + 3 + \ldots + 240}$
$= 0.50$

4) After 10 months:
$\dfrac{1 + 2}{1 + 2 + \ldots + 12}$
$= 0.038$

After 11 months: $\dfrac{1}{78} = 0.013$

5) The sum of the numbers from 1 to 12 is 78.

243

Section 6.3 Factoring Trinomials: $x^2 + bx + c$

Factoring a trinomial is treated as a step-by-step process. Students may have to see many examples before they can go through all the steps on their own.

If you are given the factors $(x + 5)(x + 2)$, you can compute the product $x^2 + 7x + 10$ using the Distributive Property, the vertical form, or FOIL.

Suppose you are given the trinomial $x^2 + 7x + 10$ and you want to find its binomial factors, $(x + 5)(x + 2)$. The process of finding the factors is called **factoring**. When the process is restricted to factors that contain integers, this process is called **factoring over the integers**.

Sample Problems

1   Find the binomial factors of $x^2 + 6x + 8$.

PROCEDURE

Treat this problem as a puzzle, and fill in the parts of the puzzle:

$x^2 + 6x + 8$

$(x \quad)(x \quad)$ The first factors of each binomial are x.

$(x + \ )(x + \ )$ Since the middle term and the third term are both positive, the signs in both binomials must be positive.

$(x + 4)(x + 2)$ The factors 4 and 2 will provide the middle term, $+6x$, and the third term, $+8$.

Therefore, $x^2 + 6x + 8 = (x + 4)(x + 2)$.

To check the factors, use FOIL:

$(x + 4)(x + 2)$
$x^2 + 2x + 4x + 8$
$x^2 + 6x + 8$ ✓

Other factors will not check; for example, try $(x + 8)(x + 1)$:

$(x + 8)(x + 1)$
$x^2 + x + 8x + 8$
$x^2 + 9x + 8$

But $x^2 + 9x + 8$ is not the same as the original trinomial $x^2 + 6x + 8$.

2   Find the binomial factors of $x^2 - 12x + 20$.

PROCEDURE

$x^2 - 12x + 20$

$(x \quad)(x \quad)$ The factors of x^2 are x and x.
The factors of $+20$ may be:

20 and 1   or -20 and -1
10 and 2   or -10 and -2
5 and 4   or -5 and -4

Both numbers must have the same sign, since their product is $+20$. Which pair of factors will give the right middle term? The factors -10 and -2 result in the middle term $-12x$.

$(x - 10)(x - 2)$

To check, use FOIL:

$(x - 10)(x - 2)$
$x^2 - 2x - 10x + 20$
$x^2 - 12x + 20 \checkmark$

At first it may be necessary to try many pairs of factors and eliminate those that do not check:

$\left.\begin{array}{l} (x + 20)(x + 1) = x^2 + 21x + 20 \\ (x - 20)(x - 1) = x^2 - 21x + 20 \\ (x + 10)(x + 2) = x^2 + 12x + 20 \\ (x + 5)(x + 4) = x^2 + 9x + 20 \\ (x - 5)(x - 4) = x^2 - 9x + 20 \end{array}\right\}$ wrong middle term

But soon patterns will be apparent. In this Sample Problem, the signs of the middle term and third term indicate that both binomial factors must contain negative signs.

3   Factor $x^2 + x - 7$ over the integers.

PROCEDURE

$x^2 + x - 7$
$(x + \quad)(x - \quad)$

The last terms would have to be 7 and 1, where one is positive and the other is negative. *Check* both $(x + 7)(x - 1)$ and $(x - 7)(x + 1)$. Neither one gives $+x$ as the middle term. Therefore, the expression $x^2 + x - 7$ cannot be factored over the integers.

ASSIGNMENT GUIDE

Basic (2 days)
(1) 5–14, 21–26
(2) 29–38

Average (2 days)
(1) 21–38
(2) 40, 42, 44, 46–48
     249: 1–8

Advanced (2 days)
(1) 28–58 (even)
(2) 249: 1–16

Problem Set **A**

1 The process of rewriting a trinomial as the product of two binomials is called __?__ .

   factoring

2 If all the signs of the trinomial are positive, then the sign of each binomial factor will be __?__ .

   positive

3 If a trinomial such as $x^2 - 6x - 16$ is factored, can both binomial factors have negative signs?

   no (the last term is negative)

4 How can you check whether the factors of a trinomial are correct?

   use FOIL

Replace the __?__ with either a "+" sign or a "−" sign to show the correct binomial factors of each trinomial.

5 $x^2 + 10x + 9 = (x \underline{\ \ ?\ \ } 9)(x \underline{\ \ ?\ \ } 1)$
   +, +

6 $x^2 - 12x + 20 = (x \underline{\ \ ?\ \ } 10)(x \underline{\ \ ?\ \ } 2)$
   −, −

7 $x^2 + 7x - 18 = (x \underline{\ \ ?\ \ } 9)(x \underline{\ \ ?\ \ } 2)$
   +, −

8 $x^2 - 2x - 35 = (x \underline{\ \ ?\ \ } 5)(x \underline{\ \ ?\ \ } 7)$
   +, −

9 $x^2 + x - 72 = (x \underline{\ \ ?\ \ } 8)(x \underline{\ \ ?\ \ } 9)$
   −, +

10 $x^2 - x - 20 = (x \underline{\ \ ?\ \ } 5)(x \underline{\ \ ?\ \ } 4)$
   −, +

11 $x^2 + 6x - 72 = (x \underline{\ \ ?\ \ } 12)(x \underline{\ \ ?\ \ } 6)$
   +, −

12 $x^2 - 8x + 16 = (x \underline{\ \ ?\ \ } 4)(x \underline{\ \ ?\ \ } 4)$
   −, −

13 $x^2 - 6x - 7 = (x \underline{\ \ ?\ \ } 7)(x \underline{\ \ ?\ \ } 1)$
   −, +

14 $x^2 + 8x - 9 = (x \underline{\ \ ?\ \ } 9)(x \underline{\ \ ?\ \ } 1)$
   +, −

Find each product. (Review: Section 6.2)

15 $(x - 2)(x + 2)$
   $x^2 - 4$

17 $(a + 9)(a - 9)$
   $a^2 - 81$

19 $(2x - 1)(2x + 1)$
   $4x^2 - 1$

16 $(y + 5)(y - 5)$
   $y^2 - 25$

18 $(x - 4)(x + 4)$
   $x^2 - 16$

20 $(3a + 7b)(3a - 7b)$
   $9a^2 - 49b^2$

Problem Set **B**

Multiple choice
For each trinomial, write the letter that corresponds to the correct binomial factors.

		a	**b**	**c**
21	$x^2 - 3x + 2$	$(x - 3)(x - 1)$	$(x - 2)(x - 1)$	$(x - 2)(x - 3)$
	b			
22	$x^2 + 3x + 2$	$(x + 3)(x + 1)$	$(x + 3)(x + 2)$	$(x + 2)(x + 1)$
	c			
23	$x^2 - 7x + 10$	$(x - 5)(x - 2)$	$(x - 10)(x - 1)$	$(x - 7)(x - 10)$
	a			
24	$x^2 - 8x + 15$	$(x - 8)(x - 1)$	$(x - 3)(x - 5)$	$(x - 15)(x - 1)$
	b			
25	$x^2 - 2x - 15$	$(x - 15)(x + 1)$	$(x - 5)(x + 3)$	$(x + 5)(x - 3)$
	b			
26	$x^2 + 3x - 18$	$(x + 9)(x - 2)$	$(x + 18)(x - 1)$	$(x + 6)(x - 3)$
	c			

Factor each trinomial over the integers.

27 $x^2 + 6x + 5$
$(x + 5)(x + 1)$

28 $x^2 + 3x + 2$
$(x + 2)(x + 1)$

29 $x^2 + 6x + 8$
$(x + 4)(x + 2)$

30 $x^2 + 7x + 10$
$(x + 5)(x + 2)$

31 $x^2 - 9x + 20$
$(x - 5)(x - 4)$

32 $x^2 - 8x + 12$
$(x - 6)(x - 2)$

33 $x^2 - 2x - 15$
$(x - 5)(x + 3)$

34 $x^2 - 4x - 12$
$(x - 6)(x + 2)$

35 $x^2 - x - 6$
$(x - 3)(x + 2)$

36 $x^2 - x - 12$
$(x - 4)(x + 3)$

37 $x^2 + 3x - 28$
$(x + 7)(x - 4)$

38 $x^2 + 2x - 24$
$(x + 6)(x - 4)$

39 $x^2 + 5x - 36$
$(x + 9)(x - 4)$

40 $x^2 + 4x - 32$
$(x + 8)(x - 4)$

41 $x^2 + x - 20$
$(x + 5)(x + 4)$

42 $x^2 + x - 72$
$(x + 9)(x - 8)$

43 $x^2 - 22x + 40$
$(x - 20)(x - 2)$

44 $x^2 - 32x + 60$
$(x - 30)(x - 2)$

45 $x^2 - 3x - 10$
$(x - 5)(x + 2)$

46 $x^2 + 2x - 3$
$(x + 3)(x - 1)$

Problem Set C

Perfect-square trinomials were introduced in the C- problems, p. 242.

The previous section used the following patterns for writing perfect-square trinomials:

$$(x + c)^2 \qquad (x - c)^2$$
$$x^2 + 2cx + c^2 \qquad x^2 - 2cx + c^2$$

When factoring a trinomial, check to see if it is a perfect-square trinomial.

EXAMPLES

- $x^2 + 16x + 64$
  $(x + 8)(x + 8)$
  $(x + 8)^2$

- $9x^2 - 30xy + 25y^2$
  $(3x - 5y)(3x - 5y)$
  $(3x - 5y)^2$

Factor the following trinomials:

47 $a^2 + 10a + 25$
  $(a + 5)^2$

48 $x^2 - 12x + 36$
  $(x - 6)^2$

49 $4x^2 - 12x + 9$
  $(2x - 3)^2$

50 $49a^2 - 70a + 25$
  $(7a + 5)^2$

51 $25c^2 + 60cd + 36d^2$
  $(5c + 6d)^2$

52 $x^2 + x + \frac{1}{4}$
  $(x + \frac{1}{2})^2$

53 $121 - 22y + y^2$
  $(11 - y)^2$

54 $r^2 + 36s^2 + 12rs$
  $(r + 6s)^2$

55 $4x^2 + 2x + \frac{1}{4}$
  $(2x + \frac{1}{2})^2$

56 $9y^2 - 2y + \frac{1}{9}$
  $(3y - \frac{1}{3})^2$

57 $a^2x^2 + 2abx + b^2$
  $(ax + b)^2$

58 $r^2y^2 - 2rsy + s^2$
  $(ry - s)^2$

The techniques of this section are repeated, in detail, in Section 12.2.

Xtending the topic: Solving Quadratic Equations

When a trinomial is set equal to zero, the result is an example of a **quadratic equation**.

- $x^2 - 3x - 10 = 0$

Some quadratic equations can be solved by factoring the trinomial, and then using the following property: If the product of two expressions equals zero, then one (or both) of the expressions must equal zero.

Sample Problem

1   Solve for x: $x^2 - 3x - 10 = 0$

PROCEDURE

First, write the factors of the trinomial:

$$x^2 - 3x - 10 = 0$$
$$(x - 5)(x + 2) = 0$$

Since the product of $(x - 5)$ and $(x + 2)$ equals zero, at least one of those factors must equal zero:

$$x - 5 = 0 \quad or \quad x + 2 = 0$$
$$x = 5 \qquad\qquad x = -2$$

Check each factor:

$$\begin{array}{cc}
x^2 - 3x - 10 = 0 & x^2 - 3x - 10 = 0 \\
5^2 - 3 \cdot 5 - 10 \overset{?}{=} 0 & (-2)^2 - 3(-2) - 10 \overset{?}{=} 0 \\
25 - 15 - 10 \overset{?}{=} 0 & 4 + 6 - 10 \overset{?}{=} 0 \\
0 \overset{?}{=} 0 \checkmark & 0 \overset{?}{=} 0 \checkmark
\end{array}$$

Problem Set **X**

Solve each quadratic equation.

1 $x^2 - 13x + 36 = 0$
    $x = 9 \quad or \quad x = 4$

2 $x^2 - 13x + 22 = 0$
    $x = 11 \quad or \quad x = 2$

3 $x^2 - x - 30 = 0$
    $x = 6 \quad or \quad x = -5$

4 $x^2 + 4x - 12 = 0$
    $x = -6 \quad or \quad x = 2$

5 $y^2 + 7y - 8 = 0$
    $y = -8 \quad or \quad y = 1$

6 $z^2 - 10z + 16 = 0$
    $z = 8 \quad or \quad z = 2$

7 $w^2 - 2w + 1 = 0$
    $w = 1$

8 $v^2 + 16v - 36 = 0$
    $v = -18 \quad or \quad v = 2$

9 $r^2 - 2r = 3$
    $r = 3 \quad or \quad r = -1$

10 $s^2 + 9s + 10 = -4$
    $s = -7 \quad or \quad s = -2$

11 $m^2 - 20 = m$
    $m = 5 \quad or \quad m = -4$

12 $n^2 - 5n - 5 = 4n + 5$
    $n = 10 \quad or \quad n = -1$

13 $n^2 - 2n = 6 - n$
    $n = 3 \quad or \quad n = -2$

14 $4a^2 = 4a - 1$
    $a = \dfrac{1}{2}$

15 $m^2 + 10 = 46 + 35m$
    $m = 36 \quad or \quad m = -1$

16 $x^2 - 2x + 5 = 5$
    $x = 0 \quad or \quad x = 2$

Section 6.4 Factoring Binomials: $x^2 - c^2$

These three binomials have something in common:

$$x^2 - 9 \qquad y^2 - 1 \qquad 9a^4b^2 - 25$$

Each binomial is the difference of two terms, and each term is a square:

$$x^2 - 9 \quad \text{is} \quad (x)^2 - (3)^2$$
$$y^2 - 1 \quad \text{is} \quad (y)^2 - (1)^2$$
$$9a^4b^2 - 25 \quad \text{is} \quad (3a^2b)^2 - (5)^2$$

In general, a variable with an even exponent is a square. A binomial of the form $x^2 - c^2$ is called the **difference of two squares.**

Sample Problems

1 Factor: $x^2 - 9$

PROCEDURE Think of $x^2 - 9$ as the trinomial $x^2 + 0x - 9$, and find the factors of that trinomial.

$$x^2 + 0x - 9$$
$(x + \ )(x - \ )$ The last term is -9, so the signs must be $+$ and $-$.
$(x + 3)(x - 3)$ These factors give the middle term
$$-3x + 3x = 0x = 0.$$

Therefore $x^2 - 9$ can be factored as $(x + 3)(x - 3)$.

The expressions $x + 3$ and $x - 3$ are called **conjugates**. Similarly, the conjugate of $y - 7$ is $y + 7$, and the conjugate of $3r + 7s^2$ is $3r - 7s^2$.

2 Factor: $2y^2 - 2$

PROCEDURE Both terms in $2y^2 - 2$ have a common factor 2:

$$2y^2 - 2$$
$$2(y^2 - 1)$$

$$2(y + \ )(y - \ )$$
$$2(y + 1)(y - 1)$$

Therefore, $2y^2 - 2$ can be factored as $2(y + 1)(y - 1)$.

3 Factor: $9a^4b^2 - 25$

PROCEDURE $9a^4b^2 - 25$ can be written as $(3a^2b)^2 - (5)^2$, which is the difference of two squares. The difference of two squares can always be factored as conjugates:

$9a^4b^2 - 25$
$9a^4b^2 + 0 - 25$
$(3a^2b + \ )(3a^2b - \ )$ Factor the first term.
$(3a^2b + 5)(3a^2b - 5)$ Factor the last term.

To check the factoring, use the FOIL pattern:

$(3a^2b + 5)(3a^2b - 5)$
$9a^4b^2 - 15a^2b + 15a^2b - 25$
$9a^4b^2 + 0 - 25$
$9a^4b^2 - 25 ✓$

Problem Set **A**

ASSIGNMENT GUIDE

Basic (1 day)
5–25

Average (1 day)
6–24 (even), 32–40 (even)

Advanced (2 days)
(1) 6–24 (even), 32–41
(2) 42–47
253: 1–7

1 Why is $x^8 - 81$ called the difference of two squares?
$x^4 - 81 = (x^2)^2 - (9)^2$

2 The squares of the first three natural numbers are 1, 4, and 9. What are the squares of the next seven natural numbers?
16, 25, 36, 49, 64, 81, 100

3 When factoring the difference of two squares, what are the signs of the binomial factors?
$+, -$

4 After factoring the difference of two squares, how can you check to determine if you have the correct factors?
use FOIL

Factor:

5 $x^2 - 4$
$(x + 2)(x - 2)$

6 $y^2 - 36$
$(y + 6)(y - 6)$

7 $64 - a^2$
$(8 + a)(8 - a)$

8 $100 - c^2$
$(10 + c)(10 - c)$

9 $x^2 - 81$
$(x + 9)(x - 9)$

10 $t^2 - 16$
$(t + 4)(t - 4)$

11 $x^4 - 9y^2$
$(x^2 + 3y)(x^2 - 3y)$

12 $25a^2 - 49b^2$
$(5a + 7b)(5a - 7b)$

13 $k^2 - m^8$
$(k + m^4)(k - m^4)$

14 $x^{16} - y^6$
$(x^8 + y^3)(x^8 - y^3)$

15 a^2b^6 minus $100y^8$
$(ab^3 + 10y^4)(ab^3 - 10y^4)$

16 z^4a^{10} subtracted from $9x^2$
$(3x + z^2a^5)(3x - z^2a^5)$

17 subtract $(a^2)^2$ from b^2
$(b + a^2)(b - a^2)$

18 subtract $\left(\dfrac{1}{4}\right)^2$ from m^4
$(m^2 + \frac{1}{4})(m^2 - \frac{1}{4}) = (m^2 + \frac{1}{4})(m + \frac{1}{2})(m - \frac{1}{2})$

19 subtract 0.01 from x^6
$(x^3 + 0.1)(x^3 - 0.1)$

For each of the following, state why it is not the difference of two squares.

20 $y^5 - 36$
exponent of y is odd

23 $x^2y - z^4$
exponent of y is odd

21 $50 - x^2$
50 is not a perfect square

24 $a^4 - bc^2$
exponent of b is odd

22 $2 - y^2$
2 is not a perfect square

25 $x^3 - 16$
exponent of x is odd

Find each product. (Review: Section 6.2)

26 $(3x + 4)(3x + 2)$
$9x^2 + 18x + 8$

29 $(6x + 1)(2x - 3)$
$12x^2 - 16x - 3$

27 $(x - 7)(5x - 3)$
$5x^2 - 38x + 21$

30 $(3x - 4)(2x + 3)$
$6x^2 + x - 12$

28 $(4x - 5)(x - 2)$
$4x^2 - 13x + 10$

31 $(x - 5)(7x + 2)$
$7x^2 - 33x - 10$

Problem Set **B**

Factor completely. First remove any common factor.

32 $3x^2 - 12$
$3(x + 2)(x - 2)$

37 $y^2 - 36y^4$
$y^2(1 + 6y)(1 - 6y)$

33 $2x^2 - 18$
$2(x + 3)(x - 3)$

38 $2x^3 - 128x$
$2x(x + 8)(x - 8)$

34 $2y^2 - 50$
$2(y + 5)(y - 5)$

39 $3x^5 - 27x^3$
$3x^3(x + 3)(x - 3)$

35 $5x^2 - 245$
$5(x + 7)(x - 7)$

40 $9x^2 - 36$
$9(x + 4)(x - 4)$

36 $x^3 - 16x$
$x(x + 4)(x - 4)$

41 $4y^2 - 64$
$4(y + 4)(y - 4)$

Problem Set **C**

Factor each difference of two squares. Simplify each factor.

42 $(x + 3)^2 - 64$
$(x + 11)(x - 5)$

45 $(x - 1)^2 - (3x + 4)^2$
$(4x + 3)(-2x - 5)$

43 $(x - 2)^2 - 16$
$(x + 2)(x - 6)$

46 $4(y - 3)^2 - (9y + 6)^2$
$11y(-7y - 12)$

44 $49y^2 - (y + 5)^2$
$(8y + 5)(6y - 5)$

47 $(x^2 - 3x + 1)^2 - 16(x + 2)^2$
$(x^2 + x + 9)(x^2 - 7x - 7)$

X tending the topic: Factoring Special Sums and Differences

Consider the following products:

$$\begin{array}{r} x^2 + x + 1 \\ \underline{x - 1} \\ x^3 + x^2 + x \\ \underline{-x^2 - x - 1} \\ x^3 \qquad\qquad - 1 \end{array}$$

$$\begin{array}{r} x^2 - x + 1 \\ \underline{x + 1} \\ x^3 - x^2 + x \\ \underline{+ x^2 - x + 1} \\ x^3 \qquad\qquad + 1 \end{array}$$

Thus $x^3 - 1$ can be factored as $(x^2 + x + 1)(x - 1)$ and $x^3 + 1$ can be factored as $(x^2 - x + 1)(x + 1)$.

In general, the difference of 2 cubes, $x^3 - a^3$, can be factored as $(x^2 + ax + a^2)(x - a)$. The sum of two cubes, $x^3 + a^3$, can be factored as $(x^2 - ax + a^2)(x + a)$.

Problem Set X

1 Multiply $(x^2 + ax + a^2)(x - a)$ to show that the product is the difference of two cubes.

$x^3 - a^3$

2 Multiply $(x^2 - ax + a^2)(x + a)$ to show that the product is the sum of two cubes.

$x^3 + a^3$

3 Multiply:
   a $(x - 1)(x^3 + x^2 + x + 1)$
   b $(x - 1)(x^4 + x^3 + x^2 + x + 1)$

   a $x^4 - 1$ b $x^5 - 1$

4 Based on problem 3, what are the factors of $x^6 - 1$? Multiply them together to check them.

   $(x - 1)(x^5 + x^4 + x^3 + x^2 + x + 1)$

5 Multiply:
   a $(x + 1)(x^4 - x^3 + x^2 - x + 1)$
   b $(x + 1)(x^6 - x^5 + x^4 - x^3 + x^2 - x + 1)$

   a $x^5 + 1$ b $x^7 + 1$

6 Based on problem 5, what are the factors of $x^9 + 1$? Multiply them together to check them.

   $(x + 1)(x^8 - x^7 + x^6 - x^5 + x^4 - x^3 + x^2 - x + 1)$

7 Factor $x^{15} - 1$ and $x^{15} + 1$.

   $x^{15} - 1 = (x - 1)(x^{14} + x^{13} + x^{12} + x^{11} + x^{10} + x^9 + x^8 + x^7 + x^6 + x^5 + x^4 + x^3 + x^2 + x + 1)$

   $x^{15} + 1 = (x + 1)(x^{14} - x^{13} + x^{12} - x^{11} + x^{10} - x^9 + x^8 - x^7 + x^6 - x^5 + x^4 - x^3 + x^2 - x + 1)$

After-School Mathematics: Restaurant Tips

Eating out is a treat that almost everybody enjoys. People eat out to enjoy the food and also to enjoy the service. Waiters and waitresses are usually paid a salary below minimum wage, and they depend on tips for their livelihood.

Angela is a waitress at a pizza restaurant in her town. Her tips usually depend on her service and courtesy, and also on the people at her table.

She often tries to play a game and guess what her tip will be. For students on a tight budget, she usually guesses 10 percent of the bill. In her mind, she moves the decimal point one place to the left; for example, 10 percent of $11.00 is $1.10. For two people enjoying a date, she sometimes guesses 20 percent of the bill. To do that, she figures 10 percent and doubles it.

Some states with sales tax provide other ways to approximate a tip; for example, if the sales tax is 5%, triple the tax.

For most people she guesses 15 percent of the bill. If the check is for $28, first she finds 10 percent, or $2.80, then she takes half of that (which is 5 percent), or $1.40, and adds them: $4.20.

Application: Grains of Wheat

There is a well-known mathematical story that a king was once asked for "a modest reward" of one grain of wheat on the first square of a chessboard, 2 grains on the second square, 4 grains on the third square, 8 grains on the fourth square, and so on. The king was ready to grant the reward, but the court mathematician told the king that there was not enough wheat in the kingdom to satisfy the request!

The nth square of the chessboard would require 2^{n-1} grains; to fill all 64 squares would require $2^{64} - 1$ grains of wheat, which is 1.845×10^{19}. At 10^{14} grains per truck, $2^{64} - 1$ grains would require 184,468 trucks.

Suppose a grain of wheat is 0.1 mm across, and you have a truck 6.25 m long, 4 m wide, and 4 m high. Then each cubic meter holds 10^{12} grains of wheat and the entire truck holds a total of 10^{14} grains of wheat.

Ten thousand trucks would provide 10^{18} grains of wheat. That would be enough for the first fifty-nine squares of the chessboard. To fill all sixty-four squares would require more than 1.8×10^{19} grains of wheat. Almost two hundred thousand trucks would be needed to haul all that wheat!

Section 6.5   Factoring Trinomials: $ax^2 + bx + c$

SECTION SCHEDULE

Basic (2 days)

Average (1 day)

Advanced (1 day)

Maxine factored $3x^2 + 7x + 2$ as $(3x + 1)(x + 2)$.   To convince her friends she was right, she used the FOIL pattern to multiply the two binomials:

$(3x + 1)(x + 2)$
$3x^2 + 6x + x + 2$
$3x^2 + 7x + 2$

"But how did you find the binomials?" they asked. Maxine explained:

First   For the first term, $3x^2$, I wrote: $(3x\quad)(x\quad)$

Second   For the last term of the trinomial, $+2$, I listed all the possible pairs of factors of $+2$; they are $+2$ and $+1$ or -2 and -1.

Third   I tried the combinations to see which one gave $+7x$ as the middle term.

I tried:	FOIL	Middle term:
$(3x + 2)(x + 1)$	$3x^2 + 3x + 2x + 2$	$5x$
$(3x + 1)(x + 2)$	$3x^2 + 6x + \ x + 2$	$7x$
$(3x - 2)(x - 1)$	$3x^2 - 3x - 2x + 2$	$-5x$
$(3x - 1)(x - 2)$	$3x^2 - 6x - \ x + 2$	$-7x$

From all the pairs, $(3x + 1)(x + 2)$ gives the original trinomial.

Maxine could have saved a little time. She could have skipped the factors -2 and -1 because the middle term, $+7x$, is positive. Also, she could have stopped as soon as she found the combination that worked.

Sample Problems

1   Factor: $3x^2 + 8x + 5$

PROCEDURE   Fill in one part of the factors at a time.

$3x^2 + 8x + 5$
$(3x\quad)(x\quad)$ The factors of $3x^2$ must be $3x$ and x.
$(3x +\ )(x +\ )$ The middle and third terms are both positive.
$(3x + 5)(x + 1)$ The other choice, $(3x + 1)(x + 5)$,   would
                          result in $3x^2 + 16x + 5$,   which has the
                          wrong middle term.

2 Factor: $6x^2 - 7x - 5$

PROCEDURE List all the combinations for the factors of $6x^2$ and of -5 and start testing them:

$$\overbrace{}^{-7x\,?}$$

$$
\begin{array}{ll}
(6x + 5)(x - 1) = 6x^2 - 6x + 5x - 5 & \text{(No)} \\
(6x - 5)(x + 1) = 6x^2 + 6x - 5x - 5 & \text{(No)} \\
(6x + 1)(x - 5) = 6x^2 - 30x + x - 5 & \text{(No)} \\
(6x - 1)(x + 5) = 6x^2 + 30x - x - 5 & \text{(No)} \\
(3x + 5)(2x - 1) = 6x^2 - 3x + 10x - 5 & \text{(No)} \\
(3x - 5)(2x + 1) = 6x^2 + 3x - 10x - 5 & \text{(Yes)} \\
\left.\begin{array}{l}
(3x + 1)(2x - 5) \\
(3x - 1)(2x + 5)
\end{array}\right\} & \text{No need to keep testing}
\end{array}
$$

Thus $6x^2 - 7x - 5$ factors as $(3x - 5)(2x + 1)$.

ASSIGNMENT GUIDE

Basic (2 days)
(1) 5–15
(2) 18, 20, 22, 24–31

Average (1 day)
10–40 (even)

Advanced (1 day)
10–40 (even), 42–45

Problem Set **A**

1 To factor $12x^2 - 7x - 10$, the positive factors of $12x^2$ may be   __?__ and __?__ ,   __?__ and __?__ ,   or   __?__ and __?__ .

    $3x, 4x;\ 6x, 2x;\ 12x, x$

2 To factor $12x^2 - 7x - 10$, the factors of -10 may be _____?_____ (list all pairs).

    $5, -2;\ -5, 2;\ 10, -1;\ -10, 1$

3 When factoring a trinomial such as $6x^2 + 13x + 5$, find the factors of the term __?__ and the term __?__ .

    $6x^2, 5$

4 To check the factors of a trinomial, __?__ them using the FOIL pattern.

    multiply

Replace each __?__ by the correct expression.

5 $2x^2 + x - 6 = (2x \underline{\ \ ?\ \ })(x + 2)$
    -3

6 $5x^2 - 17x + 14 = (5x - 7)(x \underline{\ \ ?\ \ })$
    -2

7 $6x^2 + x - 5 = (6x - 5)(\underline{\ \ \ ?\ \ \ })$
    $x + 1$

8 $6x^2 - 13x - 5 = (\underline{\ \ \ ?\ \ \ })(3x + 1)$
    $2x - 5$

9 $3x^2 - 2x - 5 = (\underline{\ \ \ ?\ \ \ })(x + 1)$
    $3x - 5$

Factor each trinomial.

10 $2x^2 + 5x + 2$
$(2x+1)(x+2)$

11 $5x^2 + 11x + 2$
$(5x+1)(x+2)$

12 $3y^2 - 4y + 1$
$(3y-1)(y-1)$

13 $2x^2 - 11x + 5$
$(2x-1)(x-5)$

14 $7x^2 - 15x + 2$
$(7x-1)(x-2)$

15 $3x^2 - 8x + 5$
$(3x-5)(x-1)$

16 $5x^2 - 2x - 7$
$(5x-7)(x+2)$

17 $3x^2 + 20x - 7$
$(3x-1)(x+7)$

18 $7x^2 - 16x + 4$
$(7x-2)(x-2)$

19 $3x^2 + 8x + 4$
$(3x+2)(x+2)$

20 $6x^2 - x - 2$
$(3x-2)(2x+1)$

21 $10x^2 + 21x + 2$
$(10x+1)(x+2)$

22 $3x^2 + 4x - 15$
$(3x-5)(x+3)$

23 $2x^2 - 9x + 10$
$(2x-5)(x-2)$

Factor by removing the GCF. (Review: Section 4.7)

24 $9x - 33$
$3(3x-11)$

25 $10y + 15$
$5(2y+3)$

26 $12x^2 - 4$
$4(3x^2-1)$

27 $6 - 18a^3$
$6(1-3a^3)$

28 $x^3 - 4x^2 + 2x$
$x(x^2-4x+2)$

29 $4x^2y - 7xy^2$
$xy(4x-7y)$

30 $3x^3 - 9x + 3x^2$
$3x(x^2+x-3)$

31 $16a^4 - 24a^3$
$8a^3(2a-3)$

Problem Set **B**

Factor.

32 $6x^2 + 19x + 10$
$(3x+2)(2x+5)$

33 $8x^2 + 22x + 15$
$(4x+5)(2x+3)$

34 $6x^2 - 5x - 6$
$(3x+2)(2x-3)$

35 $12x^2 - x - 6$
$(4x-3)(3x+2)$

36 $16x^2 + 10x - 21$
$(8x-7)(2x+3)$

37 $10x^2 + 17x - 20$
$(5x-4)(2x+5)$

Factor completely. First, remove any GCF.

38 $4x^2 + 14x + 10$
$2(2x+5)(x+1)$

39 $9x^2 - 21x + 12$
$3(3x-4)(x-1)$

40 $4x^3 + 4x^2 - 15x$
$x(2x+5)(2x-3)$

41 $15x^2y - 13xy - 6y$
$y(5x-6)(3x+1)$

Problem Set C

This BASIC language computer program factors expressions of the form $x^2 + Bx + C$. Line 40 inputs values for the coefficient of x and for the constant term.

```
10   PRINT "THIS PROGRAM WILL FACTOR EXPRESSIONS ";
20   PRINT "OF THE FORM X^2 + B*X + C."
30   PRINT "ENTER VALUES FOR B AND C SEPARATED BY A COMMA."
40   INPUT B,C
50   FOR N = 1 TO ABS(INT(C/2))
60   IF C/N <> INT(C/N) THEN 200
70   IF C < 0 THEN 140
80   IF ABS(B) <> N + ABS(C/N) THEN 200
90   IF B < 0 THEN 120
100  PRINT "(X + "; N; ")(X + "; C/N; ")"
110  GO TO 220
120  PRINT "(X - "; N; ")(X - "; C/N; ")"
130  GO TO 220
140  IF ABS(B) <> ABS(C/N) - N THEN 200
150  IF B < 0 THEN 180
160  PRINT "(X + "; ABS(C/N); ")(X - "; N; ")"
170  GO TO 220
180  PRINT "(X - "; ABS(C/N); ")(X + "; N; ")"
190  GO TO 220
200  NEXT N
210  PRINT "X^2 + "; B; "*X + "; C; " CANNOT BE FACTORED."
220  END
```

Use the program to factor the following trinomials:

42 $x^2 + 9x + 20$; $B = 9$, $C = 20$

   $(x + 5)(x + 4)$

43 $x^2 - 16$; $B = 0$, $C = -16$

   $(x - 4)(x + 4)$

44 $x^2 - 2x + 3$; $B = -2$, $C = 3$

   cannot be factored

45 $x^2 + 14x - 576$; $B = 14$, $C = -576$

   cannot be factored

As a challenge, can you expand the program to factor an expression of the form $Ax^2 + Bx + C$?

Section 6.6   Mixed Factoring

SECTION SCHEDULE

Basic (2 days)

Average (2 days)

Advanced (2 days)

This chapter treated three types of factoring situations:

   common factors   the difference of two squares   trinomials

Examine the factoring problem for clues. For an expression with any number of terms, look for a common factor. If the expression has two terms, check whether the expression is the difference of two squares. If the expression has three terms, try to find the factors of the trinomial.

Sample Problems

1   Factor: $x^4 - y^4$

   PROCEDURE   There is no common factor (other than 1), but the expression is the difference of two squares. (There are two terms, the exponents are even, the operation is subtraction.)

$$x^4 - y^4$$
$$(x^2 + y^2)(x^2 - y^2)$$
$$(x^2 + y^2)(x + y)(x - y)$$

   Thus $x^4 - y^4$ factors as $(x^2 + y^2)(x + y)(x - y)$.

2   Factor: $14b^3 - 53b^2 + 14b$

   PROCEDURE   Each term has b as common factor:

$$14b^3 - 53b^2 + 14b$$
$$b(14b^2 - 53b + 14)$$

   Now try to factor the trinomial $14b^2 - 53b + 14$. For the factors of $14b^2$, try $14b$ and b or $7b$ and $2b$.

$$b(7b - 2)(2b - 7)$$

   To check, multiply the three factors:

$$b(7b - 2)(2b - 7)$$
$$(7b^2 - 2b)(2b - 7)$$
$$14b^3 - 49b^2 - 4b^2 + 14b$$
$$14b^3 - 53b^2 + 14b \checkmark$$

3 Factor: $12t^2 - 27s^2$

PROCEDURE Start by taking out the common factor:

$$12t^2 - 27s^2$$
$$3(4t^2 - 9s^2)$$

Note that $4t^2 - 9s^2$ is the difference of two squares:

$$3(2t + 3s)(2t - 3s)$$

ASSIGNMENT GUIDE

Basic (2 days)
(1) 3–22
(2) 23–42

Average (2 days)
(1) 4–42 (even)
(2) 43–57

Advanced (2 days)
(1) 24–56 (even)
(2) 59–63
    262: 1–6

Problem Set A

1 For any factoring problem, first check whether the terms have a(n) __?__ __?__ .
    common factor (other than 1)

2 If an expression has __?__ terms, check whether it is the difference of two squares.
    two

For problems 3–22, write the GCF of the terms in each expression. (If the GCF is 1, write 1.)

3 $3m^2 - 9mn$
    $3m$

4 $7x^2 + 7x + 7$
    7

5 $x^2 - 81$
    1

6 $9y^2 - 63$
    9

7 $6a^2 - 15a + 18$
    3

8 $x^2 - 3x - 10$
    1

9 $4x^2 - 9y^2$
    1

10 $36y - 6x^2y$
    $6y$

11 $2x^2 + 10x + 2$
    2

12 $x^2 + 3x - 28$
    1

13 $x^4 - 9x^3$
    x^3

14 $3w^2y + 12y$
    $3y$

15 $49a^2 - 100b^2$
    1

16 $1 - a^4b^2$
    1

17 $9x^2 - 12x + 4$
    1

18 $10a^2 + 29a + 10$
    1

19 $64y - 36x^2y$
    $4y$

20 $2x^2 + 8x + 8$
    2

21 $45x^2 + 60x + 20$
    5

22 $4t^2 - 16s^2$
    4

For problems **23–42**, factor each expression in problems 3–22.

Solve each problem. (Review: Chapter 4, Chapter 5)

43 Find a number x such that the square of $(x + 3)$ is equal to the square of $(x + 5)$.

$x = -4$

44 During "rush hour" it takes Otis two hours to get into the city. On a Saturday, however, he can travel ten miles per hour faster and get there in an hour and a half. What is his average speed during "rush hour"?

30 m/h

45 Find two consecutive odd integers such that the first plus four times the second is one hundred twenty-three.

23, 25

23) $3m(m-3n)$
24) $7(x^2+x+1)$
25) $(x-9)(x+9)$
26) $9(y^2-7)$
27) $3(2a^2-5a+6)$
28) $(x-5)(x+2)$
29) $(2x-3y)(2x+3y)$
30) $6y(6-x^2)$
31) $2(x^2+5x+1)$
32) $(x+7)(x-4)$
33) $x^3(x-9)$
34) $3y(w^2+4)$
35) $(7a-10b)(7a+10b)$
36) $(1-a^2b)(1+a^2b)$
37) $(3x-2)(3x-2)$
38) $(5a+2)(2a+5)$
39) $4y(4+3x)(4-3x)$
40) $2(x+2)(x+2)$
41) $5(3x+2)(3x+2)$
42) $4(t-2s)(t+2s)$

Problem Set B

Factor each expression.

46 $x^8 - y^8$
$(x^4+y^4)(x^2+y^2)(x+y)(x-y)$

47 $6a^2 + ab - b^2$
$(3a-b)(2a+b)$

48 $48x^2 - 74x + 21$
$(6x-7)(8x-3)$

49 $20x^2 - 53x + 18$
$(4x-9)(5x-2)$

50 $2x^2y + 8y$
$2y(x^2+4)$

51 $7x^2y - 7y$
$7y(x-1)(x+1)$

52 $3x^2b + 6xb + 3b$
$3b(x+1)(x+1)$

53 $36y^2 - 6y - 20$
$2(6y-5)(3y+2)$

54 $225a^{10}b^2 - 144b^2$
$9b^2(5a^5-4)(5a^5+4)$

55 $x^4 - 16y^4$
$(x^2+4y^2)(x+2y)(x-2y)$

56 $6x^2y + 12xy + 15y$
$3y(2x^2+4x+5)$

57 $18a^4 + 7a^2b - b^2$
$(2a^2+b)(9a^2-b)$

Problem Set C

Find the GCF for each pair of polynomials. (Problem 58 is done as an example.)

58 $9x^2 + 6x + 1$; $9x^2 - 1$

PROCEDURE   First, factor each polynomial:

$$9x^2 + 6x + 1 = (3x + 1)(3x + 1) = (3x + 1)^2$$
$$9x^2 - 1 = (3x + 1)(3x - 1)$$

The GCF is $3x + 1$ since $3x + 1$ appears as a factor in both polynomials.

59 $9t^2 + 42t + 49$; $12t^2 + 7t - 49$
$3t + 7$

60 $4a^2 - 25$; $8a^2 + 14a - 15$
$2a + 5$

61 $35x^2 - 19x - 42$; $21x^2 - 31x - 42$
$7x + 6$

62 $8x^3 - 20x^2$; $4x^3 - 12x^2 + 5x$
$2x - 5$

63 $12y^2 + 27y + 6$; $12y^4 - 48y^2$
$3(y + 2)$

X tending the topic: Factoring by Grouping

Sometimes the terms of a polynomial can be rearranged and grouped in order to determine the factors of the polynomial.

EXAMPLES

1) $(x^2 + 6x + 9) - y^2$
$(x + 3)^2 - y^2$
$(x + 3 + y)(x + 3 - y)$

2) $4x^3 - 6x^2 + 10x - 15$
$2x^2(2x - 3) + 5(2x - 3)$
$(2x^2 + 5)(2x - 3)$

3) $a^2b^3 - b^3 + 5a^2 - 5$
$b^3(a^2 - 1) + 5(a^2 - 1)$
$(b^3 + 5)(a^2 - 1)$
$(b^3 + 5)(a + 1)(a - 1)$

4) $16x^3 + 4x^2 - 20x - 5$
$4x^2(4x + 1) - 5(4x + 1)$
$(4x^2 - 5)(4x + 1)$

5) $25a^2 - 9 + 10ab + 6b$
$(5a)^2 - (3)^2 + 10ab + 6b$
$(5a - 3)(5a + 3)$
$\qquad\qquad + 2b(5a + 3)$
$(5a - 3 + 2b)(5a + 3)$

6) $m^2 + 6mn + 9n^2$
$(m + 3n)(m + 3n)$
$(m + 3n)^2$

■ $\qquad 6x^3 + 10x^2 - 9x - 15$
$(6x^3 + 10x^2) + (-9x - 15)$
$2x^2(3x + 5) - 3(3x + 5)$
$(2x^2 - 3)(3x + 5)$

■ $\qquad x^2 - y^2 - 10x + 25$
$(x^2 - 10x + 25) - y^2$
$(x - 5)(x - 5) - y^2$
$(x - 5)^2 - y^2$
$(x - 5 - y)(x - 5 + y)$

Problem Set X

Factor each expression:

1 $x^2 + 6x + 9 - y^2$
$(x + 3 - y)(x + 3 + y)$

2 $4x^3 + 10x - 6x^2 - 15$
$(2x - 3)(2x^2 + 5)$

3 $a^2b^3 - b^3 + 5a^2 - 5$
$(b^3 + 5)(a + 1)(a - 1)$

4 $16x^3 - 5 - 20x + 4x^2$
$(4x^2 - 5)(4x + 1)$

5 $25a^2 - 9 + 10ab + 6b$
$(5a + 3)(5a - 3 + 2b)$

6 $m^2 + 3mn + 3mn + 9n^2$
$(m + 3n)(m + 3n)$

Chapter Study Guide

Skills

As you study and review this chapter, be sure that you build the useful algebraic skills including:

ASSIGNMENT GUIDE

Basic (4 days)
(1) 266: 1–20
(2) 246: 15–20
    257: 16, 17, 19
    266: 21–29
(3) 304: 1–8, 10–27
(4) 306: 28, 31–33,
    38–51

Average (1 day)
266: 1–29

Advanced (1 day)
261: 47–57 (odd)
266: 1–29

1 Finding the product of two binomials

Find the product $(3y + 1)(y - 5)$ using:

a the Distributive Property   **b** the vertical form   **c** the FOIL pattern

PROCEDURE

The assignment for Basic courses includes material from Cumulative Review 1–7 as part of the midyear review.

a The Distributive Property states that:

$$(b + c)(a) = (b)(a) + (c)(a)$$
$$(3y + 1)(y - 5) = (3y)(y - 5) + (1)(y - 5)$$
$$= 3y^2 - 15y + y - 5$$
$$= 3y^2 - 14y - 5$$

b
$$\begin{array}{r} 3y + 1 \\ \underline{y - 5} \\ 3y^2 + 1y \\ \underline{-15y - 5} \\ 3y^2 - 14y - 5 \end{array}$$

c $(3y + 1)(y - 5) = 3y^2 - 15y + y - 5$
$$= 3y^2 - 14y - 5$$

2 Factoring trinomials   Factor each trinomial:

a $z^2 - 2z - 15$
b $2y^2 + 5y - 3$
c $x^2 - 4x - 3$

PROCEDURE   Set up each problem, and fill in a part at a time.

    a $z^2 - 2z - 15$

        $(z \quad)(z \quad)$ Factors of -15 must be $+5$ and -3
                     or -5 and $+3$.
        $(z - 5)(z + 3)$ *Checking* by FOIL, this product is
                     $z^2 - 2z - 15$ ✓

b $2y^2 + 5y - 3$

$(2y \quad)(y \quad)$ Factors of -3 must be $+3$ and -1
                             or -3 and $+1$.

$(2y - 1)(y + 3)$ This product *checks*:

$$(2y - 1)(y + 3) = 2y^2 + 6y - y - 3$$
$$= 2y^2 + 5y - 3 \checkmark$$

The other possibilities do not check:

$$(2y + 1)(y - 3) = 2y^2 - 5y - 3$$
$$(2y + 3)(y - 1) = 2y^2 + \quad y - 3$$
$$(2y - 3)(y + 1) = 2y^2 - \quad y - 3$$

c $x^2 - 4x - 3$

$(x \quad)(x \quad)$

The factors of -3 are $+3$ and -1 or -3 and $+1$. Try all the possibilities:

$$(x + 3)(x - 1) = x^2 + 2x - 1$$
$$(x - 3)(x + 1) = x^2 - 2x - 1$$
$(x - 1)(x + 3)$ These two are the same as the two
$(x + 1)(x - 3)$ others.

Thus $x^2 - 4x - 3$ cannot be factored over the integers.

3 **Factoring out a GCF, Factoring the difference of two squares**
Factor each expression:

a $4y^2 + 10y - 6$ **b** $4w^2 - 81$

PROCEDURE

a Each term in the trinomial has a common factor:

$$4y^2 + 10y - 6$$
$$2(2y^2 + 5y - 3)$$
$$2(2y - 1)(y + 3)$$

b The expression $4w^2 - 81$ is the difference of two squares. It is factored as the product of two conjugates.

$4w^2 - 81$ *Check* using FOIL:
$(2w)^2 - (9)^2$
$(2w + 9)(2w - 9)$ $(2w + 9)(2w - 9)$
                        $4w^2 - 18w + 18w - 81$
                        $4w^2 - 81 \checkmark$

4   Solving verbal problems   Find a number such that the square of the number equals the square of two more than the number.

PROCEDURE   Let n represent the number. Then "two more than the number" is $n + 2$. Translate the sentence to an equation and solve it:

$$\begin{array}{ll} \text{equation:} & n^2 = (n + 2)^2 \\ \text{use FOIL:} & n^2 = n^2 + 4n + 4 \\ \text{SUB } n^2: & 0 = 4n + 4 \\ \text{SUB 4:} & -4 = 4n \\ \text{MULTBY } \frac{1}{4}: & -1 = n \end{array}$$

The number is -1.

Math History: Diophantus and Algebraic Notation

The title "the grandparent of algebra" is usually given to the Greek mathematician Diophantus, who lived in Alexandria, Egypt, during the third century B.C. The part of his work that survives is a collection of problems for which Diophantus gives a solution. The solutions use a notation that is a forerunner of modern algebraic notation.

Diophantus used letters to indicate variables, but he did not use exponents to show powers. The square of a variable was represented by a letter, such as S. A cube was shown by another letter, such as C. Diophantus would write $C\ S2\ x3$ to indicate the polynomial that we write as $x^3 + 2x^2 + 3x$. For positive numbers, he used a letter such as u. Negative numbers were placed at the end, preceded with a letter such as M, which meant that everything after M was to be subtracted. Therefore, a polynomial such as $2x^2 - 3x + 5$ would be written as $S2\ u5\ M\ x3$.

Diophantus used his notation to translate verbal problems into equations. He organized the equations into categories, and showed how to solve the different categories.

Chapter Test

In each product, one term is incorrect. Rewrite the product with the correct term.

1 $(x - 6)(x - 2) = x^2 + 8x + 12$
  $x^2 - 8x + 12$

2 $(2x - 3)(5x + 1) = 10x^2 - 13x + 3$
  $10x^2 - 13x - 3$

3 $(3x - 2)^2 = 3x^2 - 12x + 4$
  $9x^2 - 12x + 4$

Use the vertical form to find each product.

4 $(x - 3)(2x + 5)$
  $2x^2 - x - 15$

5 $(2x - 3y)^2$
  $4x^2 - 12xy + 9y^2$

6 $(x + 7)(x - 7)$
  $x^2 - 49$

7 $(x + 5)(3x^2 + 4x - 5)$
  $3x^3 + 19x^2 + 15x - 25$

8 $(2x - 1)(x^2 - 5x + 2)$
  $2x^3 - 11x^2 + 9x - 2$

9 $(x^2 - 6x + 5)^2$
  $x^4 - 12x^3 + 46x^2 - 60x + 25$

Use the FOIL pattern to find each product.

10 $(x + 3)(x - 7)$
  $x^2 - 4x - 21$

11 $(2x - 5)^2$
  $4x^2 - 20x + 25$

12 $(2x + 1)(3x - 2)$
  $6x^2 - x - 2$

13 $(3a^2 + 5)(3a^2 - 5)$
  $9a^4 - 25$

14 $(2y^2 + 1)(y + 3)$
  $2y^3 + 6y^2 + y + 3$

15 $(2x - 5)(x + 8)$
  $2x^2 + 11x - 40$

Factor completely. First remove any GCF.

16 $x^2 - 7x - 18$
  $(x - 9)(x + 2)$

17 $x^2 - 64$
  $(x - 8)(x + 8)$

18 $x^2 - 12x + 36$
  $(x - 6)(x - 6)$

19 $2y^2 - 5y + 3$
  $(2y - 3)(y - 1)$

20 $16 - 49y^2$
  $(4 - 7y)(4 + 7y)$

21 $z^4 + z^2 - 12$
  $(z^2 - 3)(z^2 + 4)$

22 $5x^2 - 125$
  $5(x - 5)(x + 5)$

23 $4x^2 + 15x + 14$
  $(4x + 7)(x + 2)$

24 $2y^2 - 8$
  $2(y - 2)(y + 2)$

25 $3z^2 + 30z + 72$
  $3(z + 6)(z + 4)$

26 $4x^3 - 32x^2 + 60x$
  $4x(x - 3)(x - 5)$

27 $20a^4 + 20a^3 - 15a^2$
  $5a^2(2a + 3)(2a - 1)$

28 $18r^3 - r^4 - 81r^2$
  $-r^2(r - 9)(r - 9)$

29 $a^4 - 16$
  $(a^2 + 4)(a - 2)(a + 2)$

Problem Set: "Computer Talk"

Students who have transferred at midyear from other textbooks can use this Problem Set to learn about "computer talk."

This text introduced a notation, called "Computer Talk," to analyze variable expressions.

> ADD 7 (12)   means "start with 12, add 7." The result is 19.
> MULTBY $\frac{1}{3}$ (36)   means "start with 36, multiply by $\frac{1}{3}$." The result is 12.
> ADD -5 $(n + 5)$ means "start with $n + 5$, add -5." The result is n.

Evaluate each expression.

1 ADD 7 (15)
22

4 MULTBY $\frac{1}{2}$ (12)
6

7 MULTBY -2 $(-\frac{1}{2}x)$
x

2 ADD 7 (-15)
-8

5 ADD -6 (6)
0

8 ADD 5 $(n - 5)$
n

3 MULTBY 6 (5)
30

6 MULTBY $\frac{5}{3}$ $(\frac{3}{5})$
1

9 ADD -2 $(3x + 2)$
$3x$

An important use of the notation is to describe how to isolate a variable in a variable expression. Write the "Computer Talk" expression that will isolate each variable.

10 $a - 7$
ADD 7 $(a-7)$

13 $x \div 10$
MULTBY 10 $(x \div 10)$

16 rst (isolate t)
MULTBY $\frac{1}{rs}$ (rst)

11 $5b$
MULTBY $\frac{1}{5}$ $(5b)$

14 $-7 + y$
ADD 7 $(-7+y)$

17 $\frac{1}{2}gt^2$ (isolate g)
MULTBY $\frac{2}{t^2}$ $(\frac{1}{2}gt^2)$

12 $8 + c$
ADD -8 $(8+c)$

15 $-3z$
MULTBY $-\frac{1}{3}$ $(-3z)$

18 $a + (n - 1)d$ (isolate d)
ADD $-a$ $(a +(n-1)d)$
MULTBY $\frac{1}{n-1}$ $((n-1)d)$

"Isolating a variable" is another way to describe how to solve an equation. Describe the step(s) in solving each equation.

19 $x - 7 = -3$
ADD 7: $x = 4$

24 $2x + 3 = 5x - 2$
$2x + 3 = 5x - 2$
$2x = 5x - 5$
$-3x = -5$
$x = \frac{5}{3}$

20 $4y = 1$
MULTBY $\frac{1}{4}$: $y = \frac{1}{4}$

25 $4 + 7y = y - 4$
$4 + 7y = y - 4$
$7y = y - 8$
$6y = -8$
$y = -\frac{4}{3}$

21 $\frac{3}{5}z + 7 = 10$
ADD -7: $\frac{3}{5}z = 3$
MULTBY $\frac{5}{3}$: $z = 5$

26 $d = rt$ (solve for r)
$\frac{d}{t} = r$

22 $-a + 5 = 12$
ADD -5: $-a = 7$
MULTBY -1: $a = -7$

27 $p = 2l + 2w$ (solve for w)
$p = 2\ell + 2w$
$p - 2\ell = 2w$
$\frac{p - 2\ell}{2} = w$

23 $\frac{1}{2}(b + 7) = 11$
MULTBY 2: $b + 7 = 22$
ADD -7: $b = 15$

28 $A = \frac{1}{2}h(B + b)$ (solve for b)
$A = \frac{1}{2}h(B + b)$
$\frac{2A}{h} = B + b$
$\frac{2A - hB}{h} = b$

Chapter 7

ALGEBRAIC FRACTIONS

CHAPTER SCHEDULE

Basic
Problem Sets   8 Days
Review   2 Days
Test   2 Days

Average
Problem Sets   9 Days
Review   3 Days
Test   2 Days

Advanced
Problem Sets   8 Days
Review   2 Days
Test   1 Day

The Chapter Schedule assumes that Average courses will reach their midyear review after this chapter.

Many of the operations on rational expressions (addition, multiplication, etc.) are similar to operations on common fractions.

Section 7.1   Simplifying Fractions

Common fractions can be written in many equivalent forms. **Equivalent fractions** are fractions equal to the same number. For example, $\frac{6}{9}$, $\frac{10}{15}$, and $\frac{-2}{-3}$ are all equivalent fractions because each one equals $\frac{2}{3}$.

Using equivalent fractions involves the **Multiplicative Property of One**:

Property

The MULTIPLICATIVE PROPERTY OF ONE is that if p is any non-zero number and a is any number, then:

$$\frac{p}{p} = 1 \quad \text{and} \quad a \cdot \frac{p}{p} = a$$

SECTION SCHEDULE

Basic ($1\frac{1}{2}$ days)

Average ($1\frac{1}{2}$ days)

Advanced (1 day)

EXAMPLES

The Multiplicative Property of One (or, more simply, the Property of 1) is used to **reduce** a fraction to lower terms:

$$\frac{12}{30} = \frac{2 \cdot 6}{5 \cdot 6} = \frac{2}{5} \cdot \frac{6}{6}$$
$$= \frac{2}{5} \cdot 1$$
$$= \frac{2}{5}$$

The Property of One is used in this chapter to reduce (or "cancel") and to find common denominators. It will also be used in Chapter 11 to simplify radical expressions.

The Property of 1 is also used to **raise** fractions to higher terms:

- $$\frac{1}{6} + \frac{2}{9} = \frac{1}{6} \cdot \frac{3}{3} + \frac{2}{9} \cdot \frac{2}{2}$$
$$= \frac{3}{18} + \frac{4}{18}$$
$$= \frac{7}{18}$$

Each of the following fractions is called an **algebraic fraction**:

$$\frac{6a^2}{4} \qquad \frac{2}{x+3} \qquad \frac{p+2}{p^2+3p+2}$$

An algebraic fraction may contain a variable in the numerator, in the denominator, or both. The Property of 1 can be used to reduce an algebraic fraction.

Sample Problems

1 Use the Property of 1 to reduce each algebraic fraction:

a $\dfrac{6a^2}{15ab}$
b $\dfrac{c^2 + cd}{c^2 - cd}$

PROCEDURE   Rewrite each fraction as a product of two fractions.

a $\dfrac{6a^2}{15ab} = \dfrac{3a \cdot 2a}{3a \cdot 5b} = \dfrac{3a}{3a} \cdot \dfrac{2a}{5b} = 1 \cdot \dfrac{2a}{5b} = \dfrac{2a}{5b}$

The original fraction was "reduced" by the factor $3a$, which is the greatest common factor (GCF) of the numerator and denominator.

b $\dfrac{c^2 + cd}{c^2 - cd} = \dfrac{c(c+d)}{c(c-d)}$
$$= \dfrac{c}{c} \cdot \dfrac{c+d}{c-d}$$
$$= 1 \cdot \dfrac{c+d}{c-d}$$
$$= \dfrac{c+d}{c-d}$$

2 Reduce each algebraic fraction:

a $\dfrac{p+2}{p^2+3p+2}$
b $\dfrac{24x^5 + 6x^4 - 9x^3}{3x^3}$

PROCEDURE

a $\dfrac{p + 2}{p^2 + 3p + 2} = \dfrac{p + 2}{(p + 1)(p + 2)}$

$\qquad\qquad = \dfrac{1 \cdot (p + 2)}{(p + 1)(p + 2)}$

$\qquad\qquad = \dfrac{1}{p + 1} \cdot \dfrac{p + 2}{p + 2}$

$\qquad\qquad = \dfrac{1}{p + 1} \cdot 1$

$\qquad\qquad = \dfrac{1}{p + 1}$

b $\dfrac{24x^5 + 6x^4 - 9x^3}{3x^3} = \dfrac{3x^3(8x^2 + 2x - 3)}{3x^3}$

$\qquad\qquad = \dfrac{3x^3}{3x^3} \cdot \dfrac{8x^2 + 2x - 3}{1}$

$\qquad\qquad = 8x^2 + 2x - 3$

Each problem has a restriction on the variable because division by zero is not defined. In part **a**, p cannot equal -1 or -2. In part **b**, x cannot equal zero.

Problem Set A

ASSIGNMENT GUIDE

Basic ($1\frac{1}{2}$ days)
(1) 5–12, 17–24, 25–27,
  34–52 (even)
(2) See p. 276

Average ($1\frac{1}{2}$ days)
(1) 26–32 (even), 48–52,
  54, 56, 58–61
(2) See p. 276.

Advanced (1 day)
44–52 (even), 59–62,
64–72 (even)

In each of problems 1–12, state what values the variables cannot have.

1 $\dfrac{5a}{25}$

no restriction $\qquad \dfrac{a}{5}$

2 $\dfrac{15mn}{25n}$

$n \neq 0 \qquad \dfrac{3m}{5}$

3 $\dfrac{24a^3}{16a^4}$

$a \neq 0 \qquad \dfrac{3}{2a}$

4 $\dfrac{45x^3y}{15y^2}$

$y \neq 0 \qquad \dfrac{3x^3}{y}$

5 $\dfrac{d}{d^2}$

$d \neq 0 \qquad \dfrac{1}{d}$

6 $\dfrac{2a^3b^2}{6a^2b^2}$

$a \neq 0,\, b \neq 0 \qquad \dfrac{a}{3}$

7 $\dfrac{-x^2y^3}{x^3y^2}$

$x \neq 0,\, y \neq 0 \qquad \dfrac{-y}{x}$

8 $\dfrac{-9xy}{30x^2y}$

$x \neq 0,\, y \neq 0 \qquad \dfrac{-3}{10x}$

9 $\dfrac{-30a^2bc}{-18a^3c}$

$a \neq 0,\, c \neq 0 \qquad \dfrac{5b}{3a}$

10 $\dfrac{5(x + 7)}{8(x + 7)}$

$x \neq -7 \qquad \dfrac{5}{8}$

11 $\dfrac{3(a + b)}{(a + b)^2}$

$a \neq -b \qquad \dfrac{3}{a + b}$

12 $\dfrac{a(x + y)^2}{b(x - y)}$

$x \neq y \qquad \dfrac{a(x+y)^2}{b(x-y)}$

For problems **13–24**, reduce each fraction in problems 1–12.

Reduce each fraction in problems 25–33.

25 $\dfrac{2x^2 + 4x}{3ax + 6a}$
$\dfrac{2x}{3a}$

28 $\dfrac{5x^2 + 10x}{6xy + 12y}$
$\dfrac{5x}{6y}$

31 $\dfrac{a^2b - ab}{a^2b^2 + ab^2}$
$\dfrac{a - 1}{b(a+1)}$

26 $\dfrac{3m + 3n}{3m - 3n}$
$\dfrac{m + n}{m - n}$

29 $\dfrac{4a^2 - 1}{2ba + b}$
$\dfrac{2a - 1}{b}$

32 $\dfrac{x^2 - 9}{x^2 - 5x + 6}$
$\dfrac{x + 3}{x - 2}$

27 $\dfrac{3x - 6y}{9x + 12y}$
$\dfrac{x - 2y}{3x + 4y}$

30 $\dfrac{4a^2 - 1}{4a^2 - 4a + 1}$
$\dfrac{2a + 1}{2a - 1}$

33 $\dfrac{x^2 - 7x + 12}{x^2 - 16}$
$\dfrac{x - 3}{x + 4}$

Evaluate. (Review: Multiplication and division of common fractions)

These problems preview multiplication and division of algebraic fractions, Section 7.2.

34 $\dfrac{3}{4} \cdot \dfrac{5}{6}$
$\dfrac{5}{8}$

37 $\dfrac{5}{9} \cdot \dfrac{1}{8}$
$\dfrac{5}{72}$

40 $\dfrac{1}{8} \div \dfrac{5}{9}$
$\dfrac{9}{40}$

35 $\dfrac{3}{4} \div \dfrac{5}{9}$
$\dfrac{27}{20}$

38 $\dfrac{5}{9} \div \dfrac{1}{8}$
$\dfrac{40}{9}$

41 $\dfrac{1}{8} \cdot \dfrac{5}{9}$
$\dfrac{5}{72}$

36 $1\frac{3}{4} \div \frac{7}{8}$
2

39 $3\frac{1}{2} \cdot 2\frac{2}{5}$
$\dfrac{42}{5}$

42 $1\frac{1}{5} \div 4\frac{4}{5}$
$\dfrac{1}{4}$

Problem Set **B**

Reduce each fraction in problems 43–52.

43 $\dfrac{x^4 - 16}{x^4 + x^2 - 20}$
$\dfrac{x^2 + 4}{x^2 + 5}$

48 $\dfrac{2b^3 - 2b^2 - 4b}{3b^3 + 3b^2 - 18b}$
$\dfrac{2(b+1)}{3(b+3)}$

44 $\dfrac{3x - 21}{3x^2 - 15x - 42}$
$\dfrac{1}{x + 2}$

49 $\dfrac{x^2 - 25}{x^2 + 10x + 25}$
$\dfrac{x - 5}{x + 5}$

45 $\dfrac{9x^2 - 12x + 4}{9x^2 - 4}$
$\dfrac{3x - 2}{3x + 2}$

50 $\dfrac{2y^2 - 2y - 12}{y^3 - 5y^2 + 6y}$
$\dfrac{2(y+2)}{y(y-2)}$

46 $\dfrac{x^2 - 9x - 22}{3x - 33}$
$\dfrac{x + 2}{3}$

51 $\dfrac{a^2 + 1}{a + 1}$
$\dfrac{a^2 + 1}{a + 1}$

47 $\dfrac{2a^2 + 2a + 4}{4a^2 - 12a - 16}$
$\dfrac{a^2 + a + 2}{2(a^2 - 3a - 4)}$

52 $\dfrac{5m - 10}{m^2 + m - 6}$
$\dfrac{5}{m + 3}$

In problems 53–58, perform the indicated operations and write each answer in reduced terms.

53 $\dfrac{7}{12} - \dfrac{3}{8}$

$\dfrac{5}{24}$

54 $\dfrac{2}{3} \cdot \dfrac{3}{4}$

$\dfrac{1}{2}$

55 $\dfrac{5}{8} \cdot \dfrac{3}{4}$

$\dfrac{15}{32}$

56 $\dfrac{10}{11} \cdot \dfrac{22}{30}$

$\dfrac{2}{3}$

57 $\dfrac{7}{3} \cdot \dfrac{9}{14}$

$\dfrac{3}{2}$

58 $\dfrac{m^2}{n^2} \cdot \dfrac{n}{m^3}$

$\dfrac{1}{mn}$

59 Solve for the variable r: $\quad ar + 3r = 4b$

$r = \dfrac{4b}{a+3}$

60 Solve: $\quad 16 - (y - 5) = 20$

$y = 1$

61 If $a = 2bc + 1$, solve for c.

$c = \dfrac{a-1}{2b}$

Problem Set **C**

Reduce each fraction in problems 62–73.

62 $\dfrac{x^2 - 5x - 5y + xy}{(x - 5)(x^2 - y^2)}$

$\dfrac{1}{x-y}$

63 $\dfrac{(4k^2 + 4ky + y^2)(k^2 - y^2)}{(k + y)(4k^2 - 4ky + y^2)}$

$\dfrac{(2k+y)^2(k-y)}{(2k-y)^2}$

64 $\dfrac{1 - 216y^3}{1 - 36y^2}$

$\dfrac{1 + 6y + 36y^2}{1 + 6y}$

65 $\dfrac{6a^2 + a - 15}{6a^2 - 13a + 6}$

$\dfrac{3a+5}{3a-2}$

66 $\dfrac{3b^2 - 27}{24 - 11b + b^2}$

$\dfrac{3(b+3)}{b-8}$

67 $\dfrac{6t^2 - 24t + 24}{4t^2 - 16}$

$\dfrac{3(t-2)}{2(t+2)}$

68 $\dfrac{(2m^2 - m)(3m + 2)(10m^2 + 3m - 1)}{(5m^2 - m)(2m^2 - m - 1)(6m^2 + m - 2)}$

$\dfrac{1}{m-1}$

69 $\dfrac{(a^2 - a - 20)(a^2 - 9)(a^2 + 5a - 6)}{(a^2 - 36)(a^2 - 6a + 5)(a^2 + 7a + 12)}$

$\dfrac{a-3}{a-6}$

70 $\dfrac{(t^2 + 3t + 2)(t^2 - 5t + 6)}{(t^2 - 2t - 3)(t^2 - 4)}$

1

71 $\dfrac{(12r^2 + 5r - 2)(4r^2 - 1)}{(6r^2 - r - 2)(8r^2 - 6r + 1)}$

$\dfrac{2r+1}{2r-1}$

72 $\dfrac{(y^2 - 5y + 6)(y + 2)}{(2y - 6)(2y + 4)(y - 2)}$

$\dfrac{1}{4}$

73 $\dfrac{(3z - 9)(8z^2)(z + 3)}{(z^3 - 9z)(4z^2)}$

$\dfrac{6}{z}$

Project: Mental Multiplication

The Distributive Property can be used to multiply by a single digit.

- $39 \cdot 7 = (40 - 1) \cdot 7$
  $= 280 - 7$
  $= 273$

- $53 \cdot 8 = (50 + 3) \cdot 8$
  $= 400 + 24$
  $= 424$

1 Find the following products without using a pencil and paper (or a calculator!).

a $21 \cdot 9 = \underline{\quad ? \quad}$ **c** $19 \cdot 8 = \underline{\quad ? \quad}$ **e** $101 \cdot 6 = \underline{\quad ? \quad}$

b $28 \cdot 7 = \underline{\quad ? \quad}$ **d** $33 \cdot 5 = \underline{\quad ? \quad}$ **f** $27 \cdot 11 = \underline{\quad ? \quad}$

The product of two conjugates is the difference of two squares.

$$(x + a)(x - a) = x^2 - a^2$$

This property can be used for certain products:

- $21 \cdot 19 = (20 + 1)(20 - 1)$
  $= 20^2 - 1^2$
  $= 400 - 1$
  $= 399$

- $38 \cdot 42 = (40 - 2)(40 + 2)$
  $= 40^2 - 2^2$
  $= 1600 - 4$
  $= 1596$

2 Compute the following products mentally:

a $31 \cdot 29 = \underline{\quad ? \quad}$ **c** $101 \cdot 99 = \underline{\quad ? \quad}$ **e** $84 \cdot 96 = \underline{\quad ? \quad}$

b $39 \cdot 41 = \underline{\quad ? \quad}$ **d** $72 \cdot 68 = \underline{\quad ? \quad}$ **f** $55 \cdot 65 = \underline{\quad ? \quad}$

If the units digit of a number is 5, the square of the number can be found quickly. The number n can be written as $n = 10a + 5$. Then:

$$n^2 = (10a + 5)^2 = 100a^2 + 100a + 25$$
$$= 100a(a + 1) + 25$$
$$= (a)(a + 1)100 + 25$$

This pattern can be used to write the square of a number that ends with 5.

- $65 = 10 \cdot 6 + 5 \quad (a = 6)$
  $65^2 = 6 \cdot 7 \cdot 100 + 25$
  $= 4200 + 25$
  $= 4225$

- $35 = 10 \cdot 3 + 5 \quad (a = 3)$
  $35^2 = 3 \cdot 4 \cdot 100 + 25$
  $= 1200 + 25$
  $= 1225$

3 Use the pattern to find each square:

a $15^2 = \underline{\quad ? \quad}$ **c** $75^2 = \underline{\quad ? \quad}$ **e** $105^2 = \underline{\quad ? \quad}$

b $45^2 = \underline{\quad ? \quad}$ **d** $25^2 = \underline{\quad ? \quad}$ **f** $195^2 = \underline{\quad ? \quad}$

1a) $(20 + 1) \cdot 9 = 180 + 9$
$= 189$

b) $(30 - 2) \cdot 7 = 210 - 14$
$= 196$

c) $(20 - 1) \cdot 8 = 160 - 8$
$= 152$

d) $(30 + 3) \cdot 5 = 150 + 15$
$= 165$

e) $(100 + 1) \cdot 6 = 600 + 6$
$= 606$

f) $27 \cdot (10 + 1) = 270 + 27$
$= 297$

2a) $(30 + 1)(30 - 1)$
$= 900 - 1 = 899$

b) $(40 - 1)(40 + 1)$
$= 1600 - 1 = 1599$

c) $(100 + 1)(100 - 1)$
$= 10,000 - 1$
$= 9999$

d) $(70 + 2)(70 - 2)$
$= 4900 - 4 = 4896$

e) $(90 - 6)(90 + 6) = 8100 - 36$
$= 8064$

f) $(60 - 5)(60 + 5) = 3600 - 25$
$= 3575$

3a) $(a = 1)$ $1 \cdot 2 \cdot 100 + 25 = 225$

b) $(a = 4)$ $4 \cdot 5 \cdot 100 + 25 = 2025$

c) $(a = 7)$ $7 \cdot 8 \cdot 100 + 25 = 5625$

d) $(a = 2)$ $2 \cdot 3 \cdot 100 + 25 = 625$

e) $(a = 10)$ $10 \cdot 11 \cdot 100 + 25$
$= 11025$

f) $(a = 19)$ $19 \cdot 20 \cdot 100 + 25$
$= 38025$

Section 7.2 Multiplying and Dividing Algebraic Fractions

SECTION SCHEDULE

Basic ($1\frac{1}{2}$ days)

Average ($1\frac{1}{2}$ days)

Advanced (2 days)

Multiplying two algebraic fractions involves the same process as multiplying two common fractions. In both cases, multiply two fractions by multiplying the numerators and multiplying the denominators.

EXAMPLES

- $\dfrac{2}{5} \cdot \dfrac{3}{7}$

  $\dfrac{2 \cdot 3}{5 \cdot 7}$

  $\dfrac{6}{35}$

- $\dfrac{a + 3}{a - 2} \cdot \dfrac{a + 1}{a + 2}$

  $\dfrac{(a + 3)(a + 1)}{(a - 2)(a + 2)}$

  $\dfrac{a^2 + 4a + 3}{a^2 - 4}$

Dividing algebraic fractions also involves the same process as dividing common fractions. To divide by a fraction, multiply by the reciprocal of that fraction.

EXAMPLES

- $\dfrac{2}{5} \div \dfrac{3}{7}$

  $\dfrac{2}{5} \cdot \dfrac{7}{3}$

  $\dfrac{2 \cdot 7}{5 \cdot 3}$

  $\dfrac{14}{15}$

- $\dfrac{a + 3}{a - 2} \div \dfrac{a + 1}{a + 2}$

  $\dfrac{a + 3}{a - 2} \cdot \dfrac{a + 2}{a + 1}$

  $\dfrac{(a + 3)(a + 2)}{(a - 2)(a + 1)}$

  $\dfrac{a^2 + 5a + 6}{a^2 - a - 2}$

Sample Problem

1 Perform each operation and then reduce:

a $\dfrac{5a + 5b}{a - b} \cdot \dfrac{a + 2b}{a^2 + 2ab + b^2}$

b $\dfrac{5x}{9wy^2} \div \dfrac{15x^3}{18w^2y^3}$

PROCEDURE

a $$\frac{5a+5b}{a-b}\cdot\frac{a+2b}{a^2+2ab+b^2}$$

$$\frac{5(a+b)\cdot(a+2b)}{(a-b)\cdot(a+b)(a+b)}$$

$$\frac{(a+b)}{(a+b)}\cdot\frac{(5)(a+2b)}{(a-b)(a+b)}$$

$$\frac{5(a+2b)}{(a-b)(a+b)}$$

$$\frac{5a+10b}{a^2-b^2}$$

b $$\frac{5x}{9wy^2}\div\frac{15x^3}{18w^2y^3}$$

$$\frac{5x}{9wy^2}\cdot\frac{18w^2y^3}{15x^3}$$

$$\frac{(5x)(18w^2y^3)}{(9wy^2)(15x^3)}$$

$$\frac{5}{15}\cdot\frac{18}{9}\cdot\frac{x}{x^3}\cdot\frac{w^2}{w}\cdot\frac{y^3}{y^2}$$

$$\frac{1}{3}\cdot\frac{2}{1}\cdot\frac{1}{x^2}\cdot\frac{w}{1}\cdot\frac{y}{1}$$

$$\frac{2wy}{3x^2}$$

*Some teachers require students to list only those restrictions that would not be apparent in the reduced form. For example, in part **b** the restrictions **w** ≠ 0, **y** ≠ 0 are not apparent in the reduced form, but **x** ≠ 0 is apparent.*

There are restrictions on the variables so that no denominator equals zero. In part **a**, $a \neq b$ and $a \neq -b$. In part **b**, w, y, and x cannot equal zero.

ASSIGNMENT GUIDE

Basic (1½ days)
(1) 1–10
     272: 28–33
(2) 11–24, 36

Average (1½ days)
(1) 1–18
     272: 43–47
(2) 25–39

Advanced (2 days)
(1) 25–42
(2) 43–47
     279: 1–6

*As oral exercises, students can be asked for the restrictions on the variables. They should include, for example, that **x** ≠ 0 in problem 14 because **x** would be in the denominator.*

Problem Set **A**

Perform each operation and then reduce:

1 $\frac{a}{b}\cdot\frac{a^2}{b^2}$

  $\frac{a^3}{b^3}$

2 $\frac{2a}{15b}\cdot\frac{5b^2}{3a}$

  $\frac{2b}{9}$

3 $\frac{10ab}{11xy}\cdot\frac{22x}{30ab}$

  $\frac{2}{3y}$

4 $\frac{x^2-9}{y^2}\cdot\frac{y}{x+3}$

  $\frac{x-3}{y}$

5 $\frac{ax}{x+a}\cdot\frac{x+a}{xa}$

  1

6 $\frac{ax}{a+x}\cdot\frac{ax}{a-x}$

  $\frac{a^2x^2}{a^2-x^2}$

7 $\frac{5x^2a}{a(x+5)}\cdot\frac{x^2-5}{5x}$

  $\frac{x(x^2-5)}{x+5}$

8 $\frac{3\pi r^2}{4}\cdot\frac{2\pi r^2}{5}$

  $\frac{3\pi^2 r^2}{10}$

9 $\frac{m-4}{12}\cdot\frac{18}{m^2-4m}$

  $\frac{3}{2m}$

10 $\frac{3a-3b}{10ab}\cdot\frac{50a^2b^2}{a^2-b^2}$

  $\frac{15ab}{a+b}$

11 $\frac{x^2+5x}{x^2-16}\cdot\frac{x^2-4x}{x^2-25}$

  $\frac{x^2}{(x+4)(x-5)}$

12 $\frac{(x-5)^3}{x}\cdot\frac{x+5}{(x-5)^2}$

  $\frac{(x-5)(x+5)}{x}$

13 $\frac{3}{4}\div\frac{1}{4}$

  3

14 $\frac{x}{2}\div\frac{3x^2}{8}$

  $\frac{4}{3x}$

15 $5xy\div\frac{10x}{y}$

  $\frac{y^2}{2}$

16 $\frac{14a^2}{10b^2}\div\frac{21a^2}{15b^2}$

  1

17 $\frac{5a^2}{8ab}\div 15a$

  $\frac{1}{24ab}$

18 $\frac{5x}{12yz^2}\div\frac{15x^3}{18y^2z^2}$

  $\frac{y}{2x^2}$

Perform each division problem. (Review: "Long division")

19 $15\overline{)255}$
17

20 $13\overline{)1417}$
109

21 $13\overline{)200}$
$15\frac{5}{13}$

22 $11\overline{)959515}$
$87228\frac{7}{11}$

23 $17\overline{)29242}$
$1720\frac{2}{17}$

24 $21\overline{)47128}$
$2244\frac{4}{21}$

These problems preview division of polynomials, Section 7.3.

Problem Set **B**

25 $\dfrac{16 - m^2}{5m - 1} \cdot \dfrac{5m^2 - m}{16 - 8m + m^2}$
$\frac{m(4+m)}{4-m}$

26 $\dfrac{a^2 - 24 - 2a}{a^2 - 30 - a} \cdot \dfrac{a + 5}{a^2 - 16}$
$\frac{1}{a-4}$

27 $\dfrac{a^4 - b^4}{3a^2} \cdot \dfrac{a^2 + b^2}{a^2 - b^2}$
$\frac{(a^2+b^2)^2}{3a^2}$

28 $\dfrac{a^2 - 7a}{a^2 - 16} \div \dfrac{a^2 - 9}{a^2 - 7a - 12}$
$\frac{a(a-7)}{(a+4)(a+3)}$

29 $\dfrac{x^3 - 6x^2 + 8x}{5a} \div \dfrac{2x - 4}{10x - 40}$
$\frac{x(x-4)^2}{a}$

30 $\dfrac{x^2 + 10x + 21}{x^2 - 2x - 15} \div (x^2 + 2x - 35)$
$\frac{1}{(x-5)^2}$

Simplify each **complex** fraction in problems 31–34.

31 $\dfrac{\frac{3}{4}}{\frac{9}{8}}$ This expression means
$\frac{3}{4} \div \frac{9}{8}$ $\frac{2}{3}$

32 $\dfrac{9}{\frac{n^2 - 9}{9}}$
$\frac{81}{n^2 - 9}$

33 $\dfrac{\frac{x^2 - 16}{25 - y^2}}{\frac{x + 4}{5 + y}}$
$\frac{x-4}{5-y}$

34 $\dfrac{2\frac{1}{2} \cdot \frac{3}{5}}{1\frac{3}{4} \cdot \frac{2}{3}}$
$\frac{9}{7}$

Section 7.2X contains additional problems with complex fractions.

35 Express nine hundred eighty-seven thousand in scientific notation.
9.78×10^5

36 Find the GCF of each set.

a 720; 120; 525

b $8x^5$; $18x^3y$; $30x^2y^5$; $20x^4y^4$

c $3x^2 + 6x - 9$; $6x^2 - 6$; $12 - 8x - 4x^2$

a 15
b $2x^2$
c $x - 1$

37 Find five consecutive odd integers whose sum is negative one hundred ninety-five.
$-43, -41, -39, -37, -35$

7.2 *Multiplying and Dividing* **277**

Perform the operations and simplify.

38 $\dfrac{x^6 - y^6}{x^3 - y^3} \cdot \dfrac{15rs}{3r^2s^2}$

$\dfrac{5(x^3+y^3)}{rs}$

39 $\dfrac{x^3 - y^3}{x - y} \div (x^2 + xy + y^2)$

1

40 $\dfrac{x + a}{x^4 - a^4} \div \dfrac{(x + a)^2}{x^2 - a^2}$

$\dfrac{1}{(x^2+a^2)(x+a)}$

41 $\dfrac{\dfrac{3x^2}{5} - 2}{\dfrac{3x^2}{5} + 2}$

$\dfrac{3x^2 - 10}{3x^2 + 10}$

42 $\dfrac{\dfrac{a^3 - b^3}{a + b}}{\dfrac{a^2 - b^2}{a + b}}$

$\dfrac{a^2 + ab + b^2}{a + b}$

43 $\dfrac{\frac{5}{12} - \frac{5}{9}}{1 - \frac{7}{15}}$

$\dfrac{-25}{96}$

44 $\dfrac{1\frac{3}{5} + 2\frac{1}{8}}{2\frac{1}{3} - 1\frac{1}{5}} \div (2\frac{1}{3} \cdot 3\frac{4}{5})$

0.3706877

45 $\dfrac{m + 2}{m + 3} \div \dfrac{m^2 - 4}{m + 3}$

$\dfrac{1}{m - 2}$

46 $\dfrac{\dfrac{r^2 + s^2}{r^2 - s^2}}{\dfrac{r - s}{r + s} - \dfrac{r + s}{r - s}}$

$\dfrac{r^2 + s^2}{-4rs}$

47 $\dfrac{x - \dfrac{4}{x}}{x - 5 + \dfrac{6}{x}}$

$\dfrac{x + 2}{x + 3}$

44) $\dfrac{1\frac{3}{5} + 2\frac{1}{8}}{2\frac{1}{3} - 1\frac{1}{5}} \div (2\frac{1}{3} \cdot 3\frac{4}{5})$

$\dfrac{\frac{8}{5} + \frac{17}{8}}{\frac{7}{3} - \frac{6}{5}} \cdot \dfrac{1}{\frac{7}{3} \cdot \frac{19}{5}} \cdot \dfrac{120}{120}$

$\dfrac{8\cdot24 + 17\cdot15}{7\cdot40 - 6\cdot24} \cdot \dfrac{3\cdot5}{7\cdot19}$

$\dfrac{192 + 255}{280 - 144} \cdot \dfrac{15}{133}$

$\dfrac{447}{136} \cdot \dfrac{15}{133}$

$\dfrac{6705}{18088} \left(= \dfrac{3\cdot3\cdot5\cdot149}{7\cdot8\cdot17\cdot19} \right)$

X tending the topic: Simplifying Complex Fractions

The Multiplicative Property of One can sometimes be used to reduce a complex fraction to a simple fraction.

Sample Problem

1   Simplify: $\dfrac{\dfrac{x^2 - 4x + 3}{x^2 - 1}}{\dfrac{x^2 - 7x + 12}{(x + 1)^2}}$

PROCEDURE

$$\frac{\dfrac{x^2 - 4x + 3}{x^2 - 1}}{\dfrac{x^2 - 7x + 12}{(x + 1)^2}} = \frac{x^2 - 4x + 3}{x^2 - 1} \div \frac{x^2 - 7x + 12}{(x + 1)^2}$$

$$= \frac{x^2 - 4x + 3}{x^2 - 1} \cdot \frac{(x + 1)^2}{x^2 - 7x + 12}$$

$$= \frac{(x - 3)(x - 1)(x + 1)(x + 1)}{(x + 1)(x - 1)(x - 4)(x - 3)}$$

$$= \frac{(x - 3)(x - 1)(x + 1)}{(x - 3)(x - 1)(x + 1)} \cdot \frac{(x + 1)}{(x - 4)}$$

$$= \frac{x + 1}{x - 4}$$

The reduced form implies that x cannot equal 4. Other restrictions on x that are not clear from the reduced form are that $x \neq -1$, 1, or 3.

Problem Set **X**

Reduce each expression, and indicate the restrictions on x that are not clear from the reduced form.

1 $\dfrac{\dfrac{x^2 - y^2}{x^2 - 3xy + 2y^2} \cdot \dfrac{xy - 2y}{y^2 + xy}}{\dfrac{(x - y)^2}{x^2 - xy}}$

$\frac{x(x-2)}{(x-2y)(x-y)} \quad y \neq 0, -x$

2 $\dfrac{\dfrac{2x - 3y}{x^2 + 4xy + 4y^2} \cdot \dfrac{5x^2 + 10xy}{3xy - 3y^2}}{\dfrac{4x^2 - 9y^2}{4x^2 - 4y^2}}$

$\frac{20x(x+y)}{3y(x+2y)(2x+3y)} \quad y \neq 0, -\frac{1}{2}x, -\frac{2}{3}x$

3 $\dfrac{\dfrac{a^2 - b^2}{a^2} \cdot \dfrac{a + b}{a - b}}{\dfrac{a^2 - b^2}{ab}}$

$\frac{b(a+b)}{a(a-b)} \quad a \neq -b, b, 0; \, b \neq 0$

4 $\dfrac{\dfrac{x^3 y^3}{x^3 - xy^2}}{\dfrac{xyz}{x - y} \cdot \dfrac{xy + yz}{xy}}$

$\frac{x^2 y^2}{z(x+y)(x+z)} \quad x \neq 0, y, -y, -z; \, y \neq 0; \, z \neq 0$

5 $\dfrac{\dfrac{2b^3}{2a + b} \cdot \dfrac{12a + 3b}{2a^2 + ab}}{\dfrac{10a^2}{4a^2 + 4ab + b^2}}$

$\frac{3b^3(4a+b)}{5a^3} \quad a \neq 0, \frac{-b}{2}$

6 $\dfrac{\left(1 - \dfrac{6}{x} + \dfrac{9}{x^2}\right)\left(2 - \dfrac{6}{x + 3}\right)}{\dfrac{9 - x^2}{x}}$

$\frac{-2(x-3)}{(x+3)^2} \quad x \neq 0, 3, -3$

Section 7.3 Dividing Polynomials

The check for long division is to multiply the quotient and divisor, and then add the remainder:

$498 \stackrel{?}{=} 21 \cdot 23 + 15$
$498 \stackrel{?}{=} 483 + 15$
$498 \stackrel{?}{=} 498 \checkmark$

Students should see that this check and the check for polynomial division, p. 281, are similar.

The procedure of "long division" sometimes involves a remainder.

EXAMPLE

$$
\begin{array}{r}
21 \\
23\overline{)498} \\
46 \\
\hline
38 \\
23 \\
\hline
15
\end{array}
$$

$\dfrac{498}{23} = 21$, remainder 15

$= 21 + \dfrac{15}{23}$

A similar "long division" procedure can be used to divide polynomials. For example, to divide $x^2 + 10x + 25$ by $x + 3$:

Step 1

$$
\begin{array}{r}
x \\
x + 3\overline{)x^2 + 10x + 25}
\end{array}
$$

The "x" in $x + 3$ divides the x^2 term. The partial quotient, x, is written above the x term.

Step 2

$$
\begin{array}{r}
x \\
x + 3\overline{)x^2 + 10x + 25} \\
x^2 + 3x \\
\hline
7x + 25
\end{array}
$$

Multiply the partial quotient x and the divisor $x + 3$. Then subtract $x^2 + 3x$ from $x^2 + 10x + 25$.

Step 3

$$
\begin{array}{r}
x + 7 \\
x + 3\overline{)x^2 + 10x + 25} \\
x^2 + 3x \\
\hline
7x + 25 \\
7x + 21 \\
\hline
4
\end{array}
$$

The "x" in $x + 3$ divides $7x$; the partial quotient is 7. Multiply 7 and the divisor, and find the remainder.

For this problem, the quotient is $x + 7$ and there is a remainder 4. Another way to write the problem, quotient, and remainder is:

$$
\frac{x^2 + 10x + 25}{x + 3} = x + 7 + \frac{4}{x + 3}
$$

Sample Problems

1 Find $(x^2 + 2x - 36) \div (x + 7)$.

PROCEDURE

$$\begin{array}{r}
x - 5 \\
x + 7 \overline{) x^2 + 2x - 36} \\
\underline{x^2 + 7x} \\
-5x - 36 \\
\underline{-5x - 35} \\
-1
\end{array}$$

The quotient is $(x - 5)$ and the remainder is -1:

$$\frac{x^2 + 2x - 36}{x + 7} = x - 5 + \frac{-1}{x - 5}$$

To check the answer, multiply $(x - 5)$ and $(x + 7)$, and then add the remainder:

$$(x - 5)(x + 7) + (-1) = (x^2 + 2x - 35) + (-1)$$
$$= x^2 + 2x - 36$$

In this problem, the polynomial $x^2 + 2x - 36$ was divided by the polynomial $x + 7$. Notice that the degree of the polynomial $x + 7$ is less than the degree of $x^2 + 2x - 36$. This division process can be used to divide a polynomial by another polynomial of lower degree.

2 Divide $6a^3 + 5a^2 + 12$ by $2a + 3$.

PROCEDURE Rewrite $6a^3 + 5a^2 + 12$ as the equivalent polynomial $6a^3 + 5a^2 + 0a + 12$.

Students should realize that the dividend must be written in descending order, with a placeholder for each degree of the variable.

$$\begin{array}{r}
3a^2 - 2a + 3 \\
2a + 3 \overline{) 6a^3 + 5a^2 + 0a + 12} \\
\underline{6a^3 + 9a^2} \\
-4a^2 + 0a \\
\underline{-4a^2 - 6a} \\
6a + 12 \\
\underline{6a + 9} \\
3
\end{array}$$

The quotient is $3a^2 - 2a + 3$ and the remainder is 3. The division problem can also be written as:

$$\frac{6a^3 + 5a^2 + 12}{2a + 3} = 3a^2 - 2a + 3 + \frac{3}{2a + 3}$$

ASSIGNMENT GUIDE

Basic (1 day)
1–15

Average (1 day)
1–9, 16–25

Advanced (1 day)
2–8 (even), 16–22, 26–31

Problem Set A

Find each quotient.

1 $(x^2 - 8x + 7) \div (x - 1)$

$x - 1$

2 $(3x^2 + 4x - 15) \div (x - 5)$

$3x + 19 + \dfrac{80}{x - 5}$

3 $(a^2 - 4ab - 32b^2) \div (a - b)$

$a - 3b + \dfrac{-35b^2}{a - b}$

4 $(56 - 15x + x^2) \div (7 - x)$

$8 - x$

5 $(6x^2 - 11x - 10) \div (3x + 2)$

$2x - 5$

6 $\dfrac{a^3 + 64}{a + 4}$

$a^2 - 4a + 16$

7 $\dfrac{x^3 + 1}{x + 1}$

$x^2 - x + 1$

8 $\dfrac{x^3 - y^3}{x - y}$

$x^2 + xy + y^2$

9 $\dfrac{x^2 + 9x + 15}{x - 3}$

$x + 12 + \dfrac{51}{x - 3}$

Write the sum or difference of each pair of common fractions. (Review: Computation)

*These problems pre-
view adding algebraic
fractions with like
denominators,
Section 7.4.*

10 $\dfrac{3}{7} + \dfrac{2}{7}$

$\dfrac{5}{7}$

11 $\dfrac{4}{9} - \dfrac{8}{9}$

$\dfrac{-4}{9}$

12 $3\tfrac{1}{2} + 7\tfrac{1}{2}$

11

13 $-\dfrac{11}{13} - \dfrac{5}{13}$

$\dfrac{-16}{13}$

14 $-\dfrac{5}{2} + \dfrac{9}{2}$

2

15 $7\tfrac{2}{5} - 15\tfrac{1}{5}$

$-\dfrac{39}{5}$

Problem Set B

16 Solve: $3y + 5y - 7 = 4y$

$y = \dfrac{7}{4}$

17 Solve: $2(x - 9) = 7(4 - x) - 6(x + 2)$

$x = \dfrac{34}{15}$

18 Factor over the integers: $7x^3 - 21x^2 - 378x$

$7x(x - 9)(x + 6)$

19 Find the GCF: $4a^2 - 10a - 24$; $8a^2 + 20a + 12$; $32a^2 + 32a - 24$

$2(2a + 3)$

20 Show a factor tree for thirty-seven thousand eight hundred.

$2^3 \cdot 3^3 \cdot 5^2 \cdot 7$

Find each quotient.

21 $(a^2 - 3ab + b^2) \div (a - b)$

$a - 2b + \dfrac{-b^2}{a - b}$

22 $(a^4 - 3a - 2) \div (a^2 + a - 1)$

$a^2 - a + 2 - \dfrac{6a}{a^2 + a - 1}$

23 $(x^3 - 1) \div (x + 1)$

$x^2 - x + 1 + \dfrac{-2}{x + 1}$

24 $\dfrac{7x^3 - 6x + 8}{x + 2}$

$7x^2 - 14x + 22 + \dfrac{-36}{x + 2}$

25 $\dfrac{2y^4 - 3y^2 + 5}{y^2 - y - 2}$

$2y^2 + 2y + 3 + \dfrac{7y + 11}{y^2 - y - 2}$

Problem Set C

Find each quotient and remainder. Check your answers.

26 $\dfrac{16x^4 + 1}{2x + 1}$

$8x^3 - 4x^2 + 2x - 1 + \dfrac{2}{2x + 1}$

27 $\dfrac{64y^6 + 1}{2y + 1}$

$32y^5 - 16y^4 + 8y^3 - 4y^2 + 2y - 1 + \dfrac{2}{2y + 1}$

28 $\dfrac{x^4 - 16}{x - 2}$

$x^3 + 2x^2 + 4x + 8$

29 $\dfrac{8x^2 + 7x + 3x^3 + 5}{3x + 2}$

$x^2 + 2x + 1 + \dfrac{3}{3x + 2}$

30 $\dfrac{5x^5 - 3x^3 - x + 1}{x^3 - 2x^2 + 1}$

$5x^2 + 10x + 17 + \dfrac{29x^2 - 11x - 16}{x^3 - 2x^2 + 1}$

31 $\dfrac{6y^5 - 4y^4 - 2y^2 + 5}{y^2 + 3y - 1}$

$-4y^2 + 12y - 36 + \dfrac{108y - 31}{y^2 + 3y - 1}$

30) The divisor is
$x^3 - 2x^2 + 0x + 1$.
The steps of obtaining the quotient are:

$$
\begin{array}{r}
5x^2 + 10x + 17 \\
x^3 - 2x^2 + 0x + 1\overline{)5x^5 + 0x^4 - 3x^3 + 0x^2 - x + 1} \\
5x^5 - 10x^4 + 0x^3 + 5x^2 \\
\hline
10x^4 - 3x^3 - 5x^2 - x \\
10x^4 - 20x^3 + 0x^2 + 10x \\
\hline
17x^3 - 5x^2 - 11x + 1 \\
17x^3 - 34x^2 + 0x + 17 \\
\hline
29x^2 - 11x - 16
\end{array}
$$

Section 7.4   Adding and Subtracting Algebraic Fractions: Like Denominators

SECTION SCHEDULE

Basic (2 days)

Average (1 day)

Advanced ($\frac{1}{2}$ day)

The process for adding or subtracting algebraic fractions is similar to the process for common fractions. If the fractions have a common denominator, simply add or subtract the numerators.

EXAMPLES

▪ $\dfrac{7}{9} - \dfrac{5}{9}$

$\dfrac{7 - 5}{9}$

$\dfrac{2}{9}$

▪ $\dfrac{5a + 4}{a + 3} - \dfrac{2a + 3}{a + 3}$

$\dfrac{(5a + 4) - (2a + 3)}{a + 3}$

$\dfrac{5a + 4 - 2a - 3}{a + 3}$

$\dfrac{3a + 1}{a + 3}$

Sample Problems

1 Find: $\dfrac{3x}{2} - \dfrac{(x + 5)}{2}$

PROCEDURE

$$\frac{3x}{2} - \frac{(x+5)}{2} = \frac{3x - (x+5)}{2}$$
$$= \frac{3x - x - 5}{2}$$
$$= \frac{2x - 5}{2}$$

2 Find the difference and reduce to simplest form: $\dfrac{x^2}{x-3} - \dfrac{9}{x-3}$

PROCEDURE

$$\frac{x^2}{x-3} - \frac{9}{x-3} = \frac{x^2 - 9}{x-3}$$
$$= \frac{(x-3)(x+3)}{x-3}$$
$$= \frac{x-3}{x-3} \cdot \frac{x+3}{1}$$
$$= x + 3$$

ASSIGNMENT GUIDE

Basic (2 days)
(1) 1–18
(2) 19–25
 288: 1–14

Average (1 day)
18–36 (even), 38–47

Advanced ($\frac{1}{2}$ day)
See p. 292.

Problem Set A

Find each sum or difference and reduce each answer to simplest form.

1 $\dfrac{4}{8} + \dfrac{3}{8}$

$\dfrac{7}{8}$

2 $\dfrac{5}{3} - \dfrac{2}{3}$

1

3 $\dfrac{a}{4} + \dfrac{a}{4}$

$\dfrac{a}{2}$

4 $\dfrac{5}{x} - \dfrac{12}{x}$

$-\dfrac{7}{x}$

5 $\dfrac{4}{a} + \dfrac{4}{a}$

$\dfrac{8}{a}$

6 $\dfrac{x}{7} - \dfrac{y}{7}$

$\dfrac{x-y}{7}$

7 $\dfrac{5}{c} - \dfrac{2}{c}$

$\dfrac{3}{c}$

8 $\dfrac{12}{a} - \dfrac{12}{a}$

0

9 $\dfrac{1}{2x} + \dfrac{1}{2x}$

$\dfrac{1}{x}$

10 $\dfrac{14}{c} + \dfrac{23}{c} - \dfrac{2}{c}$

$\dfrac{35}{c}$

14 $\dfrac{2+3x}{a} + \dfrac{1-2x}{a}$

$\dfrac{3+x}{a}$

18 $\dfrac{3r-2}{6} - \dfrac{2r-2}{6}$

$\dfrac{r}{6}$

11 $\dfrac{a}{b} + \dfrac{a}{b} + \dfrac{a}{b}$

$\dfrac{3a}{6}$

15 $\dfrac{16}{b} - \dfrac{14a-5}{b}$

$\dfrac{21-14a}{b}$

19 $\dfrac{a}{x-y} + \dfrac{b}{x-y}$

$\dfrac{a+b}{x-y}$

12 $\dfrac{x}{y} + \dfrac{x}{y} + \dfrac{w}{y}$

$\dfrac{2x+w}{y}$

16 $\dfrac{4}{b} - \dfrac{8-d}{b}$

$\dfrac{-4+d}{b}$

20 $\dfrac{a}{a+b} + \dfrac{b}{a+b}$

1

13 $\dfrac{a+1}{3} + \dfrac{2a+3}{3}$

$\dfrac{3a+4}{3}$

17 $\dfrac{2x-3}{4} - \dfrac{6x+5}{4}$

$-x-2$

21 $\dfrac{x}{x-2} - \dfrac{x}{x-2}$

0

Find each sum or difference. (Review: Computation)

These problems preview adding and subtracting algebraic fractions with unlike denominators, Section 7.5.

22 $\dfrac{3}{4} + \dfrac{3}{8}$

$\dfrac{9}{8}$

23 $\dfrac{3}{5} + \dfrac{7}{2}$

$\dfrac{41}{10}$

24 $\dfrac{2}{3} - \dfrac{3}{4}$

$-\dfrac{1}{12}$

25 $1\frac{2}{5} - 6\frac{7}{8}$

$\dfrac{219}{40}$

Problem Set B

In problems 26–37, find each sum or difference and simplify.

26 $\dfrac{4x+10}{2x^2+x-3} - \dfrac{2x+7}{2x^2+x-3}$

$\dfrac{1}{x-1}$

32 $\dfrac{3x^2-x}{2x+1} - \dfrac{x^2-2x}{2x+1}$

x

27 $\dfrac{y}{y-x} + \dfrac{x}{y-x}$

$\dfrac{y+x}{y-x}$

33 $\dfrac{a^2}{a-b} - \dfrac{b^2}{a-b}$

$a+b$

28 $\dfrac{3a-b}{a+b} - \dfrac{2a-2b}{a+b}$

1

34 $\dfrac{a+1}{(a-1)^2} - \dfrac{a+1}{(a-1)^2}$

0

29 $\dfrac{4x-5}{xy} + \dfrac{3x+5}{xy}$

$\dfrac{7}{y}$

35 $\dfrac{b^2}{5+b} - \dfrac{25}{5+b}$

$b-5$

30 $\dfrac{15a}{15a+1} + \dfrac{1}{15a+1} + \dfrac{10a}{15a+1}$

$\dfrac{25a+1}{15a+1}$

36 $\dfrac{49}{c+7} - \dfrac{c^2}{c+7}$

$7-c$

31 $\dfrac{7x^2}{3x^2-1} - \dfrac{4x^2}{3x^2-1}$

$\dfrac{3x^2}{3x^2-1}$

37 $\dfrac{y}{y-x} - \dfrac{x}{y-x}$

1

38 Simplify: $((1 \div x) \div (1 \div x)) \div (1 \div x)$

x

39 Add $\dfrac{2a + 3b}{5}$, $\dfrac{2b - 3a}{5}$, and $\dfrac{2a - 5b}{5}$.

$\dfrac{a}{5}$

40 Add $\dfrac{7x - 4y}{4}$, $\dfrac{2y - 5x}{4}$, and $\dfrac{x + y}{4}$.

$\dfrac{3x - y}{4}$

41 From $\dfrac{18}{2a - 3}$ subtract $\dfrac{13}{2a - 3}$.

$\dfrac{5}{2a - 3}$

42 Subtract $\dfrac{2x}{2x + 3}$ from $\dfrac{11}{2x + 3}$.

$\dfrac{11 - 2x}{2x + 3}$

43 Simplify:

$$-x[-x(-x - 1) - x] + x\{x + x[x - (x - 1)]\}$$

$-x^3 + 2x$

44 Divide $60x^2 + 80x - 55$ by $10x - 5$. Is $10x - 5$ a factor of $60x^2 + 80x - 55$?

yes $(10x - 5)(6x + 11)$

45 Find the average of sixteen and two thirds, eighty-seven and one half, and sixty-two and one half.

$55\frac{5}{9}$

46 The standard meter stick is thirty-nine and thirty-seven hundredths inches long. Write a formula for the number of inches in m meters.

$i = 39.37 m$

47 A formula used by automobile engineers to find the indicated horsepower of one cylinder of an automobile motor is:

$$H = \dfrac{P \cdot L \cdot A \cdot N}{33{,}000}$$

18.27 per cylinder, 109.61 for 6 cylinders

where P stands for the average pressure on the piston in pounds per square inch; L stands for the total length, in feet, of the "stroke" or effective length that the pressure is applied; A stands for the area, or cross section, of the circular piston in square inches; and N stands for the number of revolutions per 30 seconds.

An engineer wished to find the horsepower of a 6-cylinder motor, each cylinder having a 4-inch diameter and a 3.6-inch stroke, 3200 revolutions per minute, and an average effective pressure of 100 pounds per square inch. Use the formula to determine the horsepower per cylinder (to 2 decimal places). What is the horsepower (to the nearest tenth) for all six cylinders?

Problem Set C

Perform each operation and simplify the result.

48 $\dfrac{x}{x^2 + 6x + 9} + \dfrac{3}{x^2 + 6x + 9}$

$\frac{1}{x+3}$

49 $\dfrac{5a}{a^2 - 2ab + b^2} - \dfrac{5b}{a^2 - 2ab + b^2}$

$\frac{5}{a-b}$

50 $\dfrac{x^2 + 4}{x - 2} - \dfrac{4x}{x - 2}$

$x - 2$

51 $\dfrac{x^2}{y - x} - \dfrac{y^2}{y - x}$

$-(x+y)$

52 $\dfrac{x^2}{x - 3} + \dfrac{9}{x - 3} + \dfrac{6x}{3 - x}$

$x - 3$

53 $\dfrac{16 - 8r}{r - 4} - \dfrac{r^2}{4 - r}$

$r - 4$

54 $\left(\dfrac{2x}{(x + y)^2} + \dfrac{2y}{(x + y)^2}\right) \div \left(\dfrac{2x + y}{(x - y)^2} - \dfrac{x + 2y}{(x - y)^2}\right)$

$\frac{2(x-y)}{x+y}$

X tending the topic: Decimals for Common Fractions

A rational number can always be written as a decimal fraction.

EXAMPLES

Some rational numbers are equal to terminating decimals:

- $\dfrac{1}{2} = \ 0.5$

- $-\dfrac{7}{8} = -0.875$

- $\dfrac{127}{40} = \ 3.175$

Some rational numbers can only be represented by nonterminating decimal fractions:

- $\dfrac{1}{3} = 0.3333\ldots$ or $0.\overline{3}$ — The bar over the digit indicates that part of the number is a **repeating decimal**.

- $\dfrac{-10}{9} = -1.1111\ldots$ or $-1.\overline{1}$

- $\dfrac{13}{6} = 2.1666\ldots$ or $2.1\overline{6}$

Repeating decimals for common fractions may be found using a calculator or the long-division process of arithmetic.

Problem Set   X

*Brighter students can be asked about the length of the **repetend**, or repeating block of digits. They should realize, from problems like 15–21, that the length must be at most one less than the value of the denominator, because they must eventually "run out" of remainders.*

Find the decimal representation of each of the following rational numbers. If it has a repeating decimal, use a bar to indicate the repeating block of digits.

1 $\dfrac{1}{4}$

0.25

2 $-\dfrac{5}{8}$

−0.625

3 $\dfrac{7}{5}$

1.4

4 $\dfrac{1}{9}$

0.$\overline{1}$

5 $\dfrac{1}{99}$

0.$\overline{01}$

6 $\dfrac{3}{16}$

0.1875

7 $-\dfrac{33}{32}$

−1.03125

8 $\dfrac{2}{7}$

0.$\overline{285714}$

9 $-\dfrac{1}{13}$

−0.$\overline{076923}$

10 $\dfrac{1}{11}$

0.$\overline{09}$

11 $\dfrac{2}{11}$

0.$\overline{18}$

12 $\dfrac{1}{999}$

0.$\overline{001}$

13 $-\dfrac{111}{11}$

−10.$\overline{09}$

14 $\dfrac{8}{37}$

0.$\overline{216}$

15 $\dfrac{22}{23}$

0.$\overline{9565217391304347826086}$

16 $\dfrac{21}{23}$

0.$\overline{9130434782608695652173}$

17 $\dfrac{20}{23}$

0.$\overline{8695652173913043478260}$

18 $\dfrac{19}{23}$

0.$\overline{8260869565217391304347}$

19 $\dfrac{18}{23}$

0.$\overline{7826086956521739130434}$

20 $\dfrac{17}{23}$

0.$\overline{7391304347826086956521}$

21 $\dfrac{16}{23}$

0.$\overline{6956521739130434782608}$

After-School Mathematics: Making Change

Jill sells ice cream at the playground during the summer. She "totals up" each purchase in her head, and then she has to give back the correct change.

The manager taught Jill a system for making change from a five- or ten-dollar bill. The first step is to tuck the bill into her shirt pocket. That way she will remember that it is not a one-dollar bill. Then she starts with the amount of the purchase and "builds up" to the amount of money paid by the customer.

For example, a customer bought $1.38 worth of ice cream and paid with a ten-dollar bill. Jill tucked the ten into her pocket and said, "$1.38." She grabbed two pennies from her apron pockets and said, "$1.40." As she took a dime she said, "$1.50." Next she took two quarters and said, "$2.00." She took out three singles and said, "$5.00." Finally, she took out a five-dollar bill and said, "And five makes ten dollars. Thank you." Then she put away the ten-dollar bill.

By "building up" to the amount of money paid by the customer, Jill does not have to calculate, in her head, the amount of change.

Application: Laces

Laces for shoes come in many lengths: 24 inches, 18 inches, 30 inches, and so on. If you need to replace a lace, and you do not have the old lace to measure, you can estimate the length you will need by counting the number of "eyelets" over the tongue of the shoe.

Suppose that your shoes have six pairs of eyelets, and in each pair the eyelets are one inch apart. How long a lace would you need? Be sure to take into account the amount needed to tie a bow at the top. How long a lace would you need for a roller skate with twelve pairs of eyelets? For a casual shoe with two pairs of eyelets?

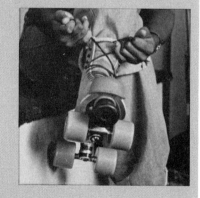

Assuming that 6 inches of lace, for each end, is needed to tie the shoe, a 12-eyelet roller skate would need $2 \cdot 6 + 2 \cdot 11 + 1$ or 35 inches of lace. A 2-eyelet shoe would need $2 \cdot 6 + 2 \cdot 1 + 1$ or 15 inches of lace.

289

Section 7.5 Adding and Subtracting Algebraic Fractions: Unlike Denominators

Two fractions must have a common denominator before they can be added or subtracted. For common fractions, finding the **least common denominator** (LCD) involves the simplest computation. In the following example, the LCD is $3 \cdot 5$ or 15. The Multiplicative Property of One is used when multiplying $\frac{2}{3}$ by $\frac{5}{5}$ and when multiplying $\frac{4}{5}$ by $\frac{3}{3}$:

EXAMPLE

■
$$\frac{2}{3} + \frac{4}{5}$$

$$\frac{2}{3} \cdot \frac{5}{5} + \frac{4}{5} \cdot \frac{3}{3}$$

$$\frac{10}{15} + \frac{12}{15}$$

$$\frac{10 + 12}{15}$$

$$\frac{22}{15}$$

Adding two algebraic fractions also involves finding a common denominator and using the Multiplicative Property of One.

EXAMPLE

■
$$\frac{4}{a + 1} + \frac{3}{a + 2}$$

$$\frac{4}{a + 1} \cdot \frac{a + 2}{a + 2} + \frac{3}{a + 2} \cdot \frac{a + 1}{a + 1}$$

$$\frac{4 \cdot (a + 2)}{(a + 1) \cdot (a + 2)} + \frac{3 \cdot (a + 1)}{(a + 2) \cdot (a + 1)}$$

$$\frac{4a + 8}{a^2 + 3a + 2} + \frac{3a + 3}{a^2 + 3a + 2}$$

$$\frac{(4a + 8) + (3a + 3)}{a^2 + 3a + 2}$$

$$\frac{7a + 11}{a^2 + 3a + 2}$$

Sample Problems

1 Add: $\dfrac{5}{12} + \dfrac{11}{18}$

PROCEDURE

$$\dfrac{5}{12} + \dfrac{11}{18}$$

$$\dfrac{5}{2 \cdot 2 \cdot 3} \cdot \dfrac{3}{3} + \dfrac{11}{2 \cdot 3 \cdot 3} \cdot \dfrac{2}{2}$$

$$\dfrac{15}{36} + \dfrac{22}{36}$$

$$\dfrac{37}{36}$$

2 Find: $\dfrac{3}{x^2} + \dfrac{7}{2xy} - \dfrac{4}{3y^2}$

PROCEDURE

$$\dfrac{3}{x^2} \qquad + \dfrac{7}{2xy} \qquad - \dfrac{4}{3y^2}$$

$$\dfrac{3}{x^2} \cdot \dfrac{6y^2}{6y^2} + \dfrac{7}{2xy} \cdot \dfrac{3xy}{3xy} - \dfrac{4}{3y^2} \cdot \dfrac{2x^2}{2x^2}$$

$$\dfrac{18y^2}{6x^2y^2} + \dfrac{21xy}{6x^2y^2} - \dfrac{8x^2}{6x^2y^2}$$

$$\dfrac{18y^2 + 21xy - 8x^2}{6x^2y^2}$$

3 Find: $\dfrac{x + 1}{x^2 - 9} - \dfrac{2}{x + 3}$

PROCEDURE

$$\dfrac{x + 1}{x^2 - 9} - \dfrac{2}{x + 3}$$

$$\dfrac{x + 1}{(x + 3)(x - 3)} - \dfrac{2}{(x + 3)} \cdot \dfrac{(x - 3)}{(x - 3)}$$

$$\dfrac{x + 1}{(x + 3)(x - 3)} - \dfrac{2x - 6}{(x + 3)(x - 3)}$$

$$\dfrac{x + 1 - 2x + 6}{(x + 3)(x - 3)}$$

$$\dfrac{-x + 7}{(x + 3)(x - 3)} \quad \text{or} \quad \dfrac{-x + 7}{x^2 - 9}$$

ASSIGNMENT GUIDE

Basic (2 days)
(1) 1–19
(2) 20–38

Average (3 days)
(1) 2–36 (even)
(2) 37–56, 73, 74
(3) 288: 1–21
    296: 1–9

Advanced ($2\frac{1}{2}$ days)
(1) 37–40, 54, 55
    285: 26–36 (even),
        48–54 (even)
(2) 41–53, 56–75
(3) 288: 1–21
    296: 1–9

Problem Set **A**

Find each sum or difference and reduce each answer to simplest form.

1 $\dfrac{1}{5} + \dfrac{2}{3}$

$\dfrac{13}{15}$

2 $\dfrac{7}{30} - \dfrac{4}{45}$

$\dfrac{13}{90}$

3 $\dfrac{3}{40} + \dfrac{5}{12}$

$\dfrac{59}{120}$

4 $\dfrac{2}{75} - \dfrac{8}{40}$

$\dfrac{-13}{75}$

5 $\dfrac{3}{7} - \dfrac{2}{5}$

$\dfrac{1}{35}$

6 $\dfrac{a}{2} + \dfrac{a}{3}$

$\dfrac{5a}{b}$

7 $\dfrac{2b}{5} - \dfrac{b}{10}$

$\dfrac{3b}{10}$

8 $\dfrac{1}{a} + \dfrac{2}{b}$

$\dfrac{b + 2a}{ab}$

9 $\dfrac{4}{a} + \dfrac{3}{2a}$

$\dfrac{11}{2a}$

10 $\dfrac{x}{10} - \dfrac{1}{5}$

$\dfrac{x - 2}{10}$

11 $\dfrac{1}{a} + \dfrac{1}{b} + \dfrac{1}{c}$

$\dfrac{bc + ac + ab}{abc}$

12 $\dfrac{a}{b} - \dfrac{b}{a}$

$\dfrac{a^2 - b^2}{ab}$

13 $\dfrac{1}{2m} + \dfrac{a - 3}{4m}$

$\dfrac{a - 1}{4m}$

14 $\dfrac{4}{5x} - \dfrac{3}{8x}$

$\dfrac{17}{40x}$

15 $\dfrac{7a}{10b} - \dfrac{2c}{5b}$

$\dfrac{7a - 4c}{10b}$

16 $\dfrac{2}{x} + \dfrac{5}{x^2}$

$\dfrac{2x + 5}{x^2}$

17 $\dfrac{6}{ab^2} - \dfrac{8}{a^2b}$

$\dfrac{6a - 8b}{a^2b}$

18 $\dfrac{3}{5x^2} - \dfrac{4}{2x}$

$\dfrac{2 - 10x}{5x^2}$

19 $\dfrac{a}{2b} + \dfrac{2a}{b} - \dfrac{1}{b^2}$

$\dfrac{5ab - 2}{2b^2}$

20 $2 + \dfrac{1}{a}$

$\dfrac{2a + 1}{a}$

21 $3 + \dfrac{1}{b}$

$\dfrac{3b + 1}{b}$

22 $\dfrac{a}{3} + 4$

$\dfrac{a + 12}{3}$

23 $\dfrac{5}{x} - 1$

$\dfrac{5 + x}{x}$

24 $6 - \dfrac{5}{n}$

$\dfrac{6n - 5}{n}$

25 $\dfrac{2}{a} - 5$

$\dfrac{2 - 5a}{a}$

26 $\dfrac{a}{b} - c$

$\dfrac{a - bc}{b}$

27 $\dfrac{c + d}{c} + \dfrac{c - d}{c}$

2

28 $\dfrac{a + b}{b} - \dfrac{a - b}{a}$

$\dfrac{a^2 + b^2}{ab}$

29 $\dfrac{2x - 6}{5} + \dfrac{x + 2}{2}$

$\dfrac{9x - 2}{10}$

30 $\dfrac{3x + 2}{4} + \dfrac{2x - 1}{6}$

$\dfrac{13x + 4}{12}$

Reduce each fraction. (Review: Section 7.1)

31 $\dfrac{4a - 8b}{12a + 16b}$

$\dfrac{a - 2b}{3a + 4b}$

32 $\dfrac{3s + 3t}{3s - 3t}$

$\dfrac{s + t}{s - t}$

33 $\dfrac{2m^2 + 4m}{3qm + 6q}$

$\dfrac{2m}{3q}$

34 $\dfrac{r^2 - rs}{2r - 2s}$

$\dfrac{r}{2}$

35 $\dfrac{4c^2 - 1}{2bc + b}$

$\dfrac{2c - 1}{b}$

36 $\dfrac{w^2 - 9}{w^2 - 5w + 6}$

$\dfrac{w + 3}{w - 2}$

Problem Set B

In problems 37–52, perform each operation and simplify.

37 $\dfrac{x}{x-y} - 3$

     $\dfrac{-2x+3y}{x-y}$

38 $\dfrac{3}{m-1} - \dfrac{2}{m-2}$

     $\dfrac{m-4}{(m-1)(m-2)}$

39 $\dfrac{2a}{(a-b)^2} + \dfrac{1}{a-b}$

     $\dfrac{3a-b}{(a-b)^2}$

40 $\dfrac{1}{a-b} - \dfrac{1}{a+b}$

     $\dfrac{2b}{(a-b)(a+b)}$

41 $\dfrac{15}{4a-4b} - \dfrac{3}{a-b}$

     $\dfrac{3}{4(a-b)}$

42 $\dfrac{6}{4x+4y} + \dfrac{3}{4}$

     $\dfrac{6+3x+3y}{4x+4y}$

43 $\dfrac{5x}{x^2-9} + \dfrac{7}{x+3}$

     $\dfrac{12x-21}{x^2-9}$

44 $\dfrac{3x}{2x^2+4x} - \dfrac{5x}{x^2+4x+4}$

     $\dfrac{6-7x}{2(x^2+4x+4)}$

45 $\dfrac{4}{x} + \dfrac{3}{x+1} - \dfrac{5}{x^2}$

     $\dfrac{7x^2-5x-1}{x^2(x+1)}$

46 $\dfrac{1}{x} - \dfrac{1}{y} + \dfrac{3}{x^2y}$

     $\dfrac{xy-x^2+3}{x^2y}$

47 $\dfrac{3}{a} - \dfrac{5}{b} - \dfrac{3}{a-b}$

     $\dfrac{-5a^2+5ab-3b^2}{ab(a-b)}$

48 $\left(\dfrac{1}{3} - \dfrac{1}{5}\right) \div \left(\dfrac{1}{7} - \dfrac{1}{9}\right)$

     $\dfrac{21}{5}$

49 $\left(3 - \dfrac{2}{x-1}\right) \div \left(2 - \dfrac{3}{1-x}\right)$

     $\dfrac{3x-5}{2x+1}$

50 $\left(\dfrac{3}{4x} + \dfrac{3}{8x}\right) \cdot \left(\dfrac{13x}{6} - \dfrac{5x}{3}\right)$

     $\dfrac{9}{16}$

51 $\left(\dfrac{7a}{12} + \dfrac{5a}{2}\right) \cdot \left(\dfrac{2}{5a} - \dfrac{4}{15a}\right)$

     $\dfrac{37}{90}$

52 $\left(1 + \dfrac{1}{x} + \dfrac{2}{x}\right) \div \left(1 + \dfrac{1}{x} - \dfrac{1}{2x}\right)$

     $\dfrac{2(x+3)}{2x+1}$

53   Solve: $2x(x-1) + 12 = x(2x-3)$

     $x = -12$

54   A sports store has forty-three pairs of ice skates. There are two kinds of skates; one kind sells for $16.50 and the other for $29.75. If all the skates are sold, the store will receive $908.25. How many pairs of each kind of skates does the store have?

     28 pairs at $16.50, 15 pairs at $29.75

     54) $29.75x + 16.50(43-x)$
             $= 908.25$
       $x = 15, \quad 43 - x = 28$

55   The cost of an airplane ticket is two hundred seventeen dollars and thirty-five cents. This price includes a special fifteen percent tax. Find the cost of the ticket before the tax.

     $189

     55) $x + 0.15x = 217.35$
            $x = 189$

56   The formula $A = \frac{1}{2}h(a+b)$ is for finding the area of a trapezoid. Rewrite and simplify this formula if $h = \frac{4}{3}a$ and $b = \frac{1}{2}a$.

     $A = a^2$

Problem Set C

In problems 57–72, perform each operation and simplify.

57 $\dfrac{x^2}{x+y} - \dfrac{y^2}{x-y} - (x-y)$

$\dfrac{-2y^3}{(x+y)(x-y)}$

63 $\dfrac{5}{x^2+x-6} + \dfrac{3x}{x^2-4x+4}$

$\dfrac{3x^2+14x-10}{(x+3)(x-2)^2}$

58 $\dfrac{5}{4x+4} + \dfrac{6}{x^2+2x+1}$

$\dfrac{5x+29}{4(x+1)^2}$

64 $\dfrac{16}{x^3-27} + \dfrac{3}{x-3}$

$\dfrac{3x^2+9x+43}{x^3-27}$

59 $\dfrac{5x}{x+3} + \dfrac{2}{x^2+5x+6}$

$\dfrac{5x^2+10x+2}{(x+3)(x+2)}$

65 $\dfrac{7(x+3)}{y^2} - \dfrac{4(y+1)}{(x+3)y}$

$\dfrac{7x^2+42x+63-4y^2-4y}{y^2(x+3)}$

60 $\dfrac{4x+1}{3x^2+33x+90} + \dfrac{3}{x+6}$

$\dfrac{13x+46}{3(x+6)(x+5)}$

66 $\dfrac{x}{a^2-b^2} + \dfrac{x}{(a-b)^2}$

$\dfrac{2xa}{(a-b)(a+b)^2}$

61 $\dfrac{5}{x^2-y^2} + \dfrac{7}{x(x+y)}$

$\dfrac{12x-7y}{x(x-y)(x+y)}$

67 $\dfrac{a}{8a^3-1} - \dfrac{a-1}{2a-1}$

$\dfrac{-4a^3+2a^2+2a+1}{8a^3-1}$

62 $\dfrac{2x}{x^2-36} - \dfrac{4(x-6)}{x+6}$

$\dfrac{-4x^2+50x-144}{(x-6)(x+6)}$

68 $\dfrac{6}{9-a^2} - \dfrac{3}{12+4a}$

$\dfrac{15+3a}{4(3-a)(3+a)^2}$

69 $\dfrac{3}{x^2+5x-14} - \dfrac{4}{x^2+14x+49} + \dfrac{7}{x^2-4x+4}$

$\dfrac{6x^2+129x+285}{(x-2)^2(x+7)^2}$

70 $\dfrac{9}{x^2-3x+2} + \dfrac{3}{x^2-5x+6} + \dfrac{2}{x^2-4}$

$\dfrac{14x^2-14x-54}{(x-1)(x-2)(x+2)(x-3)}$

71 $\left(2x - \dfrac{1}{2x}\right)\left(6x - \dfrac{x+3}{2x+1}\right)\left(\dfrac{8x^2+2}{16x^4-1}\right)$

$\dfrac{(4x+3)(3x-1)}{x(2x+1)}$

72 $\left[\left(1 - \dfrac{6}{x} + \dfrac{9}{x^2}\right)\left(2 - \dfrac{6}{x+3}\right)\right] \div \left(\dfrac{9-x^2}{x}\right)$

$\dfrac{-2(x-3)}{(x+3)^2}$

73 Evaluate: $(3\frac{3}{4} + 2\frac{1}{2}) \div (1\frac{1}{3} + 2\frac{5}{6})$

$\dfrac{3}{2}$

74 Find the average of sixteen and two thirds and sixteen and one fourth.

$16\frac{11}{24}$

75 A certain number is eight and one third less than the average of twelve and one fourth and six and one half. Find the number.

$\dfrac{25}{24}$

75) $x = \dfrac{12\frac{1}{4} + 6\frac{1}{2}}{2} - 8\frac{1}{3}$

$= \dfrac{18\frac{3}{4}}{2} - 8\frac{1}{3}$

$= 9\frac{3}{8} - 8\frac{1}{3}$

$= 9\frac{9}{24} - 8\frac{8}{24}$

$= 1\frac{1}{24}$

X tending the topic: Common Fractions for Decimals

Every terminating decimal represents a rational number.

EXAMPLES

- $2.5 = \dfrac{25}{10}$

- $-8.62 = \dfrac{-862}{100}$

- $3.1416 = \dfrac{31,416}{10,000}$

  $= \dfrac{3927}{1250}$

The rational number can often be reduced.

Every nonterminating, repeating decimal also represents a rational number. For example, the repeating decimal $0.3333\ldots$ represents the rational number $\frac{1}{3}$. The Sample Problems illustrate how to express a repeating decimal as a quotient of two integers.

Sample Problems

1   Convert $0.6666\ldots$ to a rational number.

PROCEDURE

$$\text{Let } N = 0.6666\ldots$$

MULTBY 10: $10 \cdot N = 6.6666\ldots$

$$10N - N = 6.6666\ldots - 0.6666\ldots$$

$$9N = 6.0$$

$$N = \frac{6}{9} = \frac{2}{3}$$

Therefore $0.666\ldots = \dfrac{2}{3}$

2 Find the rational number for $0.4\overline{36}$ and check your answer.

PROCEDURE

$$N = 0.4363636 \ldots$$
$$100N = 43.6363636 \ldots$$
$$99N = 43.2$$
$$N = \frac{43.2}{99} = \frac{432}{990} = \frac{18 \cdot 24}{18 \cdot 55} = \frac{24}{55}$$

Therefore $0.4\overline{36} = \dfrac{24}{55}$

$$\begin{array}{r} 0.43636 \ldots \\ 55\overline{)24.00000} \end{array}$$

To check

Problem Set **X**

Express each of the following repeating decimals as a quotient of two relatively prime integers.

1 $-2.333 \ldots$ $-\frac{7}{3}$

2 $0.4999 \ldots$ $\frac{1}{2}$

3 $5.\overline{12}$ $\frac{169}{33}$

4 $-1.\overline{2}$ $-\frac{11}{9}$

5 $2.\overline{10}$ $\frac{208}{99}$

6 $3.\overline{41}$ $\frac{338}{99}$

7 $-7.\overline{892}$ $-\frac{785}{999}$

8 $0.3\overline{69}$ $\frac{37}{100}$

9 $-0.6\overline{01}$ $\frac{601}{999}$

Section 7.6   Using the Opposites
$ax - b$ and $b - ax$ as Denominators

There is a short way to find a common denominator for a problem like:

$$\frac{4a}{x - 5} + \frac{3a}{5 - x}$$

Notice that the denominator $x - 5$ is the opposite of the denominator $5 - x$:

$$\text{OPP} (5 - x) = -5 + x$$
$$= x - 5$$

In the problem, multiply either term by $\dfrac{-1}{-1}$:

$$\dfrac{4a}{x-5}+\dfrac{3a}{5-x}$$

$$\dfrac{4a}{x-5}+\dfrac{3a}{5-x}\cdot\dfrac{-1}{-1}$$

$$\dfrac{4a}{x-5}+\dfrac{-3a}{x-5}$$

$$\dfrac{4a-3a}{x-5}$$

$$\dfrac{a}{x-5}$$

This procedure works whenever the denominators are opposites.

Sample Problems

1 Find: $\dfrac{6}{y-2x}-\dfrac{4}{2x-y}$

PROCEDURE

$$\dfrac{6}{y-2x}-\dfrac{4}{2x-y}$$

$$\dfrac{6}{(y-2x)}\cdot\dfrac{-1}{-1}-\dfrac{4}{2x-y}$$

$$\dfrac{-6}{2x-y}-\dfrac{4}{2x-y}$$

$$\dfrac{-6-4}{2x-y}$$

$$\dfrac{-10}{2x-y}$$

2 Find: $\dfrac{(x-2)\,(x-3)}{(3-x)\,(2-x)}$

PROCEDURE

$$\dfrac{(x-2)\,(x-3)}{(3-x)\,(2-x)}$$

$$\dfrac{x-2}{2-x}\cdot\dfrac{x-3}{3-x}$$

$$\dfrac{x-2}{2-x}\cdot\dfrac{-1}{-1}\cdot\dfrac{x-3}{3-x}\cdot\dfrac{-1}{-1}$$

$$\dfrac{(x-2)\,(-1)}{(x-2)}\cdot\dfrac{(x-3)\,(-1)}{(x-3)}$$

$$(-1)\,(-1)$$

$$1$$

ASSIGNMENT GUIDE

Basic (optional 1 day)
1–14

Average (1 day)
6–26, 28–38 (even)

Advanced (1 day)
15–26, 31–38
300: Problem Set X

Problem Set A

Find each sum or difference.

1 $\dfrac{2}{a-b} + \dfrac{1}{b-a}$

$\dfrac{1}{a-b}$

2 $\dfrac{3}{x-y} + \dfrac{-3}{y-x}$

$\dfrac{6}{x-y}$

3 $\dfrac{4}{3-x} - \dfrac{10}{x-3}$

$\dfrac{14}{3-x}$

4 $\dfrac{a}{x-3} - \dfrac{4a}{3-x}$

$\dfrac{5a}{x-3}$

5 $\dfrac{3x}{3y-1} + \dfrac{-8x}{1-3y}$

$\dfrac{11x}{3y-1}$

6 $\dfrac{4}{a-2} + \dfrac{2}{2-a}$

$\dfrac{2}{a-2}$

7 $\dfrac{x}{x-3} + \dfrac{1}{3-x}$

$\dfrac{x-1}{x-3}$

8 $\dfrac{3}{x^2} + \dfrac{8}{-x^2}$

$\dfrac{-5}{x^2}$

9 $\dfrac{-2x}{1-2b} + \dfrac{7x}{2b-1}$

$\dfrac{9x}{2b-1}$

10 $\dfrac{9}{3y-2} - \dfrac{5}{2-3y}$

$\dfrac{14}{3y-2}$

Perform each operation and then reduce. (Review: Section 7.2)

11 $\dfrac{a-4}{12} \cdot \dfrac{18}{a^2-4a}$

$\dfrac{3}{2a}$

12 $\dfrac{5m^2}{8mn} \div 15m$

$\dfrac{1}{24n}$

13 $\dfrac{y}{3} \div \dfrac{5y^2}{9}$

$\dfrac{3}{5y}$

14 $\dfrac{(b-7)^3}{b} \cdot \dfrac{b+7}{(b-7)^2}$

$\dfrac{(b-7)(b+7)}{b}$

Problem Set B

Find each sum or difference, and reduce each answer to simplest form.

15 $\dfrac{5}{x-2} - \dfrac{x}{4-x^2}$

$\dfrac{6x-10}{x^2-4}$

16 $\dfrac{a^2}{a^2-1} + \dfrac{a}{1-a}$

$\dfrac{-a}{a^2-1}$

17 $\dfrac{x}{x^2-1} - \dfrac{1}{1-x}$

$\dfrac{2x+1}{x^2-1}$

18 $\dfrac{a^2}{a^2-b^2} - \dfrac{a}{b-a}$

$\dfrac{2a^2+ab}{a^2-b^2}$

19 $\dfrac{a+b}{a-b} - \dfrac{b+a}{b-a}$

$\dfrac{2(a+b)}{a-b}$

20 $\dfrac{2a+3b}{2} - \dfrac{a-b}{4}$

$\dfrac{3a+7b}{4}$

Simplify each algebraic fraction.

21 $\dfrac{x - y}{y - x}$

-1

22 $\dfrac{a^2 - b^2}{b - a}$

$-a - b$

23 $\dfrac{(x - 2)(x - 5)}{(5 - x)(2 - x)}$

$+1$

24 $\dfrac{2x - 12}{36 - x^2}$

$\dfrac{-2}{x + 6}$

25 $\dfrac{a - 3}{9 - a^2}$

$\dfrac{-1}{3 + a}$

26 $\dfrac{x^2 - x - 20}{5 - x}$

$-x - 4$

In problems 27–34, find the value of each expression for $a = \tfrac{1}{2}$, $b = \tfrac{3}{4}$, and $c = 2$.

27 $a + b + c$

$\dfrac{13}{4}$

28 $ab + bc$

$\dfrac{15}{8}$

29 $\dfrac{b}{c}$

$\dfrac{3}{8}$

30 $\dfrac{a - c}{a - b}$

6

31 $\dfrac{1}{a} + \dfrac{1}{b} - \dfrac{1}{c}$

$\dfrac{17}{6}$

32 $(ab)^c$

$\dfrac{9}{64}$

33 $(a + b)^c$

$\dfrac{25}{16}$

34 $\dfrac{bc - a}{a}$

2

35 A ship left a port and averaged twenty-four miles per hour. An airplane left the same port two hours and thirty minutes later and flew in the same direction as the ship. The plane flew at two hundred forty miles per hour. How many minutes after take-off did the plane overtake the ship?

$16\tfrac{2}{3}$ minutes

36 $°F = 1.8°C + 32°$, where $°F$ represents degrees Fahrenheit and $°C$ indicates degrees Celsius. If $68°F$ is the room temperature setting used by federal buildings to conserve energy, what is the $°C$ setting? If $°K = °C + 273°$, where $°K$ stands for degrees Kelvin or absolute, what is the Kelvin temperature?

$°C = 20°$, $°K = 293°$

37 How many square feet of plywood will be required to cover the tops of one hundred twenty-five square tables, each three feet six inches on a side? How many four-by-eight foot sheets of plywood would be needed?

1531.25 sq. ft. of plywood; 48 sheets

38 If COMP $(x) = x^2 - \dfrac{1}{x}$, find COMP $\left(\dfrac{a}{2}\right)$.

$\dfrac{a^3 - 8}{4a}$

Problem Set C

$A, B, C,$ and D have the values given below. Write each expression in problems 39–44 in terms of x. Express each answer in simplest form.

$$A = \frac{x - 4}{2} \qquad B = \frac{x + 4}{2} \qquad C = \frac{x - 3}{3} \qquad D = \frac{x - 3}{x + 4}$$

39 $B + C$

$\frac{5x + 6}{6}$

40 $\dfrac{C}{D}$

$\frac{x + 4}{3}$

41 $\dfrac{1}{A} + \dfrac{1}{B}$

$\frac{4x}{(x - 4)(x + 4)}$

42 $(A \div B)(C \div D)$

$\frac{x - 4}{3}$

43 $\left(\dfrac{1}{C} - \dfrac{1}{D}\right)\left(\dfrac{1}{C} + \dfrac{1}{D}\right)$

$\frac{(x + 7)(-x - 1)}{(x - 3)^2}$

44 $\dfrac{D}{C} \div \left[\left(\dfrac{1}{A} + \dfrac{B}{C}\right)\left(\dfrac{C}{B} - \dfrac{D}{C}\right)\right]$

$\frac{6(x - 3)(x - 4)}{(3x^2 + 4x - 60)(2x - 15)}$

Xtending the topic: "2 = 1"

The "proof" below is an illustration of a **fallacy**, or error in reasoning. "2 = 1" is a false statement.

$$\text{Let } a = b$$

MULTBY a:
$$a \cdot a = a \cdot b$$
$$a^2 = ab$$

SUBTRACT b^2:
$$a^2 - b^2 = ab - b^2$$

factor:
$$(a + b)(a - b) = b(a - b)$$

MULTBY $\left(\dfrac{1}{a - b}\right)$:
$$\frac{(a + b)(a - b)}{(a - b)} = \frac{b(a - b)}{(a - b)}$$
$$(a + b) \cdot 1 = b \cdot 1$$
$$a + b = b$$

Then, since a and b are equal, substitute b for a:

$$b + b = b$$
$$2b = b$$

MULTBY $\dfrac{1}{b}$:
$$\frac{2b}{b} = \frac{b}{b}$$
$$2 = 1$$

Where is the error in this "proof"?

Since $a = b$, MULTBY $\left(\dfrac{1}{a - b}\right)$ is equivalent to dividing by zero.

Chapter Study Guide

Skills

ASSIGNMENT GUIDE

Basic (2 days)
(1) 303: 1–20
(2) 283: 21–23
      298: 11–14
      303: 21–24

Average (3 days)
(1) 300: 39–44
      303: 1–24
(2) 304: 1–31
(3) 306: 32–58

Advanced (2 days)
(1) 303: 1–24
(2) 300: 39–44
      304: 2–26 (even),

As you study and review this chapter, be sure you build the useful algebraic skills, including:

1   Using the Multiplicative Property of One   Reduce each fraction:

a $\dfrac{200}{300}$ b $\dfrac{4t}{8t}$

The Assignment Guide for Average courses includes recommendations for a midyear review.

PROCEDURE   The Multiplicative Property of One is that if p is any non-zero number and a is any number, then:

$$\frac{p}{p} = 1 \quad \text{and} \quad a \cdot \frac{p}{p} = a$$

a $\begin{aligned} \dfrac{200}{300} &= \dfrac{2 \cdot 100}{3 \cdot 100} \\ &= \dfrac{2}{3} \cdot \dfrac{100}{100} \\ &= \dfrac{2}{3} \cdot 1 \\ &= \dfrac{2}{3} \end{aligned}$

b $\begin{aligned} \dfrac{4t}{8t} &= \dfrac{1 \cdot 4t}{2 \cdot 4t} \\ &= \dfrac{1}{2} \cdot \dfrac{4t}{4t} \\ &= \dfrac{1}{2} \cdot 1 \\ &= \dfrac{1}{2} \end{aligned}$

2   Simplifying algebraic fractions   Reduce the fraction $\dfrac{p^2 + 4p + 3}{p^2 - 9}$

PROCEDURE   Rewrite the fraction as the product of two fractions:

$\dfrac{p^2 + 4p + 3}{p^2 - 9}$

$\dfrac{(p + 3)(p + 1)}{(p + 3)(p - 3)}$

$\dfrac{p + 3}{p + 3} \cdot \dfrac{p + 1}{p - 3}$

$\dfrac{p + 1}{p - 3}$

3   Dividing polynomials   Divide $10s^2 - 3s + 5$ by $2s + 3$.

PROCEDURE

$$\begin{array}{r} 5s - 9 \\ 2s + 3)\overline{10s^2 - 3s + 5} \\ 10s^2 + 15s \\ \hline -18s + 5 \\ -18s - 27 \\ \hline 32 \end{array}$$

$$\frac{10s^2 - 3s + 5}{2s + 3} = 5s - 9 \; + \; \frac{32}{2s + 3}$$

4   Multiplying and dividing algebraic fractions   Perform each operation:

a $\dfrac{2b}{15a} \cdot \dfrac{5a^2}{3b}$

b $\dfrac{8p^2}{14q^2} \div \dfrac{12p^2}{21q^2}$

PROCEDURE

a $\dfrac{2b}{15a} \cdot \dfrac{5a^2}{3b}$

$\dfrac{10a^2b}{45ab}$

$\dfrac{5ab}{5ab} \cdot \dfrac{2a}{9}$

$\dfrac{2a}{9}$

b $\dfrac{8p^2}{14q^2} \div \dfrac{12p^2}{21q^2}$

$\dfrac{8p^2}{14q^2} \cdot \dfrac{21q^2}{12p^2}$

$\dfrac{8 \cdot 21 \cdot p^2 \cdot q^2}{12 \cdot 14 \cdot p^2 \cdot q^2}$

$\dfrac{2 \cdot 4 \cdot 3 \cdot 7 \; p^2 q^2}{3 \cdot 4 \cdot 2 \cdot 7 \; p^2 q^2}$

1

5   Adding and subtracting algebraic fractions   Perform each operation:

a $\dfrac{m - 3}{3} - \dfrac{2m - 5}{4}$

b $\dfrac{7}{2a - 1} + \dfrac{5}{1 - 2a}$

PROCEDURE

a $\dfrac{m - 3}{3} \cdot \dfrac{4}{4} - \dfrac{2m - 5}{4} \cdot \dfrac{3}{3}$

$\dfrac{4m - 12}{12} - \dfrac{6m - 15}{12}$

$\dfrac{4m - 12 - (6m - 15)}{12}$

$\dfrac{4m - 12 - 6m + 15}{12}$

$\dfrac{-2m + 3}{12}$

b   Multiply either fraction by $\dfrac{-1}{-1}$:

$\dfrac{7}{2a - 1} + \dfrac{5}{1 - 2a} \cdot \dfrac{-1}{-1}$

$\dfrac{7}{2a - 1} + \dfrac{-5}{-1 + 2a}$

$\dfrac{7 - 5}{2a - 1}$

$\dfrac{2}{2a - 1}$

Chapter Test

State what values the variable cannot have.

1 $\dfrac{3 + y}{y}$

$y \neq 0$

3 $\dfrac{x + 2}{x^2 - 4}$

$x \neq 2, -2$

5 $\dfrac{a + b}{a - b}$

$a \neq b$

2 $\dfrac{x - 1}{(x + 2)(x - 3)}$

$x \neq -2, 3$

4 $\dfrac{5z}{7}$

6 $\dfrac{a - b}{a - b}$

$a \neq b$

Reduce each fraction.

7 $\dfrac{a(x + y)^2}{a(x - y)}$

$\dfrac{(x + y)^2}{x - y}$

8 $\dfrac{x^2y - xy}{x^2y^2 + xy^2}$

$\dfrac{x - 1}{y(x + 1)}$

9 $\dfrac{4y^2 - 20y + 24}{2y^2 - 2y - 12}$

$\dfrac{2(y - 2)}{y + 2}$

Divide the polynomials by long division.

10 $\dfrac{6x^2 + x - 5}{3x - 4}$

$2x + 3 + \dfrac{7}{3x - 4}$

11 $\dfrac{x^3 - 64}{x - 4}$

$x^2 + 4x + 16$

12 $\dfrac{13x + x^3 - 10 + 8x^2}{x + 5}$

$x^2 + 3x - 2$

Perform each operation and then reduce.

13 $\dfrac{3x + 2}{x + 2} + \dfrac{x + 6}{x + 2}$

4

14 $\dfrac{4a}{3a - 12} \cdot \dfrac{5a - 20}{16a^2}$

$\dfrac{5}{12a}$

15 $\dfrac{5}{c + 5} + \dfrac{c}{5 + c}$

1

16 $\dfrac{a}{b} - \dfrac{b}{a}$

$\dfrac{a^2 - b^2}{ab}$

17 $\dfrac{a + 4}{a - 4} \div \dfrac{2a + 8}{a^2 - 8a + 16}$

$\dfrac{a - 4}{2}$

18 $\dfrac{\dfrac{x}{x - 1} - \dfrac{2x}{x - 2}}{\dfrac{2x}{x - 2} - \dfrac{3x}{x - 3}}$

$\dfrac{x - 3}{x - 1}$

19 $\dfrac{x + 2}{3} + \dfrac{x - 1}{6}$

$\dfrac{3x + 1}{6}$

20 $\dfrac{5}{a - 2} + \dfrac{3}{a^2 - 4a + 4}$

$\dfrac{5a - 7}{(a - 2)^2}$

21 $\dfrac{x}{x^2 - 9} - \dfrac{1}{2x - 6}$

$\dfrac{1}{2(x + 3)}$

22 $\dfrac{a}{x - 3} + \dfrac{4a}{3 - x}$

$\dfrac{-3a}{x - 3}$

23 $\dfrac{x - 6}{x - 3} - \dfrac{x}{3 - x}$

2

24 $\dfrac{5a}{x - 5} - \dfrac{3a}{5 - x} + \dfrac{2a}{5 - x} + \dfrac{a}{x - 5}$

-8

Problem Set: Cumulative Review 1–7

Problem Set   **A**

Fill in the blank.

1 The phrase *a number minus five* can be written as a variable expression as __?__ .

  n − 5

2 To subtract a signed number, add the __?__ of that number.

  opposite

3 If no factor is zero, then the product of an even number of negative factors is __?__ and the product of an odd number of negative factors is __?__ .

  positive; negative

4 To isolate the variable in the expression $\frac{2}{3}n$, perform the operation __?__ .

  MULTIPLY BY $\frac{3}{2}$

5 The coefficient in the term $9x^2$ is __?__ .

  9

6 $8(3x - 11) = 8 \cdot 3x + $ __?__ · __?__ .

  8·(−11)

7 The pattern that can be used to find the product of two binomials is called the __?__ pattern.

  FOIL

8 To factor the trinomial $6x^2 - x - 1$, the positive factors of $6x^2$ may be __?__ and __?__ or they may be __?__ and __?__ .

  6, 1; 2, 3

9 Dividing by a fraction is equivalent to multiplying by the __?__ of the fraction.

  reciprocal

Fill in the blank with >, <, or =.

10 6 __?__ 8

  6 < 8

11 4 __?__ −3

  4 > −3

12 $-5\frac{1}{2}$ __?__ −5

  $-5\frac{1}{2}$ < −5

13 −3 __?__ 0

  −3 < 0

14 Negative seventeen __?__ twelve.

  −17 < 12

15 If $a > b$, then $-3a$ __?__ $-3b$.

  −3a < −3b

Multiple Choice

16 Find the missing number in the sequence:

$$2, 3, 5, 9, 17, \underline{} , 65$$

a	25	**c**	41
b	33	**d**	28

b

17 The smallest natural number is:

a	-1	**c**	1
b	0	**d**	n

c

18 The subtraction problem $15 - (-3)$ is equivalent to:

a	$15 - 3$	**c**	$-15 - 3$
b	$15 + 3$	**d**	$-15 + 3$

b

19 An equation that has solution $y = 17$ is:

a	$y + 10 = 7$	**c**	$y + 13 = 30$
b	$y + 2 = 17$	**d**	$y - 7 = -24$

c

20 When $n = -3$, the value of $(n^2 - n) \div 2$ is:

a	3	**c**	$\frac{3}{2}$
b	6	**d**	-3

b

Write an equation that represents each problem, and solve the equation.

21 The sum of a number and eighteen is twenty-seven.

$n + 18 = 27; n = 9$

22 A number increased by three is negative seven.

$n + 3 = -7; n = -10$

23 Twelve decreased by a number is nine.

$12 - n = 9; n = 3$

24 Three more than a number is negative thirteen.

$3 + x = -13; x = -16$

25 A waiter received fifty-three coins in quarters and dimes. Seventeen of the coins were dimes. How many were quarters?

$17 + q = 53; q = 36$

26 Angela puts two dollars into a piggy bank each week. After fourteen weeks, how much was in the bank?

$2 \cdot 14 = x; x = 28$

27 Ten fewer than the product of three and a number is negative one. Find the number.

$3n - 10 = -1; n = 3$

Problem Set **B**

Solve.

28 $26 = -8r + 2$
$r = -3$

30 $7(y - 11) = -14$
$y = 9$

29 $16x + 5x + 2 = -11 + 4x$
$x = \frac{-13}{17}$

31 $-8z < 20$
$z > -\frac{5}{2}$

Perform the indicated operation(s).

32 $(4a + 3)(a + 1)$
$4a^2 + 7a + 3$

35 $(x^2 + 3x + 2) \div (x + 2)$
$x + 1$

33 $(3n + 10)(n - 1)$
$3n^2 + 7n - 10$

36 $\frac{1}{7}(49x^2 + 14x + 7)$
$7x^2 + 2x + 1$

34 $\dfrac{x^2}{x^2 - 4x + 4} - \dfrac{4}{x^2 - 4x + 4}$
$\frac{x + 2}{x - 2}$

37 $\dfrac{6x - 3y}{x - y} \cdot \dfrac{5x}{3y}$
$\frac{5x(2x - y)}{y(x - y)}$

Factor each expression.

38 $x^2 + 7x + 10$
$(x + 5)(x + 2)$

41 $4r^2 - 4$
$4(r - 1)(r + 1)$

39 $b^2 - 36$
$(b - 6)(b + 6)$

42 $3x^2 + 13x - 30$
$(3x - 5)(x + 6)$

40 $y^2 - 6y + 9$
$(y - 3)(y - 3)$

43 $12y^2 - 78y - 42$
$6(2y + 1)(y - 7)$

Evaluate each expression for $c = 3$, $d = \frac{1}{4}$, and $e = \frac{2}{5}$.

44 $5c^2$
45

47 $(c + d) \div (d + e)$
5

45 $(5c)^2$
225

48 $c + d + e$
$\frac{73}{20}$

46 $(c \cdot d) \div e$
$\frac{15}{8}$

49 $1 \div (c + d + e)$
$\frac{20}{73}$

Perform the indicated operation(s).

50 $-9 - 4(6 + 9^2 \cdot 2)$
-681

53 $(8a^2 - 6a + 15) \div (2a - 3)$
$4a + 3, R\,24$

51 $5x^3 \cdot (4x)^2$
$80x^5$

54 $7 \div (a - 3b) + 5$
$\frac{7}{a - 3b} + 5$

52 $\dfrac{3x - 1}{5} \cdot \dfrac{7x^4 - 2x^3 + 3x - 8}{7}$
$\frac{21x^5 - 13x^4 + 2x^3 + 9x^2 - 27x + 8}{35}$

55 $\dfrac{7a}{a^2 - 4} - \dfrac{3a + 2}{a^2 - 5a + 6}$
$\frac{4a^2 - 29a - 4}{(a - 2)(a + 2)(a - 3)}$

For each problem, write an equation and solve it. Then be sure to answer the original question.

56 The length of a rectangle is $3x - 7$ and its width is $2x + 5$. Find the perimeter and the area.

$p = 10x + 4, A = 6x^2 + x - 35$

57 The area of a rhombus is one hundred twenty square centimeters and the length of one diagonal is fifteen centimeters. Find the length of the other diagonal. (Use the formula that the area of a rhombus is half the product of the diagonals.)

$d = 16$

58 The area of a trapezoid is one hundred forty square millimeters. One base is twenty-seven millimeters and the altitude is seven millimeters. Find the length of the other base. (Use the formula that the area of a trapezoid is half the product of the altitude and the sum of the bases.)

$b = 13$

Problem Set C

59 Solve the complex inequality and graph it:

$$-9x < 10 \quad or \quad -47x + 19x > -14$$

$x > -\frac{9}{10}$ or $x < \frac{1}{2}$; all real numbers

60 Factor: $8x^3 + 12x^2 + 6x + 9$

$(4x^4 + 3)(2x + 3)$

61 Add: $\dfrac{7}{b - 2a} + \dfrac{6}{4a^2 - 2ab + b^2}$

$\dfrac{-14a + 7b + 6}{(2a - b)(2a - b)}$

Write an equation and solve it. Be sure to answer the original question.

62 A rectangle and an equilateral triangle have the same perimeter. Each side of the triangle is twelve centimeters, and the length of the rectangle is four centimeters longer than the width. Find the measurements of the rectangle.

$\ell = 11, w = 7$

63 Find two consecutive even integers such that fifty more than twice the second equals three times the first.

54, 56

64 The perimeter of an equilateral triangle is $5y + 17$. If the altitude is $2y + 1$, what is the area?

$\dfrac{10y^2 + 39y + 17}{6}$

62) $36 = 2x + 2(x + 4)$
$x = 7$
$x + 4 = 11$

64) The length of each side is:
$\dfrac{5y + 17}{3}$
Thus the area is:
$A = (\frac{1}{2})(\dfrac{5y + 17}{3})(2y + 1)$
$= \dfrac{(5y + 17)(2y + 1)}{6}$
$= \dfrac{10y^2 + 39y + 17}{6}$

Chapter 8

CHAPTER SCHEDULE

Basic
Problem Sets	8 Days
Review	2 Days
Test	2 Days

Average
Problem Sets	8 Days
Review	1 Day
Test	2 Days

Advanced
Problem Sets	8 Days
Review	2 Days
Test	1 Day

PROPORTION AND VARIATION

Section 8.1   Using Fractions for Ratios

SECTION SCHEDULE

Basic (1 day)

Average (1 day)

Advanced ($1\frac{1}{2}$ days)

A comparison of two numbers or two quantities often involves division.

EXAMPLES

- In a city, there is a tax of $6 on every $100 purchase. The comparison is 6 out of 100 or $\frac{6}{100}$.

- A housepainter can prime 8 rooms in 4 hours. The comparison is 8 compared to 4, or $\frac{8}{4}$.

Each fraction $\frac{6}{100}$ or $\frac{8}{4}$ represents a **ratio**.

Definition

A RATIO is a comparison of two numbers by division. If a and b are two numbers ($b \neq 0$), the ratio of a to b can be written several ways:

$$a : b \qquad a \div b \qquad \frac{a}{b}$$

The ratio is usually reduced to simplest terms: 2:1 rather than 8:4.

EXAMPLES

Some ratios are comparisons of "like units:"

- amount of tax : amount of purchase

- circumference of a circle : diameter of the circle

Some ratios are comparisons of "unlike units:"

- number of rooms painted : number of hours worked

- number of miles : number of hours

Many ratios are familiar:

- $\dfrac{\text{circumference}}{\text{diameter}}$ is π - $\dfrac{\text{miles}}{\text{hours}}$ is velocity

Another familiar ratio of like units is percent.

- The expression 37% means 37 out of 100. The percent can be written as a fraction, $\frac{37}{100}$, or as a decimal, 0.37.

Sample Problems

1   In the rectangle, what is the ratio of the length to the width? What is the ratio of the measure of the area to the measure of the perimeter?

$$l = 12$$
$$w = 5$$

PROCEDURE   The ratio of the length to the width is $12:5$.   To compute the area and the perimeter:

$$
\begin{aligned}
\text{Area} &= \ell \cdot w \\
&= 12 \cdot 5 \\
&= 60
\end{aligned}
\qquad
\begin{aligned}
\text{Perimeter} &= 2\ell + 2w \\
&= 2 \cdot 12 + 2 \cdot 5 \\
&= 34
\end{aligned}
\qquad
\begin{aligned}
\frac{\text{area}}{\text{perimeter}} &= \frac{60}{34} \\
&= \frac{2}{2} \cdot \frac{30}{17} \\
&= \frac{30}{17}
\end{aligned}
$$

2 In a closed cube with a side of 4, find the ratio of the measure of the surface area to that of the volume.

PROCEDURE The surface consists of 6 squares, so the measure of the surface area is $6 \cdot 4 \cdot 4$. The measure of the volume is $4 \cdot 4 \cdot 4$.

$$\frac{\text{surface area}}{\text{volume}} = \frac{6 \cdot 4 \cdot 4}{4 \cdot 4 \cdot 4} = \frac{3}{2}$$

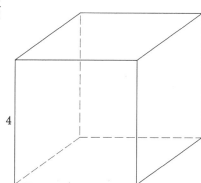

4

Problem Set **A**

In problems 1–10, write each ratio in its simplest form.

1 8 miles in 2 hours
$\frac{4}{1}$

2 40 miles per 2 gallons
$\frac{20}{1}$

3 $20x$ miles per x gallons
$\frac{20}{1}$

4 $1.38n$ dollars for n items
$\frac{1.38}{1}$

5 area to length of a rectangle
$\frac{w}{1}$

6 perimeter to side of a square
$\frac{4}{1}$

7 area to base of a triangle
$\frac{h}{2}$

8 area to radius of a circle
$\frac{\pi}{1}$

9 a distance of $2t^2 - 9t - 5$ per $2t + 1$ seconds
$\frac{t-5}{1}$

10 a distance of $8t^2 + 6t - 9$ per $4t - 3$ seconds
$\frac{2t+3}{1}$

Solve each equation. (Review: Sections 2.6, 3.6)

11 $r - 2 = -3$
$r = -1$

12 $5 = 12 + s$
$s = 7$

13 $4 - t = 9$
$t = -5$

14 $\dfrac{m}{10} = -2$
$m = -20$

15 $3n = -6$
$n = -2$

16 $\dfrac{p}{-5} = 1$
$p = -5$

Problem Set **B**

In problems 17–20, solve each equation.

17 $28 = 0.15b$

$b = 186\frac{2}{3}$

18 $\dfrac{2}{3} + \dfrac{1}{2}t = \dfrac{5}{6}$

$t = \frac{1}{3}$

19 $17 = 135p$

$p = \frac{17}{135}$

20 $\dfrac{3}{4} - \dfrac{1}{3}x = \dfrac{2}{5}$

$x = \frac{21}{20}$

Perform each of the following operations.

21 $\dfrac{1}{a} + \dfrac{2}{3a}$

$\frac{5}{3a}$

22 $\dfrac{6}{x^2 - 4} - \dfrac{4}{x + 2}$

$\frac{2(7-2x)}{x^2-4}$

23 $\dfrac{w + 4}{w^2 - 6w + 9} \cdot \dfrac{w - 3}{2w^2 + 7w - 4}$

$\frac{1}{2w^2 - 7w + 3}$

24 $\dfrac{r + 3}{1 - 2r + r^2} \cdot \dfrac{1 - r^2}{r^2 + 2r - 3}$

$\frac{1 + r}{-r^2 + 2r - 1}$

Problem Set **C**

25 The formula $s = 16t^2$ is used to compute the distance s that a dropped object on earth will fall in t seconds. The ratio of the gravity on the surface of Mars to the gravity on Earth is 0.39, and so the formula $s = (0.39) \cdot 16t^2$ describes falling objects on Mars. What distance will a dropped object fall in three seconds on Mars?

56.16

Problems 26–31 give the ratio of the surface gravity on other planets to the surface gravity on Earth. How far will a dropped object fall in two seconds on each planet?

26 Mercury: 0.37

23.68

27 Venus: 0.89

56.96

28 Jupiter: 2.54

162.56

29 Saturn: 1.06

67.84

30 Uranus: 1.09

69.76

31 Neptune: 1.41

90.24

32 On which planet (including Earth and Mars) will a dropped object fall the farthest in three seconds?

Jupiter

33 If 0.13 is the ratio of the surface gravity on Pluto to that on Earth, how far would a dropped object fall in two seconds on Pluto?

8.32

$\mathbf{X}$ tending the topic: Percent and Investments

Sample Problem

1   An investment of eight hundred dollars at ten percent per year earns eighty dollars at the end of the year. How much will the rate have to increase to earn one hundred dollars per year?

PROCEDURE   Use the formula   (principal) (rate) = (amount earned).
Let x represent the increase in the rate over ten percent. Then:

principal = 800 $p \cdot r = a$
rate = 0.10 + x $800(0.1 + x) = 100$
amount earned = 100 $80 + 800x = 100$
                                            $800x = 20$

$$x = \frac{20}{800} = \frac{1}{40} \cdot \frac{20}{20} = \frac{1}{40} = 0.025$$

The rate would have to increase 0.025 or 2.5%. (The new rate would be 12.5%.)

Problem Set $\mathbf{X}$

1   If you now get \$44.75 on an investment of \$892, how much would the rate have to be increased for you to earn \$50 a year?
    increased from 5.0% to 5.60%; 0.6%

2   Carla has some money invested at a rate of 6% a year. She discovered that she could get twice the amount each year from her investment if she saved another \$400 and bought a bond that yielded 10% a year. How much did she have invested originally?
    \$2000

2)   If the original investment was x, then:
    $p \cdot r = a$
    $x (0.06) = a$

Twice the amount is $0.12x$ and:
    $(x + 400)(0.10) = 0.12x$
    $x = 2000$

3   In earning **compound interest**, interest made during the first interest period is left in the bank to earn interest during the second period, and so on. Which of the following calculations gives the correct amount in the bank for one thousand dollars at six percent per period after three periods? Why? (More than one answer may be correct.)

a   \$1000 · (0.06)³   c   \$1000 · (1.06)³

b   (((\$1000 · 1.06) · 1.06) · 1.06)   d   \$1000 + (1.06)³
    b, c

Project: Divisibility Tests

A **divisibility test** is a short method to determine if one natural number is a factor of another natural number.

- A number is divisible by 2 if and only if it is even.

- A number is divisible by 5 if and only if it ends in a zero or a five.

- A number is divisible by 10 if and only if the last digit is zero.

A divisibility test for 3 is the following:

A number is divisible by 3 if and only if the sum of its digits is divisible by 3. For example, for the number 4851 the sum of the digits is $4+8+5+1 = 18$. Since 18 is divisible by 3, then 4851 is divisible by 3.

To understand why the divisibility test works, think of 4851 as 4 thousands, 8 hundreds, 5 tens, and 1 ones. Each time one thousand is divided by 3, the remainder is 1. Thus if 4 thousand is divided by 3, the remainder is 4. Also, each time one hundred is divided by 3, the remainder is 1, so if 8 hundred is divided by 3, the remainder is 8. Similarly, if 5 tens is divided by 3, the remainder is 5, and if 1 ones is divided by 3, the remainder is 1. To summarize, dividing 4851 by 3, place by place, gives a remainder of $4+8+5+1=18$, which is divisible by 3. Thus the overall remainder is zero, and so 4851 is divisible by 3.

1   Describe divisibility tests for 4, for 8, and for 25.

2   Try to invent divisibility tests for 6, for 9, and for 12.

3   Try to invent divisibility tests for 7 and for 11.

4   A natural number is prime if it is not divisible by smaller natural numbers (except 1). To test whether a natural number is prime, what is the smallest set of numbers that must be tested as factors?

1) For 4: last 2 digits are divisible by 4

For 8: last 3 digits are divisible by 8

For 25: last 2 digits are divisible by 25

2) For 6: divisible by 2 and by 3

For 9: sum of digits is divisible by 9

For 12: divisible by 3 and by 4

3) Answers may vary

4) test numbers $\leq \sqrt{n}$

314

Section 8.2 Using Fractions in Proportions

The scale on a map is a ratio. For this map, the scale is that 1 cm represents 100 km. This may be written several ways, including:

1 cm : 100 km

$$\frac{1 \text{ cm}}{100 \text{ km}}$$

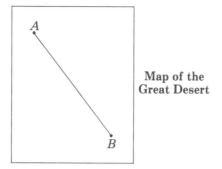

Map of the Great Desert

On the map, the distance between points A and B is 3.5 cm:

$$\frac{1}{100} = \frac{3.5}{x}$$

The value of x must be 350, and thus the actual distance represented is 350 km.

The equation $\dfrac{1}{100} = \dfrac{3.5}{350}$ is called a **proportion**.

Definition

A **PROPORTION** is a mathematical statement that two ratios are equal.

EXAMPLES

- $\dfrac{2}{5} = \dfrac{4}{10}$
- $\dfrac{7}{10} = \dfrac{700}{1000}$

Proportions usually occur in problems with a variable, such as:

- $\dfrac{3}{4} = \dfrac{6}{x}$

One way to solve for the variable is to multiply both sides of the equation by the common denominator:

$$\frac{3}{4} = \frac{6}{x}$$

MULTBY $4x$: $\quad 4x\left(\dfrac{3}{4}\right) = 4x\left(\dfrac{6}{x}\right)$

$$3x = 24$$

MULTBY $\frac{1}{3}$: $\qquad x = 8$

Thus $x = 8$.

Sample Problems

1   Rewrite the following proportion without fractions: $\dfrac{a}{b} = \dfrac{c}{d}$

PROCEDURE   Multiply both sides by the common denominator bd:

$$\frac{a}{b} = \frac{c}{d}$$

MULTBY bd: $bd\left(\dfrac{a}{b}\right) = bd\left(\dfrac{c}{d}\right)$

$$\frac{bda}{b} = \frac{bdc}{d}$$

$$ad = bc$$

The term **cross-product** *is used as an abbreviation for "multiply by the product of the denominators." Students may be familiar with this property as the statement: in a proportion, the product of the means equals the product of the extremes.*

The equation $ad = bc$ is called the **cross-product** of the original proportion. Notice how the cross-product pattern is used in the next Sample Problem.

2   Solve the following proportions:

a $\dfrac{x}{5} = \dfrac{6}{15}$ b $\dfrac{3}{4} = \dfrac{2t}{13}$ c $\dfrac{7}{2w-3} = \dfrac{8}{3w+4}$

PROCEDURE   Write the cross-product for each proportion, and solve:

a $\dfrac{x}{5} = \dfrac{6}{15}$

$$15x = 30$$
$$x = 2$$

b $\dfrac{3}{4} = \dfrac{2t}{13}$

$$39 = 8t$$
$$\frac{39}{8} = t$$

c $\dfrac{7}{2w-3} = \dfrac{8}{3w+4}$

$$7(3w + 4) = 8(2w - 3)$$
$$21w + 28 = 16w - 24$$
$$5w + 28 = -24$$
$$5w = -52$$
$$w = \frac{-52}{5}$$

3   A board is twelve feet long and weighs sixteen pounds. If a nine-foot section of the board is cut off, what would it weigh?

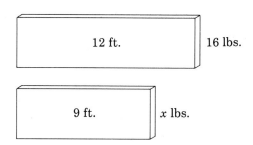

12 ft.   16 lbs.

9 ft. x lbs.

PROCEDURE   Use the ratio of the board's length to its weight:

$$\frac{\text{length}}{\text{weight}} = \frac{12}{16} = \frac{9}{x}$$
$$12x = 144 \qquad \text{(the cross-product)}$$
$$x = 12$$

The nine-foot section would weigh twelve pounds.

Problem Set **A**

In problems 1–18, solve each proportion.

1 $\dfrac{3}{8} = \dfrac{n}{32}$

    $n = 12$

2 $\dfrac{a}{5} = \dfrac{14}{35}$

    $a = 2$

3 $\dfrac{7}{x} = \dfrac{42}{36}$

    $x = 6$

4 $\dfrac{8}{9} = \dfrac{72}{y}$

    $y = 81$

5 $\dfrac{3}{4} = \dfrac{m}{5}$

    $m = \dfrac{15}{4}$

6 $\dfrac{b}{15} = \dfrac{7}{2}$

    $b = \dfrac{105}{2}$

7 $\dfrac{21}{t} = \dfrac{8}{5}$

    $t = \dfrac{105}{8}$

8 $\dfrac{16}{25} = \dfrac{6}{n}$

    $n = \dfrac{75}{8}$

9 $\dfrac{4}{5} = \dfrac{2x}{9}$

    $x = \dfrac{18}{5}$

10 $\dfrac{3n}{7} = \dfrac{15}{24}$

    $n = \dfrac{35}{24}$

11 $\dfrac{12}{5w} = \dfrac{7}{8}$

    $w = \dfrac{96}{35}$

12 $\dfrac{14}{3} = \dfrac{27}{4r}$

    $r = \dfrac{81}{56}$

13 $\dfrac{2x + 1}{3} = \dfrac{9}{25}$

    $x = \dfrac{1}{25}$

14 $\dfrac{37}{100} = \dfrac{3x - 2}{4}$

    $x = \dfrac{29}{25}$

15 $\dfrac{10}{4n + 5} = \dfrac{7}{80}$

    $n = \dfrac{765}{28}$

16 $\dfrac{n}{n + 4} = \dfrac{3}{8}$

    $n = \dfrac{12}{5}$

17 $\dfrac{12}{9} = \dfrac{n + 6}{2n}$

    $n = \dfrac{18}{5}$

18 $\dfrac{2x + 3}{x - 4} = \dfrac{1}{2}$

    $x = \dfrac{-10}{3}$

ASSIGNMENT GUIDE

Basic (2 days)
(1) 1–15, 43–46
(2) 16–27

Average (2 days)
(1) 2–18 (even), 24–30 (even), 43–47
(2) 31–42, 48–51, 58

Advanced (1½ days)
(1) 24–50 (even)
   313: 1–3
(2) 52–58

As oral exercises, students can be asked to state the cross-product for each proportion.

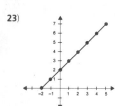

23)

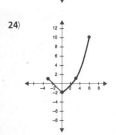

24)

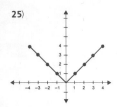

25)

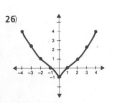

26)

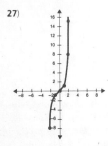

27)

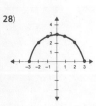

28)

19 If a piece of rope one hundred meters long has a mass of eight kilograms, what is the mass of forty meters of the rope?

$\frac{16}{5}$ kg

20 If sixty-four ounces of cold cream contain forty-five ounces of oil, how many ounces of oil will ten ounces of cold cream contain?

$7\frac{1}{32}$ ounces

21 If the scale on a road map is five centimeters for one hundred kilometers, how many centimeters would represent three hundred fifty-five kilometers?

17.75 cm

22 If a coat that has been discounted by twenty percent now sells for one hundred eighty-eight dollars, what was its original price?

$235

For each problem, draw and label a set of axes. Then graph each set of points and connect them. (Review: Graphing)

23 $(0,-2), (-1,1), (0,2), (1,3), (2,4), (3,5), (4,6), (5,7)$

24 $(-3,1), (0,-2), (3,1), (6,10)$

25 $(-4,4), (-3,3), (-2,2), (-1,1), (0,0), (1,1), (2,2), (3,3), (4,4)$

26 $(-4,4), (-3,2.25), (-2,1), (-1,0.25), (0,-1), (1,0.25), (2,1), (3,2.25), (4,4)$

27 $(-2,-8), (-1,-1), (0,0), (1,1), (2,8), (2\frac{1}{2},15\frac{5}{8})$

28 $(-3,0), (-2,2.23), (-1,2.83), (0,3), (1,2.83), (2,2.23), (3,0)$

Problem Set   **B**

In problems 29–37, solve each proportion.

29 $\dfrac{2x}{5} = \dfrac{0.07}{0.13}$

$x = \dfrac{35}{26}$

30 $\dfrac{0.5}{3n} = \dfrac{1.85}{0.72}$

$n = 0.0649$

31 $\dfrac{x-5}{x+3} = \dfrac{x+2}{x+5}$

$x = -\dfrac{31}{5}$

32 $\dfrac{n-7}{n+4} = \dfrac{n+4}{n+2}$

$n = -\dfrac{16}{13}$

33 $\dfrac{t+6}{t+9} = \dfrac{t-5}{t-3}$

$t = 27$

34 $\dfrac{2x+4}{x-3} = \dfrac{2x+1}{x-1}$

$x = \dfrac{1}{7}$

35 $\dfrac{x+5}{3x-2} = \dfrac{x+4}{3x+1}$

$w = -\dfrac{13}{6}$

36 $\dfrac{2x-5}{4x+3} = \dfrac{2x+5}{4x-3}$

$x = 0$

37 $\dfrac{5w-8}{2w+1} = \dfrac{5w+6}{2w-1}$

$w = \dfrac{1}{19}$

38 If two and three tenths centimeters on a map represents a distance of fifty-five kilometers, what distance does four and seven tenths centimeters represent?

112.3913 km

39 If a recipe calls for one and one third cups of onions to serve eight, how many cups of onions are needed to serve five?

$\frac{5}{6}$ cup

40 If a jacket that was originally one hundred thirty-six dollars has been marked down to one hundred nineteen dollars, what was the percent of discount?

12.5%

41 If you need forty-five pounds of grass seed for a lawn that is fifteen hundred square feet, how many pounds do you need for a lawn that is forty-five feet long and twenty-seven feet wide?

36.45 lbs.

42 If the subway can go from 14th Street to 51st Street in nine minutes, about how long will it take the subway to go from 14th Street to 96th Street?

about 20 minutes

Find the mystery number in each sequence.

43 1, 8, 27, a, 125

64

44 1, 2, 6, 24, 120, ___?___

720

45 16, 24, 36, b, 81, $121\frac{1}{2}$

54

46 0.5, 0.333 . . . , 0.25, 0.2, 0.1666 . . . , ___?___, 0.125

0.1428571 . . .

47 $\frac{3}{7}$, $\frac{12}{18}$, $\frac{48}{112}$, n, $\frac{768}{1792}$

$\frac{192}{448}$

48 $-\frac{5}{6}$, x, $-\frac{45}{54}$, $\frac{135}{162}$, $-\frac{405}{486}$

$\frac{15}{18}$

49 4, $4x$, $4x^2$, ___?___, $4x^4$

$4x^3$

50 1, $2x + 1$, $4x^2 - 2$, $8x^3 + 4x^2 - 2x - 1$, ___?___, $32x^5 + 16x^4 - 16x^3 - 8x^2 + 2x + 1$

$16x^4$

51 $\frac{x + 3}{1 - 3x}$, $\frac{5x + 15}{8 - 24x}$, $\frac{25x + 75}{64 - 192x}$, $\frac{?}{\rule{1cm}{0.4pt}}$, $\frac{625x + 1875}{4096 - 12288x}$

$\frac{125x + 375}{512 - 1536x}$

Problem Set C

Solve each proportion.

52 $\dfrac{\frac{1}{2}}{\frac{5}{8}} = \dfrac{x}{\frac{2}{3}}$

$x = \frac{8}{15}$

54 $\dfrac{\frac{2}{5}}{-\frac{1}{4}} = \dfrac{-\frac{7}{8}}{\frac{2}{x+1}}$

$x = \frac{93}{35}$

56 $\dfrac{\frac{5}{4}}{\frac{1}{6}} = \dfrac{x}{\frac{x+2}{\frac{2}{3}}}$

$x = -\frac{5}{2}$

53 $\dfrac{\frac{1}{x}}{\frac{3}{4}} = \dfrac{\frac{5}{6}}{\frac{3}{5}}$

$x = \frac{24}{25}$

55 $\dfrac{\frac{3}{2}}{4} = \dfrac{\frac{9}{8}}{\frac{2}{5}}$ over $2x - 5$

$x = \frac{25}{4}$

57 $\dfrac{\frac{x}{0.035}}{\frac{0.14}{2.71}} = \dfrac{\frac{3}{1.12}}{\frac{1.05}{0.75}}$

$x = 0.0171365$

58 State four proportions that have $ab = xy$ as the cross-product.

$$\frac{a}{y} = \frac{x}{b}, \frac{a}{x} = \frac{y}{b}, \frac{y}{a} = \frac{b}{x}, \frac{x}{a} = \frac{b}{y}$$

SECTION SCHEDULE

Basic (1 day)

Average (1 day)

Advanced (1 day)

Section 8.3   Inverse Variation

Problem: You have prepared 100 "muffin pizzas" for a party. If 20 people come to the party, how many pizzas can each person have? How many each for 40 people? 50 people? 200 people?

Since there are 100 pizzas,

$$\left(\begin{array}{c}\text{Number of}\\\text{persons}\end{array}\right) \cdot \left(\begin{array}{c}\text{Number of pizzas}\\\text{per person}\end{array}\right) = 100 \text{ pizzas}$$

$(20) \cdot (\underline{\ ?\ }) = 100;$ 5 pizzas/person
$(40) \cdot (\underline{\ ?\ }) = 100;$ $2\frac{1}{2}$ pizzas/person
$(50) \cdot (\underline{\ ?\ }) = 100;$ 2 pizzas/person
$(200) \cdot (\underline{\ ?\ }) = 100;$ $\frac{1}{2}$ pizzas/person

Generally, if x represents the number of persons, if y represents the number of pizzas per person, and if there are k pizzas, an equation is:

$$x \cdot y = k$$

The number k is a fixed number in this problem, and it is called a **constant** or **constant of variation**. The variables x and y have a constant product, and are said to be in **inverse variation** with each other.

Sample Problems

1 Belinda has $72 to buy grams of gold. Draw a graph of the number of grams she can buy for different prices of gold.

PROCEDURE   As the price of gold changes, the number of grams Belinda can buy with $72 will also change.

cost per gram	1	2	3	4	6	8	9	12	18	24	36	72
Number of grams for $72	72	36	24	18	12	9	8	6	4	3	2	1

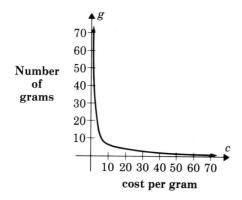

If *c* is the cost per gram, and *n* is the number of grams, then the formula $nc = 72$ describes the inverse variation between the variables.

2 If x and y vary inversely, and if $y = 3$ when $x = 8$, then:
a What is the constant of variation?
b Write the equation that relates x and y.

PROCEDURE
Since x and y vary inversely, then $xy = k$, and k is the constant of variation.
    a $xy = k$
         $(3)(8) = k$
           $k = 24$
    The constant of variation is 24.
    b The equation is $xy = 24$.

ASSIGNMENT GUIDE

Basic (1 day)
1–15, 18, 20–26

Average (1 day)
2–18 (even), 24, 25,
28–44 (even)

Advanced (1 day)
18, 20, 27–34, 43–52

Problem Set **A**

In problems 1–12, state whether or not each is an example of inverse variation. If yes, write it in the form $xy = k$.

1 $\dfrac{xy}{3} = 6$

    yes, $xy = 18$

2 $n = \dfrac{m}{7}$

    no

3 $d = 10t$

    no

4 $A = \ell \cdot 4$

    no

5 $11 = \frac{1}{2}bh$

    yes, $bh = 22$

6 $8 = 0.4rt$

    yes, $rt = 20$

7 $\dfrac{1}{4} = \dfrac{x}{y}$

    no

8 $a = \dfrac{3}{b}$

    yes, $ab = 3$

9 $20 = ab$

    yes, $ab = 20$

10 $x + y = 24$

    no

11 $xy + 8 = 15$

    yes, $xy = 7$

12 $\dfrac{1}{x} = \dfrac{y}{4}$

    yes, $xy = 4$

13   The area covered by a fixed amount of paint remains the same even if the dimensions of the region being painted vary. If a pint of paint covers a rectangle with a length of five meters and a width of three meters, use inverse variation to find the width the paint will cover when the length of the rectangle is ten meters.

    $w = 1.5m$

In problems 14–17, one variable varies inversely with the other. Write an equation that states their relationship.

14   When $r = 3$, $t = 17$.

    $rt = 51$

15   When $\ell = 8$, $w = 11$.

    $\ell w = 88$

16   When $x = 2$, $y = \dfrac{1}{4}$.

    $xy = \frac{1}{2}$

17   When $g = 0.3$, $s = 1245$.

    $gs = 373.5$

18   Graph $xy = 24$ for $x = 1, 2, 3, 4, 6, 8, 12$, and 24. Connect the points of the graph with a smooth curve.

    the graph contains the points (1,24), (2,12), (3,8), (4,6), (6,4), (8,3), (12,2), (24,1)

19   Draw a graph that shows $36 = xy$ for $x = 1, 2, 3, 4, 6, 9, 12, 18$, and 36. Connect the points with a smooth curve.

    the graph contains the points (1,36), (2,18), (3,12), (4,9), (6,6), (9,4), (12,3), (18,2), (36,1)

20   Draw a graph of $xy = 40$ for $x = 1, 2, 4, 5, 8, 10, 20$, and 40. Connect the points with a smooth curve.

    the graph contains the points (1,40), (2,20), (4,10), (5,8), (8,4), (10,4), (20,2), (40,1)

Translate each verbal expression into a variable expression. (Review: Section 1.4)

21 the sum of seventeen and twice a variable

$17 + 2n$

22 the product of negative five and the square of a variable

$-5x^2$

23 twenty-one more than the product of twenty-one and a variable

$21 + 21y$

24 a number increased by the product of itself and eight

$m + 8m$

25 seven fewer than the quotient of a number and ten

$\frac{x}{10} - 7$

26 seventeen hundredths more than the sum of seventeen hundred and a variable

$0.17 + (1700 + n)$

Problem Set **B**

27 The force that repels two particles that have the same kind of charge (positive or negative) varies inversely with the distance between the two particles. If the distance is doubled, what happens to the force (that is, how does the force change)?

the force is halved (divided by two)

28 For a given distance, if the rate is cut in half, what happens to the time?

time is doubled

29 R varies inversely with S. When R is multiplied by a constant c, what happens to S?

S is multiplied by $\frac{1}{c}$

In problems 30–34, state whether each one is an example of inverse variation.

30 The average speed and the distance, when the amount of time is constant.

no $(t = \frac{d}{r})$

31 The base and height of a triangle when the area is constant.

yes $(bh = 2A)$

32 The radius and circumference of a circle.

no $(\pi = \frac{c}{2r})$

33 The height and radius of a cylinder when the volume is constant.

no $(hr = \frac{v}{\pi}r)$

34 The height of a trapezoid and the sum of the bases when the area is constant.

yes $(A = \frac{h}{2}(b_1 + b_2))$

In problems 35–44, solve each proportion.

35 $\dfrac{7}{h} = \dfrac{5}{2}$

$h = \dfrac{14}{5}$

36 $\dfrac{n + 5}{3} = 11$

$n = 28$

37 $\dfrac{x}{x - 5} = \dfrac{3}{10}$

$x = -\dfrac{15}{7}$

38 $\dfrac{7}{m - 3} = \dfrac{5}{m + 2}$

$m = -\dfrac{29}{2}$

39 $\dfrac{x}{x + 2} = \dfrac{x - 4}{x}$

$x = -4$

40 $\dfrac{2n + 5}{n - 3} = \dfrac{2n - 7}{n + 4}$

$n = \dfrac{1}{26}$

41 $\dfrac{3m + 2}{10m + 9} = \dfrac{2}{7}$

$m = 4$

42 $\dfrac{a}{5} = \dfrac{a - 16}{3}$

$a = 4$

43 $\dfrac{t - 1}{2} = \dfrac{t + 3}{3}$

$t = 9$

44 $\dfrac{s + 1}{s - 1} = \dfrac{4}{5}$

$s = -9$

Problem Set C

In problems 45–50, solve each proportion for x.

45 $\dfrac{ax}{b} = \dfrac{cx}{d}$

0

46 $\dfrac{a + x}{b + c} = \dfrac{d}{e + f}$

$x = -a + \dfrac{bd + bc}{e + f}$

47 $\dfrac{a + x}{b + x} = \dfrac{c}{d}$

$x = \dfrac{bc - ad}{d - c}$

48 $\dfrac{ax + b}{c} = \dfrac{d}{e}$

$x = \dfrac{dc - be}{ae}$

49 $\dfrac{ax + b}{cx + d} = \dfrac{e}{f}$

$x = \dfrac{de - bf}{ab - ce}$

50 $\dfrac{ax + d}{cd + e} = \dfrac{fx + g}{hi + j}$

$x = \dfrac{cdg + eg - dhi - dj}{ahi + aj - fed - fe}$

51 The intensity of light varies inversely with the square of the distance from the light. If the intensity is three tenths at four feet, what will it be at seven feet?

0.09796

52 The frequency of a violin string varies inversely as the square root of its weight. If the frequency is four hundred forty when the weight is four units, what is the frequency when the weight is nine units?

$293\frac{1}{3}$

After-School Mathematics: Bike Trip

After Jerry bought his new bicycle, he began to take long bike trips. He liked riding along an old country road. When he traveled north on the road, which was mostly downhill, he averaged 20 miles per hour. When he returned south, he only averaged 12 miles per hour.

On a Saturday when he was not working, Jerry road north to Springfield, 60 miles away. He returned the same day. When he got home, he tried to figure out his average speed.

The trip north took 3 hours, and the trip south took 5 hours. Therefore, Jerry traveled 120 miles in 8 hours, for an average speed of 15 miles per hour.

Jerry's young brother Frankie thought Jerry had made a mistake. Frankie figured that Jerry's average should have been halfway between his northbound average and his southbound average, or 16 miles per hour. Jerry explained to Frankie that he hadn't traveled the same amount of time at each rate, so he couldn't take an average of his rates. Frankie remained unconvinced, and he ran off to his mom to check who was really right.

A method to average two rates is to use the harmonic mean:

$$HM = \frac{2ab}{a+b}$$
$$= \frac{2(20)(12)}{20+12}$$
$$= \frac{480}{32}$$
$$= 15$$

Application: Lumber for the Set

Jeanine and David are in charge of the set for the school play. To construct the set, their first task is to order two-by-fours to frame the backdrops and to support the backdrops.

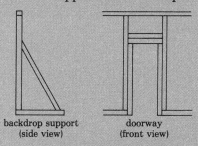

backdrop support
(side view)

doorway
(front view)

The smaller flats each need one internal vertical piece, and the longer flat needs two internal vertical pieces.

The backdrop is to consist of three flats, each one ten feet tall. At stage right is a flat that is six feet long. The flat for center stage is eleven feet long, and the flat at stage left is eight feet long. Each flat needs a vertical piece at least every four feet. Also, every vertical piece, including the ends, needs a support: a five-foot horizontal piece and a nine-foot angled brace. In addition, there are two doorways that need "double framing" so that they appear solid.

How many feet of lumber should Jeanine and David order?

		running feet
verticals:	10 @ 10 ft	100
tops/btms:	2 @ 6 ft	12
	2 @ 11 ft	22
	2 @ 8 ft	16
supports for the verticals:	10 @ 5 ft	50
	10 @ 9 ft	90
the doorways:	4 @ 8 ft	32
	4 @ $2\frac{1}{2}$ ft	10
	Total:	332

Section 8.4   Setting Up Solutions to Problems

The previous sections presented two kinds of problems.

Proportions   In these problems, two ratios are equal:

$$\frac{a}{b} = \frac{c}{d}$$

- $\dfrac{x}{5} = \dfrac{7}{2};\quad x = \dfrac{35}{2}$

Inverse variation   In these problems, the product of two variables is constant:

$$x \cdot y = k$$

- $xy = 12;\quad (x,y) = (1,12),\ (2,6)\ (3,4)\ \ldots$

The solution is expressed as a list of ordered pairs.

To solve these kinds of problems, two of the first steps are to identify the variables in the problem and to write an equation for the variables. The key to writing an equation is to analyze the problem and find two quantities that are equal.

Sample Problems

1   Two work crews start on the same day on opposite sides of a mountain to build a tunnel. Crew A builds at a rate of 5 meters a day, and Crew B builds 6 meters a day. When the tunnels meet, Crew B has gone 25 meters further than Crew A. How much of the tunnel did Crew A build?

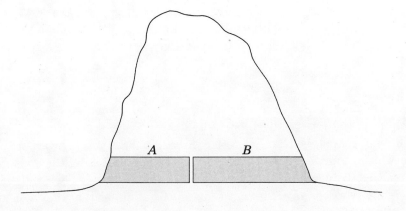

PROCEDURE

First step   Use a variable to help describe the problem. Let x represent the number of meters in Crew A's tunnel. Thus the length of Crew B's tunnel is $x + 25$.

Second step   Set up and solve an equation. Both crews worked the same number of days, so the two times are equal.

$$\frac{\text{distance for } A}{\text{rate for } A} = \frac{\text{distance for } B}{\text{rate for } B}$$

$$\frac{x}{5} = \frac{x + 25}{6}$$

$$6x = 5(x + 25) \quad \text{(the cross-product)}$$
$$6x = 5x + 125$$
$$x = 125$$

Thus Crew A built 125 meters of tunnel.

Third step   To check the answer, Crew A needed 25 days to build its 125-foot tunnel. In those 25 days, Crew B built $6 \cdot 25 = 150$ meters of tunnel, which is 25 meters more than Crew A. ✓

---

2   A department store advertises a "storewide" sale with "all prices reduced proportionally." A $7 crystal glass is now $6, and a reclining chair has been reduced by $50. What was the original price of the chair? What is the sale price?

PROCEDURE   Since all prices are reduced by the same proportion, the ratio old price : sale price   will be constant for all items in the store.

Let y represent the old price of the chair, and so the sale price must be $y - 50$.   The old price and sale price of the glass are 7 and 6, respectively. This leads to the proportion:

$$\frac{y}{y - 50} = \frac{7}{6}$$
$$7(y - 50) = 6y \quad \text{(cross-product)}$$
$$7y - 350 = 6y$$
$$y = 350$$

Since the old price of the chair was $350, the sale price must be $300.

3 The treasurer noticed that his boss was usually a little late for meetings. Then he noticed that the number of minutes she was late varied inversely with the amount of money being discussed. She was 10 minutes late to a meeting involving $2000. How late is she expected for a meeting to discuss $10,000?

PROCEDURE For inverse variation, the product of the variables is constant:

$$\left(\begin{array}{c}\text{number of} \\ \text{minutes late}\end{array}\right) \cdot \left(\begin{array}{c}\text{amount} \\ \text{of money}\end{array}\right) = k$$

Letting ℓ represent the number of minutes late:

$$(10)\,(2000) = (\ell)\,(10,000)$$
$$20,000 = 10,000 \cdot \ell$$
$$\ell = 2$$

She is expected to be two minutes late.

ASSIGNMENT GUIDE

Basic (1 day)
1–12, 25–27

Average (1 day)
1–15, 19–27

Advanced (1 day)
1–6, 13–30

Problem Set **A**

1 Elise and Becky jog together but Elise always goes a mile farther at the same rate after Becky stops. If Becky jogs twenty minutes a day and Elise jogs thirty minutes a day, how far does each run?

Becky: 2 miles, Elise: 3 miles

Find the missing dimensions of each of the rectangles:

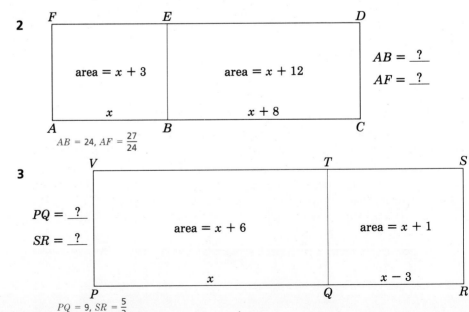

2

area = $x + 3$ area = $x + 12$

x $x + 8$

$AB = \underline{\ ?\ }$
$AF = \underline{\ ?\ }$

$AB = 24,\ AF = \dfrac{27}{24}$

3

$PQ = \underline{\ ?\ }$
$SR = \underline{\ ?\ }$

area = $x + 6$ area = $x + 1$

x $x - 3$

$PQ = 9,\ SR = \dfrac{5}{3}$

4 Jack noticed from a newspaper report that a pound of hamburger had increased from \$1.89 to \$1.99. The article went on to say that the change would mean that the cost of a backyard barbecue would go up \$10. Jack was skeptical, so he calculated the number of pounds of hamburger the newspaper writer had in mind for the backyard barbecue. What was it?

> 100 pounds

5 Maria and Adelle each have the same amount invested, but Maria gets a rate of return each year that is two percent higher. If Maria gets seventy dollars each year and Adelle gets sixty dollars, what are the rates for each investment?

> Maria: 14%   Adelle: 12%

6 In a far-off galaxy, a long, long time ago, they measured the lengths and widths of rectangles in pallups. If a saloop of paint would cover a rectangle eight pallups long and eleven pallups wide, how wide a rectangle that is three pallups long could a saloop of paint cover?

> $29\frac{1}{3}$

Find the least common denominator for each set of fractions, and then calculate the sum of the fractions. (Review: Computation)

7 $\dfrac{1}{3}$ $\dfrac{3}{4}$

> $12, \frac{13}{12}$

8 $\dfrac{2}{5}$ $\dfrac{2}{6}$ $\dfrac{4}{7}$

> $105, \frac{137}{105}$

9 $\dfrac{a}{x}$ $\dfrac{b}{x^2}$

> $x^2, \frac{ax+b}{x^2}$

10 $\dfrac{1}{a}$ $\dfrac{1}{ab}$ $\dfrac{2}{b}$

> $ab, \frac{2a+b+1}{ab}$

11 $\dfrac{3}{x+5}$ $\dfrac{4}{x-5}$

> $x^2-25, \frac{7x}{x^2-25}$

12 $\dfrac{a}{a-1}$ $\dfrac{1}{a+1}$ $\dfrac{a+1}{a^2-1}$

> $a^2-1, \frac{a^2+3a}{a^2-1}$

Problem Set **B**

13 Mark and his cousin Luke leave their houses at 10:00 A.M. and bicycle toward each other until they meet. Mark averages fifteen miles an hour, but Luke has more uphill travel and only averages ten miles an hour. As a result, they are ten miles farther from Mark's house than Luke's when they meet. What time did they meet?

> 12:00 noon

14 The intensity of light varies inversely with the square of the distance from the light source. If the intensity is six at eight feet, at what distance is the intensity twenty-four?

> 4 feet

15 If you can buy a jacket for fifty-eight dollars and fifty cents after a discount of twenty-two percent, what was the original price?

> \$75

13) First find the distances:

> Luke: x
> Mark: $10 + x$

Their times are equal, so:

$$\frac{d}{r} = \frac{x}{10} = \frac{10+x}{15}$$

$$x = 20$$
$$10 + x = 30$$

Luke and Mark each needed 2 hours to travel the 20 and 30 miles, respectively. They met at noon.

Problem Set C

16) The trapezoid and the triangle have the same height. The area of the trapezoid is:
$A = \frac{1}{2}h(b + B)$
where $A = 18$, $b = x + 4$, $B = x + 8$. Thus:
$h = \dfrac{18}{x + 6}$
The area of triangle BCD is:
$A = \frac{1}{2}bh$

where $A = 6$ and $b = x$. Thus:
$h = \dfrac{12}{x}$

Then:
$\dfrac{18}{x + 6} = \dfrac{12}{x}$
$x = 12 = DC$

16 In the drawing (not to scale), AB is eight centimeters longer than DC and DE is four centimeters long. $ABCE$ is a trapezoid. If the area of $ABCE$ is eighteen square centimeters and the area of BCD is six square centimeters, how long is DC?

$DC = 12$ cm

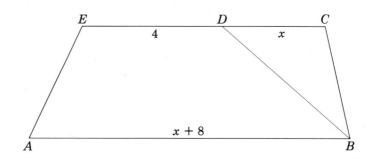

17 If five gallons of gasahol contain thirty-two ounces of ethanol, how much ethanol is in a full gas tank that holds fourteen and one half gallons of gasahol?

92.8 ounces

18 If the gravitational attraction between two steel balls is three millionths of a newton at one thousand meters, what will be the attraction between them at five hundred meters?

0.000006 newton

In problems 19–24, solve each proportion.

19 $\dfrac{n - 5}{n + 3} = \dfrac{n - 2}{n + 4}$

$n = -7$

20 $\dfrac{x}{x + 8} = \dfrac{2x}{2x + 3}$

$x = 0$

21 $\dfrac{3}{2t + 4} = \dfrac{5}{6 - 5t}$

$t = -\dfrac{7}{25}$

22 $\dfrac{7b + 3}{2b - 4} = \dfrac{5 + 7b}{4 + 2b}$

$b = -\dfrac{8}{13}$

23 $\dfrac{4 + 2w}{w - 4} = \dfrac{2w + 3}{4 + w}$

$w = -\dfrac{28}{17}$

24 $\dfrac{5 - w}{3 + w} = \dfrac{4 + w}{5 + w}$

$w = -13$

Factor each polynomial.

25 $3xy^2 - 52x^2y$

$xy(3y - 52x)$

26 $5ab^3 - 20a^3b$

$5ab(b - 2a)(b + 2a)$

27 $14w^2 - 27w - 20$

$(7w + 4)(2w - 5)$

28 $x^2 + rx + sx + rs$

$(x + s)(x + r)$

29 $abx^2 + adx + b^2x + bd$

$(ax + b)(bx + d)$

30 $abx^2 + adx - b^2x - bd$

$(ax - b)(bx + d)$

28) $x(x + r) + s(x + r)$
$(x + s)(x + r)$

29) $ax(bx + d) + b(bx + d)$
$(ax + b)(bx + d)$

30) $ax(bx + d) - b(bx + d)$
$(ax - b)(bx + d)$

Section 8.5   Using Fractions in Equations

SECTION SCHEDULE

Basic (2 days)

Average (2 days)

Advanced (2 days)

Sometimes a mathematical situation leads to an equation that involves fractions, such as:

$$\frac{5x}{6} + \frac{2}{3} = \frac{1}{6}$$

One method to solve such an equation is to multiply both sides by a number that will remove the denominators.

$$\frac{5x}{6} + \frac{2}{3} = \frac{1}{6}$$

$$6 \cdot \left(\frac{5x}{6} + \frac{2}{3}\right) = \left(\frac{1}{6}\right) \cdot 6$$

$$\frac{6 \cdot 5x}{6} + \frac{6 \cdot 2}{3} = \frac{1 \cdot 6}{6}$$

$$5x + 4 = 1$$

$$5x = -3$$

$$x = -\frac{3}{5}$$

Notice that 6, the number that was used, is the **least common multiple** (**LCM**) of the denominators.

Sample Problems

1   Solve for the variable: $\dfrac{2}{3x} - \dfrac{3}{4} = \dfrac{1}{2}$

PROCEDURE   Multiply both sides of the equation by $12x$, which is the LCM of the denominators.

$$(12x)\left(\frac{2}{3x} - \frac{3}{4}\right) = \frac{1}{2}(12x)$$

$$\frac{12x \cdot 2}{3x} - \frac{12x \cdot 3}{4} = \frac{12x}{2}$$

$$\frac{3x \cdot 4 \cdot 2}{3x} - \frac{4 \cdot 3x \cdot 3}{4} = \frac{2 \cdot 6x}{2}$$

$$8 - 9x = 6x$$

$$8 = 15x$$

$$x = \frac{8}{15}$$

2   Solve for w:

$$\frac{5}{w-1} + \frac{3}{w+1} = \frac{16}{w^2-1}$$

PROCEDURE   The LCM of the denominators is $(w+1)(w-1)$:

$$(w+1)(w-1)\left(\frac{5}{w-1} + \frac{3}{w+1}\right) = \left(\frac{16}{w^2-1}\right)(w+1)(w-1)$$

$$\frac{(w-1)\,5(w+1)}{(w-1)} + \frac{(w+1)\,3(w-1)}{(w+1)} = \frac{16(w+1)(w-1)}{(w+1)(w-1)}$$

$$5w + 5 + 3w - 3 = 16$$

$$8w + 2 = 16$$

$$8w = 14$$

$$w = \frac{14}{8} = \frac{7}{4}$$

3   Jack can pick all the apples from the orchard in five hours and Jill can pick all the apples in three hours. How many hours will it take them to pick all the apples from the orchard if they work together?

These problems are often referred to as "work problems." The general procedure is to find the total rate at which the task is being done.

PROCEDURE   The key to this type of problem is that Jack's rate ($\frac{1}{5}$ job per hour) and Jill's rate ($\frac{1}{3}$ job per hour) can be added. The total rate is $\frac{1}{5} + \frac{1}{3}$ job per hour. Let x represent the number of hours they worked together to complete the job.

(rate)·(hours) = number of jobs

$$\left(\frac{1}{5} + \frac{1}{3}\right)(x) = 1$$

$$\frac{x}{5} + \frac{x}{3} = 1$$

$$15\left(\frac{x}{5} + \frac{x}{3}\right) = 1 \cdot 15 \qquad \text{(15 is the LCM)}$$

$$\frac{15 \cdot x}{5} + \frac{15 \cdot x}{3} = 15$$

$$3x + 5x = 15$$

$$8x = 15$$

$$x = \frac{15}{8}$$

They worked $1\frac{7}{8}$ hours together and picked all the apples.

Problem Set **A**

ASSIGNMENT GUIDE

Basic (2 days)
(1) 1–10, 22–28
(2) 16–21, 48, 49, 51, 52

Average (2 days)
(1) 2–14 (even), 29–38
(2) 16–21, 39–42, 48–53

Advanced (2 days)
(1) 29–38, 48–54
(2) 16–21, 39–47

1 $\dfrac{b}{2} - \dfrac{2}{5} = \dfrac{7}{10}$

$b = \dfrac{17}{5}$

6 $\dfrac{5}{6} + \dfrac{3k}{8} = \dfrac{5}{12}$

$k = -\dfrac{10}{9}$

11 $\dfrac{a}{2-a} - \dfrac{4}{5} = \dfrac{7}{10}$

$a = \dfrac{6}{5}$

2 $\dfrac{1}{6} - \dfrac{d}{4} = \dfrac{5}{12}$

$d = -1$

7 $\dfrac{4}{x} - \dfrac{1}{2} = \dfrac{1}{4}$

$x = \dfrac{16}{3}$

12 $\dfrac{2s}{1-s} + \dfrac{1}{2} = \dfrac{5}{6}$

$s = \dfrac{1}{7}$

3 $\dfrac{x}{3} + \dfrac{3}{5} = \dfrac{x}{15}$

$x = -\dfrac{9}{4}$

8 $\dfrac{3}{4} + \dfrac{2}{y} = \dfrac{3}{8}$

$y = -\dfrac{16}{3}$

13 $\dfrac{2}{3x} + \dfrac{5}{2} = \dfrac{3}{2x}$

$x = \dfrac{1}{3}$

4 $\dfrac{3}{4} - \dfrac{n}{2} = \dfrac{n}{8}$

$n = \dfrac{6}{5}$

9 $\dfrac{n}{n-4} + \dfrac{5}{8} = \dfrac{3}{2}$

$n = -28$

14 $\dfrac{4}{3} - \dfrac{5}{4n} = \dfrac{1}{6n}$

$n = \dfrac{17}{16}$

5 $\dfrac{2t}{5} - \dfrac{t}{4} = \dfrac{3}{10}$

$t = 2$

10 $\dfrac{g}{g+3} - \dfrac{2}{3} = 10$

$g = -\dfrac{96}{29}$

15 $\dfrac{5}{x-3} + \dfrac{2}{x^2-9} = \dfrac{3}{x+3}$

$x = -13$

16 Harry can clean up the kitchen in ten minutes, Mary can clean it up in fifteen minutes, but it takes Barry twenty-five minutes to do the same job. How fast can they clean it up if all three work together?

4.8 min

16) $\dfrac{x}{10} + \dfrac{x}{15} + \dfrac{x}{25} = 1$

$775x = 3750$

$x = 4.84$

minutes

17 If someone can mow a certain lawn in two hours using a ride-on lawn-mower, but it takes three hours using a power mower that must be pushed, how long will it take to mow the lawn if two people use both mowers at the same time?

$\dfrac{6}{5}$ hrs

18 Jerry estimates that he can build a new deck for his house in six days. His brother, who is a carpenter, thinks that he could build it in three days. If they work together, can they build it during a two-day weekend?

yes

19) Let x represent the time needed to bike to town. Since the distances are equal:

$10x = 30(x - \dfrac{1}{3})$

$x = \dfrac{1}{2}$

She lives $10 \cdot \dfrac{1}{2}$ or 5 miles from town.

19 Michelle can bicycle to town at ten miles an hour, or she can drive to town at thirty miles an hour, which gets her there twenty minutes faster. How far does Michelle live from town? (HINT: Since the rates are in miles per hour, the time must be expressed in hours.)

5 mi

20) If x is the time at 450 mph:

$450x = 500 (x - \dfrac{1}{2})$

$x = 5$

It is $450 \cdot 5$ or 2250 miles from Here to Yon.

20 An airplane can fly from Here, NY, to Yon, CO, at four hundred fifty mph, but it gets to Yon a half hour faster if it has a tailwind of fifty mph. How far is it from Here to Yon?

2250 mi

21 When the big drain on the water tank is open, the tank empties in forty-five minutes. When the small drain is open (and the big one closed), it empties in one hour. How fast does the tank empty when both are open?

25.71 min

21) $\dfrac{x}{45} + \dfrac{x}{60} = 1$

$105x = 2700$

$x = 25.71$

minutes

Write each computer expression as a variable expression. (Review: Section 1.5)

22 MULTIPLYBY $\frac{1}{3}$ (3n)
    n

23 MULTIPLYBY 3 (7)
    21

24 MULTIPLYBY $\frac{3}{4}$ (− 8)
    −6

25 ADD −7 (n + 7)
    n

26 MULTIPLYBY $\frac{2}{3}$ $\left(\dfrac{3t}{2}\right)$
    t

27 ADD g $(s - g)$
    s

28 MULTIPLYBY $-\dfrac{a}{b}\left(\dfrac{-bx}{a}\right)$
    x

Problem Set **B**

Solve each equation in problems 29–38.

29 $\dfrac{3t}{2t - 3} - \dfrac{3}{4} = \dfrac{7}{8}$
    $t = \frac{39}{2}$

30 $\dfrac{5}{6} = \dfrac{2}{3} - \dfrac{5r}{2r + 1}$
    $n = \frac{39}{12}$

31 $\dfrac{3}{v + 3} - \dfrac{2}{v + 3} = \dfrac{1}{v^2 + 6v + 9}$
    $v = -2$

32 $\dfrac{8}{2n - 7} + \dfrac{3}{4n^2 - 28n + 49} = \dfrac{2}{2n - 7}$
    $n = \frac{39}{12}$

33 $\dfrac{4}{r + 5} - \dfrac{2}{r + 6} = \dfrac{9}{r^2 + 11r + 30}$
    $r = -\frac{5}{2}$

34 $\dfrac{5}{2x - 3} + \dfrac{7}{3x + 5} = \dfrac{8}{6x^2 + x - 15}$
    $x = \frac{4}{29}$

35 $\dfrac{2}{x^2 + 4x + 3} + \dfrac{3}{x^2 + 3x + 2} = \dfrac{4}{x^2 + 5x + 6}$

$x = -9$

36 $\dfrac{1}{n^2 - 7n + 12} - \dfrac{5}{n^2 - 8n + 15} = \dfrac{7}{n^2 - 9n + 20}$

$n = \dfrac{36}{11}$

37 $\dfrac{9}{4t^2 - 4t + 1} - \dfrac{6}{4t^2 + 4t + 1} = \dfrac{3}{4t^2 - 1}$

$t = -\dfrac{1}{10}$

38 $\dfrac{8}{2x^2 - 5x - 12} = \dfrac{2}{3x^2 - 13x + 4} + \dfrac{5}{6x^2 + 7x - 3}$

$x = -\dfrac{2}{5}$

39 If a gallon of syrup contains a pint of maple syrup, how much maple syrup does a pint of the mixture contain?

$\dfrac{1}{4}$ pint

40 A rectangle can be divided so that the longer part is three centimeters longer than the shorter part and the area of the longer part is twice the area of the shorter part. What is the length of the rectangle?

9 cm

41 Find a number such that when three fourths of the number is added to one half, the result is eight.

10

42 Find consecutive integers such that when three times the reciprocal of the first is added to two times the reciprocal of the second, the result is four times the reciprocal of the first. (HINT: Recall that the reciprocal of a number n is $1 \div n$.)

1, 2

43 Mercedes is tiling a room in a pattern that uses five blue tiles for every three red tiles. If the tiles are one-foot squares and the room is eight feet by ten feet, how many tiles of each color should she order? (HINT: If there are n red tiles, then there will be $\frac{5}{3}n$ blue tiles.)

30 red tiles, 50 blue tiles

44 An astronaut on an asteroid measures the gravitational attraction between his asteroid and another at three newtons when they are twelve kilometers apart. How far apart are they when the gravitational force is measured at five tenths of a newton?

72 km

45 C.B. flies between his home in Texas and his eastern office in a plane with average air speed of two hundred seventy-five miles per hour. When the jet stream is flowing at a rate of seventy-five miles an hour from west to east, the trip west takes two hours longer than the trip east. How far is his home from the office?

$2566\frac{2}{3}$ mi

39) There are 8 pints in a gallon, so:

$\dfrac{8}{1} = \dfrac{1}{x}$

$x = \dfrac{1}{8}$

40)

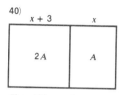

The widths are the same, so:

$\dfrac{2A}{x + 3} = \dfrac{A}{x}$

$2Ax = Ax + 3A$

$2Ax - Ax = 3A$

$Ax = 3A$

$x = 3$

The length of the rectangle is 6 + 3 or 9 cm.

41) $\dfrac{3}{4}x + \dfrac{1}{2} = 8$

$3x + 2 = 32$

$3x = 30$

$x = 10$

42) If the first integer is x:

$3 \cdot \dfrac{1}{x} + 2 \cdot \dfrac{2}{x + 1} = \dfrac{4}{x}$

$x = 1$

$x + 1 = 2$

43) The room will require 80 tiles:

$n + \dfrac{5}{3}n = 80$

$3n + 5n = 240$

$8n = 240$

$n = 30$

$\dfrac{5}{3}n = 50$

45) Let x represent the time needed to fly east. Since the distances are the same:

$(275 + 75)x = 275(x + 2)$

$x = 7\dfrac{1}{3}$ hours

The distance is $350 \cdot 7\dfrac{1}{3}$ or $2566\dfrac{2}{3}$ miles.

Problem Set **C**

46)
$$r \cdot t = j$$
$$(\tfrac{1}{20} - \tfrac{1}{25})x = 1$$
$$20 \cdot 25(\tfrac{1}{20} - \tfrac{1}{25})x$$
$$= 1 \cdot 20 \cdot 25$$
$$5x = 500$$
$$x = 100 \text{ minutes}$$

47) $\quad (\tfrac{1}{3})(1 + x) + \tfrac{1}{2}x = 1$

$$6((\tfrac{1}{3})(1 + x) + (\tfrac{1}{2}x))$$
$$= 1 \cdot 6$$
$$2(1 + x) + 3x = 6$$
$$2 + 2x + 3x = 6$$
$$5x = 4$$
$$x = \tfrac{4}{5} \text{ hours}$$

Tom will have worked

$1 + \tfrac{4}{5}$ hours.

46 It takes twenty minutes to fill a tank for a chemical process. Then, after the process is complete, it takes twenty-five minutes to empty the tank. If someone accidentally leaves the drain open, how long will it take to fill the tank?

100 min

47 Tom figures that it will take him three hours to dig up his garden. After he has been working for one hour, his father, who could complete the job by himself in two hours, starts digging from the other end. How many hours will Tom have worked?

$\tfrac{9}{5}$ hrs.

Solve each of the following equations.

48 $\quad 5x - 9 = 31$

$x = 8$

49 $\quad \dfrac{5x}{4} - \dfrac{9}{5} = \dfrac{31}{60}$

$x = \dfrac{139}{75}$

50 $\quad \dfrac{5}{4x} - \dfrac{9}{5} = \dfrac{31}{6x}$

$x = -\dfrac{235}{108}$

51 $\quad \dfrac{3}{n} = \dfrac{5}{4}$

$n = \dfrac{12}{5}$

52 $\quad \dfrac{2n}{3n - 1} = 15$

$n = \dfrac{15}{43}$

53 $\quad \dfrac{3}{5a + 2} - \dfrac{4}{5a - 2} = \dfrac{5}{25a^2 - 4}$

$a = -\dfrac{19}{5}$

54 $\quad \dfrac{2}{x^2 + 8x + 15} - \dfrac{1}{x^2 + 3x - 10} = \dfrac{4}{x^2 + x + 6}$

$x = -\dfrac{25}{3}$

55 $\quad \dfrac{x^2 + x - 12}{x^2 - x - 20} = 7 \qquad$ (Simplify the fraction before solving.)

$x = \dfrac{16}{3}$

56 $\quad \dfrac{5}{x - 3} = \dfrac{2}{2x + 1} - \dfrac{4}{x - 3}$

$x = -\dfrac{15}{16}$

57 $\quad \dfrac{a}{x} + b = c \qquad$ (a, b, and c are constants)

$x = \dfrac{a}{c - b}$

Section 8.6   Using Fractions in Formulas

SECTION SCHEDULE

Basic (1 day)

Average (1 day)

Advanced (1 day)

Isolate R in the electricity formula: $I = \dfrac{E}{R}$

MULTBY R: $IR = E$

MULTBY $\dfrac{1}{I}$: $R = \dfrac{E}{I}$

Isolating variables in formulas often involves fractions.

Sample Problems

1   Solve $S = \dfrac{a}{1 - r}$ for r.

PROCEDURE
$$S = \frac{a}{1 - r}$$

MULTBY $(1 - r)$: $S(1 - r) = \dfrac{a}{1 - r}(1 - r)$

$$S - Sr = a$$

SUBT S: $-Sr = a - S$

MULTBY $\dfrac{1}{-S}$: $\dfrac{-Sr}{-S} = \dfrac{a - S}{-S}$

$$r = \frac{a - S}{-S} = -\frac{a - S}{S} = \frac{S - a}{S}$$

Some students may be interested that this is the formula for the sum of an infinite series such as:

$$\frac{1}{2} + \frac{1}{4} + \frac{1}{8} + \ldots$$

*where **r** is the common ratio.*

2   Solve $\dfrac{1}{f} = \dfrac{1}{p} + \dfrac{1}{q}$ for q. (This formula is for the focal length of a lens.)

PROCEDURE   Multiply both sides by $f \cdot p \cdot q$, the LCM of the denominators.

$$f \cdot p \cdot q \left(\frac{1}{f} \right) = \left(\frac{1}{p} + \frac{1}{q} \right) \cdot f \cdot p \cdot q$$

$$\frac{f \cdot pq}{f} = \frac{p \cdot fq}{p} + \frac{q \cdot fp}{q}$$

$$pq = fq + fp$$

SUBT (fq): $pq - fq = fp$

$$q(p - f) = fp$$

MULTBY $\dfrac{1}{p - f}$: $\dfrac{q(p - f)}{p - f} = \dfrac{fp}{p - f}$

$$q = \frac{fp}{p - f}$$

ASSIGNMENT GUIDE

Basic (1 day)
1–14

Average (1 day)
1–20

Advanced (1 day)
5–8, 15–30

Problem Set **A**

Solve each formula for the variable indicated.

1 $b = \dfrac{2A}{h}$ for h

$h = \frac{2A}{b}$

2 $w = \dfrac{V}{\ell w}$ for ℓ

$\ell = \frac{V}{u\,2}$

3 $h = \dfrac{2A}{B + b}$ for A

$A = \frac{h(B+6)}{2}$

4 $S = \dfrac{a}{1 - r}$ for a

$a = S(1-r)$

5 $I = \dfrac{E}{R}$ for E

$E = IR$

6 $p = \dfrac{i}{rt}$ for r

$r = \frac{i}{pt}$

7 $F = \dfrac{Mv^2}{gr}$ for r

$r = \frac{Mv^2}{Fg}$

8 $S = \tfrac{1}{2}gt^2$ for g

$g = \frac{2S}{t\,2}$

Solve each proportion by finding the cross-product. (Review: Section 8.2)

9 $\dfrac{2n}{9} = \dfrac{2}{3}$

$n = 3$

10 $\dfrac{5}{2} = \dfrac{-5p}{8}$

$p = -4$

11 $\dfrac{3x - 2}{5} = \dfrac{14}{10}$

$x = 3$

12 $\dfrac{p - 2}{p - 7} = \dfrac{7}{2}$

$p = 9$

13 $\dfrac{4}{3 - 2r} = \dfrac{10}{4r + 3}$

$r = \frac{1}{2}$

14 $\dfrac{2p - 1}{4} = \dfrac{3 - p}{-4}$

$p = -2$

Problem Set **B**

Solve each formula for the variable indicated.

15 $h = \dfrac{2A}{B + b}$ for B

$B = \frac{2A - Bh}{h}$

16 $M = \dfrac{25}{f} + \dfrac{25}{d}$ for f

$f = \frac{25d}{Md - 25}$

17 $\dfrac{1}{f} = \dfrac{1}{p} + \dfrac{1}{q}$ for f

$f = \frac{pq}{q + p}$

18 $A = p + prt$ for p

$p = \frac{A}{1 + rt}$

19 $f = \dfrac{gm - t}{m}$ for m

$m = \frac{t}{g - f}$

20 $\dfrac{1}{R} = \dfrac{1}{r_1} + \dfrac{1}{r_2} + \dfrac{1}{r_3}$ for r_3

$r_3 = \frac{Rr_1r_2}{r_1r_2 - Rr_1 - R_2}$

Problem Set C

Solve each formula for the variable(s) indicated.

21 $A^2 = s(s - a)(s - b)(s - c)$ for a

$a = s - \dfrac{A^2}{s(s-b)(s-c)}$

22 $s = a + ar + ar^2 + ar^3 + \ldots$ for a

(see pages 295–296)

$a = \dfrac{s}{1 + r + r2 + r3 + \ldots}$

23 $\dfrac{a + b}{b} = \dfrac{c + d}{d}$ for $\dfrac{a}{b}$

$\dfrac{a}{b} = \dfrac{c}{d}$

24 $\dfrac{a - 2b}{b} = \dfrac{c - 2d}{d}$ for $\dfrac{c}{d}$

$\dfrac{c}{d} = \dfrac{a - 2b}{b} + 2$

25 $\dfrac{a - b}{b} = \dfrac{c - d}{d}$ for $\dfrac{a}{c}$

$\dfrac{a}{c} = \dfrac{b}{d}$

26 If one child can build a snow fort in forty minutes and another can build a snow fort in thirty-five minutes, how long will it take to build one if they work together?

$18\frac{2}{3}$ min.

27 You can get to the top of the ski lift in fifteen minutes, and, skiing along the path of the lift, you can get down the slope in four minutes. You estimate that you travel ten miles per hour faster on your skis than on the lift. How long would you estimate the lift to be? (NOTE: the time is given in minutes, but the rate is given in miles per hour.)

$\frac{10}{11}$ mile, 4800 feet

28 A rectangle is divided in two so that the larger part is six inches longer than the shorter part. The area of the smaller part is two fifths the area of the larger. How long is the rectangle?

10 inches

29 Find two consecutive even integers so that three times the reciprocal of the first plus four times the reciprocal of the second is equal to five times the reciprocal of the first.

2, 4

30 Filling her backyard pool with a hose takes Maria two hours. When the water use is restricted, Maria fills it from a spring using buckets, which takes five hours. How long would it take to fill the pool using the hose from the house and buckets from the spring at the same time?

$1\frac{3}{7}$ hours

21) $A^2 = s(s-a)(s-b)(s-c)$

$\dfrac{A^2}{s(s-b)(s-c)} = s - a$

$\dfrac{A^2}{s(s-b)(s-c)} - s = -a$

$s - \dfrac{A^2}{s(s-b)(s-c)} = a$

26) $\left(\dfrac{1}{40} + \dfrac{1}{35}\right)x = 1$

$(35 + 40)x = (35)(40)$

$75x = 1400$

$x = 18\frac{2}{3}$

27) Let x represent the rate up the slope. Since the distances are the same:

$\dfrac{1}{15}x = \dfrac{1}{4}(x - 10)$

$x = 13\frac{7}{11}$ mph

Thus the distance is

$(13\frac{7}{11})(\frac{1}{15})$ which is $\dfrac{10}{11}$

miles or 4800 ft.

28) Since the widths are the same,

$\dfrac{A}{x + 6} = \dfrac{\frac{2}{5}A}{x}$

$x = 4$

The length of the rectangle is $x + 6$ or 10 in.

29) $3(\frac{1}{x}) + 4(\dfrac{1}{x + 2}) = 5(\frac{1}{x})$

$x = 2$

$x + 2 = 4$

30) $(\frac{1}{2} + \frac{1}{5})x = 1$

$(5 + 2)x = 10$

$7x = 10$

$x = \dfrac{10}{7}$

It would take about 1 hour and 26 minutes.

ASSIGNMENT GUIDE

Basic (2 days)
(1) 342: 1–14
(2) 318: 29, 30
    322: 16, 17, 35, 36
    333: 11–15

Average (1 day)
333: 43–45
339: 26, 29
342: 1–14

Advanced (2 days)
(1) 319: 29–41 (odd)
    333: 2–14 (even),
        55–57
    342: 1–14
(2) 306: 28–64

Chapter Study Guide

Vocabulary

As you study and review this chapter, be sure to learn the important mathematics vocabulary, including:

1   **Ratio**   A RATIO is a comparison of two numbers by division.
- The ratio of 3 teachers to 87 students can be written several ways:

$$3:87 \qquad 3 \div 87 \qquad \frac{3}{87}$$

2   **Proportion**
A PROPORTION is a mathematical statement that two ratios are equal.
The following equations are proportions:

- $\dfrac{3}{5} = \dfrac{9}{15}$
- $\dfrac{x}{2} = \dfrac{7}{5}$

Skills

Be sure you build the useful algebraic skills, including:

3   **Using the cross-product to solve a proportion**   Solve for x:

$$\frac{x}{2} = \frac{7}{5}$$

PROCEDURE

$$5x = 14 \quad \text{(the cross-product)}$$
$$x = \frac{14}{5}$$

4   **Solving equations and formulas involving fractions**   Solve for x:

a $\dfrac{3x}{4} - \dfrac{x+1}{5} = 2$ b $a = \dfrac{xt^2}{2}$

PROCEDURE

a Multiply both sides of the equation by 20, the LCM of the denominators.

$$\frac{3x}{4} - \frac{x+1}{5} = 2$$

$$20\left(\frac{3x}{4} - \frac{x+1}{5}\right) = 20\,(2)$$

$$5 \cdot 3x - 4(x+1) = 40$$

$$15x - 4x - 4 = 40$$

$$11x - 4 = 40$$

$$11x = 44$$

$$x = 4$$

b Isolate the variable x:

$$a = \frac{xt^2}{2}$$

MULTBY 2: $\quad 2a = xt^2$

MULTBY $\dfrac{1}{t^2}$: $\quad \dfrac{2a}{t^2} = x$

5 **Solving problems involving fractions** Solve: Tom could whitewash his fence in three hours, and his friend Huck could whitewash it in four hours. Working together, how long would the job take?

PROCEDURE Let x represent the time.

(rate) (time) = (jobs):

$$r \cdot t = j$$

$$\left(\frac{1}{3} + \frac{1}{4}\right)x = 1$$

MULTBY 12: $\quad 12\left(\frac{1}{3} + \frac{1}{4}\right)x = 12(1)$

$$(4 + 3)x = 12$$

$$7x = 12$$

$$x = \frac{12}{7}$$

It would take $\dfrac{12}{7}$ hours, or approximately 1 hour, 43 minutes.

Chapter Test

A cube has a side of measure 5. Write each ratio in simplest form.

1 perimeter of one face to area of one face

$\frac{4}{5}$

2 sum of all the edges to total surface area

$\frac{2}{5}$

3 total surface area to volume

$\frac{6}{5}$

Solve the proportions.

4 $\dfrac{18}{7} = \dfrac{12}{5x}$

$x = \frac{14}{15}$

5 $\dfrac{3x + 5}{4} = \dfrac{3 + 2x}{3}$

$x = -3$

State whether or not each is an example of inverse variation.

6 $\dfrac{x}{2} = \dfrac{3}{y}$

yes

7 $\dfrac{5}{x} = \dfrac{8}{y}$

no

Solve each equation.

8 $\dfrac{3}{4x} - \dfrac{3}{2} = \dfrac{7}{8x}$

$x = -\frac{1}{12}$

9 $\dfrac{2}{x + 4} + \dfrac{1}{4 - x} = \dfrac{-15}{x^2 - 16}$

$x = -3$

Solve each formula for the letter indicated.

10 $Ft = \dfrac{Wv^2}{gr}$ for r

$r = \frac{Wv^2}{Ftg}$

11 $M = \dfrac{t}{g - f}$ for f

$f = \frac{t - Mg}{-M}$

Write an equation for each problem. Then solve the equation and answer the original question.

12 If three yards of fabric cost \$7.50, what is the cost of $10\frac{1}{2}$ yards?

\$26.25

13 Find a number such that two thirds of the number is the same as one fourth of the number increased by five.

12

14 A train runs between two cities 240 miles apart at an average rate of 48 mph. To cut its running time by one hour, by how much should its rate be increased or decreased?

60 m/h

Problem Set: Variation as the Square

In many physical situations, the magnitude of one number is a function of the square of a second number. For example, the surface area A of a cube is six times the square of the edge of the cube:

If $e = 4$, then $A = 6e^2 = 6 \cdot 4^2 = 96$.
If $e = 10$, then $A = 6e^2 = 6 \cdot 10^2 = 600$.

In general, the formula for variation as the square is $y = kx^2$, and k is called the **constant of variation**.

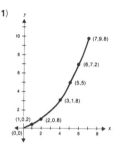

Problems

1 Graph the relationship between y and x if they are related by the formula $y = 0.2x^2$.

2 Graph the relationship between y and x if they are related by the formula $y = x^2 \div 10$.

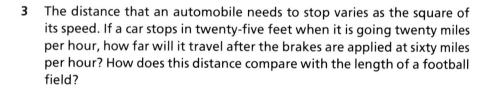

3 The distance that an automobile needs to stop varies as the square of its speed. If a car stops in twenty-five feet when it is going twenty miles per hour, how far will it travel after the brakes are applied at sixty miles per hour? How does this distance compare with the length of a football field?

4 Find the formula that describes the approximate distance d that an object falls in t seconds (assuming no air resistance) using the following observations: A stone dropped from an airplane falls sixty-four feet in two seconds and four hundred feet in five seconds.

5 The variable d varies with the square of e. Find the formula relating d and e if d is one and eight tenths when e is two and d is sixteen and two tenths when e is six.

6 Einstein proposed that mass m and energy e vary with the square of the speed of light c: $e = mc^2$. If the speed of light is about 300,000,000 centimeters per second, what is the energy released in a nuclear explosion if ten grams of matter completely turn to energy?

3) $d = ks^2$
$25 = k \cdot 20^2$
$k = \dfrac{1}{16}$
$d = \dfrac{1}{16}60^2$
$d = 225$

The distance is $\frac{3}{4}$ of the length of a football field

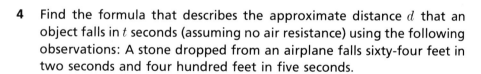

5) $\quad d = ke^2 \qquad\qquad d = ke^2$
$1.8 = k \cdot 2^2 \qquad 16.2 = k \cdot 6^2$
$k = 0.45 \qquad\qquad k = 0.45$
$d = 0.45e^2$

6) $e = mc^2$
$= (10g)(3 \times 10^8 \, cm/s)$
$= 3 \times 10^9 \, g - cm/s$

Chapter 9

LINEAR EQUATIONS

CHAPTER SCHEDULE

Basic
Problem Sets 13 Days
Review 2 Days
Test 2 Days

Average
Problem Sets 11 Days
Review 1 Day
Test 2 Days

Advanced
Problem Sets 12 Days
Review 1 Day
Test 1 Day

For accurate graphs, students should be encouraged to use graph paper, to label the axes and the points that are plotted, and to use a straightedge.

Section 9.1   Graphing Points and Lines

Jan makes and sells eggshell faces. She sells her artwork for one dollar more than the cost of her materials.

SECTION SCHEDULE

Basic (2 days)

Average (1 day)

Advanced (1 day)

If x stands for her cost of materials, and y stands for her selling price, then the relationship between her cost and revenue can be represented by the equation:

$$y = x + 1$$

This equation can be shown as a graph:

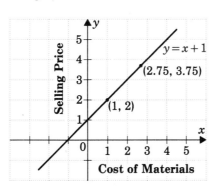

The labeled points on the graph indicate that if her cost is $1 then the selling price is $2, and if her cost is $2.75 then the selling price is $3.75.

The graph $y = x + 1$ is a straight line, and so the equation $y = x + 1$ is called a **linear equation**. In general, a linear equation is any equation that can be graphed as a straight line. For any graph, there are three vocabulary terms associated with the ordered pair of numbers (x, y). The x-value is called the **abscissa** and the y-value is called the **ordinate**. Together, the x- and y-values are called the **coordinates**.

Problem Set C in Section 9.6 (p. 383) describes the algebraic conditions for a linear equation.

The x-axis and the y-axis determine four regions called **quadrants**. (The axes are not part of the quadrants.) The intersection of the two axes, called the **origin**, has the coordinates (0,0).

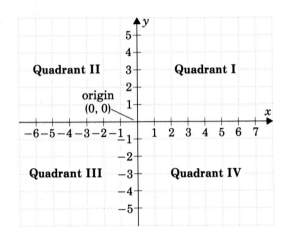

Sample Problems

1   Graph: $2x + y = 8$

Plotting three points for a line provides a check. If the three points are not collinear, the student has made an error.

Students should realize that:
a *It is easier to calculate values for **y** if the equation is solved for **y**:*
   $y = -2x + 8$
b *Any 3 **x**-values can be selected, and the value **x** = 0 is an easy and useful selection.*

PROCEDURE   Select any three values for x, say -1, 3, and 4, and calculate the corresponding values for y:

If $x = -1$:
$2(-1) + y = 8$
$-2 + y = 8$
$y = 10$

If $x = 3$:
$2(3) + y = 8$
$6 + y = 8$
$y = 2$

If $x = 4$:
$2(4) + y = 8$
$8 + y = 8$
$y = 0$

The completed chart is:

x	-1	3	4
y	10	2	0

The three points are $(-1, 10)$, $(3,2)$, and $(4,0)$. **Plot** the three points (label them on a set of axes), draw the line for the equation, and label the line with its equation:

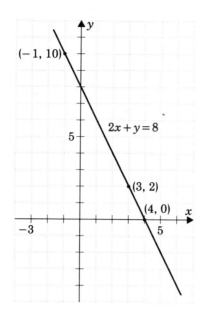

2   Graph: $y = -\dfrac{2}{3}x + 4$

PROCEDURE   Choose at least three values for x, say -3, 3, and 9, and calculate the corresponding values for y.

x	-3	3	9
y	6	2	-2

The value $x = 0$ is another convenient value to use. When $x = 0$,

$y = -\dfrac{2}{3}(0) + 4 = 4$.

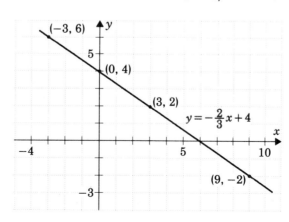

ASSIGNMENT GUIDE

Basic (2 days)
(1) 11–22
(2) 23–31

Average (1 day)
24–40 (even)

Advanced (1 day)
32–40 (even), 41–45

Problem Set A

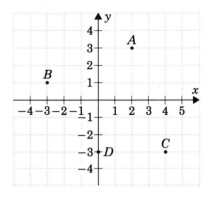

1 What is the abscissa
(x-coordinate) of point A?

  2

2 What are the coordinates of B?

  (−3,1)

3 Which point is not in any
quadrant?

  D

4 In which quadrant is point B?

  2

5 Which labeled point has a positive abscissa and a negative ordinate?

  C

6 If both coordinates of a point are negative, in which quadrant is the
point?

  3

What value of y corresponds to the given value of x for the following equations?

7 $y = x + 7$; $x = 3$

  10

9 $2x + y = 4$; $x = -3$

  10

8 $y = x - 5$; $x = 2$

  −3

10 $-x + y = 6$; $x = -4$

  2

Fill in a table for each linear equation.

11 $y = x + 5$; $x = 2, 0, -3$

  (2,7), (0,5), (−3,2)

12 $y = x - 7$; $x = 11, 0, -3$

  (11,4), (0,−7), (−3,−10)

13 $y = 2x + 3$; $x = 4, 0, -2$

  (4,11), (0,3), (−2,−1)

14 $y = -3x + 1$; $x = 9, 0, -1$

  (9,−26), (0,1) (−1,4)

15 $x + y = -5$; $x = 0, -2; y = 0$

  (0,5), (−2,7), (5,0)

16 $2x + y = 10$; $x = 4, -5$;
  $y = 0$

  (4,2), (−5,20), (5,0)

17 $y = \dfrac{1}{3}x + 7$; $x = 3, 0, -6$

  (3,8), (0,7), (−6,5)

18 $y = \dfrac{2}{5}x - 4$; $x = 5, 0, -10$

  (5,−2), (0,−4), (−10,8)

Evaluate each formula for the given value of the variable. (Review: Section 1.2)

19 $F = \dfrac{9}{5}C + 32$; $C = 0$

  $F = 32$

21 $y = \dfrac{x^2}{16}$; $x = 0$

  $y = 0$

20 $y = 4x - \dfrac{1}{2}x$; $x = 0$

  $y = 0$

22 $y = mx + b$; $x = 0$

  $y = b$

Problem Set B

Select three values for x, calculate corresponding y-values, and graph the following equations.

23 $y = x + 2$
some points are
$(-2,0)$, $(-1,1)$, $(0,2)$

24 $y = x - 5$
some points are
$(5,0)$, $(3-2)$ $(0,-5)$

25 $x + y = 10$
some points are $(0,10)$, $(1,9)$,
$(2,8)$, $(8,2)$, $(9,1)$, $(10,0)$

26 $2x + y = 0$
some points are
$(0,0)$, $(1,-2)$ $(2,-4)$

27 $9 = y + 4x$
some points are
$(0,9)$, $(1,5)$, $(2,1)$, $(\frac{9}{2},0)$

28 $4 = x - y$
some points are
$(0,-4)$, $(4,0)$, $(3,-1)$, $(10,6)$

29 $y - 2x = 12$
some points are $(2,16)$, $(1,14)$
$(0,12)$, $(-1,10)$, $(-2,8)$, $(6,0)$

30 $y - 3x = -1$
some points are
$(0,-1)$, $(1,2)$, $(3,8)$, $(5,14)$

31 $y = 4x$
some points are
$(0,0)$, $(1,4)$, $(2,8)$, $(3,12)$

For each equation, select three values of x, calculate corresponding y-values, and graph each linear equation.

32 $y = -2x - 3$

3 points are
$(0,-3)$, $(1,-5)$, $(2,-7)$

33 $2x - y = 4$

3 points are

$(-2,-8)$, $(0,-4)$, $(2,2)$

34 $3x - y = -2$

3 points are
$(0,2)$, $(1,5)$, $(-1,-1)$

35 $y = \frac{1}{2}x + 8$

3 points are
$(10,0)$, $(0,5)$, $(2,4)$

36 $y = \frac{3}{4}x + 2$

3 points are
$(0,2)$, $(4,5)$, $(\frac{-8}{3},0)$

37 $y = -\frac{1}{3}x$

3 points are
$(5,0)$, $(0,5)$, $(2,3)$

38 $y = -\frac{2}{5}x$

3 points are
$(0,0)$, $(5,-2)$, $(10,-4)$

39 $y = 5 - \frac{x}{2}$

3 points are
$(-3,0)$, $(0,-2)$, $(2,-\frac{10}{3})$

40 $y = 4 - \frac{x}{3}$

3 points are
$(0,4)$, $(3,3)$, $(12,0)$

Problem Set C

Graph each equation.

41 $2x + 4y = 16$

3 points are $(4,0)$, $(0,4)$, $(2,2)$

42 $3x - 2y = 8$

3 points are $(0,-4)$, $(\frac{8}{3},0)$, $(6,5)$

43 $x - \frac{y}{2} = 3$

3 points are $(\frac{5}{2},0)$, $(0,3)$, $(2,\frac{5}{3})$

44 Jake wants to put a rectangular fence around part of his side yard. The area to be fenced can only be six meters wide, but it can be any length up to twenty meters. Make a graph showing the possible perimeters of such a fenced rectangle. (Use the vertical axis for the perimeter and the horizontal axis for the length of the rectangle.)

points are $(1,14)$, $(2,16)$, $(3,18)$, $(9,20)$, . . . , $(19,50)$

44) An equation for the graph is:
$p = 12 + 2\ell$
$0 < \ell < 20$

45 Lynn wants to fence in a rectangular region using one side of her house as one side of the fenced rectangle. The area to be fenced can only be eight meters wide, but along the side of the house the length can be up to fifteen meters. Make a graph showing the possible total amounts of fencing. (Use the vertical axis for the total amount of fencing and the horizontal axis for the length of the rectangle.)

points are $(1,18)$, $(2,20)$, $(3,22)$, . . . , $(14,44)$

45) An equation for the graph is:
$p = 16 + \ell$, $0 < \ell < 15$

Project: A Game of Battleship

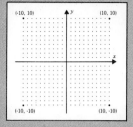

Many versions of Battleship are played on the Cartesian plane. This version uses integers for x and y to locate a point on a 21-by-21 grid (where $-10 \le x \le 10$ and $-10 \le y \le 10$).

Player 1 selects point (a,b) and writes it on a card. Player 2 makes a guess, and Player 1 responds with a clue:

Player 2's Guess:	Player 1 says:
x is correct $(x = a)$, y is too low $(y < b)$	"Go North"
$x = a, y > b$	"Go South"
$x < a, y = b$	"Go East"
$x > a, y = b$	?
$x < a, y < b$	"Go Northeast"
$x > a, y < b$	?
$x < a, y > b$	?
$x > a, y > b$	?
$x = a, y = b$	"Lifeboats!"

The object is for Player 2 to make as few guesses as possible.

1 Copy the table and fill in the missing clues.

2 How many possible locations are there for the battleship?

3 If you are Player 1, what clue should you give for each guess?

Your point is:	The guess is:	Give clue:
$(-3,9)$	0,0	?
$(1,0)$	$(-5,-5)$	?
$(5,6)$	$(7,2)$	?

4 What would be a good second guess for Player 2?

First guess	Clue	Second guess
$(3,5)$	Go NE	?
$(4,-3)$	Go S	?
$(9,3)$	Go E	?

5 Write a computer program: the computer randomly selects the point (a,b) and tells Player 2 (you!) the appropriate clue.

1)

$x = a, y < b$ Go N
$x = a, y > b$ Go S
$x < a, y = b$ Go E
$x > a, y = b$ Go W
$x < a, y < b$ Go NE
$x > a, y < b$ Go NW
$x < a, y > b$ Go SE
$x > a, y > b$ Go SW
$x = a, y = b$ "Lifeboats!"

2) $21^2 = 441$

3) Go NW
       Go NE
       Go NW

4) $x > 3, y > 5$
       $x = 4, y < -3$
       $(10,3)$

5) Programs will vary.

350

Section 9.2   The x-intercept and the y-intercept

SECTION SCHEDULE

Basic (2 days)

Average (2 days)

Advanced (1 day)

This graph shows that Joy's age and Rex's age differ by five years.

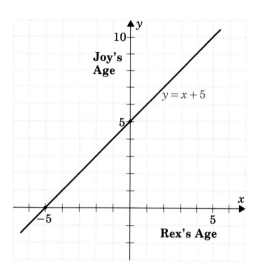

*The negative values for **y** and **x** can be interpreted as "before Rex (or Joy) was born."*

The equation for this graph is $y = x + 5$.
   The line crosses the y-axis at the point (0,5) and crosses the x-axis, at the point $(-5,0)$. In general, when a line crosses the x-axis, the value of y must be zero. Similarly, when a line crosses the y-axis, the value of x must be zero.

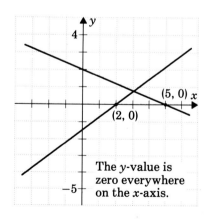

The y-value is zero everywhere on the x-axis.

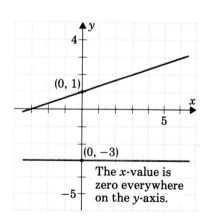

The x-value is zero everywhere on the y-axis.

When a line crosses an axis, it determines an **intercept** of the graph.

Definition

An x-INTERCEPT of a graph is a value of x for which $y = 0$. A y-INTERCEPT of a graph is a value of y for which $x = 0$.

EXAMPLES

■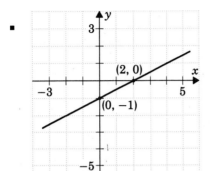

■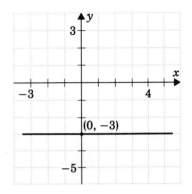

The x-intercept is 2.
The y-intercept is -1.

The y-intercept is -3.
There is no x-intercept.

Note that the x-intercept and the y-intercept are numbers, not points.

Sample Problems

1 Find the x-intercept and the y-intercept for the graph of $3x - 4y = 12$.

PROCEDURE   To find the x-intercept, let $y = 0$:

$$3x - 4y = 12$$
$$3x - 4(0) = 12$$
$$3x = 12$$
$$x = 4$$

The x-intercept is 4, so the graph goes through the point (4,0).

To find the y-intercept, let $x = 0$:

$$3x - 4y = 12$$
$$3(0) - 4y = 12$$
$$-4y = 12$$
$$y = -3$$

The y-intercept is -3, and so the graph goes through the point (0,-3).

2 State the x- and y-intercepts and then use them to draw the graph of $2(y - 4) = -3x + 16$.

PROCEDURE   Find the two intercepts:

When $y = 0$,
$$2(0 - 4) = -3x + 16$$
$$2(-4) = -3x + 16$$
$$-8 = -3x + 16$$
$$-24 = -3x$$
$$8 = x$$

When $x = 0$,
$$2(y - 4) = -3(0) + 16$$
$$2(y - 4) = 0 + 16$$
$$2(y - 4) = 16$$
$$y - 4 = 8$$
$$y = 12$$

The line contains the points (8,0) and (0,12).

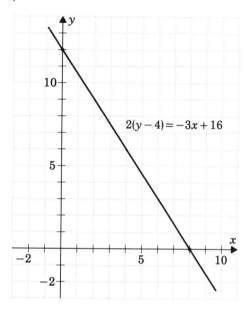

$2(y - 4) = -3x + 16$

Students could be asked to find additional points on the line as a check.

Problem Set **A**

1 What is the x-intercept of a line that passes through the origin?

0

2 If you know the equation of a line, how do you find the y-intercept of the line? the x-intercept?

substitute $x = 0$; substitute $y = 0$

3 The following six points are all on the same line. State the x-intercept and the y-intercept for the graph of the line.

x	1	0	2	−1	4	3
y	4	6	2	8	−2	0

x-intercept is 3, y-intercept is 6

4 The points (3,2) and (0,5) are on a line. Which intercept is known? How could the other intercept be determined?

y; Find the equation of the line and substitute $y = 0$

ASSIGNMENT GUIDE

Basic (2 days)
(1) 1–20
(2) 21–32

Average (2 days)
(1) 6–32 (even)
(2) 34–44 (even), 45
256: 1–13

Advanced (1 day)
8, 18, 34–44 (even), 45,
46–52 (even)
356: 1–13

State the x- and y-intercepts of each graph.

5

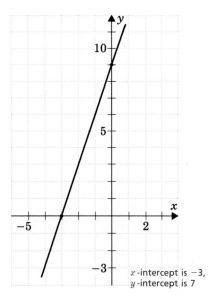

x-intercept is -3,
y-intercept is 7

7

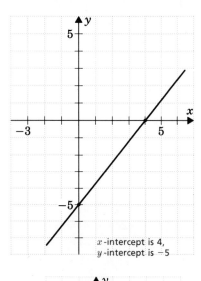

x-intercept is 4,
y-intercept is -5

6

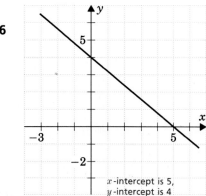

x-intercept is 5,
y-intercept is 4

8

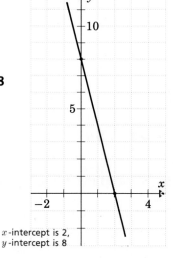

x-intercept is 2,
y-intercept is 8

Without drawing the graphs, determine the x-intercept and the y-intercept for the following:

9 $x + y = 5$
  x-intercept is 5,
  y-intercept is 5

10 $x + y = -3$
  x-intercept is -3,
  y-intercept is -3

11 $x + 3y = 9$
  x-intercept is 9,
  y-intercept is 3

12 $2x + y = 10$
  x-intercept is 5,
  y-intercept is 10

13 $3x - 4y = 12$
  x-intercept is 4,
  y-intercept is -3

14 $5x + 4y = -20$
  x-intercept is -4,
  y-intercept is -5

15 $5x - y = 15$
  x-intercept is 3,
  y-intercept is -15

16 $x - y = 7$
  x-intercept is 7,
  y-intercept is -7

17 $12 = x - 4y$
  x-intercept is 12,
  y-intercept is -3

18 $6 = 2x - y$
  x-intercept is 3,
  y-intercept is -6

19 $-x + 6y = 3$
  x-intercept is -3,
  y-intercept is $\frac{1}{2}$

20 $4x - y = -2$
  x-intercept is $-\frac{1}{2}$,
  y-intercept is 2

Find the x- and y-intercepts, plot them on a graph, and sketch the line. Use a separate pair of axes for each equation.

21 $x + y = 4$
some points are
(4,0), (2,2), (0,4)

22 $2x + y = 2$
some points are
(0,2), (2,2), (1,0)

23 $x - 2y = 8$
some points are
(-4,0), (2,-3), (0,-4)

24 $3x - y = 6$
some points are
(0,6), (1,3), (2,0)

25 $5x - 2y = 10$
some points are
(2,0), (-2,-10), (0,5)

26 $-3x + 5y = 15$
some points are
(-5,0), (0,3), (5,6)

Reduce each fraction. (Review: Section 2.4)

These problems preview the algebraic calculation of slope, Section 9.3X.

27 $\dfrac{3 - (-2)}{10 - 5}$
1

29 $\dfrac{-1 - (-1)}{4 - 10}$
0

31 $\dfrac{1 - 5}{5 - 1}$
-1

28 $\dfrac{4 - 3}{6 - (-8)}$
$\frac{1}{14}$

30 $\dfrac{-6 - (-4)}{6 - 8}$
1

32 $\dfrac{-3 - 3}{7 - (-8)}$
0

Problem Set B

Find the x- and y-intercepts and use them to graph each equation.

33 $y = 3x + 6$
3 points are
(-2,0), (1,9), (0,6)

34 $y = -2x + 8$
3 points are
(0,8), (2,4), (4,0)

35 $\dfrac{x}{2} + y = 5$
3 points are
(10,0), (0,5), (2,4)

36 $\dfrac{x}{3} - y = 1$
3 points are
(0,-1), (3,0), (6,1)

37 $2(x + y) = 10$
3 points are
(5,0), (0,5), (2,3)

38 $-3(x - y) = 6$
3 points are
(-2,0), (0,2), (1,3)

39 $10 + 2x = 4 - 3y$
3 points are
(-3,0), (0,-2), (2,-$\frac{10}{3}$)

40 $2(x + 3) = y - 8$
3 points are
(-7,0), (-4,6), (0,14)

41 $\dfrac{x + y}{4} = 1$
3 points are
(4,0), (0,4), (2,2)

42 $\dfrac{2x - 3y}{3} = -2$
3 points are
(-3,0), (0,2), (3,4)

43 $2x + 3y = 9$
3 points are ($\frac{9}{2}$,0), (0,3), (2,$\frac{5}{3}$)

44 $4x - y = 6$
3 points are
(0,-6), (1,-2), ($\frac{3}{2}$,0)

45 The Sellsellsell Company sells materials that other companies have discontinued. They use the formula $p = 3c + 5$ to price the materials, where p is the selling price, in cents, and c is the company's cost, in cents. If the company gets something free, at what price do they sell it?

5 cents

Problem Set C

Students can graph these nonlinear equations by plotting and connecting a sufficient number of points.

Determine the x-intercept(s) and y-intercept(s) for each of the following:

46 $y = x^2 + 4x + 4$
x-intercept is -2;
y-intercept is 4

47 $y = x^2 - 5x - 14$
x-intercepts are 7, -2;
x-intercept is -14

48 $x^2 + y^2 = 25$
x-intercepts are 5, -5;
y-intercepts are 5, -5

49 $3x^2 + xy + 9y^2 = 27$
x-intercepts are 3, -3;
y-intercepts are $+\sqrt{3}$, $-\sqrt{3}$

50 $-4x^2 + 3xy - 5y^2 = -20$
x-intercepts are $+\sqrt{5}$, $-\sqrt{5}$;
y-intercepts are 2, -2

51 $x^2 - 3x - 2y^2 = 10$
x-intercepts are 5, -2;
no y-intercepts

52 $(x - 5)^2 + (y - 2)^2 = 9$
x-intercepts are $5+\sqrt{5}$, $5-\sqrt{5}$
no y-intercept in reals

53 $(x + 1)^2 + (y + 3)^2 = 16$
x-intercepts are $-1+\sqrt{7}$, $-1-\sqrt{7}$
y-intercepts are $-3+\sqrt{15}$, $-3-\sqrt{15}$

X tending the topic: **Subscripts**

Subscripts are a useful notation in many algebraic topics. In this text, they are used in Section 9.3X for slope and Section 9.6X for equations of a line.

The ordered pair (x,y) refers to a general point in the coordinate plane (also called the **Cartesian plane**, named after Rene Descartes (dā kärt'), a 17th century mathematician and philosopher). Sometimes it is useful to name specific points by using **subscripts**. The points (x_1,y_1), (x_2,y_2), etc. refer to specific points in the plane. (The point (x_1,y_1) is read, "x sub one, y sub one" or "x-one, y-one.")

- If the point (x_1,y_1) is the y-intercept of $y = 3x + 5$, then $x_1 = 0$ and $y_1 = 5$. The point (x_1,y_1) is $(0,5)$.

- If the point (x_2,y_2) is three units to the right of the origin and two units down, then $x_2 = 3$ and $y_2 = -2$. The point (x_2,y_2) is $(3,-2)$.

Problem Set **X**

1 The point (x_1,y_1) locates the y-intercept of $y = -3x - 5$. Find y_1.
$(0,-5)$

2 Find x_2 and y_2 if (x_2,y_2) locates the x-intercept of $y = -4x + 3$.
$(\frac{3}{4},0)$

3 The points $(5,-1)$ and (x_3,y_3) coincide. What are the values of x_3 and y_3?
$x_3 = 5$, $y_3 = -1$

In problems 4–9, name the numerical coordinates for each point.

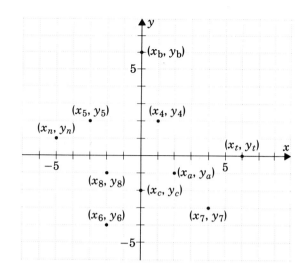

4 (x_4, y_4)

    (1,2)

5 (x_5, y_5)

    (−3,2)

6 (x_6, y_6)

    (−2,−4)

7 (x_a, y_a)

    (2,−1)

8 (x_b, y_b)

    (0,6)

9 (x_n, y_n)

    (−5,1)

10 Which point is (4,− 3)?

    (x_7, y_7)

11 Which point is (− 2,− 1)?

    (x_8, y_8)

12 Which point is (0,− 2)?

    (x_c, y_c)

13 Which point is (6,0)?

    (x_t, y_t)

Section 9.3 Slope

SECTION SCHEDULE

Basic (3 days)

Average (2 days)

Advanced (2 days)

Chemical reactions generate heat. For two different reactions, the relationships between the temperature C (in degrees Celsius) and the time t (in seconds) are described by the following equations:

$$C = 3t + 4$$
$$C = \tfrac{1}{2}(t + 8)$$

These two equations can be drawn on a graph that has a horizontal t-axis and a vertical C-axis.

Notice that both equations have the same C-intercept; that is, when $t = 0$, $C = 4$. However, $C = 3t + 4$ goes through the points (2,10) and (3,13), while $C = \tfrac{1}{2}(t + 8)$ goes through (2,5) and (4,6).

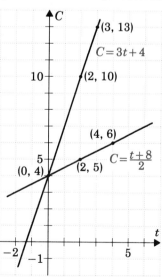

The graph of $C = 3t + 4$ is "steeper" than the graph of $C = \frac{1}{2}(t + 8)$. The number that describes the steepness of a line is called the **slope** of the line.

Definition

This geometric meaning of slope precedes the algebraic interpretation in Section 9.3X.

The SLOPE of a line is the ratio:

$$\frac{\textbf{difference along the vertical axis}}{\textbf{corresponding difference along the horizontal axis}}$$

EXAMPLE

- Select any two points on the line, say (2,5) and (4,6).

  $$\frac{\text{difference along the vertical axis}}{\text{difference along the horizontal axis}} = \frac{6 - 5}{4 - 2}$$

  $$= \frac{1}{2}$$

  Thus for the line $C = \frac{1}{2}(t + 8)$

  the slope is $\dfrac{1}{2}$.

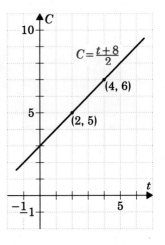

Sample Problems

1 Calculate the slope of each line:

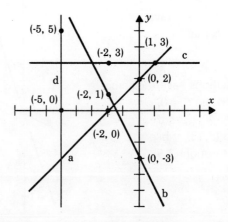

PROCEDURE   For each pair of points, calculate the slope ratio. Be sure that the order in which the y-values are subtracted corresponds to the order in which the x-values are subtracted.

Students should be encouraged to describe the general relationship between the sign of the slope and the inclination of the line:
*   Positive slope: rises to the right*
*   Negative slope: falls to the right*
*   Zero slope: horizontal line*
*   No slope: vertical line*

a   two points are (0,2) and (−2,0):   slope $= \dfrac{2-0}{0-(-2)} = \dfrac{2}{2} = 1$

b   two points are (−2,1) and (0,−3):   slope $= \dfrac{1-(-3)}{-2-0} = \dfrac{4}{-2} = -2$

c   two points are (−2,3) and (1,3):   slope $= \dfrac{3-3}{-2-1} = \dfrac{0}{-3} = 0$

d   two points are (−5,5) and (−5,0):   slope $= \dfrac{5-0}{-5-(-5)} = \dfrac{5}{0}$

Division by zero is not defined mathematically, and so a vertical line is said to have **no slope**. The horizontal line in part **c** has a slope of zero, which should not be confused with no slope.

2   Graph the line that contains (2,1) and has slope $\frac{3}{4}$.

PROCEDURE
Use the point (2,1) and the slope $\frac{3}{4}$ to find other points on the line. The slope indicates that the vertical change is 3 when the horizontal change is 4. Thus other points on the line are (−2,−2), (6,4), (10,7), etc.

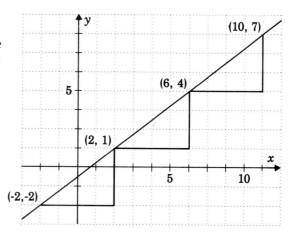

A "shorthand" way to describe the slope of a line is "rise over run."

$$\text{slope} = \frac{\text{rise}}{\text{run}} = \frac{3}{4}$$

For this line, the rise is 3 when the run is 4.

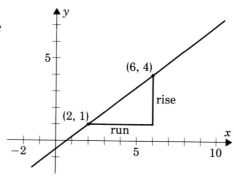

Basic (3 days)
(1) 1–12, 15–23
(2) 13, 14, 24–20 (even),
    34, 37, 41, 42
(3) 35, 36, 43–45
    356: 1–12 (even)
    264: 1–6

Average (2 days)
(1) 13, 14, 24, 31, 32–40
(2) 41–45
    264: 1–8

Advanced (2 days)
(1) 13, 14, 32–45
(2) 46–56 (even)
    364: 1–12

Problem Set **A**

Find the slope of each line.

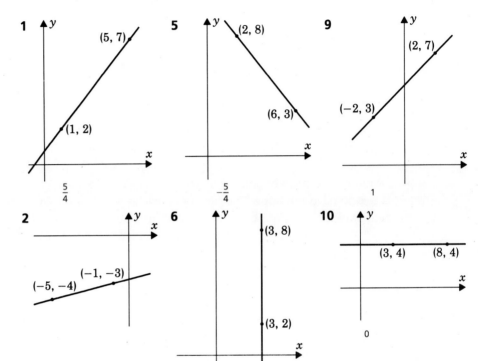

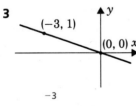

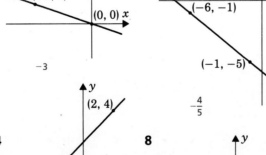

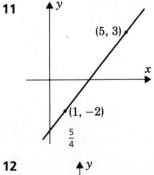

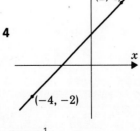

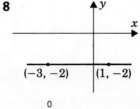

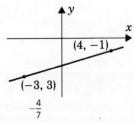

13 On a topographic map, the horizontal distance between Liu's house and Kwan's house is 500 meters. Their houses differ in elevation: Kwan's house is higher, on an evenly-rising hill, by 20 meters. What is the slope of the hill that rises from Liu's house to Kwan's house?

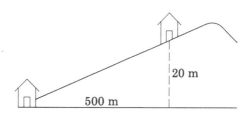

$\frac{1}{25}$

14 A cable car runs up the side of a mountain. The horizontal distance from the bottom of the cable car ride to the top is 1200 feet. The station at the bottom of the mountain has an elevation of 600 feet. The station at the top has an elevation of 1000 feet. What is the slope of the cable car ride?

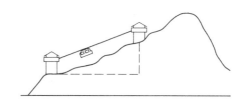

$\frac{1}{3}$

Use this graph to calculate the slope of the line joining each pair of points.

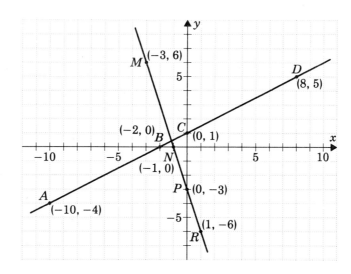

15 C and D
$\frac{1}{2}$

16 B and C
$\frac{1}{2}$

17 A and C
$\frac{1}{2}$

18 A and D
$\frac{1}{2}$

19 R and M
-3

20 P and M
-3

21 R and P
-3

22 R and N
-3

23 Describe a property of the slope of a line based on problems 15–22.
The slope is the same, no matter what pair of points is used.

Evaluate each expression. (Review: Section 1.2)

24 $A = \frac{1}{2}h(B + b)$ find h if $A = 54, B = 6, b = 3$.
  h = 12

25 $A = \pi r^2$ find r if $A = 154, \pi = \dfrac{22}{7}$.
  r = 49

26 $V = \frac{4}{3}\pi r^3$ find V if $\pi = \dfrac{22}{7}, r = 21$.
  V = 38808

27 $s = \frac{1}{2}gt^2$ find t if $s = 256, g = 32$.
  t = 4

28 $t = rs + p$ find p if $t = -5, r = 4, s = -3$.
  p = 7

29 $\ell = (n - 1)d + a$ find a if $\ell = -37, n = 8, d = -5$.
  a = -2

30 $y = mx + b$ find b if $y = 10, m = -3, x = -2$.
  b = 5

31 $y = mx + b$ find b if $x = -5, y = -5, m = \dfrac{2}{5}$.
  b = -3

Problem Set **B**

Graph each line and then find its slope.

32 $2x + y = 6$
  3 points are (0,6), (2,2), (3,0); slope is -2

33 $x + 3y = 3$
  3 points are (0,1), (3,0), (6,-1); slope is $-\frac{1}{3}$

34 $x + y = 4$
  3 points are (0,4), (2,2), (4,0); slope is -1

35 $-x + y = 5$
  3 points are (-5,0), (0,5), (5,10); slope is 1

36 $y = 3x - 4$
  3 points are (0,-4), (1,-1), (3,5); slope is 3

37 $y = -2x + 1$
  3 points are (0,1), ($\frac{1}{2}$,0), (1,-1); slope is -2

38 $x - 2y = 8$
  3 points are (0,-4), (8,0), (10,1); slope is $\frac{1}{2}$

39 $3x - y = 0$
  3 points are (0,0), (1,3), (2,6); slope is 3

40 $6 = 4y - x$
  3 points are (-6,0), (3,6); slope is $\frac{1}{4}$

Graph each line, given the slope and the indicated point. Use a separate pair of axes for each graph.

41 slope $\dfrac{1}{2}$; (2,3)
  2 other points are (0,2), (4,4)

42 slope $-\dfrac{2}{3}$; (-8,4)
  (Treat either the 2 or the 3 as negative, but not both.)
  2 other points are (-8,4), (-5,2)

43 slope 3 $\left(\text{or } \dfrac{3}{1}\right)$; (2,-1)
  2 other points are (1,-4), (3,2)

44 slope -4; (-1,-5)
  2 other points are (-1,-5), (-9,0)

45 slope 0; (3,-2)
  2 other points are (0,-2), (5,-2)

Problem Set C

Graph each line and then find its slope.

46 $2x - 4y = 6$

     3 points are $(1,-1)$, $(3,0)$, $(5,1)$, slope is $\frac{1}{2}$

47 $4x + 2y = 5$

     3 points are $(0,\frac{5}{2})$, $(2,-\frac{3}{2})$, $(\frac{5}{4},0)$, slope is -2

48 $y = \frac{1}{4}x - 3$

     3 points are $(0,-3)$, $(4,-2)$, $(8,-1)$, slope is $\frac{1}{4}$

49 $y = -\frac{2}{3}x + 1$

     3 points are $(0,1)$, $(3,0)$, $(6,-1)$, slope is $-\frac{2}{3}$

50 $2x = 3y + 6$

     3 points are $(0,-2)$, $(3,0)$, $(6,2)$, slope is $\frac{2}{3}$

51 $-5x = 2y - 3$

     3 points are $(0,\frac{3}{2})$, $(\frac{3}{5},0)$, $(4,\frac{17}{2})$, slope is $-\frac{5}{2}$

52   Etta wants to build a rectangular garden in a location where the garden can be five feet wide, but it can be any length from five to thirty feet.

   a   Make a graph showing the perimeter of the garden as the length goes from five feet to thirty feet. (Use the vertical axis for the perimeter and the horizontal axis for the length.)

     some points are $(5,20)$, $(10,30)$, $(30,70)$

   b   Find the slope of the graph.

     slope is 2

   c   Extend the graph to find the point where it intercepts the vertical axis. What is the physical interpretation of this intercept?

     as length approaches 0, perimeter approaches 10

Notice what happens if two x-values differ by one unit:

$$\text{slope} = \frac{\text{difference in } y\text{-values}}{\text{corresponding difference in } x\text{-values}}$$

$$= \frac{\text{difference in } y\text{-values}}{1}$$

$$= \text{difference in } y\text{-values}$$

Thus the slope can be calculated by changing the x-values by one unit.

53   Calculate the change in y-values for $y = -2x + 7$ when x changes from 2 to 3.

     -2

54   Calculate the change in y-values for $y = 5x - 3$ when x changes from 12 to 13.

     5

55   Calculate the change in y-values for $y = x$ when x changes from k to $k + 1$.

     1

56   Calculate the change in y-values for $y = 3x + 2$ when x changes from $k - 1$ to k.

     3

X tending the topic: Describing Slope Algebraically

Subscripts can be used to provide an algebraic definition of the slope of a line:

Definition

If (x_1,y_1) and (x_2,y_2) are two different points on a line, $x_1 \neq x_2$, then the **SLOPE** of the line is: $\dfrac{y_2 - y_1}{x_2 - x_1}$

EXAMPLE

- The order of the x-values must correspond with the order of the y-values, but either point can be used first. For $(1,7)$ and $(-3,-1)$:

$$\frac{y_2 - y_1}{x_2 - x_1} = \frac{7 - (-1)}{1 - (-3)} = \frac{8}{4} = 2 \qquad \frac{y_2 - y_1}{x_2 - x_1} = \frac{-1 - 7}{-3 - 1} = \frac{-8}{-4} = 2$$

The value for the slope is the same.

Problem Set X

Find the slope of the line that contains each pair of points.

1 $(2,2)$ and $(3,5)$

3

3 $(4,1)$ and $(-2,-2)$

$\frac{1}{2}$

5 $(2,-2)$ and $(-1,3)$

$-\frac{5}{3}$

2 $(2,1)$ and $(4,3)$

1

4 $(2,0)$ and $(-1,-3)$

1

6 $(3,-1)$ and $(-4,2)$

$-\frac{3}{7}$

7 A line has a slope of 2. If it passes through the points $(2,5)$ and $(x,6)$, find the value of x.

$2\frac{1}{2}$

8 A line has a slope of -3. If it passes through the points $(3,2)$ and $(4,y)$, find the value of y.

-1

9 A line contains the points $(-2,1)$ and $(x,3)$. Its slope is $-\frac{2}{5}$. Find x.

-3

10 A line contains the points $(-3,-2)$ and $(5,y)$. If its slope is $\frac{3}{4}$, find y.

4

11 A horizontal line passes through the points $(6,y)$ and $(-3,4)$. Find y.

4

12 A vertical line passes through the points $(7,5)$ and $(x,-3)$. Find x.

7

Section 9.4 The Slope-Intercept Form of a Linear Equation

SECTION SCHEDULE

Basic (2 days)

Average (2 days)

Advanced (2 days)

To establish the menu price, y, of an entree, a restaurant manager doubles the restaurant's purchase price, x, and then adds three dollars. This relationship translates to the equation $y = 2x + 3$. The equation can be graphed:

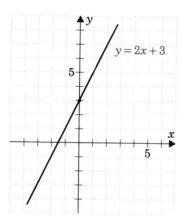

The slope of the line is 2 and the y-intercept is 3. (The graph includes negative values of x and y even though the restaurant prices would not be negative!)

Whenever a linear equation is written so that it is "solved" for y in the form $y = mx + b$, then m is the slope of the line and b is the y-intercept. This form of an equation, $y = mx + b$, is called the **slope-intercept form** of a linear equation.

Definition

The **SLOPE-INTERCEPT FORM** of a linear equation is $y = mx + b$. In this form, the slope of the line is m and the y-intercept is b.

EXAMPLES

- $y = 5x - 8$
  slope is 5
  y-intercept is -8

- $y = -x + 3$
  slope is -1
  y-intercept is 3

- $y = x$
  slope is 1
  y-intercept is 0

- $y = -\frac{1}{3}x - \frac{2}{3}$
  slope is $-\frac{1}{3}$
  y-intercept is $-\frac{2}{3}$

The **slope-intercept form** *is one form of a linear equation. Students will see the* **standard form** *in Section 9.6 and the* **point-slope form** *and the* **two point form** *in Section 9.6X.*

Students can graph the 4 lines and use the methods of Sections 9.2 and 9.3 to calculate the slopes and y-intercepts.

Sample Problems

1   Find the slope and y-intercept for each line:

    a $2x + 2y + 3 = 0$

    b $\dfrac{2x - 3y}{4} = 5$

PROCEDURE

Solve each equation for y so that the equation is in slope-intercept form:

    a $\qquad\qquad\qquad 2x + 2y + 3 = 0$

    ADD $-2x$: $\qquad\qquad 2y + 3 = -2x$

    ADD -3: $\qquad\qquad\; 2y = -2x - 3$

    MULTBY $\frac{1}{2}$: $\qquad\qquad y = -x - \frac{3}{2}$

    The slope is -1 and the y-intercept is $-\frac{3}{2}$.

    b $\qquad\qquad\qquad \dfrac{2x - 3y}{4} = 5$

    MULTBY 4: $\quad 2x - 3y = 20$

    ADD $-2x$: $\qquad\; -3y = -2x + 20$

    MULTBY $-\frac{1}{3}$: $\qquad\quad y = \frac{2}{3}x - \frac{20}{3}$

    The slope is $\frac{2}{3}$ and the y-intercept is $-\frac{20}{3}$.

2   Find the slope and y-intercept of:

    a   the horizontal line $y = 7$ **b**   the vertical line $x = -4$

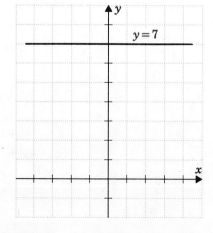

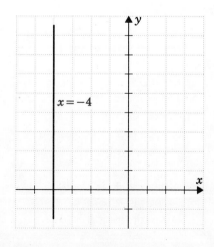

PROCEDURE

a The equation $y = 7$ can be thought of as $y = 0x + 7$. The slope is zero and the y-intercept is 7.
  Every horizontal line has a slope of zero.

b In general, slope is not defined for a vertical line. Also, a vertical line does not cross the y-axis, and so it does not have a y-intercept.

Problem Set A

ASSIGNMENT GUIDE

Basic (2 days)
(1) 1–4, 5–25 (odd)
(2) 6–32 (even)

Average (2 days)
(1) 1–4, 6–26 (even)
(2) 28–52 (even)

Advanced (2 days)
(1) 24–46 (even)
(2) 48–56 (even), 58–60

1 The slope-intercept form of an equation provides the slope and the ___?___ .

  y-intercept

2 For the equation $y = mx + b$, the slope of the line is ___?___ and the y-intercept is ___?___ .

  m, b

3 Does the equation $y = 5$ represent a horizontal line or a vertical line?

  horizontal

4 Does the equation $x = 2$ represent a horizontal line or a vertical line?

  vertical

The following equations are in slope-intercept form. State the slope and the y-intercept.

5 $y = 2x + 5$

  $m = 2$, $b = 5$

6 $y = 3x - 4$

  $m = 3$, $b = -4$

7 $y = -\dfrac{1}{2}x - 1$

  $m = -\dfrac{1}{2}$, $b = -1$

8 $y = -\dfrac{2}{3}x + 3$

  $m = -\dfrac{2}{3}$, $b = 3$

9 $y = 4x - \dfrac{1}{3}$

  $m = 4$, $b = -\dfrac{1}{3}$

10 $y = x + 3$

  $m = 1$, $b = 3$

11 $y = -2x + \dfrac{3}{5}$

  $m = -2$, $b = \dfrac{3}{5}$

12 $y = -x + 2$

  $m = -1$, $b = 2$

13 $y = 2x$

  $m = 3$, $b = 0$

Rewrite each of the following equations in $y = mx + b$ form. Then state the slope and the y-intercept.

14 $y = -5x$

  $y = -5x$, $m = -5$,
  $b = 0$

15 $y - x = 11$

  $y = x + 11$, $m = 1$,
  $b = 11$

16 $x + y = 9$

  $y = -x + 9$, $m = -1$,
  $b = 9$

17 $x - y = 5$

  $y = x - 5$, $m = 1$,
  $b = -5$

18 $6x - y = -2$

  $y = 6x + 2$, $m = 6$,
  $b = 2$

19 $3y = 12x - 6$

  $y = 4x - 2$, $m = 4$,
  $b = -2$

20 $-2y = -10x + 4$

  $y = 5x - 2$, $m = 5$,
  $b = -2$

21 $6y = 2x - 12$

  $y = \dfrac{1}{3}x - 2$, $m = \dfrac{1}{3}$, $b = -2$

22 $-5y = 10x + 3$

  $y = -2x - \dfrac{3}{5}$, $m = -2$,
  $b = -\dfrac{3}{5}$

9.4 Slope-Intercept Form **367**

Graph each line, given the slope and a point. (Review: Section 9.3)

23 slope 3; (0,2)

  2 other points are (−1,−1), (1,5)

24 slope $-\dfrac{2}{3}$; (0,1)

  2 other points are (3,−1), (6,−3)

25 slope −2; (0,3)

  2 other points are (−1,5), (1,1)

26 slope $\dfrac{1}{2}$; (0,2)

  2 other points are (2,3), (4,4)

Problem Set **B**

For each equation state whether the graph of the line is horizontal, vertical, or neither. Then list two points that lie on the line and, if possible, calculate the slope.

27 $y = x + 3$

  neither, $m = 1$

28 $y = x + 4$

  neither, $m = 1$

29 $x = 2$

  vertical, slope is undefined

30 $x = -1$

  vertical, slope is undefined

31 $y = -3$

  horizontal, $m = 0$

32 $y = 4$

  horizontal, $m = 0$

33 $x + y = 8$

  neither, $m = -1$

34 $2x + y = 6$

  neither, $m = -2$

35 $x = 0$

  vertical, slope is undefined

36 $y = 0$

  horizontal, $m = 0$

37 $y = x$

  neither, $m = 1$

38 $y = -3x$

  neither, $m = -3$

Rewrite the following in slope-intercept form. Then state the slope and the y-intercept.

39 $3x - 4y + 5 = 0$

  $y = \dfrac{3}{4}x + \dfrac{5}{4}, \ m = \dfrac{3}{4}, \ b = \dfrac{5}{4}$

40 $5x + 5y - 7 = 0$

  $y = -x + \dfrac{7}{5}, \ m = -1, \ b = \dfrac{7}{5}$

41 $x = \dfrac{1}{2}y - 3$

  $y = 2x + 6, \ m = 2, \ b = 6$

42 $2x = \dfrac{1}{3}y + 1$

  $y = 6x - 3, \ m = 6, \ b = -3$

43 $\dfrac{-2x + 3y}{5} = 1$

  $y = \dfrac{2}{3}x + \dfrac{5}{3}, \ m = \dfrac{2}{3}, \ b = \dfrac{5}{3}$

44 $\dfrac{x - y}{6} = -4$

  $y = x + 24, \ m = 1, \ b = 24$

45 $y + \dfrac{2}{3}x = -\dfrac{1}{3}$

  $y = -\dfrac{2}{3}x - \dfrac{1}{3}, \ m = -\dfrac{2}{3}, \ b = -\dfrac{1}{3}$

46 $\dfrac{1}{2}x + 12 = 2y$

  $y = \dfrac{1}{4}x + 6, \ m = \dfrac{1}{4}, \ b = 6$

Problem Set C

Use the following method to graph each equation: First, use the y-intercept to locate one point on the line. Then, use that point and the slope to locate a second point on the line.

47 $y = \dfrac{1}{2}x + 2$

2 points are (0,2), (2,3)

48 $y = \dfrac{2}{3}x + 1$

2 points are (0,1), (3,3)

49 $y = 2x - 5$

2 points are (0,−5), (1,−3)

50 $y = 3x - 1$

2 points are (0,−1), (1,2)

51 $y = -5x$

2 points are (0,0), (1,−5)

52 $y = 4x$

2 points are (0,0), (1,4)

53 $y = -\dfrac{3}{4}x + 2$

2 points are (0,2), (4,−1)

54 $y = -\dfrac{1}{2}x + 3$

2 points are (0,3), (2,2)

55 $y = -2$

2 points are (0,−2), (2,−2)

56 $y = x - 3$

2 points are (0,−3), (1,−2)

57 $y = -x + 2$

2 points are (0,2), (1,1)

58 $y = 4$

2 points are (0,4), (1,4)

Use the given information to draw a graph for each problem. Then use the graph to answer the question.

59 When $x = -2, y = -7$. Also $y = 13$ when $x = 3$. Determine the value of y when $x = 1$.

$y = 5$ when $x = 1$

59) From the line through (−2,−7) and (3,13), read the y-value for $x = 1$.

60 Sid and Tina needed to cut down several trees near their cabin in order to build a barn. In two hours they cut down six trees. In five hours they had leveled thirteen trees. About how many trees could they cut down in eleven hours?

27

60) Extend the line through (2,6) and (5,13) to read the y-value for $x = 11$.

61 Rona was inspecting light bulbs during her job. She found that one bulb out of the first seven was defective and three out of the first twenty-two were defective. How many bulbs could she expect to test before she found five defective ones?

37

61) Extend the line through (1,7) and (3,22) to read the y-value for $x = 5$.

62 Cindy and James ran twenty miles together one day while training for a marathon. They ran the first six miles in forty-two minutes. It took them a total of one hundred two minutes to run the first twenty-four miles. How many minutes would be expected for them to run the twenty-six miles?

$108\dfrac{2}{3}$

62) Extend the line through (6,42) and (24,102) to read the y-value for $x = 26$.

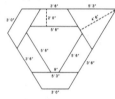

After-School Mathematics: Sailing

This method of successive approximations is common in algebra. Students can study the technique for approximating a cube root, p. 443.

Sara saved her money and bought a little Sunfish sailboat. Since she lives near a lake, she sails almost every day. Sara discovered that it usually takes her longer to make the trip back across the lake than to cross in the first place. The wind is usually against her on the way back. One day she timed it: it took one hour to cross the lake and two hours to return.

One day Sara had only two and a half hours. She had to figure how many minutes she could sail out before turning back. She knew that she couldn't cross the lake because she didn't have three hours. If she sailed out for half an hour, she would need one hour to return. That was too short a trip; she would have an hour left over. So she added ten minutes. If she sailed out for forty minutes, she would need eighty minutes to return, for a total of one hundred twenty minutes, or two hours. That still gave her an extra half hour. Then she tried fifty minutes. Fifty minutes out and one hundred minutes back would be one hundred and fifty minutes, just right! Assuming the wind conditions remained the same, Sara would make it home on time.

Reasonably accurate measurements can be taken from a scale drawing of the steps.

Application: Carpet Repair

The lounge area was designed so that students can sit on the carpeted top step. Thus the carpeting on the lower step, which students walk on, wears out more quickly than the carpeting on the upper step.

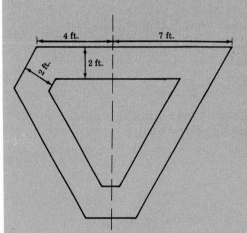

The area consists of:

1 triangle:
$$A = \tfrac{1}{2}bh$$
$$= (\tfrac{1}{2})(5\tfrac{1}{4})(4\tfrac{1}{2})$$
$$= 11\tfrac{13}{16}$$

3 trapezoids:
$$A = \tfrac{1}{2}h(B + h)$$
$$= \tfrac{1}{2}(2)(5\tfrac{1}{2} + 3\tfrac{1}{2})$$
$$= 9$$

2 trapezoids:
$$A = \tfrac{1}{2}h(B + h)$$
$$= \tfrac{1}{2}(2)(5\tfrac{1}{4} + 3)$$
$$= 8\tfrac{1}{4}$$

The riser:
$$A = \tfrac{1}{3}(3 \cdot 5\tfrac{1}{2} + 3 \cdot \tfrac{3}{4})$$
$$= \tfrac{1}{3}(16\tfrac{1}{2} + 2\tfrac{1}{4})$$
$$= \tfrac{1}{3}(18\tfrac{3}{4})$$
$$= 6\tfrac{1}{3}$$

The total area is:
$$11\tfrac{13}{16} + 3(9) + 2(8\tfrac{1}{4}) + 6\tfrac{1}{3}$$
$$= 11\tfrac{13}{16} + 27 + 16\tfrac{1}{2} + 6\tfrac{1}{3}$$
$$= 61\tfrac{31}{48} \text{ square feet}$$

or almost 7 square yards of carpeting.

How many square yards of carpeting will be necessary to recarpet the lower step along with the four-inch riser that leads up to the lower step?

Section 9.5 Parallel Lines and Perpendicular Lines

SECTION SCHEDULE

Basic (2 days)

Average (2 days)

Advanced (3 days)

Line **a** and line **b** are **parallel**, which means that they are in the same plane and they do not meet. Calculate the slope of each line:

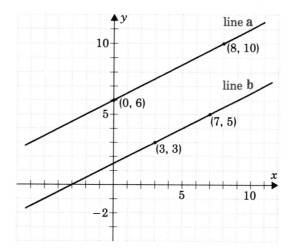

Line **a** contains (0,6) and (8,10):

$$\text{slope} = \frac{10 - 6}{8 - 0}$$

$$= \frac{4}{8}$$

$$= \frac{1}{2}$$

Thus the two parallel lines have equal slopes.

Line **c** and line **d** are perpendicular, which means that they form an angle of 90°. Calculate the slope of each line:

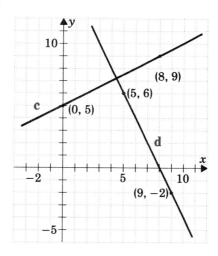

Line **c** contains (0,5) and (8,9):

$$\text{slope} = \frac{9 - 5}{8 - 0}$$

$$= \frac{4}{8}$$

$$= \frac{1}{2}$$

Line **d** contains (5,6) and (9,−2):

$$\text{slope} = \frac{-2 - 6}{9 - 5}$$

$$= \frac{-8}{4}$$

$$= -2$$

Notice that the product of the two slopes is $\left(\frac{1}{2}\right)\left(-2\right) = -1$. In general, if two lines are perpendicular, and neither line is vertical, the product of their slopes is −1.

Property

*The two lines must be distinct. See Sample Problem **1d** for two equations that represent the same line.*

If two lines are parallel, then their slopes are equal. Also, if two lines have equal slopes, then the lines are parallel.

If two lines are perpendicular, then the product of their slopes is − 1. Also, if the product of two slopes is − 1, then the lines are perpendicular.

An exception to these properties must be made for vertical lines, since the slope of a vertical line is not defined.

Sample Problems

1 State whether each pair of equations represents parallel lines, perpendicular lines, or neither.

a $y = 3x + 5$
 $y = 3x - 4$

b $2x - y = 1$
 $x + 2y = -2$

c $x - y = -5$
 $x + 3y = -12$

d $2x + 2y = 10$
 $y = 5 - x$

e $y = 3$
 $x = -2$

f $x = 3$
 $x = -1$

PROCEDURE   Find the slope of each line.

a   The slope of each line is 3; the lines are parallel.

b   The equations can be rewritten in slope-intercept form:

$$2x - y = 1$$
$$-y = -2x + 1$$
$$y = 2x - 1$$

$$x + 2y = -2$$
$$2y = -x - 2$$
$$y = -\frac{1}{2}x - 1$$

The two slopes are 2 and $-\frac{1}{2}$. Since $(2)\left(-\frac{1}{2}\right) = -1$, the two lines are perpendicular.

Two numbers are **reciprocals** if their product is 1. If the product of two numbers is -1, they can be called **negative reciprocals**. Thus two lines are perpendicular if their slopes are negative reciprocals.

c   Rewrite the equations in slope-intercept form:

$$x - y = -5$$
$$-y = -x - 5$$
$$y = x + 5$$

$$x + 3y = -12$$
$$3y = -x - 12$$
$$y = -\frac{1}{3}x - 4$$

The slopes are 1 and $-\frac{1}{3}$; the lines are neither parallel nor perpendicular.

d   Rewrite the equations in slope-intercept form:

$$2x + 2y = 10 \qquad\qquad y = 5 - x$$
$$2y = -2x + 10 \qquad\qquad y = -x + 5$$
$$y = -x + 5$$

Notice that both lines have the same equation. Therefore, both equations represent the same line.

e   The equation $y = 3$ represents a horizontal line and the equation $x = -2$ represents a vertical line. The lines are perpendicular.

f   The two equations $x = 3$ and $x = -1$ represent vertical lines. Although the slopes are not defined, the lines are parallel.

2   Write the equations of two lines that are parallel to $y = 3x + 2$.

PROCEDURE

Lines with slope 3 will be parallel to $y = 3x + 2$. Some equations are:

$$y = 3x + 4$$
$$y = 3x - 7$$

ASSIGNMENT GUIDE

Basic (2 days)
(1) 1–17
(2) 18–30

Average (2 days)
(1) 1–24, 29, 30
(2) 31–43

Advanced (3 days)
(1) 15–20, 29–42
(2) 43–48, 50–60 (even)
(3) 377: 1–8

Problems 5–14 can be used as oral exercises by asking students to state the slope of each line.

Problem Set **A**

1 Two lines that have the same slope are __?__.
   parallel

2 If two lines are parallel, then their slopes are __?__.
   equal

3 If two lines are perpendicular, then their slopes are __?__.
   negative reciprocals

4 Every vertical line is __?__ to every horizontal line.
   perpendicular

State whether each pair of equations represents parallel lines, perpendicular lines, or neither.

5 $y = 2x + 3$
    $y = 2x - 3$
    parallel

6 $y = 2x + 3$
    $y = 3x - 2$
    neither

7 $y = 3 + x$
    $y = 4 - x$
    perpendicular

8 $y = x - 5$
    $y = 5 - x$
    perpendicular

9 $y = 2x + 3$
    $y = -\dfrac{1}{2}x - 3$
    perpendicular

10 $y = -1$
     $x = -1$
     perpendicular

11 $y = 2$
     $x = 3$
     perpendicular

12 $y = 5$
     $y = -3$
     parallel

13 $x = 7$
     $x = 2$
     parallel

14 $y = \dfrac{3}{5}x - 6$
     $x = \dfrac{5}{3}x + 1$
     neither

For each problem, find a value of k so that the lines are parallel and find a value of k so that the lines are perpendicular.

15 $y = 2x + 10$
     $y = kx - 2$ parallel; $K = 2$
         perpendicular; $K = -\dfrac{1}{2}$

16 $y = \dfrac{3}{2}x - 8$
     $y = kx$ parallel; $K = \dfrac{3}{2}$
         perpendicular; $K = -\dfrac{2}{3}$

17 $y = -\dfrac{1}{5}x + 7$
     $y = kx - 5$ parallel; $K = -\dfrac{1}{5}$
         perpendicular; $K = 5$

18 $y = -4x + 3$
     $y = kx - 2$ parallel; $K = -4$
         perpendicular; $K = \dfrac{1}{4}$

19 $y = \dfrac{2}{7}x + 1$
     $y = -kx + 4$ parallel; $K = -\dfrac{2}{7}$
         perpendicular; $K = \dfrac{7}{2}$

20 $y = x + 6$
     $y = kx - 3$
         parallel; $K = 1$
         perpendicular; $K = -1$

Solve for b. (Review: Section 2.6)

21 $0 = 4(3) + b$
      $b = -12$

22 $-2 = 3(-2) + b$
      $b = 4$

23 $6 = 5(2) + b$
      $b = -4$

24 $4 = -3(6) + b$
      $b = 22$

25 $-3 = 2(7) + b$
      $b = -17$

26 $-1 = 4(-2) + b$
      $b = 7$

27 $0 = -1(3) + b$
      $b = 3$

28 $-8 = \dfrac{1}{2}(0) + b$
      $b = -8$

Problem Set   B

State whether each system represents parallel lines, perpendicular lines, or neither.

29 $3x + y = 6$
      $3x + y = 2$
      parallel

30 $-\frac{1}{2}x + y = 4$
      $\frac{1}{2}x + y = 8$
      neither

31 $4x + y = 2$
      $-4x - y = 1$
      parallel

32 $x + y = 2$
      $x - y = 1$
      perpendicular

33 $x - 3y = -6$
      $9x + 3y = 12$
      perpendicular

34 $2y = 4x + 8$
      $x + 2y = 10$
      perpendicular

35 $2x + 3y = 5$
      $6y = 10 - 4x$
      parallel

36 $3x - 2y - 1 = 0$
      $-2x + 3y + 5 = 0$
      neither

Write the equation of each line in slope-intercept form.

37   parallel to the line with the equation $y = 2x - 7$
      $y = 2x + b$

38   parallel to the line with the equation $y = -3x + 2$
      $y = -3x + b$

39   perpendicular to the line with the equation $y = -\dfrac{1}{4}x$
      $y = 4x + b$

40   perpendicular to the line with the equation $y = 5x + 1$
      $y = -\frac{1}{5}x + b$

41   parallel to the line with the equation $x = 3$
      $x = a$

42   perpendicular to the line with the equation $y = -1$
      $x = a$

Problem Set C

43 Graph the line that is perpendicular to the graph of $x + y = 12$ and that passes through the origin.

3 points are (0,0), (1,1), (2,2)

44 Graph the line that is perpendicular to the graph of $x - y = 8$ and that passes through the point (2,-6).

3 points are (0,-4), (2,-6), (4,-8)

45 Graph the line that is perpendicular to the graph of $2x + y = 4$ and that passes through the y-intercept of the line with an equation $y = 3x - 8$.

3 points are (0,-8), (4,-6), (8,-4)

46 Graph the line that is parallel to the graph of $x - 2y = 4$ and that passes through the x-intercept of the line with an equation $x - 2y = 1$.

3 points are (1,0), (3,1), (5,2)

47 The Mongrebian spy set his surveillance drone on a course that was described by $3n + 5e = 15$, where n is north and e is east. The Grebmongian counterspy was watching from five miles north. She wanted her surveillance drone to fly on a parallel course (so that it could spy on the Mongrebian drone). What course should she set?

$3n + 5e = 30$

Three or more points are **collinear** if they can all be contained by one line. Determine whether the points are collinear.

48 (2,1), ($-1,2$), ($-4,4$)

noncollinear

50 ($-2,1$), ($-6,-1$), ($-4,0$), ($-7,1$)

noncollinear

49 ($-4,-4$), (3,-2), ($-1,-3$)

noncollinear

51 (8,1), (5,-5), (6,-3), (7,-1)

collinear

Find values of k so that the following points are collinear.

52 (3,0), (8,3), and ($k,-9$)

$k = -12$

57 (2,9), (6,10), (5,k)

$k = \frac{39}{4}$

53 (2,-4), ($-3,-2$), $\left(-\frac{21}{2},k\right)$

$k = 1$

58 (0,-3), (6,-5), ($k,-7$)

$k = 12$

54 (2,9), ($-4,-21$), ($k,14$)

$k = 3$

59 (3,-7), (5,-7), (2,k)

$k = -7$

55 (0,1), $\left(-\frac{1}{2},0\right)$, (5,$k$)

$k = 11$

60 ($k,7$), ($-5,-14$), ($-1,-2$)

$k = 2$

56 (1,4), ($-1,-4$), ($k,2$)

$k = \frac{1}{2}$

61 (8,k), (3,1), ($-5,-2$)

$k = \frac{23}{8}$

X tending the topic: A BASIC Program to Compute Slope

The following program calculates the slope determined by a pair of points:

```
10   PRINT "ENTER TWO ORDERED PAIRS (X1,Y1) AND (X2,Y2)."
20   INPUT X1, Y1, X2, Y2
30   M = (Y2 - Y1)/(X2 - X1)
40   PRINT "THE SLOPE IS "; M
50   PRINT "DO YOU HAVE ANOTHER PAIR OF POINTS?"
60   PRINT "IF YES, ENTER 1.  IF NO, ENTER 0."
70   INPUT A
80   IF A = 1 THEN 10
90   END
```

Problem Set X

Use the program to find the slope determined by the following pairs of points:

1 (2,3) and (−3,4)
$m = -\frac{1}{5}$

2 (8,−30) and (−5,2)
$m = -\frac{32}{13}$

3 (5,6) and (−102,6)
$m = 0$

4 (0,5) and (5,0)
$m = -1$

5 (0,−5) and (−5,0)
$m = -1$

6 (0,0) and (3,4)
$m = \frac{4}{3}$

7 The program above does not test whether the points determine a vertical line. Modify the program so that it handles that case effectively. Test your modified program with the pair of points (2,1) and (2,6).

   slope is undefined

8 Modify the program again (or write a new program) that determines whether three points are collinear. Test your program with the following sets of points:

a (1,1), (4,4), (7,7)   collinear $(y = x)$

b (0,−1), (4,11), (−2,−6)   noncollinear

c (−2,7), (1,−2), ($\frac{1}{3}$,0)   noncollinear

d (−3,5), (6,5), (2,5)   collinear $(y = 5)$

e (4,−3), (4,5), (4,−1)   collinear $(x = 4)$

f (5,2), (9,4) (13,7)   noncollinear

55) $\frac{1 - 0}{0 - (-\frac{1}{2})} = \frac{k - 1}{5 - 0}$

$\frac{1}{\frac{1}{2}} = \frac{k - 1}{5}$

$\frac{10}{5} = \frac{k - 1}{5}$

$k = 11$

56) $\frac{4 - (-4)}{1 - (-1)} = \frac{2 - 4}{k - 1}$

$\frac{8}{2} = \frac{-2}{k - 1}$

$\frac{4}{1} = \frac{-2}{k - 1}$

$4k - 4 = -2$

$4k = 2$

$k = \frac{1}{2}$

57) $\frac{10 - 9}{6 - 2} = \frac{k - 9}{5 - 2}$

$\frac{1}{4} = \frac{k - 9}{3}$

$4k - 36 = 3$

$4k = 39$

$k = \frac{39}{4}$

58) $\frac{-5 - (-3)}{6 - 0} = \frac{-7 - (-3)}{k - 0}$

$\frac{-2}{6} = \frac{-4}{k}$

$\frac{-1}{3} = \frac{-4}{k}$

$3k \quad -k = -12$

$k = 12$

59) The points are on the horizontal line $y = -7$.

60) $\frac{-14 - (-2)}{-5 - (-1)} = \frac{7 - (-2)}{k - (-1)}$

$\frac{-12}{-4} = \frac{9}{k + 1}$

$\frac{3}{1} = \frac{9}{k + 1}$

$3k + 3 = 9$

$3k = 6$

$k = 2$

61) $\frac{1 - (-2)}{3 - (-5)} = \frac{k - 1}{8 - 3}$

$\frac{3}{8} = \frac{k - 1}{5}$

$8k - 8 = 15$

$8k = 23$

$k = \frac{23}{8}$

Section 9.6   Writing the Equation for a Line

Trudy plotted the value of her stocks for a two-week period. At the beginning of the period, her stocks were worth $6 per share. She noticed that the price per share increased by $0.25 per day.

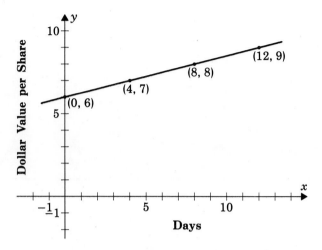

The equation for the graphed line can be determined by finding the slope and the y-intercept:

$$\frac{\text{change in } y}{\text{change in } x} = \frac{9 - 7}{12 - 4} = \frac{2}{8} = \frac{1}{4}$$

The y-intercept is 6.

Using the general equation $y = mx + b$, the equation of the graphed line is:

$$y = \frac{1}{4}x + 6.$$

Sometimes it is useful to write the equation without fractions and with all the variables on one side of the equation:

$$y = \frac{1}{4}x + 6$$

MULTBY 4: $4y = x + 24$
ADD $-x$: $-x + 4y = 24$

The two equations $y = \frac{1}{4}x + 6$ and $-x + 4y = 24$ represent the same line; the equations are equivalent. The equation $-x + 4y = 24$ is said to be in **standard linear equation form**.

Definition

A linear equation is said to be in **STANDARD LINEAR EQUATION FORM** (or, more simply, **STANDARD FORM**), if it is expressed in the form:

$$Ax + By = C$$

where A, B, C are integers.

Two other forms of linear equations, the **point-slope form** *and the* **two point form**, *are presented in Section 9.6X.*

EXAMPLES

- The equation $y = -3x + 5$ can be written in standard form as $3x + y = 5$.

- The equation $\frac{1}{3}x + \frac{1}{5}y = 1$ can be written in standard form as $5x + 3y = 15$.

Sample Problems

1 A line with slope 2 contains the point $(0,-3)$. Write the equation in slope-intercept form and write the equation in standard form.

PROCEDURE

Since the line contains $(0,-3)$, the y-intercept is -3. The slope is 2, so the equation is: $y = 2x - 3$

Collect all the variables on one side of the equation: $-2x + y = -3$

2 Write the equations, in standard form, of the following lines:

a a vertical line through $(6,-2)$

b a horizontal line through $(6,-2)$

PROCEDURE

a For a vertical line, the x-value is constant. The equation is $x = 6$ since the line contains $(6,-2)$. Both the equations $x = 6$ and $x + 0y = 6$ are considered to be in standard form.

b The y-value is constant for a horizontal line. The equation is $y = -2$ or $0x + y = -2$.

3 A line with slope $-\frac{1}{8}$ contains the point $(4,-7)$. Write the equation in standard from.

PROCEDURE First write the equation in slope-intercept form. The ordered pair $(4,-7)$ gives a particular pair of values for x and y, namely $x = 4$ and $y = -7$. Substitute these values into $y = mx + b$ along with $m = -\frac{1}{8}$:

$$y = mx + b$$
$$-7 = (-\tfrac{1}{8})\,(4) + b$$
$$-7 = -\tfrac{1}{2} + b$$
$$-\tfrac{13}{2} = b$$

Thus the slope-intercept form is $y = -\frac{1}{8}x - \frac{13}{2}$.
For the standard form, write the equation without fractions and collect the variables on one side of the equation:

$$y = -\tfrac{1}{8}x - 6\tfrac{1}{2}$$
$$\text{MULTBY 8:} \quad 8y = -x - 52$$
$$\text{ADD } x: \quad x + 8y = -52$$

The standard form is $x + 8y = -52$.

ASSIGNMENT GUIDE

Basic (2 days)
(1) 1–13, 19–21
(2) 14–18, 22–28

Average (2 days)
(1) 1–4, 6–24 (even)
(2) 15–21 (odd), 26–38 (even)

Advanced (3 days)
(1) 10–38 (even)
(2) 31, 33, 35, 40–48 (even), 50–58
(3) 37, 39
385: 2–16 (even)

Problem Set **A**

1 What is the **standard linear equation form** of an equation?
$Ax + By = C$

2 What is the general **slope-intercept form** of a linear equation?
$y = mx + b$

3 Write the standard form of the equation $y = 2x - 5$.
$-2x + y = -5$

4 Write the slope-intercept form of the equation $3x + 2y = 9$.
$y = -\dfrac{3}{2} + \dfrac{9}{2}$

Write each equation in $Ax + By = C$ form where A, B, and C are integers. Then list the values of A, B, and C.

5 $2x = y - 3$
$2x - y = -3;\ A = 2,\ B = -1,\ C = -3$

6 $\dfrac{1}{2}x - \dfrac{2}{3}y = 4$
$3x - 4y = 24;\ A = 3,\ B = -4,\ C = 24$

7 $4x + 7 = -6y$
$4x + 6y = -7;\ A = 4,\ B = 6,\ C = -7$

8 $\dfrac{2}{5}x - \dfrac{1}{3}y = \dfrac{1}{6}$
$12x - 10y = 5;\ A = 12,\ B = -10,\ C = 5$

Write the equation for each line in slope-intercept form and in standard linear equation form.

9 $m = 1; b = 3$

  $y = x + 3, x - y = 3$

10 $m = -2; b = 4$

  $y = -2x + 4, 2x + y = 4$

11 slope 5; y-intercept -2

  $y = 5x - 2, -5x + y = -2$

12 slope -3; y-intercept 0

  $y = -3x, 3x + y = 0$

13 slope $\frac{1}{2}$; y-intercept -8

  $y = \frac{1}{2}x - 8, -x + 2y = -16$

14 slope -1; through $(0,-3)$

  $y = -1x - 3, x + y = -3$

15 slope 1; through $(0,2)$

  $y = x + 2, -x + y = 2$

16 slope $-\frac{2}{3}$; y-intercept 1

  $y = -\frac{2}{3}x + 1, 2x + 3y = 3$

17 horizontal through $(2,3)$

  $y = 3, y = 3$

18 vertical through $(-1,4)$

  $x = -1, x = -1$

Find the slope determined by the following pairs of points. (Review: Section 9.3)

19 $(0,0)$ and $(2,5)$

  $m = \frac{5}{2}$

20 $(0,2)$ and $(1,6)$

  $m = 4$

21 $(5,7)$ and $(-10,1)$

  $m = \frac{2}{5}$

22 $(1,2)$ and $(-5,-3)$

  $m = \frac{5}{6}$

23 $(-2,-1)$ and $(-2,-4)$

  slope is undefined

24 $(8,-4)$ and $(-4,-4)$

  $m = 0$

Problem Set **B**

Write the equation of the line, in slope-intercept form, for each set of conditions:

25 slope 2; passes through the point $(3,4)$

  $y = 2x - 2$

26 slope -3; passes through the point $(2,0)$

  $y = -3x + 6$

27 slope 5; passes through the point $(-1, 4)$

  $y = 5x + 9$

28 slope -1; passes through the point $(-3,-2)$

  $y = -x - 5$

29 slope $\frac{1}{2}$; passes through the point $(4,-6)$

  $y = \frac{1}{2}x - 8$

30 slope $\frac{2}{3}$; passes through the point $(-9,4)$

  $y = \frac{2}{3}x - \frac{35}{3}$

Write the equation of each line in standard form.

31 horizontal and passes through the point $(-3,2)$

$y = 2$

32 vertical and passes through the point $(2,1)$

$x = 2$

33 parallel to the line with the equation $y = 2x - 3$ and passing through the point $(-4,2)$

$y = 2x + 10$

34 parallel to the line with the equation $y = \frac{1}{2}x + 4$ and passing through the point $(-2,1)$

$y = \frac{1}{2}x + 2$

35 perpendicular to the line with the equation $y = \frac{1}{3}x + 14$ and passing through the point $(-2,-7)$

$y = -3x - 13$

36 perpendicular to the line with the equation $y = 4x - 7$ and passing through the point $(8,-2)$

$y = -\frac{1}{4}x$

37 slope is negative of the slope of the graph of $2x - 3y = 7$; passes through the point $(-6,5)$

$y = -\frac{2}{3}x - \frac{8}{3}$

38 x-intercept 4; slope is the reciprocal of the slope of the line with the equation $4x - \frac{1}{2}y = 0$

$y = \frac{1}{8}x - \frac{1}{2}$

39 horizontal, through the intersection of $y = 2x$ and $y = 5x + 3$

$y = -2$

Problem Set C

When two points on a line are given, first use the two points to calculate the slope. Then use that slope, and either one of the points, to calculate the y-intercept.

■ Find the equation of the line that contains $(-2,5)$ and $(4,0)$.

First, calculate the slope:
$$m = \frac{0 - 5}{4 - (-2)} = -\frac{5}{6}$$

Next, use the slope and either point, say (4,0), to calculate the y-intercept:

$$y = mx + b$$

$$0 = \left(-\frac{5}{6}\right)(4) + b$$

$$0 = -\frac{20}{6} + b$$

$$b = \frac{20}{6} = \frac{10}{3}$$

The equation is: $y = -\frac{5}{6}x + \frac{10}{3}$

Write the equation of the line, in slope-intercept form, through each pair of points:

40 (3,−6) and (0,0)

$y = -2x$

41 (0,2) and (1,5)

$y = 3x + 2$

42 (1,8) and (0,−3)

$y = 11x - 3$

43 (1,1) and (4,4)

$y = x$

44 (−5,3) and (3,−5)

$y = -x - 2$

45 (3,4) and (−5,4)

$y = 4$

46 (−2,−2) and (3,−2)

$y = -2$

47 (5,1) and (−1,5)

$y = -\frac{2}{3}x + \frac{13}{3}$

48 (−1,0) and (2,5)

$y = \frac{5}{3}x + \frac{5}{3}$

49 (−1,3) and (−3,4)

$y = -\frac{1}{2}x + \frac{1}{2}$

It is possible to tell, without graphing, if an equation is a linear equation. The conditions are:

1. The equation contains one or two variables.
2. The equation does not contain the product of the variables.
3. The variable(s) are to the first power.

The third condition means that the squares, cubes, etc. of variables are ruled out. It also means that a variable cannot be in a denominator.

Tell whether or not each equation is a linear equation. If not, identify the condition that is not met.

50 $y = x + 4$

linear

51 $\frac{5y}{7} = 25$

linear

52 $x^3 + 3y = 9$

not linear (3)

53 $xy = 24$

not linear (2)

54 $3x = 2y + 5$

linear

55 $3(5 + x) = 2 + 4y$

linear

56 $\frac{y - 4}{3} = 4$

linear

57 $(x + y)^2 = 49$

not linear (2,3)

58 $A = 4w + 6$

linear

Xtending the topic: Forms of Linear Equations

This chapter discussed two forms of a linear equation:

slope-intercept form: $y = mx + b$ where m is the slope and b is the y-intercept

standard form: $Ax + By = C$ where A, B, and C are integers

There are two other useful forms of a linear equation. They can each be derived from the same two properties. First, for any particular line, all forms of the slope of that line must be equal. Second, if (x_1, y_1) represents a particular point on a line, then (x, y) can be used to represent the general point on the line (x and y are variables).

1   Given the slope m of a line and a particular point (x_1, y_1):

slope $= m$ Given

slope $= \dfrac{y - y_1}{x - x_1}$ Use (x_1, y_1), the particular point, and (x, y), the general point.

The slopes must be equal: $\dfrac{y - y_1}{x - x_1} = m$

This equation is called the **point-slope form** of a linear equation.

■   Use the point-slope form to find the equation of the line with slope $\frac{2}{3}$ that contains the point (6,9).

$$\frac{y - y_1}{x - x_1} = m$$

$$\frac{y - 9}{x - 6} = \frac{2}{3}$$

$$3y - 27 = 2x - 12 \qquad \text{(cross-product)}$$
$$3y = 2x + 15$$
$$y = \frac{2}{3}x + 5$$

2   Given the two particular points (x_1, y_1) and (x_2, y_2) on a line:

slope $= \dfrac{y_2 - y_1}{x_2 - x_1}$ Use the two particular points.

slope $= \dfrac{y - y_1}{x - x_1}$ Use the general point (x, y) and either particular point.

The slopes must be equal: $\dfrac{y - y_1}{x - x_1} = \dfrac{y_2 - y_1}{y_2 - x_1}$

This equation is called the **two point form** of a linear equation.

- Find the equation of the line through (6,9) and $(-3,3)$.

$$\frac{y - y_1}{x - x_1} = \frac{y_2 - y_1}{x_2 - x_1}$$

$$\frac{y - 9}{x - 6} = \frac{3 - 9}{-3 - 6}$$

$$\frac{y - 9}{x - 6} = \frac{-6}{-9}$$

$$\frac{y - 9}{x - 6} = \frac{2}{3}$$

$$3y - 27 = 2x - 12 \qquad \text{(cross-product)}$$

$$3y = 2x + 15$$

$$y = \frac{2}{3}x + 5$$

Problem Set X

Use the point-slope form or the two point form to find the equation of each line.

1 slope is 2; through (3,5)

$y = 2x - 1$

2 through (4,7) and $(-6,2)$

$y = \frac{1}{2}x + 5$

3 through (0,7) and $(-6,11)$

$y = -\frac{2}{3}x + 7$

4 slope is -5; through $(-2,7)$

$y = -5x - 3$

5 slope is $-\frac{3}{10}$; through $(20,-4)$

$y = -\frac{3}{10}x + 2$

6 through $(-5,-5)$ and (2,2)

$y = x$

7 through $(-5,5)$ and $(2,-2)$

$y = -x$

8 through $(\frac{17}{2},0)$ and $(\frac{1}{2},-16)$

$y = 2x - 17$

9 slope $\frac{3}{2}$; through (1,1)

$y = \frac{3}{2}x - \frac{1}{2}$

10 slope $\frac{5}{3}$; through (2,4)

$y = \frac{5}{3}x + \frac{3}{2}$

11 through $(-1,0)$ and $(\frac{1}{2},-6)$

$y = -4x - 4$

12 through (1,27) and $(-2,-3)$

$y = 10x + 17$

13 through $(1,-4)$ and $(2,-8)$

$y = -4x$

14 through (3,2) and $(-5,2)$

$y = 2$

15 through $(7,-3)$ and (7,2)

$x = 7$

16 slope m; through $(3,3m + b)$

$y = mx + b$

ASSIGNMENT GUIDE

Basic (2 days)
(1) 390: 1–12
(2) 362: 32, 33
   368: 27–33 (odd)
   390: 13–17

Average (1 day)
369: 47, 49, 51
382: 31–37 (odd)
390: 1–17

Advanced (1 day)
369: 53, 57
376: 49, 60
385: 11, 13, 15
390: 1–17

Chapter Study Guide

Vocabulary

As you study and review this chapter, be sure to learn the important mathematics vocabulary, including:

1 **x-intercept, y-intercept**   An x-INTERCEPT of a graph is a value of x for which $y = 0$. A y-INTERCEPT of a graph is a value of y for which $x = 0$.

   - For the equation $y = 3x - 6$, when x is zero, y is -6. When y is zero, x is 2. The x-intercept is 2 and the y-intercept is -6.

2 **slope**   The SLOPE of a line is the ratio:

$$\frac{\text{difference along the vertical axis}}{\text{corresponding difference along the horizontal axis}}$$

   - Find the slope of the line containing $(-4, 3)$ and $(2, -1)$.

$$\text{slope} = \frac{3 - (-1)}{-4 - 2}$$

$$= \frac{4}{-6}$$

$$= -\frac{2}{3}$$

The slope of the line is $-\frac{2}{3}$.

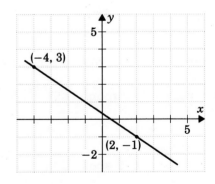

3 **Slope-intercept form, standard linear equation form**
   The SLOPE-INTERCEPT FORM of a linear equation is $y = mx + b$, where m represents the slope and b is the y-intercept. The STANDARD LINEAR EQUATION FORM (more simply, STANDARD FORM) is $Ax + By = C$, where A, B, and C are integers.

   - The equation $y = -\frac{2}{3}x - 5$ is in slope-intercept form. The same equation, in standard form, is $2x + 3y = -15$.

Skills

Be sure you build the useful algebraic skills, including:

4 **Graphing linear equations**
Draw the graph of the
equation $y = 3x - 2$.

PROCEDURE   Choose at least three
values for x, say $-2, 0,$ and 2, and
calculate the corresponding values
for y. Then plot the points and draw
the graph.

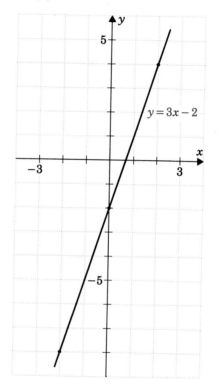

x	-2	0	2
y	-8	-2	4

5 **Finding the slope of a line**   Find the slope of:
  a   the line through $(0, -3)$ and $(6, 7)$ **b** $5x - 3y = 9$

PROCEDURE

   a   Use the definition:

$$\text{slope} = \frac{\text{difference in } y\text{-values}}{\text{corresponding difference in } x\text{-values}}$$

$$= \frac{7 - (-3)}{6 - 0} = \frac{10}{6} = \frac{5}{3}$$

   b   Solve the equation for y: $5x - 3y = 9$
$$-3y = -5x + 9$$
$$y = \tfrac{5}{3}x - 3$$

   The slope is $\tfrac{5}{3}$.

6 **Writing the equation of a line** Write the equation of each line in slope-intercept form and in standard form.
a slope is -2; contains $(0,-4)$
b contains $(0,-3)$ and $(6,7)$
c contains $(4,2)$; parallel to $y = \frac{1}{2}x - 7$
d contains $(6,11)$, perpendicular to $y = -\frac{1}{3}x + 1$

PROCEDURE

a The slope and y-intercept are given. The slope intercept form is $y = -2x - 4$. In standard form, the equation is $2x + y = -4$.

b Use the two points to find the slope, and then find the value of b.

$$\text{slope} = \frac{-3 - 7}{0 - 6} = \frac{-10}{-6} = \frac{5}{3} \qquad y = mx + b$$

$$7 = \left(\frac{5}{3}\right)(6) + b$$

$$7 = 10 + b$$

$$-3 = b$$

The equation is $y = \frac{5}{3}x - 3$. For the standard form:

$$y = \frac{5}{3}x - 3$$
$$3y = 5x - 9$$
$$-5x + 3y = -9$$

c The line is parallel to $y = \frac{1}{2}x - 7$, so its slope must be $\frac{1}{2}$.

$$y = mx + b$$
$$2 = \left(\frac{1}{2}\right)(4) + b$$
$$2 = 2 + b$$
$$0 = b$$

The slope-intercept form is $y = \frac{1}{2}x + 0$ or $y = \frac{1}{2}x$.
The standard form is $x - 2y = 0$.

d The line is perpendicular to $y = -\frac{1}{3}x + 1$ so its slope must be 3. Find the value of b:

$$y = mx + b$$
$$11 = (3)(6) + b$$
$$11 = 18 + b$$
$$-7 = b$$

The slope-intercept form is $y = 3x - 7$. In standard form, the equation is $3x - y = 7$.

Math History: Archimedes and an Analogy

Many discoveries in mathematics are made by guessing an answer and then carefully showing that the guess is correct. Many times the guess is made by an **analogy** in which two objects or structures are thought of as similar. Archimedes, a mathematician who lived in Greece in the third century B.C., used an analogy to guess a formula for the volume of a sphere.

 Archimedes had noted that a triangle and a circle would have the same area if the base of the triangle was the circumference of the circle and if the height of the triangle was the radius of the circle:

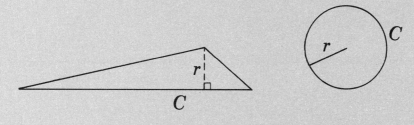

$$A = \tfrac{1}{2}bh = \tfrac{1}{2}(C)\,(r) = \tfrac{1}{2}(2\pi r)\,(r) = \pi r^2$$

He knew the formula for the volume of a cone, $V = \tfrac{1}{3}Bh$, where B was the base area and h was the height. He also knew that the area of a sphere was $4\pi r^2$.

 His analogy was: Just as the area of a circle is the same as the area of a triangle, if the base of the triangle is the circumference of the circle and the height of the triangle is the radius of the circle; then by analogy the volume of a sphere might be the same as the volume of a cone, if the base area of the cone is the area of the sphere and the height of the cone is the radius of the sphere.

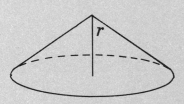 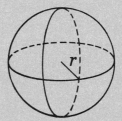

$$V = \tfrac{1}{3}Bh = \tfrac{1}{3}(4\pi r^2)r = \tfrac{4}{3}\pi r^3$$

Then he proved that his guess was correct.

Chapter Test

Determine whether each statement is true or false.

1 The ordered pair $(-5,3)$ represents a point in the third quadrant.

    false

2 All the points (x,y) for which $x > 0$ and $y < 0$ lie in the fourth quadrant.

    true

3 The x-intercept of the graph of $2x + 5y = 10$ is 2.

    false

4 The y-intercept of the graph of $y = 3x - 4$ is -4.

    true

5 The slope of the graph of $y = 2x + 3$ is 2.

    true

6 The slope of the line passing through the points (4,6) and (5,8) is $\frac{1}{2}$.

    false

7 The slope of a line parallel to the x-axis is zero.

    false

8 The slope of a line which slants upward to the right is negative.

    false

9 The graphs of the equations $y = 3x - 5$ and $y = 3x + 2$ are parallel lines.

    true

Find the slope of the line through each pair of points.

10 (0,−4), (−3,5) **11** (4,3), (4,−5) **12** (−2,1), (−5,−1)

slope is −3 no slope (vertical line) slope $\frac{2}{3}$

Write an equation of the line meeting each pair of conditions. (First, write the equation in slope-intercept form and then write the equation in standard linear equation form.)

13 slope 3; passes through point (0,2)

$y = 3x + 2$; $-3x + y = 2$

14 horizontal; passes through point $(-2,-6)$

$y = -6$; $y = -6$

15 passes through points (3,3) and $(-2,-1)$

$y = \frac{4}{5}x + \frac{3}{5}$; $4x - 5y = -3$

State whether the pairs of lines are parallel, perpendicular, or neither.

16 $2x + 3y$
    $3x - 2y = 5$

    perpendicular

17 $5x - y + 10 = 0$
    $y = 5x + 10$

    neither

Problem Set: Slope and Grade

When a road climbs or descends a hill, the slope of the climb or descent is called the **grade** of the road. Grade is usually expressed as a percent: if a road rises fifteen meters for a horizontal run of one hundred meters, the road is said to have a grade of fifteen percent.

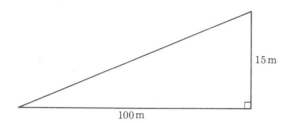

$$\text{grade} = \frac{15m}{100m} = 15\%$$

Major highways are constructed so that the grade is always low. For example, the steepest part of the Pennsylvania Turnpike has a grade of three percent.

1   A street in San Francisco rises thirteen feet for every fifty feet of horizontal run. What is the grade of the street?

2   An automotive test hill for bulldozers has a three meter drop for every five meters of horizontal run. What is the slope of the test hill?

3   One stretch of Pikes Peak Road has a grade of eleven percent. If that stretch of road climbs eighty feet, what is the horizontal run for that part of the road? What is the length of that part of the road?

4   A diving submarine drops five meters for every thirteen meters of horizontal travel. Express its descent grade as a negative percent.

5   Design specifications require that the grade of a state highway cannot exceed six percent. How many miles of horizontal run will be necessary for a vertical climb of seventy-five hundredths miles? How many miles of horizontal run will be necessary for a drop of thirty-five hundredths miles?

6   A climbing path goes straight up a hill at a grade of seventeen percent. What is the actual distance walked by a climber after ascending one hundred fifty meters?

1) $\dfrac{13}{50} = 26\%$

2) $\dfrac{-3}{5} = -60\%$

3)

$\dfrac{80}{r} = 11\%$
$r = 727$ ft.
$\ell^2 = h^2 + 80^2$
$\ell = 731$ ft.

4) $\dfrac{-5}{13} = -38\%$

5) $\dfrac{0.75}{r} \le 0.06$
$r \ge 12.5$ mi.
$\dfrac{0.35}{r} \le 0.06$
$r \ge 5.8$ mi.

6)

$\dfrac{150}{r} = 0.17$
$r = 882$
$\ell^2 = r^2 + 150^2$
$\ell = 895$ m

Chapter 10

CHAPTER SCHEDULE

Basic
Problem Sets	7 Days
Review	3 Days
Test	2 Days

Average
Problem Sets	9 Days
Review	2 Days
Test	2 Days

Advanced
Problem Sets	9 Days
Review	2 Days
Test	1 Day

SYSTEMS OF LINEAR EQUATIONS

Section 10.1   Finding a Solution for a Pair of Equations

SECTION SCHEDULE

Basic (1 day)

Average (1 day)

Advanced (1 day)

Roseanne said, "I am 4 years older than Steve." Steve said, "Roseanne is twice as old as I am." These two sentences can be translated into two equations:

$$r = s + 4$$
$$r = 2s$$

The values $r = 8$ and $s = 4$ satisfy both equations (and they are the only values that make both equations true).

When two (or more) equations involve the same variables, they are called a **system of equations**. Finding values for the variables that satisfy both equations is called **solving** the system of equations.

Sample Problems

1   Josie said she had 3 times as many albums as Ronnie had, but Ronnie said that Josie only had 4 more albums than he. If both were right, how many albums does each have?

PROCEDURE Let x represent the number that Ronnie has, and let y represent the number that Josie has.

$$y = 3x$$
$$y = x + 4$$

Find numbers (x, y) that satisfy both equations. For the first equation, $y = 3x$, values could be (0,0), (1,3) (2,6), (3,9), . . . Checking each of these in the second equation, the ordered pair (2,6) also satisfies $y = x + 4$. Thus the **solution** to the system is the ordered pair (2,6). The solution can also be expressed $x = 2, y = 6$. Ronnie has 2 albums and Josie has 6 albums.

The method of solution for these two sample problems is a simple, intuitive procedure, introduced only to present the concepts of a system of equations and its solution. The method is extended to graphing equations in Section 10.2 and to algebraic techniques in Sections 10.3–10.5.

2 Solve the system of equations: $x + y = 7$
$$x - y = 1$$

PROCEDURE Try pairs of numbers to find the pair that satisfies both equations. The numbers 3 and 4 will work, but the order is important:

$$x = 4, y = 3$$

The solution to the system is (4,3).

ASSIGNMENT GUIDE

Basic (1 day)
2–14 (even), 15–21, 25

Average (1 day)
15–20, 22, 25, 30–38
(even), 39

Advanced (1 day)
15–20, 30–36 (even),
38–40, 42–46 (even)

Problem Set **A**

Find a solution for each system of equations.

1 $y = x + 2$
$y = 2x$
   (2,4)

2 $y = x + 1$
$y = 2x$
   (1,2)

3 $x + y = 5$
$x - y = 1$
   (3,2)

4 $x + y = 6$
$x - y = 2$
   (4,2)

5 $x + y = 7$
$x - y = -1$
   (4,3)

6 $x + y = 5$
$x - y = -3$
   (1,4)

7 $2x + y = 7$
$x + y = 5$
   (2,3)

8 $3x + y = 6$
$x + y = 4$
   (1,3)

9 $x + 3y = 9$
$x + y = 5$
   (3,2)

10 $x + 2y = 11$
$x + y = 7$
   (3,4)

11 $x + 2y = 6$ and $x - y = 3$

(4,1)

12 $3x - y = 4$ and $x + y = 8$

(3,5)

13 $y = x + 2$ and $y = 2x - 1$

(3,5)

14 $y = x - 3$ and $2y = x + 1$

(7,4)

15 Sally has guessed three more winning teams than Fred, and Sally has guessed twice as many winning teams as Fred. How many winners has each guessed?

Sally guessed 6, Fred guessed 3

16 Angelo lives six blocks farther from school than Linda does, and Angelo lives three times as far from school as Linda does. How far does each live from school?

Linda, 3 blocks; Angelo, 9 blocks

17 What figure contains all the points inside rectangle ABCD and inside triangle RST?

trapezoid *PMNO*

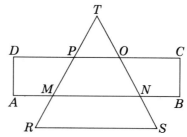

18 What figure contains all the points inside parallelogram ABCD and all the points inside triangle BCD?

triangle *BCD*

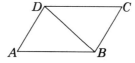

19 The drugstore is between the grocery and the ice cream parlor. The flower shop is between the drugstore and the grocery. Which two stores are farthest apart?

grocery store and Ice Cream Parlor

19)

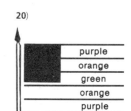

20 The national flag of Revultania has five stripes. There is a green stripe between two orange stripes, and each orange stripe is between a green and a purple stripe. Draw a picture of the flag of Revultania with the colors labeled.

the stripes are in the following order:
purple, orange, green, orange, purple

20)

	purple
	orange
	green
	orange
	purple

Draw a graph of each equation by finding the two intercepts. (Review: Section 9.2)

21 $x + y = 10$

3 points are (0,10), (10,0), (5,5)

22 $x - y = 8$

3 points are (0,−8), (8,0), (4,−4)

23 $2x + y = 6$

3 points are (0,6), (3,0), (1,4)

24 $x + 3y = 6$

3 points are (0,2), (3,1), (6,0)

25 $2x + 3y = 12$

3 points are (0,4), (5,0), (3,2)

26 $3x - 4y = 12$

3 points are (0,−3), $(2, -\frac{3}{2})$, (4,0)

27 $4x - 20 = 5y$

3 points are (0,−4), (5,0), (10,4)

28 $4x = 5y + 1$

3 points are $(0, -\frac{1}{5})$, $(2, \frac{7}{5})$, $(\frac{1}{4}, 0)$

29 $2x + y = 5$

3 points are (5,0), $(\frac{5}{2}, 0)$, (1,3)

Problem Set B

Find a solution for each system of equations.

30 $x - 2 = 4y$
$2x - 9 = 3y$
(6,1)

31 $10 - x = y - 1$
$3 + x = 2y + 2$
(7,4)

32 $3 + x = y - 1$
$1 + 2x = y + 1$
(4,8)

33 $2x + y = -1$
$x + 2y = 4$
(−2,3)

34 $x - y = 8$
$x + y = 2$
(5,−3)

35 $x - y = 1$
$2x = -y$
$(\frac{1}{3}, -\frac{2}{3})$

36 $x - y = 4$
$3x + y = 2$
$(\frac{3}{2}, -\frac{5}{2})$

37 $2x + y = 5$
$3x - y = -10$
(−1,−7)

38 What are two consecutive even numbers such that five times the first is equal to four times the second?
8, 10

39 Two years from now Mark will be twice as old as Meredith, but one year ago Mark was three times Meredith's age. How old is each?
Mark is 10, Meredith is 4

Problem Set C

Students would have to develop some kinds of algebraic techniques for these systems.

Solve each system of equations.

40 $x - 3y = -8$
$x + 3y = 10$
(1,3)

41 $2x + y = 2$
$4x - y = 1$
$(\frac{1}{2},1)$

42 $x + 3y = 4$
$x - 6y = 1$
$(3,\frac{1}{3})$

43 $2x + 4y = 2$
$3x - 2y = 1$
$(\frac{1}{2},\frac{1}{4})$

44 $3x + 2y = 4$
$y - 3x = 1$
$(\frac{2}{9},\frac{5}{3})$

45 $2x - y = -1$
$x + 3y = 3$
(0,1)

46 $y = 2x + 1$
$x = 2y + 1$
(−1,−1)

47 $y = 3x - 2$
$3x = y + 7$
no solution, lines are parallel

Section 10.2 Graphing a System of Equations

SECTION SCHEDULE

Basic (1 day)

Average (2 days)

Advanced (2 days)

A system of linear equations can be interpreted as two lines on a graph. The intersection of the lines corresponds to the solution of the system.

EXAMPLE

All of the systems in the main part of this section have unique solutions. Inconsistent systems and dependent systems are discussed in Section 10.2X.

- $2x + 4y = 16$ $x - 2y = -1$

   A quick method to graph the equations is to find the two intercepts of each. The equation $2x + 4y = 16$ contains (0,4) and (8,0). The equation $x - 2y = -1$ contains (0, $\frac{1}{2}$) and (−1,0).

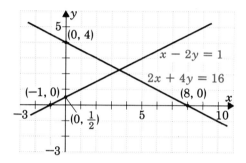

The point of intersection is $(3\frac{1}{2}, 2\frac{1}{4})$. *Check* these values in each of the original equations:

$$2x + 4y = 16$$

$$2\left(\frac{7}{2}\right) + 4\left(\frac{9}{4}\right) \overset{?}{=} 16$$

$$7 + 9 \overset{?}{=} 16$$

$$16 \overset{?}{=} 16 \checkmark$$

$$x - 2y = -1$$

$$\left(\frac{7}{2}\right) - 2\left(\frac{9}{4}\right) \overset{?}{=} -1$$

$$\frac{7}{2} - \frac{9}{2} \overset{?}{=} -1$$

$$\frac{-2}{2} \overset{?}{=} -1$$

$$-1 \overset{?}{=} -1 \checkmark$$

Sample Problems

1   Use graphs to find two numbers that have a sum of two and a difference of twelve.

PROCEDURE
Letting x and y represent the two numbers, the two equations can be written:

$$x + y = 2$$
$$x - y = 12$$

Find the intercepts and graph each line.

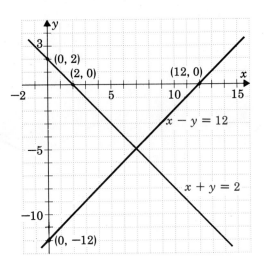

The point of intersection is $(7, -5)$; the two numbers are 7 and -5.

> *To check*   The sum is $7 + (-5) = 2$ and the difference is $7 - (-5) = 12$.

2   Use a graph to solve the system of equations: $y = \frac{1}{3}x + 1$

$$y = \frac{1}{4}x + 2$$

PROCEDURE   Three points on $y = \frac{1}{3}x + 1$ are (0,1), (3,2), and (6,3). Three points on $y = \frac{1}{4}x + 2$ are (0,2), (4,3), and (8,4). Graph each line:

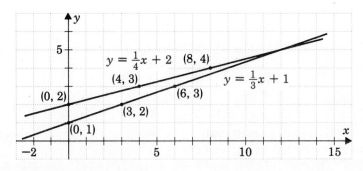

The two lines meet at (12,5).

Problem Set A

ASSIGNMENT GUIDE

Basic (1 day)
2–8 (even), 10–13, 16–18,
20, 21

Average (2 days)
(1) 3, 6, 10–13, 17, 21,
   24, 28, 32, 35
(2) 26, 30
   404: 2–14 (even)

Advanced (2 days)
(1) 14, 15, 26–32 (even),
   35, 38, 40, 42
(2) 44, 46, 48
   404: 2–10 (even),
   11–15

Use a graph to solve each system of equations.

1 $x + y = 8$
    $x - y = 2$
    (2,4)

2 $x + y = 11$
    $x - y = 3$
    (7,4)

3 $2x + y = 7$
    $x + 2y = 8$
    (3,2)

4 $3x + y = 15$
    $x + 2y = 15$
    (3,6)

5 $x + 2y = 0$
    $y = x + 6$
    (4,3)

6 $x + 4y = 1$
    $y = x + 4$
    (−3,1)

7 $2x + y = 3$
    $x - y = 9$
    (2,3)

8 $x + y = 4$
    $x - y = 10$
    (7,−3)

9 $x - 2y = 1$
    $x + 2y = -7$
    (3,2)

10 Find two numbers with difference nine and sum five.
    7, −2

11 What are these two numbers: their sum is three and their difference
    is eleven.
    7, −4

12 Find two numbers with sum twenty and difference two.
    9, 11

13 Find two consecutive odd numbers such that twice the first plus the
    second is seventeen.
    5, 7

14 An airplane takes off from a field at
    the base of a cliff on a secret mis-
    sion. As it climbs, its slope is $\frac{1}{7}$. At the
    same time, a spy plane takes off
    from the top of the cliff and stays
    above the first plane. If the spy
    plane climbs with a slope of $\frac{1}{10}$, and
    the cliff is 750 meters high, at what
    height will the plane on the secret
    mission hit the spy plane?
    2500 m

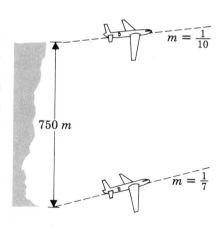

14) $y = \frac{1}{7}x$
    $y = \frac{1}{10}x + 750$

15 A train is going down a mountain that has a slope of one fifth. When
    the train is three kilometers above sea level, a helicopter is three kilome-
    ters above the top of the train. If the helicopter descends with a slope
    of one half, staying above the train, at what height above sea level will
    the helicopter be able to land on one of the train's flatcars?
    1 km

15) $y = \frac{1}{5}x + 3$
    $y = \frac{1}{2}x + 6$

Find the slope of each line. (Review: Sections 9.3 and 9.5)

16 $3x + 2y = 5$
   $m = -\frac{3}{2}$

17 perpendicular to $3x + y = 2$
   $m = \frac{1}{3}$

18 parallel to $x - 4y = 1$
   $m = \frac{1}{4}$

19 $\dfrac{x + 2y}{3} = 8$
   $m = -\frac{1}{2}$

20 through $(-2,-6)$ and $(3,9)$
   $m = 3$

21 through $(4,4)$ and $(0,2)$
   $m = \frac{1}{2}$

22 perpendicular to $x = -3$
   $m = 0$

23 parallel to $3x - y = 2$
   $m = 3$

Problem Set **B**

Use a graph to solve each system of equations.

24 $\dfrac{x}{2} - y = 1$

   $\dfrac{x}{3} + y = 4$

   (6,2)

25 $\dfrac{x}{2} + y = 10$

   $x - \dfrac{y}{4} = 2$

   (4,8)

26 $\dfrac{x}{2} - \dfrac{y}{2} = 4$

   $x - \dfrac{y}{3} = 4$

   (2,−6)

27 $\dfrac{x}{2} + y = 4$

   $x + \dfrac{y}{5} = -1$

   (−2,5)

28 $x + \dfrac{y}{2} = 4$

   $2x - \dfrac{y}{3} = 4$

   $(\frac{5}{2},3)$

29 $\dfrac{x}{2} + y = 4$

   $\dfrac{x}{2} + \dfrac{y}{7} = 2$

   (4,0)

30 $\dfrac{x}{3} - \dfrac{y}{9} = 1$

   $3x + \dfrac{y}{3} = -3$

   $(\frac{3}{2},-\frac{9}{2})$

31 $\dfrac{x}{7} - y = 2$

   $x - \dfrac{y}{5} = 3$

   approx. (2.7,−1.6)

32 $\dfrac{4a}{3} + \dfrac{3b}{4} = 7$

   $\dfrac{5a}{6} - \dfrac{4b}{8} = 2$

   approx. (3.9,2.5)

33 $\dfrac{3m}{2} + \dfrac{4n}{5} = \dfrac{5}{2}$

   $\dfrac{m}{4} + \dfrac{3n}{2} = \dfrac{29}{4}$

   (−1,5)

34 Find two numbers with sum two and difference nine.

$(\frac{11}{2}, -\frac{7}{2})$

35 Find two numbers with difference seven halves and sum twenty-five halves.

$(8, \frac{7}{2})$

36 If one child can make a snowperson in forty minutes and another child can make a snowperson in half an hour, how long will it take the two children working together to make a snowperson?

$\frac{120}{7}$

37 If the area of a square is $36t^2 + 60t + 25$ square meters, what is the length of one side?

$(6t + 5)$ meters

38 Ten times the square of a number plus twenty-nine times the number is equal to twenty-one. If the number is shown by a positive decimal, what is the number?

0.6

36) $(\frac{1}{40} + \frac{1}{30})x = 1$

$(\frac{3 + 4}{120})x = 1$

$x = \frac{120}{7} = 17\frac{1}{7}$ min.

37) $\sqrt{36t^2 + 60t + 25}$
$= \sqrt{(6t + 5)^2}$
$= \quad 6t + 5$

Problem Set **C**

Write parallel, perpendicular, or neither to describe each pair of equations.

Some of the equations are already in slope-intercept form.

Section 10.2X relates parallel lines to inconsistent systems.

39 $y = \frac{x}{3} - 11$

$y = -3x + 13$

perpendicular

40 $3x + 2y = 8$
$3x + 2y = 0$

neither

41 $y = 4x + 17$
$y = 4x - 6$

parallel

42 $y = \frac{5}{3}x + 14$

$y = -\frac{3}{5}x + 14$

perpendicular

43 $y = 5x + 2$

$y = \frac{1}{5}x - 8$

neither

44 $3x + 2y = 8$
$2x - 3y = 0$

perpendicular

45 $4x - y = 11$
$4x + y = 11$

neither

46 $2x + 5y = 7$
$4x + 10y = 7$

neither

47 $\frac{2}{3}x + \frac{1}{5}y = 7$

$10y = 3x - 5$

perpendicular

48 $4x - 3y = 4$
$\frac{3}{5}y = \frac{4}{5}x - 5$

parallel

Xtending the topic: Inconsistent and Dependent Systems

Theresa and Steven released balloons at the same time, Theresa's from ten meters above sea level, and Steven's from two meters above sea level. Each balloon ascended at five meters per second. Did the two balloons ever meet?

The equations are:

$$y = 5x + 10 \quad \text{(Theresa's balloon)}$$
$$y = 5x + 2 \quad \text{(Steven's balloon)}$$

The lines are parallel: they do not intersect. Therefore, there is no ordered pair (x,y) that satisfies both equations. A system of equations that represents parallel lines is said to be **inconsistent** because the system cannot be solved.

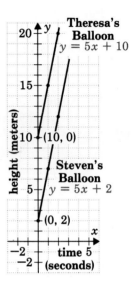

Sometimes both equations in a system represent the same line:

$$y = x - 1$$
$$2y = 2x - 2$$

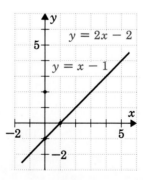

In this case, every point on the line satisfies both equations, so there is no unique solution to the system. The equations are called **dependent**.

Definitions

A system of two equations is **INCONSISTENT** when the system does not have a solution. The graphs of the equations of an inconsistent system are parallel lines.

A system of equations is **DEPENDENT** when the system does not have a unique solution, so that many ordered pairs satisfy the equations. The graph of two equations of a dependent system consists of a single line.

EXAMPLES

- This system of equations is inconsistent: $3x + 2y = 7$
$$3x + 2y = -3$$

    Both equations represent lines that have slope $-\frac{3}{2}$, but they have different y-intercepts.

- This system of equations is dependent: $3x + 2y = 7$
$$6x + 4y = 14$$

    Both equations represent the line with slope $-\frac{3}{2}$ and y-intercept $(0, -\frac{7}{2})$.

> *Dividing both sides of the second equation by 2 also shows that the two equations represent the same line.*

Sample Problem

1   Without graphing, find the solution or state whether the system is inconsistent or dependent.

$$2x + 3y = 5$$
$$x + \frac{3}{2}y = 4$$

PROCEDURE   Rewrite each equation in slope-intercept form:

$$2x + 3y = 5 \qquad\qquad x + \frac{3}{2}y = 4$$
$$3y = -2x + 5 \qquad\qquad \frac{3}{2}y = -x + 4$$
$$y = -\frac{2}{3}x + \frac{5}{3} \qquad\qquad y = -\frac{2}{3}x + \frac{8}{3}$$

The two equations $y = -\frac{2}{3}x + \frac{5}{3}$ and $y = -\frac{2}{3}x + \frac{8}{3}$ represent parallel lines. Thus there is no ordered pair that satisfies both equations, and the system is inconsistent.

Problem Set **X**

Tell whether each of the following systems of equations is inconsistent, dependent, or neither.

1 $4x - 3y = 12$

$2x - \dfrac{3}{2}y = 6$
    dependent

2 $6x + 18y = 48$

$x + 3y = 7$
    inconsistent

3 $111x - 87y = 129$

$74x - 58y = 86$
    neither

4 $\dfrac{2}{3}x - \dfrac{4}{7}y = 10$

$\dfrac{5}{3}x - \dfrac{10}{7}y = 25$
    neither

5 $5x = 3y - 18$

$\dfrac{5}{3}x - y = 9$
    inconsistent

6 $\dfrac{2}{3}x + \dfrac{5}{3}y = 18$

$x + 10y = 12$
    neither

7 $217x + 161y = 287$

$93x + 69y = 82$
    inconsistent

8 $51x - 3y = 57$

$y = 19x - 17$
    neither

9 $\dfrac{4}{5}x - \dfrac{2}{3}y = 12$

$\dfrac{y}{2} = 9 - \dfrac{3}{5}x$
    neither

10 $6x - 9y = 21$

$6y = 4x - 12$
    inconsistent

11 $3x = 5y + 19$

$3y = 5x + 19$
    neither

12 $x = 7$

$y = -1$
    neither

13 $x = \pm\, y$
    neither

14) $\dfrac{3}{5}a - \dfrac{3}{4}p = 15$

$\dfrac{1}{2}p = \dfrac{2}{5}a - 10$

$12a - 15p = 300$

$5p = 4a - 100$

The equations are dependent; many solutions are possible:
$(a,p) = (25,0), (30,4), (35,8), \ldots$

14 In Toni's Grocery, the produce manager noticed a peculiar relation between the sales of apples and pears. On any given day, if he took three fifths of the apples sold and subtracted the number that was three fourths of the pears sold, he got fifteen. He told Toni about it, but Toni said that he had it all wrong. On any given day, half the number of pears sold was equal to two fifths the number of apples sold minus ten. If they were both right, how many apples and pears were sold each day?
    the equations are dependent; there is not a unique solution

15 The City of Peoria is a train that leaves from the station in Chicago at 3:00 P.M. It travels at eighty-five mph. The Springfield Special leaves from the same station in Chicago at 4:00 P.M. on a parallel track. It also travels at eighty-five mph. How far from Chicago is it when the Springfield Special catches up to The City of Peoria?
    the train does not catch up

Project: Logic Puzzles

Some logic puzzles can be solved clue by clue:

1   Five friends were sitting on one side of a table in the cafeteria.
   a Bill sat next to Sally.
   b Joe sat next to Ed.
   c Ruth sat in the third seat from Sally.
   d Bill sat in the third seat from Joe.
   Who sat on the other side of Ed?
   From clues **a** and **c**, the seating plan is:

<u>(Ruth)</u> <u> ? </u> <u>Bill</u> <u>Sally</u> <u> ? </u>   <u> ? </u> <u>(Ruth)</u>

Can you finish the puzzle and answer the question?

For some logic puzzles, start with a table of all the combinations. Then use the clues to eliminate the impossible combinations.

2   Four married couples play on the same volleyball team. The women's names are Ann, Betty Carol, and Doris. The men's names are Ed, Frank, George, and Henry. Use the clues to identify the couples:

   a Carol is Frank's sister.
   b Ann is married to George.
   c Henry is not married to Carol.
   d Doris' husband is an only child.

	Ed	Frank	George	Henry
Ann	X	X	O	X
Betty	?	?	X	?
Carol	?	X	X	?
Doris	?	?	X	?

To start, clue **a** implies that Carol and Frank are not married. From clue **b**, eliminate the other boxes in the row for Ann and in the column for George. Can you finish the puzzle?

3   Five snowmobiles were in a race. Use the clues to find the exact order of finish.
   a The Rupp did not finish last.
   b The Snow Jet finished neither first nor last.
   c The Arctic Cat finished in a lower position than the Polaris.
   d The Polaris did not win the race.
   e The Snow Jet did not finish immediately ahead of or behind either the Polaris or the Ski Doo.

---

1) Use clue **d** to locate Joe, then clue **b** to locate Ed.

2) From clue **c**, Carol must be married to Ed. From clues **a** and **d**, Frank has a sister, so Frank can't be married to Doris.

3)

	Rupp	SnowJet	Arctic Cat	Polaris	SkiDoo
1		X (**b**)	X (**c,d**)	X (**d**)	
2					
3				X (**e**)	X (**e**)
4					
5	X (**a**)	X (**b**)		X (**c**)	

If the Polaris or SkiDoo came in 3rd, the SnowJet would have to come in 2nd or 4th, which would contradict clue **e**.

Suppose the Polaris came in 4th. Then the Arctic Cat came in last (clue **c**). The SnowJet came in 2nd (clue **e**), leaving 1st for the SkiDoo. But this violates clue **e**.

Thus the Polaris came in 2nd. The SnowJet came in 4th (clue **e**) and the SkiDoo came in 1st (clue **e**). The Rupp came in 3rd and the Arctic Cat came in 5th.

Section 10.3   Adding to Solve Systems of Equations

There is an algebraic method to solve systems of equations. Consider the system:

$$x + y = 8$$
$$x - y = 2$$

Notice what happens when the two equations are added. The left-hand sum is $(x + y) + (x - y) = 2x$. The right-hand sum is $8 + 2 = 10$, and the two sums are equal:

$$x + y = 8$$
$$x - y = 2$$

ADD EQS: $2x \quad = 10$

MULTBY $\frac{1}{2}$: $x \quad = 5$

Use the value $x = 5$ in either equation to find the value of y:

$$x + y = 8$$
$$(5) + y = 8$$
$$y = 3$$

Students can check the solution (5,3) in each equation.

The ordered pair (5,3) is the solution to the system of equations.

Sample Problems

1   Maria's and Juan's ages sum to thirty, and Maria is six years older than Juan. Find their ages.

   PROCEDURE   Let j and m represent Juan's and Maria's ages, respectively. Then the equations are:

$$m + j = 30$$
$$m = j + 6$$

   Rewrite the equations as a system:

$$m + j = 30$$
$$m - j = 6$$

ADD EQS: $2m \quad = 36$

MULTBY $\frac{1}{2}$: $m \quad = 18$

Substitute $m = 18$ into either equation:

$$m + j = 30$$
$$(18) + j = 30$$
$$j = 12$$

Juan's age is 12, Maria's age is 18.

2 Solve the system:

$$2x + y = 19$$
$$x + y = 23$$

PROCEDURE Introduce a negative sign by multiplying one of the equations by -1. Using the second equation, $x + y = 23$:

equation: $\quad x + y = 23$
MULTBY -1: $\quad -x - y = -23$

The system can be rewritten as:

$$2x + y = 19$$
$$\underline{-x - y = -23}$$

ADD EQS: $\quad x \qquad = -4$

Substitute $x = -4$ into either equation:

$$2x + y = 19$$
$$2(-4) + y = 19$$
$$-8 + y = 19$$
$$y = 27$$

The solution to the system is $(-4, 27)$.

Problem Set **A**

ASSIGNMENT GUIDE

Basic (1 day)
2–20 (even), 21, 24, 27

Average (1 day)
8–20 (even), 30–34 (even), 36, 37

Advanced (1 day)
10, 12, 16–20, 30–34 (even), 36, 37, 46, 48

Solve each system of equations.

1 $x + y = 9$
$x - y = 3$
(6,3)

3 $x + y = 2$
$x - y = 16$
(9,7)

5 $2x + y = 17$
$x + y = 14$
(3,11)

2 $x + y = 15$
$x - y = 1$
(8,7)

4 $x + y = 4$
$x - y = 10$
(7,−3)

6 $3x + y = 15$
$x + y = 3$
(6,−3)

7 $x + 2y = 13$
$x + y = 5$
$(-3,8)$

10 $3x - y = 13$
$x + y = 3$
$(5,-2)$

13 $2x + y = 11$
$3x - y = 4$
$(3,5)$

8 $x + 4y = 23$
$x + y = 5$
$(-1,6)$

11 $x + 5y = 24$
$x - y = 6$
$(\frac{3}{2}, -\frac{9}{2})$

14 $x + 5y = 23$
$x + 2y = 2$
$(-14,7)$

9 $2x + y = 12$
$x - y = 3$
$(5,2)$

12 $x - 3y = 5$
$x + y = 25$
$(20,5)$

15 $x + 3y = -8$
$-x - 4y = 11$
$(1,-3)$

16) $B + G = 32$
$G = B - 4$

16 The sum of Bill's and Gerry's ages is thirty-two. Gerry is four years younger than Bill. What are their ages?
Bill is 18, Gerry is 14

17) $M + J = 9$
$M - J = 1$

17 When Jack stands on Manny's shoulders, the top of his head is nine feet high. When Jack stands next to Manny, the top of his head is a foot beneath Manny's shoulders. How tall is Jack?
Manny is 5 feet tall, Jack is 4 feet tall

18) $2a + o = 19$
$a = o + 2$

18 Laurie thought that if she had twice as many apples, then with the oranges she had, she would have nineteen pieces of fruit. If she had two more apples than oranges to start with, how many of each did she have?
7 apples, 5 oranges

19) $x + y = 350$
$2x + y = 600$

19 Melinda had two savings accounts, with a total of three hundred fifty dollars in the two. If she saved enough to double one of the accounts, she would have six hundred dollars. How much was in each account?
$250 in one account, $100 in the other account

20) $3s + 2a = 7$
$s + 2a = 5$

20 Chris was making some crunchies to take camping. His friend told him that three packages of sunflower seeds and two packages of almonds would be a good mixture, and that this ought to make about seven ounces. But Chris forgot the recipe and used one package of sunflower seeds to two packages of almonds. He only got five ounces of crunchies. How much was in each package?
1 ounce of sunflower seeds, 2 ounces of almonds

Express each equation in standard form. (Review: Section 9.6)

21 $y = \frac{4}{3}x - 2$
$4x - 3y = 6$

25 $\frac{x + 4y}{3} = \frac{2x + 4}{5}$
$x - 20y = -12$

22 $\frac{y - 2}{x - 1} = 3$
$3x - y = 1$

26 $\frac{y - 5}{x + 4} = \frac{3}{2}$
$3x - 2y = -22$

23 $y \div 4 = 5$
$y = 20$

27 $y = 3x + 7$
$3x - y = -7$

24 $y = 6 - \frac{x}{2}$
$x + 2y = 12$

28 $x = \frac{y}{5} + 2$
$5x - y = 10$

Problem Set B

Solve each system of equations.

29 $\dfrac{x}{2} + \dfrac{y}{4} = 7$

$\dfrac{x}{3} = \dfrac{y}{4}$

$(8.4, 11.2)$

30 $\dfrac{x}{2} + y = 1$

$y = \dfrac{3x}{2}$

$(\frac{1}{2}, \frac{3}{4})$

31 $2x - y = 1$

$4x + y = 4$

$(\frac{5}{6}, \frac{2}{3})$

32 $\dfrac{x}{3} + \dfrac{y}{5} = -1$

$\dfrac{x}{3} - \dfrac{y}{2} = -8$

$(-9, 10)$

33 $2x = y + \dfrac{3}{2}$

$y = 6x$

$(-\frac{3}{8}, -\frac{9}{4})$

34 $2x + y = 2$

$2x - 3y = 4$

$(\frac{5}{4}, -\frac{1}{2})$

35 $\dfrac{x}{2} + y = 1$

$\dfrac{x}{2} + 13y = 15$

$(-\frac{1}{3}, \frac{7}{6})$

36 $x - 2y = -1$

$y = x + \dfrac{1}{2}$

$(0, \frac{1}{2})$

37 Iris makes \$260 a year in interest from the combination of her NOW account that pays 5% and her savings account that pays 7% interest. A friend at the bank told her that she could make \$330 a year if she moved her savings into a bank certificate that pays 11%. How much does Iris have in each account?

37) $0.05x + 0.07y = 260$
$0.05x + 0.11y = 330$

38 George and Traci worked together one day building a toy boat. George came late, so he worked four hours and Traci worked five. They finished the boat. They decided to make a summer business of it, but George could only work half time, so every day Traci worked eight hours and George four. They could build two boats a day. How long would it take George to build a boat by himself?

38) $\dfrac{4}{G} + \dfrac{5}{T} = 1$
$\dfrac{4}{G} + \dfrac{8}{T} = 2$

Subtracting:
$\dfrac{5}{T} - \dfrac{8}{T} = -1$
$\dfrac{-3}{T} = -1$
$T = 3$
$G = -6$

The algebraic solution $G = -6$ indicates that George dismantles the toy boats, 1 every 6 hours, while Traci builds. The problem has no "real," or practical, solution.

Complete the multiplication and simplify.

39 $5(2x - 6y)$
$10x - 30y$

40 $-4(5x + 9y)$
$-20x - 36y$

41 $-8(3x - 7y)$
$24x + 56y$

42 $2(3x + 5y) - 3(2x + 4y)$
$6x - 2y - 6$

43 $5(7x + 8y) + 8(4x - 5y)$
$67x$

44 $3(9x - 4y) + 4(5x + 3y)$
$47x$

Problem Set C

Solve each system of equations.

45 $x^2 + y = 11$
      $x^2 + 2y = 13$
       $(3,2), (-3,2)$

46 $\dfrac{1}{x} + \dfrac{1}{y} = 6$

      $\dfrac{1}{x} - \dfrac{1}{y} = 2$
       $(\frac{1}{4},\frac{1}{2})$

47 $x + 2y^2 = 13$
      $3x - 2y^2 = 8$
      $(\frac{21}{4}, \frac{\sqrt{62}}{2}), (\frac{21}{4}, \frac{-\sqrt{62}}{2})$

48 $x^2 + 2y^2 = 19$
      $3x^2 + 2y^2 = 21$
      $(1,3), (1,-3), (-1,3), (-1,-3)$

Section 10.4   Multiplying to Solve Systems of Equations

Who had more desserts, Laird or Michael:
Laird said, "If I had twice as many desserts as I had tonight, then between us we'd have seven." Michael replied, "And if I had twice as many desserts as I had, between us we'd have eight!"

     Equations that represent this problem are: $2\ell + m = 7$
                           $\ell + 2m = 8$

     The key to solving this system of equations is to get coefficients of one variable that add to zero. For example, notice what happens when the second equation is multiplied by -2: $2\ell + m = 7$
                $-2\ell - 4m = -16$

The coefficients of ℓ will add to zero if you add the equations:

$$2\ell + m = 7$$
$$-2\ell - 4m = -16$$

ADD EQS: $-3m = -9$
MULTBY $-\frac{1}{3}$: $m = 3$

Substitute $m = 3$ into either equation: $2\ell + m = 7$
                                      $2\ell + (3) = 7$
                                          $2\ell = 4$
                                            $\ell = 2$

Thus Laird had two desserts and Michael had three desserts. Michael had more.

Sample Problems

1 Solve the system of equations:

$$3x + y = 13$$
$$x - 3y = 11$$

PROCEDURE
Multiply the first equation by 3 to get $9x + 3y = 39$. Then the system is:

*Another appropriate procedure would be to multiply the second equation by −3 to eliminate the **x** terms.*

$$9x + 3y = 39$$
$$x - 3y = 11$$

ADD EQS: $\quad 10x \qquad = 50$

MULTBY $\frac{1}{10}$: $\qquad x \qquad = 5$

Substitute $x = 5$ into either equation:

$$3x + y = 13$$
$$3(5) + y = 13$$
$$15 + y = 13$$
$$y = -2$$

The solution is $(5, -2)$.

2 Solve the system:

$$5x + 3y = 23$$
$$4x + 2y = 16$$

PROCEDURE   In this case it is necessary to multiply each equation by a number. Consider the y-coefficients. Multiplying the first equation by -2 and the second equation by 3 will change the y-coefficients to -6 and 6. The system of equations can be rewritten as:

$$-10x - 6y = -46$$
$$12x + 6y = 48$$

ADD EQS: $\quad 2x \qquad = 2$

MULTBY $\frac{1}{2}$: $\qquad x \qquad = 1$

Substitute $x = 1$ into either equation:

$$5x + 3y = 23$$
$$5(1) + 3y = 23$$
$$3y = 18$$
$$y = 6$$

The solution to the system is $(1, 6)$.

3 Solve the systems of equations:

   a $x + 2y = 5$ **b** $2x + y = 12$
       $-3x - 6y = -15$ $4x + 2y = 6$

PROCEDURE

   a Multiply the first equation by 3 so the system of equations becomes:

$$3x + 6y = 15$$
$$-3x - 6y = -15$$

ADD EQS: $0 = 0$

The result $0 = 0$ indicates that the two equations represent the same line; the system is dependent. To check, notice that both equations contain $(0, \frac{5}{2})$ and $(5, 0)$, so both equations represent the same line. A dependent system has no unique solution.

   b Multiply the first equation by -2 so the system becomes:

$$-4x - 2y = -24$$
$$4x + 2y = 6$$

ADD EQS: $0 = -18$

This false statement, $0 = -18$, indicates that the two equations represent parallel lines; the system is inconsistent. An inconsistent system has no solution.

ASSIGNMENT GUIDE

Basic (2 days)
(1) 1–13 (odd), 16–18
(2) 2–14 (even), 15, 19–21, 28

Average (2 days)
(1) 2–12 (even), 13–18
(2) 19–22, 24, 25, 28–32

Advanced (2 days)
(1) 9–15, 22, 24, 26
(2) 28–40

As oral exercises, students could be asked how they would manipulate the equations to solve each system.

Problem Set **A**

Solve each system of equations.

1 $x + 2y = 5$
     $2x + y = 7$
     (3,1)

2 $3x + y = 10$
     $x + 3y = 14$
     (2,4)

3 $3x - y = 3$
     $x + 3y = 11$
     (2,3)

4 $x + 4y = 27$
     $4x - y = 23$
     (7,5)

5 $x + 2y = 20$
     $3x + y = 20$
     (4,8)

6 $4x - 3y = 18$
     $x + y = 8$
     (6,2)

7 $x + 3y = 5$
     $3x + 2y = 1$
     (−1,2)

8 $2x + 3y = 11$
     $x + 2y = 8$
     (−2,5)

9 $y = 2x - 13$
     $x + 2y = -1$
     (5,−3)

10 $2x - 3y = 10$
     $y = 2x - 2$
     (−1,−4)

11 $y = 3x$
     $x + 2y = 14$
     (2,6)

12 $4x + 3y = 6$
     $y = 4x - 14$
     (3,−2)

13 Leslie was supposed to mix one bag of white gravel with two bags of blue gravel to get the right amount to cover forty square meters of a walk. By mistake Leslie used two bags of white gravel and one of blue. The mixture covered only thirty-five square meters. How much of the walk would each type of gravel cover per bag?

white; 10 sq m blue; 15 sq m.

14 Mrs. Lopez ordered twenty petunia plants. She told the salesperson that she wanted two boxes of the small, white petunias and one box of the big, red ones. The salesperson just wrote down twenty petunias. The company delivered twenty petunias, but there was only one box of white and three boxes of red. How many petunias of each color did Mrs. Lopez want? How many did she get?

Mrs. Lopez wanted 16 white and 4 red; she got 8 white and 12 red

15 The punch recipe called for five tins of punch mix and seven bottles of club soda, which was to make one hundred eighty-three ounces of punch. Meredith used five bottles of club soda and seven tins of punch mix. She got two hundred thirteen ounces of punch. How many ounces were in each tin of punch mix and in each bottle of club soda?

tin: 24 oz., bottle: 9 oz.

Solve each equation. (Review: Section 3.7)

16 $\dfrac{s + 3}{2} = 1$

$s = -1$

17 $3t - 4 = 11$

$t = 5$

18 $-2 - 3m = 4$

$m = -2$

19 $\dfrac{4}{3}n + \dfrac{1}{3} = 7$

$n = 5$

20 $-8 = -5p + 2$

$p = 2$

21 $3q - 20 = -5q$

$q = \dfrac{5}{2}$

Problem Set **B**

Solve each system of equations.

22 $\dfrac{x}{2} + \dfrac{y}{3} = 17$

$\dfrac{x}{3} + \dfrac{y}{2} = 18$

(18,24)

23 $\dfrac{x}{3} + \dfrac{y}{4} = 13$

$\dfrac{x}{4} - \dfrac{y}{3} = -8$

(13.44,34.08)

24 $\dfrac{3x}{5} = \dfrac{2y}{3}$

$3x + 2y = 8$

$(\tfrac{5}{3},\tfrac{3}{2})$

25 $0.7x + 0.5y = 320$

$0.6x + 0.6y = 360$

(100,500)

26 $\dfrac{7x}{5} - \dfrac{3y}{2} = -1$

$\dfrac{3x}{5} + \dfrac{7y}{2} = 41$

(10,10)

27 $\dfrac{3x}{2} - \dfrac{5y}{4} = 14$

$\dfrac{5x}{2} - \dfrac{3y}{4} = 34$

(16,8)

28) $3x + 17 = 8$

28 I'm thinking of a number. If I triple it and add seventeen, the result is eight. What is the starting number?

−3

29) $0.45a + 0.30o = 9$
$o = a + 10$

29 Jack bought some apples for forty-five cents and ten more oranges than apples at thirty cents each. He spent nine dollars on apples and oranges. How many of each did he buy?

8 apples, 18 oranges

30) $0.01ar = 75$
$0.01a(r + 3) = 120$

30 Anne and Arnie each have the same amount invested, but Anne gets a rate of return that is three percent higher. If Anne gets one hundred twenty dollars each year and Arnie gets seventy-five dollars, what are the rates for each investment?

Arnie, 5%; Anne, 8%

31) $x^2 + x = 6, \quad x < 0$

31 The square of a negative number plus the number itself is six. What is the number?

−3

32) $11c + 13f = 167$
$17c + 9f = 166$

32 Diet Formula Number 1 includes eleven units of carbohydrates and thirteen units of fat in each package. Diet Formula Number 2 includes seventeen units of carbohydrates and nine units of fat. If one package of Formula Number 1 has one hundred sixty-seven calories, and one package of Formula Number 2 has one hundred sixty-six calories, how many calories are there in a unit of carbohydrates? in a unit of fat?

carbohydrates, about 5.4; fat, about 8.3

Problem Set C

Solve each system of equations.

33 $2x^2 + 3y = 23$
$x^2 + 2y = 14$

(2,5), (−2,5)

34 $3x + 5y^2 = 23$
$4x − 3y^2 = 23$

$(\frac{184}{29}, \sqrt{\frac{23}{29}}), (\frac{184}{29}, -\sqrt{\frac{23}{29}})$

35 $7x^2 − 3y^2 = 15$
$6x^2 − 2y^2 = 22$

(3,4), (3,−4), (−3,4), (−3,−4)

36 $9x^2 + 4y^2 = 72$
$5x^2 − 3y^2 = −7$

(4,3), (4,−3), (−4,3), (−4,−3)

37 $\dfrac{9x}{2} = \dfrac{8y}{5}$
$\dfrac{9y}{2} = \dfrac{8x}{5} + \dfrac{1769}{720}$

$(\frac{2}{9}, \frac{5}{8})$

38 $3x + 5y = 1$
$2x − 3y = \dfrac{7}{15}$

$(\frac{16}{57}, \frac{3}{95})$

39 $0.08x + 0.04y = 20$
$0.09x − 0.03y = 15$

(200,100)

40 $2x − 8y = 5$
$7x + 10y = 8$

$(\frac{3}{2}, -\frac{1}{4})$

After-School Mathematics: Party Favors

Jerry, the busboy, helped plan a birthday party for his young brother Frankie. Planning the food and the games was easy. What stumped Jerry was finding favors that would appeal to eight-year-olds. Everything he liked in the toy store cost too much for his budget.

Jerry decided to use his ingenuity. He folded over a piece of paper, drew half a bird, and cut out the bird pattern from brightly colored cardboard, one for each child. Then he glued a penny under each wing tip to balance the weight of the tail. Each bird could balance on the tip of its beak!

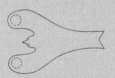

By weighting the wing tips with coins, and then trimming the tail, the cardboard bird can be adjusted so that its center of gravity is at its beak. Thus the bird will balance on its beak.

As a surprise, Jerry balanced the birds around the corners of the tables in the dining room. When Frankie and his guests walked into the room, they couldn't believe their eyes.

"It's magic," said Jerry, pleased with the reaction of the children.

One order could be:

M
S
M } 62 min.
S
C

M
S
M } 62 min.
S
C

M
S } 26 min.

Another order could be:

M
S
C } 50 min.
S

M
S
C } 50 min.
S

M
S
C } 50 min.
S

Application: Parade Music

The marching band has prepared three pieces. The Sousa march takes twelve minutes to play, the school song takes fourteen minutes to play, and the classic piece, in an up-beat arrangement, takes ten minutes to play.

The band must play music for a parade that will take two and a half hours. It wants to play all three of its pieces, and it does not want to play any piece twice in a row. Write two different orders for the songs that will exactly fill the two and a half hours.

Section 10.5 Substituting to Solve Systems of Equations

There is another method for solving systems of equations:

$$x + y = 19$$
$$y = x + 3$$

Notice that the second equation gives an expression for y: $y = x + 3$. Use that expression for y in the first equation:

$$x + (y) = 19$$
$$x + (x + 3) = 19$$
$$2x + 3 = 19$$
$$2x = 16$$
$$x = 8$$

Then use the value $x = 8$ in either original equation:

$$x + y = 19$$
$$8 + y = 19$$
$$y = 11$$

The solution is (8,11). This method is called **solving by substitution**.

Sample Problems

1 Use substitution to solve the system of equations: $y = x + 1$
$x + y = 7$

PROCEDURE Substitute the value of y from the first equation into the second equation:

$$x + (y) = 7$$
$$x + (x + 1) = 7$$
$$2x + 1 = 7$$
$$2x = 6$$
$$x = 3$$

Then substitute $x = 3$ into either equation: $y = x + 1$
$y = (3) + 1$
$y = 4$

The solution is (3,4).

2 Use substitution to solve the system:

$$5x + y = -13$$
$$2x - 3y = -29$$

PROCEDURE The first step is to solve one of the equations for one of the variables. The easiest situation is to solve the first equation for y:

$$5x + y = -13$$
$$y = -5x - 13$$

Substitute $y = -5x - 13$ into the second equation:

$$2x - 3y = -29$$
$$2x - 3(-5x - 13) = -29$$
$$2x + 15x + 39 = -29$$
$$17x + 39 = -29$$
$$17x = -68$$
$$x = -4$$

Substituting $x = -4$ into the first equation:

$$5x + y = -13$$
$$5(-4) + y = -13$$
$$-20 + y = -13$$
$$y = 7$$

An exception is shown in problem 34, p. 419, where it is not necessary to isolate the variable.

The solution is $(-4,7)$.

Notice that substitution is generally easier if one of the equations has a variable with the coefficient 1 or -1.

ASSIGNMENT GUIDE

Basic (1 day)
1–15

Average (2 days)
(1) 1–15
(2) 16–28 (even), 30–33

Advanced (2 days)
(1) 10–26 (even), 28–30
(2) 31–34, 36–44 (even)

Problem Set A

Solve each of the following systems of equations using substitution.

1 $y = x - 1$
$x + y = 7$
$(4,3)$

4 $x - y = 8$
$x + y = 2$
$(5,-3)$

7 $y = x + 2$
$x - 3y = 2$
$(-4,-2)$

2 $x + y = 8$
$y = x + 4$
$(2,6)$

5 $y = x + 3$
$x + 2y = 18$
$(4,7)$

8 $2x - 3y = 0$
$x - 3 = y$
$(9,6)$

3 $x + y = -2$
$x - y = -4$
$(-3,1)$

6 $x + 3y = -17$
$y = x + 3$
$(-\frac{13}{2}, -\frac{7}{2})$

9 $x + 2y = 3$
$x + y = 5$
$(7,-2)$

As oral exercises, students could be asked to read off the equation after substitution. For example, problem 1 would be: "Equation 2; x + (x − 1) = 7."

10.5 Substituting **417**

Use the cross-product to solve each proportion. (Review: Section 8.2)

10 $\dfrac{u + 3}{7} = \dfrac{5u}{14}$

$u = 2$

11 $\dfrac{v - 10}{5} = \dfrac{v + 2}{-15}$

$v = 7$

12 $\dfrac{1 - 2w}{4} = \dfrac{-w - 4}{-4}$

$w = -1$

13 $\dfrac{x - 1}{7} = \dfrac{x + 2}{10}$

$x = 8$

14 $\dfrac{y}{6} = \dfrac{2y}{7}$

$y = 0$

15 $\dfrac{3}{z} = \dfrac{4}{z - 2}$

$z = -6$

Problem Set B

Solve each of the following systems of equations using substitution.

16 $2x + y = 3$
$4x - 2y = -2$

$(\tfrac{1}{2}, 2)$

17 $x + 4y = 4$
$\dfrac{x}{2} - 2y = 1$

$(3, \tfrac{1}{4})$

18 $8x + 6y = 2$
$\dfrac{x}{3} - y = -\dfrac{1}{8}$

$(\tfrac{1}{8}, \tfrac{1}{6})$

19 $3x + 4y = 1$
$x - \dfrac{y}{3} = \dfrac{3}{4}$

$(\tfrac{2}{3}, -\tfrac{1}{4})$

20 $x + y = 10$
$9x - 9y = 36$

$(7, 3)$

21 $2x + \dfrac{y}{3} = 6$
$3x - y = 0$

$(2, 6)$

22 $5x + 25y = 175$
$x + y = 15$

$(10, 5)$

23 $29x - 13y = 355$
$17x + y = 165$

$(10, -5)$

24 $\dfrac{x}{2} - \dfrac{y}{4} = -1$
$x - 3y = 3$

$(-3, -2)$

25 $\dfrac{x}{3} - \dfrac{y}{2} = 4$
$2x + y = 0$

$(3, -6)$

26 $2x + y = 17$
$x - \dfrac{y}{3} = 6$

$(7, 3)$

27 $x + y = 8$
$20x + 2y = 52$

$(2, 6)$

28 $x + 5y = 6$
$\dfrac{x}{2} + 3y = 4$

$(-4, 2)$

29 $129x + 189y = 1530$
$x + y = 10$

$(6, 4)$

30 Connie invested three thousand dollars, part of it at five percent per year and part of it at eleven percent per year. If her yearly income from the investments is three hundred dollars, how much is invested at each rate?

$5000 at 5%, $2500 at 11%

31 The average of two numbers is nineteen. Their range is eight. What are the numbers?

15, 23

32 The average of a positive number and its square is sixty-six. What is the number?

33 The following data are arranged by size: 3, 5, x, y, 10, 16
The median for the data is seven. What is the mean?

8

30) $\begin{aligned} x + \quad\; y &= 300 \\ 0.05x + 0.11y &= 300 \end{aligned}$

31) $\dfrac{x + y}{2} = 19$

$x - y = 8$

32) $\dfrac{x^2 + x}{2} = 66$

33) Both x and y must be 7, so the mean is $48 \div 6$ or 8.

Problem Set C

Solve each of the following systems of equations by substitution.

34 $7x + 3y = 23$
$3y = 2x + 5$
(substitute the value of $3y$)
(2,3)

35 $9x - 11y = 25$
$11y = 4x - 5$
(4,1)

36 $5x + 6y = 3$
$7x + 6y = 9$
(3,−2)

37 $4x - 3y = -11$
$4x + 5y = -35$
(−5,−3)

38 $\dfrac{x}{2} + \dfrac{y}{3} = 8$

$\dfrac{x}{2} + \dfrac{y}{4} = 7$

(4,12)

39 $\dfrac{x}{2} + \dfrac{y}{3} = 2$

$\dfrac{x}{6} - \dfrac{y}{3} = 2$

(6,−3)

40 $3x + 5y = 2$
$3x - 5y = -38$
(−6,4)

41 $2m - \quad n = \quad 8$
$3m - 2n = -15$
$m = -31, n = -70$

42 $3r + 22s = -30$
$15r = 12 - 2s$
$(1, -\frac{3}{2})$

43 $2p = -48 + 8q$
$4p + 7q = -4$
$p = -3, q = -\frac{100}{23}$

44 $-2 = \dfrac{a}{5} - \dfrac{b}{5}$

$-4 = \dfrac{a}{3} + \dfrac{b}{3}$

(−11,−1)

45 $\dfrac{x}{4} - \dfrac{y}{8} = \quad 1$

$\dfrac{x}{5} - \dfrac{2y}{15} = -1$

(31,54)

34) $7x + (2x + 5) = 23$

35) $9x - (4x - 5) = 25$

36) $5x + (9 - 7x) = 3$

37) $(-35 - 5y) - 3y = -11$

38) $(7 - \frac{y}{4}) + \frac{y}{3} = 8$

39) $\frac{x}{2} + (\frac{x}{6} - 2) = 2$

40) $(5y - 38) + 5y = 2$

41) $3m - 2(2m - 8) = -15$

42) $3r + 11(12 - 15r) = -30$

43) $2(-48 + 8q) + 7q = -4$

44) $\begin{aligned} -10 &= a - b \\ -12 &= a + b \\ -10 &= a - (-12 - a) \end{aligned}$

45) $\begin{aligned} 2x - \quad y &= 8 \\ 3x - 2y &= -15 \\ 3x - 2(2x - 8) &= -15 \end{aligned}$

Section 10.6 Solving Number Problems

My house has a two-digit street number, and the sum of the digits is four. If I reverse the digits, the new number is eighteen less than the old number. What is my house number?

This problem, and others like it, can be solved using the following algebraic technique. The number 47 can be thought of as $4 \cdot 10 + 7$ and the number 31 can be thought of as $3 \cdot 10 + 1$. Similarly, an *unknown* two-digit number, where x is the tens digit and y is the units digit, can be expressed as $10 \cdot x + y$.

For my street number, if x is the tens digit and y is the units digit, then the street number is $10x + y$, and "the sum of the digits is four" can be represented as $x + y = 4$. The reverse of the street number is $10y + x$. Thus the system of equations is:

$$x + y = 4$$
$$10y + x = 10x + y - 18$$

This system can be rewritten as:

$$x + y = 4$$
$$-9x + 9y = -18$$

Multiply the first equation by 9, to get:

$$9x + 9y = 36$$
$$\underline{-9x + 9y = -18}$$

ADD EQS:
$$18y = 18$$
$$y = 1$$

Substitute $y = 1$ into either equation:
$$x + y = 4$$
$$x + (1) = 4$$
$$x = 3$$

The solution is (3,1), and so my street number is 31.

Sample Problems

1   Two angles are complementary (which means that the sum of their measures is 90). When 24° is subtracted from two times one of the angles, the result is the same size as the other angle. What are the original measures of the two angles?

PROCEDURE   Let the measures of the angles be represented by x and y. Then:

$$x + y = 90$$
$$2x - 24 = y$$

Rewrite the equations as:

$$\begin{aligned} x + y &= 90 \\ 2x - y &= 24 \end{aligned}$$

ADD EQS: $\quad 3x \quad\quad = 114$

MULTBY $\tfrac{1}{3}$: $\quad\; x \quad\quad = 38$

Substitute $x = 38$ into either equation:

$$\begin{aligned} x + y &= 90 \\ (38) + y &= 90 \\ y &= 52 \end{aligned}$$

The solution is (38,52). The two angles are 38° and 52°.

2 Anya had 11 coins in dimes and quarters. The amount she had was $1.85. How many coins of each did she have?

PROCEDURE Let d represent the number of dimes and let q represent the number of quarters. She had 11 coins, so $d + q = 11$. They were worth 185 cents, so $10d + 25q = 185$. Multiply the first equation by -10, and rewrite the system:

$$\begin{aligned} -10d - 10q &= -110 \\ 10d + 25q &= 185 \end{aligned}$$

ADD EQS:
$$\begin{aligned} 15q &= 75 \\ q &= 5 \end{aligned}$$

Since $d + q = 11$, d must equal 6. Anya had 6 dimes and 5 quarters.

3 Monica mixed cashews, at $3.00 per pound, and Brazil nuts, at $4.00 per pound. The resulting mixture weighed 10 pounds and cost $3.35 per pound. How many pounds of each nut were in the mixture?

PROCEDURE If x represents the number of pounds of cashews, and y represents the number of pounds of Brazil nuts, then the equations are:

$$\begin{aligned} x + y &= 10 \\ 3x + 4y &= (3.35)(10) \end{aligned}$$

Multiply the first equation by -4, and rewrite the system as:

$$\begin{aligned} -4x - 4y &= -40 \\ 3x + 4y &= 33.5 \end{aligned}$$

ADD EQS:
$$\begin{aligned} -x &= -6.5 \\ x &= 6.5 \end{aligned}$$

Since $x + y = 10$, then $y = 3.5$. There were 6.5 pounds of cashews and 3.5 pounds of Brazil nuts in the mixture.

ASSIGNMENT GUIDE
Basic (1 day)
2, 4, 5–10, 12

Average (1 day)
1–4, 6, 8, 10, 15–19

Advanced (1 day)
1–4, 8, 10, 14, 16–24

Problem Set A

1 The sum of the digits of a two-digit number is seventeen. Two times the number is one hundred seventy-eight. What is the original number?

89

2 The sum of the digits of a two-digit number is ten. Three times the number is one hundred ninety-two. What is the number?

64

3 The sum of the digits of a two-digit number is ten. If you reverse the digits, the new number is thirty-six more than the original number. What is the original number?

37

4 Chico had a card in his store where people could put nickels and dimes in thirty-four little pockets for charity. Each pocket held one coin. When the card was full, it turned out to be worth two dollars and thirty-five cents. How many people put nickels in the pockets? dimes?

21 nickels, 13 dimes

1) $t + u = 17$
   $2(10t + u) = 178$

2) $t + u = 10$
   $3(10t + u) = 192$

3) $t + u = 10$
   $10u + t = 10t + u + 36$

4) $n + d = 34$
   $0.05n + 0.10d = 2.35$

Solve each system of equations. (Review: Section 10.4)

5 $2x - 3y = 11$
   $x + 2y = -5$
   $(1, -5)$

8 $4x + 6y = -36$
   $6x + 9y = -54$
   all real numbers

6 $4x + 3y = 14$
   $3x + 4y = 14$
   $(2, 2)$

9 $2x + y = -7$
   $x - 3y = 7$
   $(-2, -3)$

7 $2x - 7y = -7$
   $5x + 6y = 6$
   $(0, 1)$

10 $3x + y = 2$
   $5x + 3y = 10$
   $(-1, 5)$

Problem Set B

Find the solution to each of the following equations.

11 $2(x + 3) + x = 21$
   $x = 5$

14 $3(5y + 4) + 7y = 78$
   $y = 3$

12 $2x - 3(x + 4) = -5$
   $x = -7$

15 $4x - 5(3x - 11) = 77$
   $x = -2$

13 $4(y - 1) - 5y = -5$
   $y = 1$

16 $5x - 3 = 7x + 19$
   $x = -11$

17   Fernando invested seven thousand dollars, part of it at six percent a year and part at nine percent a year. If his yearly income is five hundred seventy dollars from these investments, how much is invested at each rate?

     $2000 at 6%, $5000 at 9%

18   Adult tickets for the play cost $2.50 and student tickets cost $1.75. Every seat in the 350-seat auditorium was sold, and the amount collected at the box office was $742.25. When they count the tickets, how many should be adult and how many student?

     173 adult, 177 student

19   An airplane flew three thousand one hundred fifty miles across the country in seven hours. It made the return trip in nine hours. If the average speed of the airplane in still air was the same both ways, and the average wind speed and direction were the same both ways, what was the average airspeed (in still air) and the average wind velocity?

     average air speed: 400 mph, average wind velocity: 50 mph

Problem Set C

NUMBER PUZZLES

20   Take any two-digit number. Reverse the digits. Subtract the smaller of the two numbers from the larger. Add nine to the result. Now add together the digits in that sum. Multiply by fifty-seven. What is the result?

21   What happens when you take any two-digit number, reverse the digits, and subtract? That is, if the digits of the original number are x and y, what is the difference?

     $9(t - u)$

22   Of what natural number is the answer to problem 21 always a multiple?

     9

23   Take any two-digit number. Reverse it and add the reversed number to the original number. Divide by eleven. What is always the result?

     The sum of the digits of the original number

24   Show that if you add the digits of a number that is a multiple of nine, then the result will be a multiple of nine or zero. (One way is to solve the system $10x + y = 9n$ and $x + y = 9m$ for x and y. Then use this result and the fact that n is a whole number to show that m must also be a whole number.)

     $(10x + y) - 9x = 9n - 9x$; $x + y = 9(n - x)$

---

17) $x + y = 7000$

     $0.06x + 0.09y = 570$

18) $x + y = 350$
     $2.50x + 1.75y = 742.25$

19) $x + y = 450$
     $x - y = 350$

20) $|(10t + u) - (10u + t)|$
  $+ 9$ simplifies to
  $9t - 9u + 9$.   The sum of the digits of the number $9t - 9u + 9$ will be 9, and $(9)(57)$ is 513.

21) $(10t + u) - (10u + t)$
        $= 9t - 9u$
        $= 9(t - u)$

22) $9(t - u)$ is a multiple of 9.

23) $\dfrac{(10t + u) + (10u + t)}{11}$
   $= \dfrac{11t + 11u}{11}$
   $= t + u$

The result is the sum of the digits of the original number.

24)   If a number is a multiple of 9, then:

   $10x + y = 9n$

where n is an integer. Subtract the value $9x$ from both sides:

   $10x + y - 9x = 9n - 9x$
    $x + y = 9(n - x)$

This equation says that the sum of the digits is the product of $(n - x)$, which is an integer, and 9. Thus $x + y$ is a multiple of 9.

ASSIGNMENT GUIDE

Basic (3 days)
(1) 408: 11, 15
    422: 1, 3
    427: 1–15 (odd)
(2) 413: 25
    418: 16
    427: 2–14 (ven)
(3) 428: 1–27

Average (2 days)
(1) 427: 1–15
    428: 1–11
(2) 429: 12–41

Advanced (2 days)
(1) 410: 45, 47
    419: 41, 43
    427: 1–15
(2) 428: 1–52 (even)

Chapter Study Guide

Skills

As you study and review this chapter, be sure to build the useful algebraic skills, including:

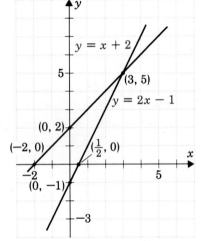

1 **Graphing a system of equations**

Graph and solve this system:

$$y = 2x - 1$$
$$y = x + 2$$

PROCEDURE
Use the two intercepts
to graph each equation:

The lines intersect at (3,5).

2 **Adding to solve a system of equations**

Solve the system:

$$2x + y = 2$$
$$3x - y = -7$$

PROCEDURE   Add the left-hand sides and add the right-hand sides of the two equations:

$$
\begin{array}{l}
2x + y = 2 \\
\underline{3x - y = -7} \\
\end{array}
$$

ADD EQS: $5x = -5$
MULTBY $\tfrac{1}{5}$: $x = -1$

Substitute $x = -1$ in either equation:

$$
\begin{aligned}
2x + y &= 2 \\
2(-1) + y &= 2 \\
-2 + y &= 2 \\
y &= 4
\end{aligned}
$$

The solution is $(-1, 4)$.

3   Multiplying to solve a system of equations

Solve the system: $2x + 4y = -2$

$$3x + 5y = -1$$

PROCEDURE

Multiply the first equation by -3 and the second equation by 2:

$$-6x - 12y = 6$$
$$6x + 10y = -2$$

ADD EQS: $-2y = 4$

MULTBY $-\frac{1}{2}$: $y = -2$

Substitute $y = -2$ into either equation:

$$2x + 4y = -2$$
$$2x + 4(-2) = -2$$
$$2x - 8 = -2$$
$$2x = 6$$
$$x = 3$$

The solution is $(3, -2)$.

4   Substituting to solve a system of equations

Solve the system:

$$y = 2x - 1$$
$$3x + 2y = -16$$

PROCEDURE

Substitute the value for y into the second equation:

$$3x + 2y = -16$$
$$3x + 2(2x - 1) = -16$$
$$3x + 4x - 2 = -16$$
$$7x - 2 = -16$$
$$7x = -14$$
$$x = -2$$

Now substitute $x = -2$ into either equation:

$$y = 2x - 1$$
$$y = 2(-2) - 1$$
$$y = -4 - 1$$
$$y = -5$$

The solution is $(-2, -5)$.

5   Solving number problems   For a two-digit number, the sum of the digits is six. The units digit is four more than the tens digit. What is the number?

PROCEDURE   Let t represent the tens digit and let u represent the units digit. The system of equations is:

$$t + u = 6$$
$$u = t + 4$$

Rewrite the system in standard form:

$$\begin{aligned} t + u &= 6 \\ -t + u &= 4 \end{aligned}$$

ADD EQS: $\qquad 2u = 10$

MULTBY $\frac{1}{2}$: $\qquad u = 5$

Substitute $u = 5$ into either equation:

$$\begin{aligned} t + u &= 6 \\ t + 5 &= 6 \\ t &= 1 \end{aligned}$$

The original number is 15.

Math History: *The Beginning of Modern Algebra*

Algebra goes back at least some 4000 years. Yet the first algebra to be written with letters for unknown numbers is only about 400 years old. And only for 150 years have mathematicians been studying systems of variables.

In 1830, George Peacock proposed that variables do not have to stand for numbers. He also made the first attempt at stating the distributive and commutative properties. That same year, Augustus De Morgan wrote that variables and operations could be studied alone; they did not necessarily represent numbers. Soon, Sir William Rowan Hamilton described algebraic rules for a system in which the commutative property did not hold. By 1847, George Boole had developed an algebra with two distributive laws.

These steps are considered the beginning of "modern algebra." Today, algebra is the study of systems of mathematical properties, not a search for unknown numbers.

Chapter Test

Solve each system using multiplication and/or addition.

1 $x + y = 3$
$3x - y = 1$
(1,2)

4 $2x + 3y = 11$
$5x - 4y = 16$
(4,1)

2 $x - 3y = 9$
$x - 4y = 11$
(3,−2)

5 $0.2a - 0.3b = 0.1$
$0.5a - 0.2b = 3$
(8,5)

3 $2x - y = 5$
$x + 2y = 25$
(7,9)

6 $\dfrac{x}{2} - \dfrac{y}{3} = \dfrac{5}{9}$
$\dfrac{x}{5} - \dfrac{y}{2} = \dfrac{7}{15}$
$\left(\dfrac{2}{3}, -\dfrac{2}{3}\right)$

Solve each system using the method of substitution.

7 $y = 2x - 4$
$3x + 2y = 13$
(3,2)

9 $x - 4y = 0$
$\frac{1}{3}x - \frac{2}{3}y = 2$
(12,3)

8 $x - 3y = 1$
$2x + y = 9$
(4,1)

10 $3x - y = 3$
$2x + 3y = 2$
(1,0)

Solve by graphing.

11 $x + y = 4$
$y = 2x + 1$
(1,3)

12 $y = -2x + 2$
$y = \frac{3}{2}x - 5$
(2,−2)

Identify two variables, set up a system of equations, and solve.

13 A two-digit number is one more than five times the sum of its digits. If the digits are reversed, the new number is greater by nine.

56

13) $10t + u = 5(t + u) + 1$
$10u + t = (10t + u) + 9$

14 If Joe were two years older, he would be half as old as Fred is now. If Fred were six years older, he would be three times as old as Joe is now. How old is each now?

Joe is 10, Fred is 24

14) $J + 2 = \frac{1}{2}F$
$F + 6 = 3J$

15 The butcher prepared one hundred pounds of a mixture of hamburger and soy protein to sell for $2.08 per pound. If hamburger sells for $2.40 and soy protein for 80 cents a pound, how may pounds of each are used in the mixture?

80 pounds hamburger, 20 pounds soy protein

15) $h + s = 100$
$2.40h + 0.80s = 100(2.08)$

Problem Set: Cumulative Review 1–10

Problem Set A

Multiple choice

1 The expression $(8 - 3 \cdot 4)^2$ is equal to: *d*

   a 8   **c** -16

   b 400   **d** 16

2 Solve for m: $13 - 5m = 11$ *b*

   a $m = \frac{24}{5}$ **c** $m = \frac{5}{2}$

   b $m = \frac{2}{5}$ **d** $m = 120$

3 Solve for x: $5 > 9 + x$ *c*

   a $x > -4$ **c** $-4 > x$

   b $14 > x$ **d** $-4 < x$

4 Solve for m: $\dfrac{3m}{m + 2} = \dfrac{5}{2}$ *b*

   a $m = 2$ **c** $m = 6$

   b $m = 10$ **d** $m = \frac{10}{11}$

5 Solve for x: $\dfrac{3}{4x} + \dfrac{5}{3} = \dfrac{2}{3x}$ *c*

   a $x = \frac{20}{17}$ **c** $x = -\frac{1}{20}$

   b $x = 6$ **d** $x = \frac{17}{20}$

6 Which point is in Quadrant III? *d*

   a $(5,7)$ **c** $(6,-2)$

   b $(-1,3)$ **d** $(-1,-4)$

7 The x-value which satisfies both $y = 2x - 5$ and $x - y = 2$ is: *d*

   a 7   **c** 1

   b -3 **d** 3

Translate each variable expression to a verbal expression.   answers will vary

8 $2a$

9 $n + 20$

10 $16 \div x$

11 $r - 17$

Solve for the indicated variable.

12 $C = 2\pi r$ for r

$r = \dfrac{C}{2\pi}$

13 $\dfrac{a}{b} = \dfrac{c}{d}$ for d

$d = \dfrac{bc}{a}$

Perform the indicated operations.

14   Add $11m^2 + 3m - 2$
and $m^2 - 8m - 3$

$12m^2 - 5m - 5$

15   Subtract $m^2 - 8m - 3$
from $11m^2 + 3m - 2$

$10m^2 + 11m + 1$

16   Factor: $x^2 - 3x + 2$

$(x - 2)(x - 1)$

17   Factor: $c^2 + 9c + 20$

$(c + 4)(c + 5)$

18   Divide $x^2 - 8x - 48$ by $x + 4$

$x - 12$

19   Subtract $\dfrac{6y + 3}{2y^2 - 2}$ from $\dfrac{6}{y - 1}$

$\dfrac{6y - 9}{2(2y - 1)(y - 1)}$

20   Multiply: $(x - 3)(x + 2)$

$x^2 - x - 6$

21   Simplify: $6xy \div 9y$

$\dfrac{2x}{3}$

22   Solve and check

a $\dfrac{x}{3} - \dfrac{1}{6} = \dfrac{4}{9}$

$x = \dfrac{11}{6}$

b $\dfrac{2}{x - 2} + \dfrac{5}{x + 3} = \dfrac{7}{x^2 + x - 6}$

$x = \dfrac{11}{7}$

23   Find the slope of the line through (3, −5) and (1, 1).

-3

24   Solve each system of equations.

a $x + 2y = 6$
$x - 2y = -1$

$\left(\dfrac{5}{2}, \dfrac{7}{4}\right)$

b $x = 3y - 1$
$x + 4y = 13$

$(5, 2)$

Write each verbal expression as a variable expression.

25   seven more than three times a number

$3x + 7$

26   four decreased by twice the sum of a number and six

$4 - 2(x + 6)$

27   the quotient of a number and seven, added to the product of three and half the number

$\dfrac{x}{7} + \left(3 \cdot \dfrac{1}{2}x\right)$

Problem Set B

28 Perform the indicated operations:

a $3(4 - 2) + 18 \div (5 + 4) - 3^2$ **b** $-(6 + 3) \div 3 + 4(2 - 6)^3$

  -1 -259

29 Solve and check:

a $k \div 11 - 3 = 8$ **b** $\dfrac{3}{4}x + 9 = 12$

  $k = 121$ $x = 4$

30) $0.70x = 38.80$

30 Sarah bought an outfit on sale for thirty-eight dollars and eighty cents. If that price was seventy percent of the original price, what was the original price?

  $55.43

31 Write each expression as a product of the GCF and a polynomial:

a $72a^2b^3 + 18ab^2 - 27a$ **b** $100x^4y + 1000xy + 10,000y$

  $9a(8ab^3 + 2b^2 - 3)$ $100y(x^4 + 10x + 100)$

32) $5x - 1 \geq 19$

32 A variable has values such that five times the number, decreased by one, is at least nineteen. What are the values for the variable?

  $x \geq 4$

33 Write an inequality for each description:

a k is between zero and three, including zero but not three

b y is greater than six *or* less than negative six

  $0 \leq k < 3$ $y > 6$ *or* $y < -6$

Perform the indicated operation.

34 Multiply $x + 3$
      by $6x^2 + 3x - 2$

  $6x^3 + 21x^2 + 7x - 6$

35 Factor: $25x^2 - 9$

  $(5x - 3)(5x + 3)$

36 Factor: $9y^2 - 30y + 25$

  $(3y - 5)^2$

37 Simplify: $\dfrac{1}{a} + \dfrac{1}{b} + \dfrac{3}{ab^2} - 2$

  $\dfrac{b^2 + ab + 3 - 2ab^2}{ab^2}$

38 Divide $x^3 + 3x^2 + 7x - 9$
      by $x + 3$

  $x^2 + 7 - \dfrac{30}{x + 3}$

39 Factor: $2c^2 - 28c + 98$

  $2(c - 7)^2$

40 Factor: $20x^2 - 6x^4 - 26x^3$

  $-2x^2(3x - 2)(x + 5)$

41 Simplify: $\dfrac{y - 3}{7 - x} + \dfrac{3 - y}{x - 7}$

  $\dfrac{6 - 2y}{x - 7}$

42 The variables a and b are in inverse variation, and $a = 6$ when $b = 7$.

a What is the constant of variation?

b Write the equation that relates a and b.

c Find the value of a when b is fourteen.

  42

  $ab = 42$

  3

Problem Set C

43 Solve each system of equations:

a $3x + y = -12$
$-8x = y + 16$

$(-\frac{4}{5}, -9\frac{3}{5})$

b $\dfrac{x}{2} - \dfrac{y}{3} = \dfrac{5}{9}$

$\dfrac{x}{5} - \dfrac{y}{2} = \dfrac{7}{15}$

$x = \frac{2}{3}, y = -\frac{2}{3}$

44 State whether each system of equations is inconsistent, dependent, or neither.

a $3x + 4y = 5$
$12x + 16y = 20$
dependent

b $5x - 2y = 16$
$4y = 10x + 23$
inconsistent

45 Find two numbers such that half their sum is eight, and twice their difference is twelve.

11, 5

45) $\frac{1}{2}(x + y) = 8$
$2(x - y) = 12$

46 Graph each compound inequality:

a $n \geq 2 \text{ and } n < -3$
all real numbers

b $n < 0 \text{ or } n > -5$
no solution

47 Solve the system of equations: $3x + 2y - 4z = -4$
$-2x + 5y + 3z = 15$
$8z = -8$

$(-4, 2, -1)$

48 Solve for x: $\dfrac{2}{5x^2 - 7x - 6} + \dfrac{3}{8 - 2x - x^2} = \dfrac{1}{5x^2 + 23x + 12}$

$x = \frac{1}{14}$

49 Factor: $3x^3 + 6x^2 - 27x - 54$

$3(x + 2)(x + 3)(x - 3)$

50 Use one set of axes to graph all four equations:

$y = -x + 3 \qquad 0 \leq x \leq 3$
$y = x - 3 \qquad 0 \leq x \leq 3$
$y = -x - 3 \qquad -3 \leq x \leq 0$
$y = x + 3 \qquad -3 \leq x \leq 0$

Can you describe the result?

a square with vertices at (3,0), (0,3), (−3,0), (0,−3)

51 Warren used his ten percent employee discount to buy a jacket that was already on sale for twenty percent off the original price. If he paid eighty-six dollars and thirty-nine cents, what was the original price of the coat?

$119.99

51) $(0.9)(0.8x) = 86.39$

52 How many birds and how many beasts are in a zoo that has thirty heads and one hundred feet?

10 birds, 20 beasts

52) No. of heads: $x + y = 30$

No. of feet: $2x + 4y = 100$

Chapter 11

CHAPTER SCHEDULE

Basic
Problem Sets   12 Days
Review   2 Days
Test   2 Days

Average
Problem Sets   10 Days
Review   1 Day
Test   2 Days

Advanced
Problem Sets   11 Days
Review   1 Day
Test   1 Day

RADICALS

Section 11.1   Square Roots

SECTION SCHEDULE

Basic (2 days)

Average (2 days)

Advanced (2 days)

The area of a square parking lot is eighty-one square meters. What is the length of each side?

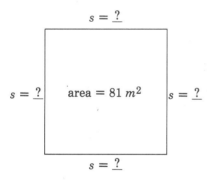

$$\ell \cdot w = A$$
$$s \cdot s = 81$$
$$s^2 = 81$$
$$s = \ \ 9$$

The length of each side is nine meters.

A way to express the mathematical relationship is "9 is **a square root of 81**."

Definition

A SQUARE ROOT of a number or expression is one of its two equal factors.

EXAMPLES

- $(-4)(-4) = 16$, so -4 is a square root of 16.

- $(4)(4) = 16$, so 4 is a square root of 16.

- $(10)(10) = 100$ and $(-10)(-10) = 100$, so 10 and -10 is each a square root of 100.

- $0 \cdot 0 = 0$, so 0 is a square root of 0.

The nonnegative value is called **the principal square root**.

- The principal square root of 16 is 4. Similarly, the principal square roots of 100, 49, and $\frac{1}{4}$ are 10, 7, and $\frac{1}{2}$, respectively.

- If x is a nonnegative number, the principal square root of x^2 is x.

The symbol, or notation, for principal square root is $\sqrt{}$. It is called a **radical sign**.

- $\sqrt{25} = 5$

- $\sqrt{\frac{9}{64}} = \frac{3}{8}$

- $\sqrt{144} = 12$

- $\sqrt{p^2} = p$ if $p \geq 0$

Note that if $x^2 = 64$, then x can be 8 or -8. Using the symbol for principal square root, this can be expressed as:

If $x^2 = 64$, then $x = \sqrt{64} = 8$ or $x = -\sqrt{64} = -8$

Finally, even though the expression $\sqrt{x}$ is often read, "the square root of x," $\sqrt{x}$ always means "the principal square root of x."

Sample Problems

1   Find all the integers that satisfy the equation $x^2 = 49$.

PROCEDURE   There are two values for x:

$$x = \sqrt{49} = 7$$
$$x = -\sqrt{49} = -7$$

Thus the solutions to the equation $x^2 = 49$ are $x = 7$ or $x = -7$. The notation "$x = \pm 7$" can be used as an abbreviation for "$x = 7$ or $x = -7$."

While the common reading of $x = \pm 7$ is "x equals plus or minus seven," students should realize that the signs are used to indicate integers, not operations. A more accurate description would be "x equals positive or negative seven."

2   Evaluate: $\sqrt{7^2 5^4}$

PROCEDURE   To find the principal square root of a positive number, first write the number as a product of two equal positive factors:

$$\sqrt{7^2 5^4} = \sqrt{(7 \cdot 5^2)(7 \cdot 5^2)}$$
$$= 7 \cdot 5^2$$
$$= 7 \cdot 25$$
$$= 175$$

3   Evaluate each expression:

a $-\sqrt{256}$

b $\sqrt{5^2 - 3^2}$

c $\sqrt{\dfrac{64}{9}x^4 y^8}$

PROCEDURE

a $-\sqrt{256} = -\left(\sqrt{16 \cdot 16}\right)$

$$= -(16)$$
$$= -16$$

b $\sqrt{5^2 - 3^2} = \sqrt{(25 - 9)}$

$$= \sqrt{16}$$
$$= \sqrt{4 \cdot 4}$$
$$= 4$$

c $\sqrt{\dfrac{64}{9}x^4 y^8} = \sqrt{\left(\dfrac{8}{3}x^2 y^4\right)\left(\dfrac{8}{3}x^2 y^4\right)}$

$$= \dfrac{8}{3}x^2 y^4$$

All students should be aware of the difference between $-\sqrt{256}$, which is -16, and $\sqrt{-256}$, which is not a real number.

Some students may need additional examples of the square root of an even power.

The main part of Section 11.1 considers only positive-valued variables (or variables with exponents that are multiples of four.). The consideration of roots of negative-valued variables is in Section 11.1X.

ASSIGNMENT GUIDE

Basic (2 days)
(1) 1–20, 22–30 (even)
(2) 438: 1–16

Average (2 days)
(1) 2–38 (even), 40–42
(2) 15, 17, 19, 37, 39
    438: 1–16

Advanced (2 days)
(1) 16–38 (even), 40–42,
    44–54 (even)
(2) 43–53 (odd)
    438: 1–16

Problem Set A

Evaluate each expression.

1 $\sqrt{64}$
    8

2 $\sqrt{81}$
    9

3 $-\sqrt{100}$
    −10

4 $\sqrt{1}$
    1

5 $\sqrt{2^4}$
    4

6 $\sqrt{\dfrac{9}{49}}$
    $\frac{3}{7}$

7 $-\sqrt{\dfrac{25}{16}}$
    $-\frac{5}{4}$

8 $\sqrt{.36}$
    0.6

9 $\sqrt{.04}$
    0.2

10 $\sqrt{1600}$
    40

11 $-\sqrt{400}$
    −20

12 $\sqrt{144}$
    12

13 $\sqrt{225}$
    15

14 $-\sqrt{196}$
    −14

15 $\sqrt{7\dfrac{1}{9}}$ $\frac{8}{3}$

16 $\sqrt{6\frac{1}{4}}$ $\frac{5}{2}$

17 $\sqrt{3^2 \cdot 4^2}$
    12

18 $\sqrt{5^4 \cdot 6^2}$
    150

19 $-\sqrt{2^{10}\left(\frac{1}{2}\right)^2}$
    −16

20 $\sqrt{\left(\dfrac{3}{4}\right)^6}$
    $\frac{27}{64}$

Evaluate each expression. (Review: Section 3.1)

21 4^3
    64

22 6^4
    1296

23 $\left(\dfrac{1}{3}\right)^5$
    $\frac{1}{243}$

24 $\left(\dfrac{3}{4}\right)^3$
    $\frac{27}{64}$

25 $\dfrac{2^8}{2^{11}}$
    $\frac{1}{8}$

26 $(2 \cdot 3)^2$
    36

27 $(3)(2 \cdot 3)^3$
    648

28 $\left(\dfrac{5}{4}\right)^4$
    $\frac{625}{256}$

29 $(1\frac{3}{4})^2$
    $\frac{49}{16}$

30 $\dfrac{5^7}{5^4}$
    125

Problem Set B

Write each expression without a radical sign. (Assume that all variables represent positive numbers.)

The square root of an expression that may have negative values is presented in Section 11.1X. Students who are assigned Section 11.1X can be required to express $\sqrt{x^2}$ as $|x|$ through the remainder of the chapter.

31 $\sqrt{9^2}$

9

32 $-\sqrt{12^2}$

-12

33 $\sqrt{(x+4)^2}$

$x + 4$

34 $\left(\sqrt{25}\right)^2$

25

35 $\left(-\sqrt{61}\right)^2$

61

36 $\left(\sqrt{x^4}\right)^2$

x^4

37 $\sqrt{11^2 - 21}$

10

38 $\sqrt{6^2 + 8^2}$

10

39 $\sqrt{2^3 + 7 \cdot 8}$

8

40 $\sqrt{1^3 + 2^3 + 3^3}$

6

41 $\sqrt{1^3 + 2^3 + 3^3 + 4^3}$

10

42 If the pattern shown in problems 40 and 41 continues, evaluate
$$\sqrt{1^3 + 2^3 + 3^3 + \ldots + n^3}$$

$1 + 2 + 3 + \ldots + n$

Problem Set C

Simplify problems 43–54. (All variables represent positive numbers.)

43 $\sqrt{\dfrac{12}{27}}$

$\dfrac{2}{3}$

44 $\sqrt{\dfrac{180}{320}}$

$\dfrac{3}{4}$

45 $\sqrt{\dfrac{x^5}{x}}$

x^2

46 $-\sqrt{\dfrac{20x^2}{45x^6}}$

$-\dfrac{2}{3x^2}$

47 $\sqrt{x^2 + 10x + 25}$

$x + 5$

48 $\sqrt{9x^2 + 24x + 16}$

$3x + 4$

49 $\sqrt{\dfrac{-4x^2}{-25}}$

$\dfrac{2x}{5}$

50 $-\sqrt{\dfrac{x^2 - 9}{x + 3}}$

$-\sqrt{x - 3}$

51 $\sqrt{\dfrac{a^2 b^4}{a^4 b^2}}$

$\dfrac{b}{a}$

52 $\sqrt{\dfrac{(x - 2)^6}{(x - 2)^4}}$

$x - 2$

53 $\sqrt{a^2 + 2ab + b^2}$

$a + b$

54 $\sqrt{4r^2 - 12rs + 9s^2}$

$2r - 3s$

Xtending the topic: The Square Root of a Variable

The principal square root is always positive (or zero). Since an unknown variable may have a negative value, a careful definition of principal square root is the following:

Definition

If a is any real number, and if $x = a^2$, then the PRINCIPAL SQUARE ROOT of x is the absolute value of a. In symbols:

If $x = a^2$, then $\sqrt{x} = |a|$.

EXAMPLES

- If $a = -3$,
  and if $x = a^2$,
  then $\sqrt{x} = \sqrt{a^2}$
  $\phantom{then \sqrt{x}} = \sqrt{(-3)^2}$
  $\phantom{then \sqrt{x}} = \sqrt{9}$
  $\phantom{then \sqrt{x}} = 3$
  $\phantom{then \sqrt{x}} = |a|$

- If $a = -\dfrac{1}{2}$,
  and if $x = a^2$,
  then $\sqrt{x} = \sqrt{a^2}$
  $\phantom{then \sqrt{x}} = \sqrt{\left(-\dfrac{1}{2}\right)^2}$
  $\phantom{then \sqrt{x}} = \sqrt{\dfrac{1}{4}}$
  $\phantom{then \sqrt{x}} = \dfrac{1}{2}$
  $\phantom{then \sqrt{x}} = |a|$

Problem Set X

Write each expression without a radical sign.

1 $\sqrt{x^2}$
$|x|$

2 $\sqrt{16y^2}$
$4|y|$

3 $\sqrt{a^4b^2c^6}$
$a^2|bc^3|$

4 $-\sqrt{9q^2s^4}$
$-3s^2|q|$

5 $-\sqrt{4x^2}$
$-2|x|$

6 $\sqrt{\dfrac{81b^6}{16c^2}}$
$\dfrac{9}{4}\left|\dfrac{b^3}{c}\right|$

7 $-\sqrt{\dfrac{25x^6}{9y^2}}$
$-\dfrac{5|x^3|}{3|y|}$

8 $\sqrt{\dfrac{12a^4}{3b^2}}$
$\dfrac{2a^2}{|b|}$

9 $\sqrt{p^2q^4}$
$q^2|p|$

10 $-\sqrt{(3)(27)w^2}$
$-9|w|$

11 $-\sqrt{(-5)(-125)m^2n^2}$
$-25|mn|$

12 $\sqrt{0.0001m^4n^2}$
$0.01m^2|n|$

13 $\sqrt{0.04r^2t^2}$
$0.2|rt|$

14 $\sqrt{\dfrac{p^2}{100q^4}}$
$\dfrac{|p|}{10q^2}$

15 $\sqrt{\dfrac{1}{0.09t^2}}$
$\dfrac{1}{0.3|t|}$

16 $\sqrt{\dfrac{t^2r^3}{s^2r}}$
$\left|\dfrac{tr}{s}\right|$

Section 11.2 Cube Roots, Fourth Roots, . . . , n^{th} Roots

SECTION SCHEDULE

Basic (1 day)

Average (1 day)

Advanced (1 day)

A radical sign can be used to indicate cube roots, fourth roots, etc.

- $\sqrt[3]{8}$ is read "the cube root of 8." The number 3 is the **index**, and the 8 is called the **radicand**.

$$\sqrt[3]{8} = \sqrt[3]{2 \cdot 2 \cdot 2} = 2$$

- $\sqrt[5]{32}$ is read "the fifth root of 32." The index is 5 and the radicand is 32.

$$\sqrt[5]{32} = \sqrt[5]{2 \cdot 2 \cdot 2 \cdot 2 \cdot 2} = 2$$

- $\sqrt[3]{-64} = \sqrt[3]{(-4)(-4)(-4)} = -4$

- $\sqrt{9x^4} = 3x^2$ The index for a square root is omitted.

In general, if $n \geq 2$, the nth root of a number or expression is one of its n equal factors. In symbols, if $n \geq 2$:

$$\sqrt[n]{b} = a \quad \text{means that} \quad b = a^n$$

If n is an odd number, note that $\sqrt[n]{b}$ may be equal to a positive number or a negative number:

- $\sqrt[3]{-8} = -2$

- $\sqrt[3]{27} = 3$

If n is even, however, $\sqrt[n]{b}$ must be positive (or zero). Thus the radicand must be nonnegative.

- $\sqrt[4]{81} = 3$

- $\sqrt[4]{(-2)^4} = \sqrt[4]{16} = 2$

- $\sqrt[4]{-16} = \underline{?}$ Since the radicand is negative, this expression is not part of the real number system.

- $-\sqrt[4]{625} = -(5) = -5$

- $\sqrt[4]{-625} = \underline{?}$ This expression is not a real number.

Sample Problems

1   Write the expression $\sqrt[6]{x^6y^{12}z^{24}}$ without a radical sign.

PROCEDURE   The sixth root of an expression is one of its six equal factors:

$$\sqrt[6]{x^6y^{12}z^{24}}$$
$$\sqrt[6]{(xy^2z^4)\,(xy^2z^4)\,(xy^2z^4)\,(xy^2z^4)\,(xy^2z^4)\,(xy^2z^4)}$$
$$xy^2z^4$$

A briefer way to write the problem is:

$$\sqrt[6]{x^6y^{12}z^{24}} = \sqrt[6]{(xy^2z^4)^6} = xy^2z^4$$

2   Evaluate each expression:
a $-\sqrt[3]{-8}$
b $\sqrt[3]{512}\cdot 27$

PROCEDURE

a   Use parentheses to help keep track of the negative signs:

$$-\sqrt[3]{-8} = -\left(\sqrt[3]{-8}\right)$$
$$= -(-2)$$
$$= 2$$

b   Note that the "27" is not part of the radicand:

$$\sqrt[3]{512}\cdot 27 = \sqrt[3]{8\cdot 8\cdot 8}\cdot 27$$
$$= 8\cdot 27$$
$$= 216$$

3   Simplify the expression: $\sqrt[4]{(9x^4)^2 + 5\cdot 243x^8}$

PROCEDURE   Simplify the radicand first:

$$\sqrt[4]{(9x^4)^2 + 5\cdot 243x^8}$$
$$\sqrt[4]{81x^8 + 1215x^8}$$
$$\sqrt[4]{1296x^8}$$
$$\sqrt[4]{(6x^2)^4}$$
$$6x^2$$

Historical note: The radical sign is actually composed of two parts:
$\sqrt{}$ and $\overline{}$. The bar, or **vinculum**, is a grouping symbol.

Problem Set A

ASSIGNMENT GUIDE

Basic (1 day)
1–20, 25–27

Average (1 day)
2–16 (even), 17–20,
26–38 (even)

Advanced (1 day)
2–16 (even), 26–48 (even)

Write each expression without a radical sign.

1 $\sqrt[3]{64}$

  4

2 $-\sqrt[4]{625}$

  -5

3 $\sqrt[5]{-32}$

  -2

4 $\sqrt[7]{-128}$

  -2

5 $\sqrt[5]{7776}$

  6

6 $-\sqrt[4]{4096}$

  -8

7 $\sqrt[3]{\dfrac{27}{125}}$

  $\dfrac{3}{5}$

8 $\sqrt[4]{0.0001}$

  0.1

9 $-\sqrt[7]{-1}$

  1

10 $\sqrt[15]{0}$

  0

11 $3\sqrt[3]{8}$

  6

12 $-5\sqrt[4]{16}$

  -10

13 $4\sqrt[7]{2^{14}}$

  16

14 $-2\sqrt[4]{3^8}$

  -18

15 $-\sqrt[5]{x^{50}}$

  $-x^{10}$

16 $\sqrt[3]{(-x)^6}$

  x^2

Evaluate each expression. (Review: Section 11.1)

17 $\sqrt{4} \cdot \sqrt{9}$

  6

18 $\sqrt{4} + \sqrt{9}$

  5

19 $\sqrt{4} - \sqrt{9}$

  -1

20 $\sqrt{4} \div \sqrt{9}$

  $\dfrac{2}{3}$

21 $\sqrt{125} + \sqrt{36}$

  $5\sqrt{5} + 6$

22 $\sqrt{125} \cdot \sqrt{36}$

  $30\sqrt{5}$

23 $\sqrt{125} \div \sqrt{36}$

  $\dfrac{5\sqrt{5}}{6}$

24 $\sqrt{125} - \sqrt{36}$

  $5\sqrt{5} - 6$

Problem Set B

Write each expression without a radical sign.

25 $\sqrt[4]{x^4 y^8}$

  xy^2

26 $\sqrt[3]{x^{12} y^6}$

  $x^4 y^2$

27 $\sqrt[3]{6^2 - 4 \cdot 7}$

  2

28 $\sqrt[10]{\dfrac{a^{40} b^{10}}{c^{20}}}$

  $\dfrac{a^4 b}{c^2}$

29 $2\sqrt[3]{125 x^3}$

  $10x$

30 $-3\sqrt[3]{-y^9}$

  $3y^3$

Write each expression without a radical sign.

31 $\frac{1}{2}\sqrt[4]{16x^4}$

x

32 $\frac{2}{3}\sqrt[4]{81x^{12}}$

$2x^3$

33 $-5\sqrt[3]{-0.008a^{30}}$

$-a^{10}$

34 $-2x\sqrt[3]{3\frac{3}{8}}$

$-3x$

35 $\sqrt[6]{\dfrac{a^{12}}{b^6}}$

$\frac{a^2}{b}$

36 $-\sqrt[4]{2 \cdot 3 + 5 \cdot 2}$

-2

37 $4\sqrt[6]{10^2 - 6^2}$

8

38 $\frac{1}{2}\sqrt[5]{-8(8 \cdot 2 \div 2^2)}$

-1

Problem Set **C**

Write each expression without a radical sign.

39 $\sqrt[4]{(a^4b^2)\left(\dfrac{a^9b}{ab^7}\right)}$

$\frac{a^3}{b}$

40 $-\sqrt[4]{(2x + 3)^8}$

$-(2x+3)^2$

41 $4\sqrt[5]{(3x + 1)^5}$

$12x + 4$

42 $-\sqrt[7]{\dfrac{256x^3y^{10}}{-2x^{10}y^3}}$

$\frac{2y}{x}$

43 $\sqrt[3]{\dfrac{x^7y^5}{xy^2}}$

x^2y

44 $\sqrt[3]{(x + 4)^6}$

$(x+4)^2$

45 $-\sqrt[5]{(-8x^2)(4x^8)}$

$2x^2$

46 $\frac{1}{2}\sqrt[3]{(2x + 6)^3}$

$x + 3$

47 Evaluate $-5\sqrt[3]{v^2}$ for $v = 8$.

-20

48 Evaluate $\frac{1}{2}\sqrt[4]{c^2 - b^2}$ for $c = 5$ and $b = 3$.

1

Project: Approximating a Cube Root

This is a method for finding the cube root of a number. (A calculator should be used for the computations.)

- Find $\sqrt[3]{10}$ to 2 decimal places.

Step 1	Start with any estimate R_1	$R_1 = 2$
Step 2	Use the equation $R_1 \cdot R_1 \cdot Q_1 = 10$ and find Q_1.	$R_1 \cdot R_1 \cdot Q_1 = 10$ $2 \cdot 2 \cdot Q_1 = 10$ $Q_1 = 2.5$
Step 3	The second estimate, R_2, is the average of R_1 and Q_1.	$R_2 = (R_1 + Q_1) \div 2$ $= (2 + 2.5) \div 2$ $= 2.25$
Step 4	Use the equation $R_2 \cdot R_2 \cdot Q_2 = 10$ and find Q_2.	$R_2 \cdot R_2 \cdot Q_2 = 10$ $(2.25)(2.25)Q_2 = 10$ $Q_2 = 1.9753$
Step 5	The third estimate, R_3, is the average of R_2 and Q_2.	$R_3 = (R_2 + Q_2) \div 2$ $= (2.25 + 1.9753) \div 2$ $= 2.1126$

Continue finding values for R and Q until they are equal (to 2 decimal places).

$Q_3 = 2.2406$
$R_4 = 2.1766$
$Q_4 = 2.1108$
$R_5 = 2.1437$
$Q_5 = 2.1761$
$R_6 = 2.1599$
$Q_6 = 2.1436$
$R_7 = 2.1518$
$Q_7 = 2.1597$

$\sqrt[3]{10} = 2.15$ (to 2 decimal places)

This method is called "Newton's Method of Successive Approximations."

1   Use Newton's Method to approximate each of the following cube roots.
   a $\sqrt[3]{100}$ to the nearest hundredth
   b $\sqrt[3]{12,345}$ to the nearest unit
   c $\sqrt[3]{77}$ to the nearest thousandth (3 decimal places)
   d $\sqrt[3]{3}$ to the nearest ten-thousandth (4 decimal places)

2   Try to use Newton's Method to approximate the fifth root of a number. (To find $\sqrt[5]{100}$, $R_1 \cdot R_1 \cdot R_1 \cdot R_1 \cdot Q_1 = 100$)

1a)

R	Q
4.6	4.7258 ...
4.6629 ...	4.5991 ...
4.6310 ...	4.6627 ...
4.6468 ...	4.6310 ...
4.6389 ...	4.6468 ...
4.6429 ...	4.6389 ...
4.6409 ...	

Thus $\sqrt[3]{100} = 4.64$

b)   Suppose $R_1 = 22$:

R	Q
22.	25.5 ...
23.7 ...	21.8 ...
22.8 ...	23.7 ...
23.2 ...	22.8 ...
23.0 ...	23.2 ...
23.1 ...	

Thus $\sqrt[3]{12345} = 23$

c)

R	Q
4.3	4.164 ...
4.2322 ...	4.2988 ...
4.2655 ...	4.2319 ...
4.2487 ...	4.2654 ...
4.2571 ...	4.2487 ...
4.2529 ...	4.2571 ...
4.2550 ...	4.2529 ...
4.2539 ...	4.2550 ...
4.2544 ...	4.2539 ...
4.2542 ...	

Thus $\sqrt[3]{77} = 4.254$

d)

R	Q
1.4422	1.4423 ...
1.44227 ...	1.44219 ...
1.44223 ...	

Thus $\sqrt[3]{3} = 1.4422$

2)   This method diverges! However, change Step 3 to the weighted average:

$R_2 = (4 \cdot R_1 + Q_1) \div 5$

R	Q
2.5	2.56
2.512	2.5114 ...
2.511886 ...	2.511886 ...

To the nearest millionth, $\sqrt[5]{100}$ is 2.511886.

443

Section 11.3   Multiplying Radicals

Is $\sqrt{9} \cdot \sqrt{4} = \sqrt{9 \cdot 4}$?

To answer this question, check the computation by evaluating the two sides separately:

$$\sqrt{9} \cdot \sqrt{4} \overset{?}{=} \sqrt{9 \cdot 4}$$
$$3 \cdot 2 \overset{?}{=} \sqrt{36}$$
$$6 \overset{?}{=} 6 \checkmark$$

Notice that the left-hand side of the equation is the product of two square roots, and the right-hand side is the square root of a product. The two sides are equal as long as all radicals have the same index and the radicands are not negative.

Property

The restriction on the radicand is for an even-numbered index.

If $\sqrt[n]{a}$ and $\sqrt[n]{b}$ are two radicals, $a \geq 0$ and $b \geq 0$, then:

$$\sqrt[n]{a} \cdot \sqrt[n]{b} = \sqrt[n]{a \cdot b}$$

EXAMPLES

- $\sqrt[3]{8} \cdot \sqrt[3]{64} = 2 \cdot 4 = 8 = \sqrt[3]{512} = \sqrt[3]{8 \cdot 64}$

- $\sqrt{100} \cdot \sqrt{9} = 10 \cdot 3 = 30 = \sqrt{900} = \sqrt{100 \cdot 9}$

If the index is odd, then the radicands can also have negative values:

- $\sqrt[3]{-8} \cdot \sqrt[3]{27} = (-2)(3) = -6 = \sqrt[3]{-216} = \sqrt[3]{(-8)(27)}$

- $\sqrt[3]{-64} \cdot \sqrt[3]{-8} = (-4)(-2) = 8 = \sqrt[3]{512} = \sqrt[3]{(-64)(-8)}$

Sample Problems

1   Write without a radical sign: $3\sqrt{2} \cdot \sqrt{8}$

PROCEDURE

$$3 \cdot \sqrt{2} \cdot \sqrt{8}$$
$$3 \cdot \sqrt{16}$$
$$3 \cdot 4$$
$$12$$

2 Write each expression so that no square root contains a perfect square and no cube root contains a perfect cube:

a $\sqrt{27}$ b $\sqrt[3]{40a^7}$ c $3x\sqrt[3]{5x} \cdot 2\sqrt[3]{25x^2}$

PROCEDURE

a $\sqrt{27} = \sqrt{9 \cdot 3}$
$= \sqrt{9} \cdot \sqrt{3}$
$= 3 \cdot \sqrt{3}$

b $\sqrt[3]{40a^7} = \sqrt[3]{8 \cdot 5 \cdot a^6 \cdot a}$
$= \sqrt[3]{8a^6} \cdot \sqrt[3]{5a}$
$= 2a^2\sqrt[3]{5a}$

c $3x\sqrt[3]{5x} \cdot 2\sqrt[3]{25x^2} = 3x \cdot 2\sqrt[3]{5x}\sqrt[3]{25x^2}$
$= 6x\sqrt[3]{125x^3}$
$= 6x \cdot 5x$
$= 30x^2$

Writing a radical so that no square root contains a perfect square, no cube root contains a perfect cube, etc., is part of the process called **simplifying a radical.**

> *Sections 11.3–11.5 each present part of the process of simplifying a radical. The parts are summarized in Section 11.6.*

Problem Set A

Simplify each radical.

1 $\sqrt{5} \cdot \sqrt{5}$
  5

2 $\sqrt{7} \cdot \sqrt{7}$
  7

3 $\sqrt{12} \cdot \sqrt{3}$
  6

4 $\sqrt{2} \cdot \sqrt{50}$
  10

5 $4\sqrt{27} \cdot \sqrt{3}$
  36

6 $2\sqrt{2} \cdot \sqrt{2}$
  4

7 $-7\sqrt{28}$
  $-14\sqrt{7}$

8 $3\sqrt{40}$
  $6\sqrt{10}$

9 $\sqrt{0.5x} \cdot \sqrt{8x}$
  $2x$

10 $\sqrt{490x^3} \cdot \sqrt{0.1x}$
  $7x^2$

11 $\sqrt[3]{4x} \cdot \sqrt[3]{2x^2}$
  $2x$

12 $\sqrt[3]{4x^2} \cdot \sqrt[3]{16x^4}$
  $4x^2$

13 $\sqrt{24}$
  $2\sqrt{6}$

14 $\sqrt{8}$
  $2\sqrt{2}$

15 $\sqrt{12}$
  $2\sqrt{3}$

16 $\sqrt{18}$
  $3\sqrt{2}$

17 $-\sqrt{98}$
  $-7\sqrt{2}$

18 $\sqrt{75}$
  $5\sqrt{3}$

19 $-2\sqrt{27} \cdot \sqrt{\dfrac{1}{3}}$
  -6

20 $-5\sqrt{\dfrac{1}{2}} \cdot \sqrt{32}$
  -20

21 $\dfrac{1}{2}\sqrt{52}$
  $\sqrt{13}$

22 $\dfrac{3}{4}\sqrt{32}$
  $3\sqrt{2}$

ASSIGNMENT GUIDE

Basic (2 days)
(1) 2–28 (even)
(2) 449: 2–26 (even)

Average (2 days)
(1) 2–38 (even), 40–42
(2) 449: 2–30 (even)

Advanced (2 days)
(1) 10, 12, 20, 22, 30–38
  (even), 40–49
(2) 449: 2–30 (even),
  32–37

Find each product. (Review: Section 6.2)

23 $(a + 2b)(a - 2b)$
$a^2 - 4b^2$

24 $(2x - 5y)(2x + 5y)$
$4x^2 - 25y^2$

25 $(4m - n)(4m + n)$
$16m^2 - n^2$

26 $(n - 3p)(n + 3p)$
$n^2 - 9p^2$

27 $(2q + 1)(2q - 1)$
$4q^2 - 1$

28 $(5r + 6s)(5r - 6s)$
$25r^2 - 36s^2$

Problem Set B

Simplify each radical.

29 $\sqrt[3]{16}$
$2\sqrt[3]{2}$

30 $-\sqrt[3]{54}$
$-3\sqrt[3]{2}$

31 $\sqrt[3]{24x^5}$
$2x\sqrt[3]{3x^2}$

32 $\sqrt[3]{250x^4}$
$5x\sqrt[3]{2x}$

33 $4\sqrt{5} \cdot \sqrt{8}$
$8\sqrt{10}$

34 $-3\sqrt{48}$

$-12\sqrt{3}$

35 $5\sqrt{54}$
$15\sqrt{6}$

36 $2\sqrt{6} \cdot 4\sqrt{2}$
$16\sqrt{3}$

37 $-8\sqrt{3} \cdot 5\sqrt{15}$
$-120\sqrt{5}$

38 $7\sqrt{72x^3}$
$42x\sqrt{2x}$

39 $x^2\sqrt{x^7y^2}$
$x^5y\sqrt{x}$

40 $\frac{1}{2}x\sqrt{12x^5}$

$x^3\sqrt{3x}$

If a car skids to a stop, police can approximate the car's prior speed by measuring the length of the skid marks. For the length d (in feet) of the skid, the speed s (in miles per hour) is found by one of the formulas:

$$s = \sqrt{12d} \quad \text{(for wet pavement)}$$

$$s = \sqrt{24d} \quad \text{(for dry pavement)}$$

Use the appropriate formula and a calculator (or the table on page 448) for problems 41 and 42.

41 Find the speed (to the nearest tenth) on wet pavement if $d = 60$ ft.
26.8

42 Find the speed (to the nearest tenth) on dry pavement if $d = 360$ ft.
93.0

Problem Set C

43 The height of a roof can be calculated by using the formula $a = \sqrt{c^2 - b^2}$. Find a to the nearest hundredth if $c = 20$ and $b = 15$.

$a = 13.2$

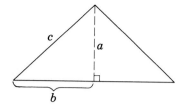

This is a form of the Pythagorean Theorem. An explcit statement of the theorem is in Chapter 14, p. 578.

Simplify each radical.

44 $3x\sqrt{12x} \cdot 5x\sqrt{2x}$

$30x^2\sqrt{6}$

45 $-8xy\sqrt{3y^3} \cdot \sqrt{36y}$

$-48xy^2\sqrt{3}$

46 $\dfrac{1}{2}\sqrt{5x} \cdot 7\sqrt{8x^4}$

$7x^2\sqrt{10x}$

47 $6a^2\sqrt[3]{4a^5} \cdot \sqrt[3]{6a^2}$

$12a^4\sqrt[3]{3a}$

48 $-9c^2\sqrt[3]{4c^2} \cdot \left(-\dfrac{1}{2}\right)\sqrt[3]{32c}$

$18c^3\sqrt[3]{2}$

49 $2x^2y^3\sqrt[3]{\dfrac{1}{2}x^5y^2} \cdot \sqrt[3]{-250x^7y^4}$

$-10x^6y^5$

X tending the topic: Decimal Approximations for Radicals

When a calculator is used for radicals, it is useful to check the calculator reading by approximating the value. To approximate a radical, use the property that, for non-negative radicands, the order of the radicals is the same as the order of the radicands. In symbols, if $a, b, c \geq 0$, then:

If $\qquad a < \quad b < \quad c$
then $\quad \sqrt[n]{a} < \sqrt[n]{b} < \sqrt[n]{c}$

EXAMPLES

- To approximate $\sqrt{8}$:

$$4 < \quad 8 < \quad 9$$
Thus $\sqrt{4} < \sqrt{8} < \sqrt{9}$
$$2 < \sqrt{8} < \quad 3$$

$\sqrt{8}$ is between 2 and 3.

- To approximate $\sqrt[3]{72}$

$$64 < \quad 72 < \quad 125$$
Thus $\sqrt[3]{64} < \sqrt[3]{72} < \sqrt[3]{125}$
$$4 < \sqrt[3]{72} < \quad 5$$

$\sqrt[3]{72}$ is between 4 and 5.

Sample Problems

1   Locate between two consecutive integers:

a $-\sqrt{54}$

b $\sqrt{\dfrac{25}{19}}$

PROCEDURE   Order each radicand between two perfect squares. In part **a**, first work with the radicand and then consider the negative sign.

a $49 < 54 < 64$

$\sqrt{49} < \sqrt{54} < \sqrt{64}$

$7 < \sqrt{54} < 8$

Since $\sqrt{54}$ is between 7 and 8, then $-\sqrt{54}$ is between -8 and -7:

$$-8 < -\sqrt{54} < -7$$

b   The radicand $\dfrac{25}{19}$ equals $1\dfrac{6}{19}$:

$$1 < 1\dfrac{6}{19} < 4$$

$$\sqrt{1} < \sqrt{1\dfrac{6}{19}} < \sqrt{4}$$

$$1 < \sqrt{1\dfrac{6}{19}} < 2 \quad \text{or} \quad 1 < \sqrt{\dfrac{25}{19}} < 2$$

2   Use the table to approximate, to the nearest tenth, the value of $4\sqrt[3]{6}$.

n	1	2	3	4	5	6	7	8
$\sqrt{n}$	1.	1.414	1.732	2.	2.236	2.449	2.646	2.828
$\sqrt[3]{n}$	1.	1.260	1.442	1.587	1.710	1.817	1.913	2.

n	9	10	11	12	13	14	15	16
$\sqrt{n}$	3.	3.162	3.317	3.464	3.606	3.742	3.873	4.
$\sqrt[3]{n}$	2.080	2.154	2.224	2.289	2.351	2.410	2.466	2.520

PROCEDURE   From the table, $\sqrt[3]{6} \doteq 1.817$ ("the cube root of six **is approximately equal to** one and eight hundred seventeen thousandths").

$$4\sqrt[3]{6} \doteq (4)(1.817)$$
$$\doteq 7.268$$
$$= 7.3 \quad \text{(to the nearest tenth)}$$

3 The formula for the distance that a body travels in free fall is $s = \frac{1}{2}gt^2$. Use the table from problem **2** to approximate the value of t, to the nearest hundredth, if $s = 176$ and $g = 32$.

PROCEDURE   First solve the equation for t, and then evaluate it:

$$s = \frac{1}{2}gt^2$$

$$2s = gt^2$$

$$\frac{2s}{g} = t^2$$

$$t = \sqrt{\frac{2s}{g}}$$

$$= \sqrt{\frac{2(176)}{32}}$$

$$= \sqrt{\frac{176}{16}}$$

$$= \sqrt{11}$$

$$= 3.317 \quad \text{(from the table)}$$

$$= 3.32 \quad \text{(to the nearest hundredth)}$$

Brighter students may appreciate the distinction between the last two steps of this problem (and of Sample Problem 2): $\sqrt{11}$ is approximately equal to 3.317. But, to the nearest hundredth, $\sqrt{11}$ is exactly equal to 3.32.

Problem Set **X**

Locate each number between consecutive integers.

1 $\sqrt{10}$

$3 < \sqrt{10} < 4$

2 $\sqrt{32}$

$5 < \sqrt{32} < 6$

3 $\sqrt{89}$

$8 < \sqrt{89} < 9$

4 $\sqrt{\dfrac{739}{8}}$

$9 < \sqrt{\dfrac{739}{8}} < 10$

5 $-\sqrt{23}$

$-5 < -\sqrt{23} < -4$

6 $-\sqrt{8}$

$-3 < -\sqrt{8} < -2$

7 $\sqrt{3.6}$

$1 < \sqrt{3.6} < 2$

8 $\sqrt{0.05}$

$0 < \sqrt{0.05} < 1$

9 $-\sqrt{\dfrac{15}{22}}$

$-1 < -\sqrt{\dfrac{15}{22}} < 0$

Use the table (or a calculator) to order each set of numbers from smallest to largest.

10 $2 \cdot 3 \cdot \sqrt{5},\ 2 \cdot 5\sqrt{3},\ 3 \cdot 5\sqrt{2}$

$6\sqrt{5} < 10\sqrt{3} < 15\sqrt{2}$

11 $1.5,\ \sqrt{2},\ \sqrt[3]{3}$

$\sqrt{2} < \sqrt[3]{3} < 1.5$

12 $\sqrt{6},\ \dfrac{5}{2},\ \sqrt[3]{15}$

$\sqrt{6} < \sqrt[3]{15} < \dfrac{5}{2}$

13 $\sqrt[3]{9},\ 1.9,\ \sqrt{4}$

$1.9 < \sqrt{4} < \sqrt[3]{9}$

14 $\left(\sqrt{5}\right)^2,\ 25,\ 2\sqrt[3]{14}$

$(\sqrt{5})^2 < 2 \cdot \sqrt[3]{14} < 25$

15 $3 \cdot 5,\ \left(\sqrt{5}\right)^3,\ \left(\sqrt{3}\right)^5$

$(\sqrt{5})^3 < 3 \cdot 5 < (\sqrt{3})^5$

Use the table to find each value to the nearest tenth.

16 $\frac{1}{2}\sqrt{3}$

0.9

19 $\sqrt[3]{7}$

1.9

17 $4\sqrt[3]{5}$

6.8

20 $\frac{1}{4}\sqrt[3]{12}$

0.6

18 $3\sqrt{13}$

10.8

21 $\sqrt{6}\cdot\sqrt[3]{14}$

5.9

For each pair of numbers, use the table (or a calculator) and state which number is greater. If the numbers are equal, write equal.

22 $2\sqrt{2},\ \sqrt{8}$

equal

27 $2\sqrt{12},\ 4\sqrt{3}$

equal

23 $(1.5)^2,\ \sqrt{5}$

$(1.5)^2$

28 $3\sqrt[3]{2},\ \sqrt{10}$

$3\sqrt[3]{2}$

24 $\sqrt{4},\ \sqrt[3]{9}$

$\sqrt[3]{9}$

29 $\left(\sqrt{2}\cdot\sqrt{8}\right),\ 2$

$\sqrt{2}\cdot\sqrt{8}$

25 $\left(3\sqrt{3}+4\sqrt{3}\right),\ 7\sqrt{6}$

$7\sqrt{6}$

30 $\left(\sqrt[3]{3}\cdot\sqrt{8}\right),\ 4$

$(\sqrt[3]{3}\cdot\sqrt{8})$

26 $\left(\sqrt{3}\right)^2,\ 3$

equal

31 $\left(\sqrt[3]{14}\cdot\sqrt{7}\right),\ 2\sqrt{5}$

$2\sqrt{5}$

Use the table (or a calculator) for problems 32–37.

32 If the area of a square is fifteen square meters, find the length of one side to the nearest hundredth.

3.87

33 Use $s=\sqrt{\frac{1}{2}t^2}$ and find s to the nearest thousandth if $t=2$.

1.414

34 Use $s=\sqrt{\frac{1}{2}t^2}$ and find s to the nearest whole number if $t=8$.

6

35 If $c=\sqrt{a^2+b^2}$, find c to the nearest hundredth for $a=2$ and $b=3$.

3.61

36 $t=\sqrt{\dfrac{d^3}{216}}$ Find t to the nearest tenth when $d=12$.

2.8

37 The formula of Hero for the area of a triangle is $A=\sqrt{s(s-a)(s-b)(s-c)}$, where a, b, and c are the lengths of the sides and $s=\frac{1}{2}(a+b+c)$. Find A to the nearest tenth for $a=3$, $b=2$, $c=3$.

2.8

Section 11.4 Dividing Radicals

SECTION SCHEDULE

Basic (2 days)

Average (1 day)

Advanced (1 day)

Is $\dfrac{\sqrt{36}}{\sqrt{4}} = \sqrt{\dfrac{36}{4}}$?

To answer the question, evaluate the two sides separately:

$$\dfrac{\sqrt{36}}{\sqrt{4}} \overset{?}{=} \sqrt{\dfrac{36}{4}}$$

$$\dfrac{6}{2} \overset{?}{=} \sqrt{9}$$

$$3 \overset{?}{=} 3 \checkmark$$

In general, if two radicals have the same index and if the radicands are nonnegative, then the quotient of the radicals is equal to the root of the quotient.

Property

If $\sqrt[n]{a}$ and $\sqrt[n]{b}$ are two radicals, $a \geq 0$ and $b \geq 0$, then:

$$\dfrac{\sqrt[n]{a}}{\sqrt[n]{b}} = \sqrt[n]{\dfrac{a}{b}}$$

The restriction on the radicand is for an even-numbered index.

EXAMPLES

■ $\dfrac{\sqrt[3]{64}}{\sqrt[3]{8}} = \dfrac{4}{2}$

$= 2$

$= \sqrt[3]{8}$

$= \sqrt[3]{\dfrac{64}{8}}$

■ $\dfrac{\sqrt{25}}{\sqrt{100}} = \dfrac{5}{10}$

$= \dfrac{1}{2}$

$= \sqrt{\dfrac{1}{4}}$

$= \sqrt{\dfrac{25}{100}}$

If the index is odd, then the radicands can also have negative values:

■ $\dfrac{\sqrt[3]{1000}}{\sqrt[3]{-125}} = \dfrac{10}{-5}$

$= -2$

$= \sqrt[3]{-8}$

$= \sqrt[3]{\dfrac{1000}{-125}}$

■ $\dfrac{\sqrt[3]{-64}}{\sqrt[3]{-8}} = \dfrac{-4}{-2}$

$= 2$

$= \sqrt[3]{8}$

$= \sqrt[3]{\dfrac{-64}{-8}}$

Sample Problems

1   Simplify the expression:

$$\frac{\sqrt[3]{128}}{\sqrt[3]{-2}}$$

PROCEDURE

$$\frac{\sqrt[3]{128}}{\sqrt[3]{-2}} = \sqrt[3]{\frac{128}{-2}}$$
$$= \sqrt[3]{-64}$$
$$= -4$$

2   Write each expression so that there are no radicals in the denominator.

a $\sqrt{\dfrac{2}{5}}$ b $\dfrac{2\sqrt{10}}{\sqrt{8x}}$ c $\dfrac{6}{\sqrt[3]{3}}$

PROCEDURE
Use the Multiplicative Property of One:

$$\frac{a}{a} = 1 \qquad (a \neq 0)$$

In each case, select a value of a that makes the denominator a perfect square (or a perfect cube).

a $\sqrt{\dfrac{2}{5}} = \sqrt{\dfrac{2}{5} \cdot \dfrac{5}{5}}$
$= \sqrt{\dfrac{10}{25}}$
$= \dfrac{\sqrt{10}}{\sqrt{25}}$
$= \dfrac{\sqrt{10}}{5}$

b $\dfrac{2\sqrt{10}}{\sqrt{8x}} = \dfrac{2\sqrt{10}}{\sqrt{8x}} \cdot \dfrac{\sqrt{2x}}{\sqrt{2x}}$
$= \dfrac{2\sqrt{20x}}{\sqrt{16x^2}}$
$= \dfrac{2\sqrt{4}\sqrt{5x}}{4x}$
$= \dfrac{4\sqrt{5x}}{4x}$
$= \dfrac{\sqrt{5x}}{x}$

c $\dfrac{6}{\sqrt[3]{3}} = \dfrac{6}{\sqrt[3]{3}} \cdot \dfrac{\sqrt[3]{9}}{\sqrt[3]{9}}$
$= \dfrac{6\sqrt[3]{9}}{\sqrt[3]{27}}$
$= \dfrac{6\sqrt[3]{9}}{3}$
$= 2\sqrt[3]{9}$

This statement is repeated in Section 11.6, which summarizes all the steps of simplifying a radical.

The expression "rationalizing the denominator" is introduced in the C problems of Section 11.6, p. 463.

Writing a radical expression so that no radicals are in the denominator is part of the process of simplifying a radical.

Problem Set A

ASSIGNMENT GUIDE

Basic (2 days)
(1) 1–29 (odd)
(2) 2–30 (even), 32, 33, 37

Average (1 day)
2–40 (even)

Advanced (1 day)
18–24 (even), 32–50 (even)

Simplify each radical.

1 $\dfrac{\sqrt{20}}{\sqrt{5}}$

2

2 $\dfrac{\sqrt{32}}{\sqrt{2}}$

4

3 $\sqrt{\dfrac{18}{2}}$

3

4 $-\sqrt{\dfrac{75}{3}}$

−5

5 $\sqrt{\dfrac{28x^3}{7x}}$

2x

6 $\sqrt{\dfrac{72x^7}{8x^3}}$

3x²

7 $\dfrac{\sqrt[3]{-56}}{\sqrt[3]{7}}$

−2

8 $\dfrac{\sqrt[3]{54}}{\sqrt[3]{2}}$

3

9 $2\sqrt{\dfrac{80}{5}}$

8

10 $-4\sqrt{\dfrac{252}{7}}$

−24

11 $\sqrt{\dfrac{3}{5}}$

$\frac{\sqrt{15}}{5}$

12 $\sqrt{\dfrac{2}{7}}$

$\frac{\sqrt{14}}{7}$

13 $\sqrt{\dfrac{3}{10}}$

$\frac{\sqrt{30}}{10}$

14 $-\sqrt{\dfrac{5}{11}}$

$-\frac{\sqrt{55}}{11}$

15 $\dfrac{\sqrt{3}}{\sqrt{2}}$

$\frac{\sqrt{6}}{2}$

16 $\dfrac{\sqrt{1}}{\sqrt{3}}$

$\frac{\sqrt{3}}{3}$

17 $-\dfrac{\sqrt{5x}}{\sqrt{6}}$

$\frac{\sqrt{30x}}{6}$

18 $\dfrac{\sqrt{7}}{\sqrt{x}}$

$\frac{\sqrt{7x}}{x}$

19 $\sqrt{\dfrac{y}{x}}$

$\frac{\sqrt{xy}}{x}$

20 $\sqrt{\dfrac{3}{x^3}}$

$\frac{\sqrt{3x}}{x^2}$

21 $\dfrac{\sqrt{4}}{\sqrt{6}}$

$\frac{\sqrt{6}}{3}$

22 $\dfrac{\sqrt{8}}{\sqrt{5}}$

$\frac{2\sqrt{10}}{5}$

23 $\dfrac{4}{\sqrt{3}}$

$\frac{4\sqrt{3}}{3}$

24 $\dfrac{-7}{\sqrt{6}}$

$-\frac{7\sqrt{6}}{6}$

Combine the like terms. (Review: Section 4.2)

25 $12xy - 5xy + 2x + xy - 6x$

−4x + 8xy

26 $3r^2s + 5rs^2 - 3rs^2 - 5r^2s$

2rs² − 2r²s

27 $3ab - 2a + 4ab + a$

7ab − a

28 $5p^2q - 7pq^2 + 12pq^2 - p^2q$

4p²q + 5pq²

29 $3x^2 + 2xy - 4(2xy + x^2)$

−x² − 6xy

30 $5x(y + 7) + 3y(x - 1) + 2(4x + y)$

8xy + 43x − y

These review problems can be used to preview the addition and subtraction of like radicals, Section 11.5.

Problem Set B

Simplify each radical.

31 $\dfrac{\sqrt{9}}{\sqrt{5x^3}}$

$\quad \frac{3\sqrt{5x}}{5x^2}$

32 $\dfrac{\sqrt{36}}{\sqrt{7x^2}}$

$\quad \frac{6\sqrt{7}}{7x}$

33 $\dfrac{\sqrt{45}}{\sqrt{4}}$

$\quad \frac{3\sqrt{5}}{2}$

34 $-\dfrac{\sqrt{54}}{\sqrt{16x^2}}$

$\quad \frac{-3\sqrt{6}}{4x}$

35 $\dfrac{50}{\sqrt[3]{-4}}$

$\quad -25\sqrt[3]{2}$

36 $\dfrac{15}{\sqrt[3]{9x}}$

$\quad \frac{5\sqrt[3]{3x^2}}{x}$

Simplify each expression, and then use a calculator (or the table on page 448) to evaluate each of the following to the nearest tenth.

37 $\dfrac{4\sqrt{30}}{\sqrt{2}}$

$\quad 4\sqrt{15} = 15.5$

38 $\dfrac{-3\sqrt{10}}{\sqrt{6}}$

$\quad -\sqrt{15} = -3.9$

39 $\dfrac{1}{3}\sqrt{\dfrac{2}{3}}$

$\quad \frac{\sqrt{6}}{9} = 0.3$

40 $\dfrac{2}{5}\sqrt{\dfrac{8}{3}}$

$\quad \frac{4\sqrt{6}}{15} = 0.7$

Problem Set C

Simplify each expression.

41 $5x\sqrt{(2\frac{2}{5})x^3}$

$\quad 2x^2\sqrt{15x}$

42 $-\dfrac{x}{3y}\sqrt{(5\frac{1}{3})x^3y^5}$

$\quad -\frac{4x^2y\sqrt{3xy}}{9}$

43 $\dfrac{1}{\sqrt{(x+y)}}$

$\quad \frac{\sqrt{x+y}}{x+y}$

44 $\sqrt{\dfrac{3}{(x+3)^3}}$

$\quad \frac{\sqrt{3(x+3)}}{(x+3)^2}$

45 $\sqrt{\dfrac{x}{x^2+14x+49}}$

(Hint: factor) $\quad \frac{\sqrt{x}}{x+7}$

46 $\sqrt{4x^3}\sqrt{\frac{1}{16}x^5}$

$\quad \frac{1}{2}x^4$

47 $a\sqrt{1+\dfrac{2}{a}+\dfrac{1}{a^2}}$

$\quad a+1$

48 $\dfrac{5}{\sqrt{2}-\sqrt{3}}$

$\quad -5(\sqrt{2}+\sqrt{3})$

49 $\sqrt{\dfrac{(r-s)^2}{(s-r)^2}}$

$\quad 1$

50 $\sqrt{\dfrac{(y-5)^3}{(-1)(5-y)^3}}$

$\quad 1$

After-School Mathematics: Ballpark Vendor

Marty works as a vendor at the stadium during football season. Sometimes he sells soft drinks, hot dogs, or peanuts. Other times he sells programs and souvenirs. He walks up and down the aisles selling his merchandise. He wears a change-maker to help him make change quickly.

One afternoon on a slow day, Marty began wondering how many different ways there were to make change for a dollar. That problem seemed too difficult, so he tried making change for a quarter. He used his change-maker to help him. First he tried combinations with two dimes. There were only two possibilities: two dimes and one nickel, and two dimes and five pennies. Then he tried with only one dime. He found four possibilities: one dime and three nickels; one dime, two nickels, and five pennies; one dime, one nickel, and ten pennies; and one dime and fifteen pennies. Lastly, he found the possible combinations with no dimes: five nickels, four nickels and five pennies, three nickels and ten pennies, two nickels and fifteen pennies, one nickel and twenty pennies, and twenty-five pennies. Altogether, Marty found twelve ways to make change for a quarter.

At this point, Marty decided he would try to figure out all the different ways to make change for a dollar when he had more time.

$2h$		(1 way)
$1h, 2q$		(1 way)
$1h, 1q$		(12 ways to make change for the last 25¢)
$1h, 0q$:		
	$5d$	(1 way)
	$4d$	(3 ways: $2n$, $1n$, or $0n$)
	$3d$	(5 ways: $4n$ to $0n$)
	$2d$	(7 ways)
	$1d$	(9 ways)
	$0d$	(11 ways)
$4q$:		(1 way)
$3q$:		(12 ways)
$2q$:		(36 ways)
$1q$:	$7d$	(2 ways)
	$6d$	(4 ways)
	$5d$	(6 ways)
	$4d$	(8 ways)
	$3d$	(10 ways)
	$2d$	(12 ways)
	$1d$	(14 ways)
	$0d$	(16 ways)
$0q$:	$10d$	(1 way)
	$9d$	(3 ways)
	$8d$	(5 ways)
	$7d$	(7 ways)
	$6d$	(9 ways)
	$5d$	(11 ways)
	$4d$	(13 ways)
	$3d$	(15 ways)
	$2d$	(17 ways)
	$1d$	(19 ways)
	$0d$	(21 ways)

Total: 292 ways

Application: Viewing Region

The computer video display tube can pivot 90° horizontally and can turn 45° vertically. If the display tube is ten feet from a wall, what is the perimeter of the region that would have sight lines to the display tube?

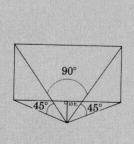

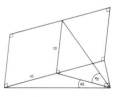

The perimeter of the viewing region is 60 feet.

Section 11.5 Adding and Subtracting Radicals

The Distributive Property was used to combine like terms in a variable expression:

- $2a + 5a$
  $(2 + 5)a$
  $7a$

- $2x^2y - 5x^2y$
  $(2 - 5)x^2y$
  $-3x^2y$

Similarly, the Distributive Property can be used to combine "like radicals:"

- $2\sqrt{3} + 5\sqrt{3}$
  $(2 + 5)\sqrt{3}$
  $7\sqrt{3}$

- $2\sqrt[8]{73} - 5\sqrt[8]{73}$
  $(2 - 5)\sqrt[8]{73}$
  $-3\sqrt[8]{73}$

"Like radicals" must have the **same index** and the **same radicand**.
  Sometimes the terms in an expression must be simplified before they can be combined:

- $$\sqrt{75} - \sqrt{48}$$
  $$\sqrt{25 \cdot 3} - \sqrt{16 \cdot 3}$$
  $$\sqrt{25}\sqrt{3} - \sqrt{16}\sqrt{3}$$
  $$5\sqrt{3} - 4\sqrt{3}$$
  $$(5 - 4)\sqrt{3}$$
  $$\sqrt{3}$$

Sample Problems

1 Simplify the expression: $\left(5 + 3\sqrt{6}\right)\left(2 - 4\sqrt{6}\right)$

PROCEDURE The multiplication of two binomials can use the FOIL pattern:

$$\left(5 + 3\sqrt{6}\right)\left(2 - 4\sqrt{6}\right)$$

$$= (5)(2) + (5)\left(-4\sqrt{6}\right) + \left(3\sqrt{6}\right)(2) + \left(3\sqrt{6}\right)\left(-4\sqrt{6}\right)$$

$$= 10 - 20\sqrt{6} + 6\sqrt{6} - (12)(6)$$

$$= 10 - (12)(6) - 20\sqrt{6} + 6\sqrt{6}$$

$$= (10 - 72) + (-20 + 6)\sqrt{6}$$

$$= -62 - 14\sqrt{6}$$

2 Simplify each expression:

a $\quad x\sqrt{125x^3} - \dfrac{3}{2}x^2\sqrt{20x}$

b $\quad 3\sqrt[3]{16} + \sqrt[3]{\dfrac{1}{4}}$

PROCEDURE

In each case, the radicands already have the same index.

a $\quad x\sqrt{125x^3} - \dfrac{3}{2}x^2\sqrt{20x}$

$\quad x\sqrt{25x^2 \cdot 5x} - \dfrac{3}{2}x^2\sqrt{4 \cdot 5x}$

$\quad (x)(5x)\sqrt{5x} - \left(\dfrac{3}{2}x^2\right)(2)\sqrt{5x}$

$\qquad 5x^2\sqrt{5x} - 3x^2\sqrt{5x}$

$\qquad\quad (5-3)\,x^2\sqrt{5x}$

$\qquad\qquad 2\,x^2\sqrt{5x}$

b $\quad 3\sqrt[3]{16} + \sqrt[3]{\dfrac{1}{4}}$

$\quad 3\sqrt[3]{8 \cdot 2} + \sqrt[3]{\dfrac{2}{8}}$

$\quad (3)(2)\sqrt[3]{2} + \dfrac{\sqrt[3]{2}}{2}$

$\qquad 6\sqrt[3]{2} + \dfrac{1}{2}\sqrt[3]{2}$

$\qquad \left(6 + \dfrac{1}{2}\right)\sqrt[3]{2}$

$\qquad\qquad \dfrac{13}{2}\sqrt[3]{2}$

Problem Set **A**

ASSIGNMENT GUIDE

Basic (2 days)
(1) 1–19 (odd)
(2) 2–22 (even)

Average (1 day)
2–30 (even)

Advanced (1 day)
2–36 (even)
459: 2–10 (even)

Find each sum or difference.

1 $3\sqrt{7} + 2\sqrt{7}$
$\quad 5\sqrt{7}$

2 $4\sqrt[3]{5} - 3\sqrt[3]{5}$
$\quad \sqrt[3]{5}$

3 $6\sqrt{2} + \sqrt{2}$
$\quad 7\sqrt{2}$

4 $9\sqrt{x} - 5\sqrt{x}$
$\quad 4\sqrt{x}$

5 $-6\sqrt[3]{3} + 2\sqrt[3]{3}$
$\quad -4\sqrt[3]{3}$

6 $5\sqrt{2x} - 5\sqrt{2x}$
$\quad 0$

7 $\sqrt[3]{6} - 10\sqrt[3]{6}$
$\quad -9\sqrt[3]{6}$

8 $\sqrt{2} + 5\sqrt{2} - 6\sqrt{2}$
$\quad 0$

9 $\sqrt{8} + 3\sqrt{2}$
$\quad 5\sqrt{2}$

10 $\sqrt{12} - 4\sqrt{3}$
$\quad -2\sqrt{3}$

11 $\sqrt{50} + \sqrt{32}$
$\quad 9\sqrt{2}$

12 $\sqrt{8} - \sqrt{72}$
$\quad -4\sqrt{3}$

13 $\sqrt{24} - 2\sqrt{6}$
$\quad 0$

14 $4\sqrt{12} + 3\sqrt{27}$
$\quad 17\sqrt{3}$

As oral exercises, students could be asked to state an index and radicand for each problem.

11.5 Adding and Subtracting **457**

Find each product. (Review: Section 6.1)

15 $(x + 3)(x - 7)$

$x^2 - 4x - 21$

16 $(2y + 1)(2y + 1)$

$4y^2 + 4y + 1$

17 $(3z - 1)(2z + 4)$

$6z^2 + 10z - 4$

18 $(r - 2s)(r + 2s)$

$r^2 - 4s^2$

19 $(3 - t)(4 + t)$

$12 - t - t^2$

20 $(a + b)(c + d)$

$ac + ad + bc + bd$

Problem Set **B**

Find each sum or difference.

21 $\sqrt{5x^3} - x\sqrt{80x}$

$-3x\sqrt{5x}$

22 $-7x\sqrt{24x} + 6\sqrt{54x^3}$

$4x\sqrt{6x}$

23 $\frac{1}{2}\sqrt{28} - 3\sqrt{7}$

$-2\sqrt{7}$

24 $2\sqrt{45} - 6\sqrt{5} + \sqrt{32}$

$4\sqrt{2}$

25 $\sqrt{27} + 5\sqrt{8} - 4\sqrt{3}$

$10\sqrt{2} - \sqrt{3}$

26 $\sqrt{\frac{2}{5}} - \sqrt{40}$

$-\frac{9\sqrt{10}}{5}$

Simplify each expression.

27 $\sqrt{6}\left(\sqrt{2} + \sqrt{3}\right)$

$2\sqrt{3} + 3\sqrt{2}$

28 $\sqrt{8}\left(\sqrt{5} - \sqrt{2}\right)$

$2\sqrt{10} - 4$

29 $\sqrt{14}\left(3\sqrt{2} + 5\right)$

$6\sqrt{7} + 5\sqrt{14}$

30 $-\sqrt{4x}\left(2\sqrt{3} - 3\right)$

$-4\sqrt{3x} + 6\sqrt{x}$

Problem Set **C**

Simplify each expression.

31 $5x\sqrt{72x^3} - 2x^2\sqrt{18x}$

$24x^2\sqrt{2x}$

32 $-3x^2\sqrt{\frac{3}{5}} + \frac{1}{2}\sqrt{60x^4}$

$\frac{2x^2\sqrt{15}}{5}$

33 $6\sqrt{x}\left(3\sqrt{x} - \frac{2}{3}\right) - \frac{7}{3\sqrt{x}}$

$18x - 4\sqrt{x} - \frac{7\sqrt{x}}{3x}$

34 $2x\sqrt{3x}\left(4 - \sqrt{3x}\right)\left(7 + 5\sqrt{3x}\right)$

$78x^2 + 56x\sqrt{3x} - 30x^2\sqrt{3x}$

35 $\left(6\sqrt{x^3} + \sqrt{2}\right)^2 - \left(\sqrt{72x^3} + 2\right)$

$36x^3 + 6x\sqrt{2x}$

36 $\left(6 + \sqrt{3}\right)\left(-5 + 2\sqrt{3}\right)$

$-24 + 7\sqrt{3}$

X tending the topic: $\sqrt{-1}$

The square of any real number must be positive (or zero). Thus there is no number in the real number system such that its square is -1, and there is no real number that can represent $\sqrt{-1}$.

Mathematicians use the symbol i to represent $\sqrt{-1}$; i is not part of the real number system. It is called an **imaginary number** (although it is no less real than "4" or "0" or "pi").

This section can serve as a preview, for able students, to the properties of imaginary numbers and the development of the complex number system, which are major topics in second-year algebra.

Sample Problem

1 Use the symbol i to simplify each expression:

a $\sqrt{-16}$ c $\sqrt{-x^4}$

b $\sqrt{-25}$ d $\sqrt{-49a^2b^6}$

PROCEDURE   Write each radicand as the product of a perfect square and $\sqrt{-1}$. Then simplify the expression.

a $\sqrt{-16} = \sqrt{(16)(-1)}$
$\qquad\quad = 4\sqrt{-1}$
$\qquad\quad = 4i$

c $\sqrt{-x^4} = \sqrt{x^4(-1)}$
$\qquad\quad = x^2 i$

b $\sqrt{-25} = \sqrt{(25)(-1)}$
$\qquad\quad = 5i$

d $\sqrt{-49a^2b^6} = \sqrt{(49a^2b^6)(-1)}$
$\qquad\qquad\quad = 7|ab^3|i$

*In part **d**, the expression $a^2 b^6$ must be nonnegative, so it will have a real square root. However, if **a** or **b** (but not both) is negative, ab^3 will be negative. Thus the absolute value symbols are needed to represent the principal square root.*

Problem Set X

Simplify each expression.

1 $\sqrt{-225}$
$\quad$ $15i$

6 $\sqrt{-2}$
$\quad$ $\sqrt{2}i$

2 $\sqrt{-400}$
$\quad$ $20i$

7 $\sqrt{-36m^2n}$
$\quad$ $6m\sqrt{n}i$

3 $\sqrt{-\dfrac{1}{16}r^4}$
$\quad$ $\frac{1}{4}r^2 i$

8 $\sqrt{-\dfrac{9}{25}s^2}$
$\quad$ $\frac{3}{5}si$

4 $\sqrt{-4a^2b^2}$
$\quad$ $2abi$

9 $\sqrt{(-1)^2}$
$\quad$ 1

5 $-\sqrt{-16t^8}$
$\quad$ $-4t^4 i$

10 $\left(\sqrt{-1}\right)^2$
$\quad$ -1

Section 11.6 Writing Radicals in Standard Form

The three previous sections presented parts of a process that was called **simplifying a radical.** In general, a radical is in **simplest exact form** (or **simplest form**), if:

A   no square root contains a perfect square, no cube root contains a perfect cube, etc.

B   the radicand is not a fraction

C   there are no radicals in a denominator

D   all like radicals are combined

Sample Problem

1   Write each expression in simplest exact form.

a $\sqrt[3]{54}$

b $\sqrt{\dfrac{3}{4}}$

c $\dfrac{\sqrt{3}}{\sqrt{2}}$

d $2\sqrt{3} - 4\sqrt{27}$

PROCEDURE

a $\sqrt[3]{54}$ contains a perfect cube:

$$\sqrt[3]{54} = \sqrt[3]{27}\ \sqrt[3]{2}$$
$$= 3\sqrt[3]{2}$$

b   The radicand of $\sqrt{\dfrac{3}{4}}$ is a fraction:

$$\sqrt{\frac{3}{4}} = \frac{\sqrt{3}}{\sqrt{4}}$$
$$= \frac{\sqrt{3}}{2}$$

c $\dfrac{\sqrt{3}}{\sqrt{2}}$ contains a radical in the denominator:

$$\frac{\sqrt{3}}{\sqrt{2}} = \frac{\sqrt{3}}{\sqrt{2}} \cdot \frac{\sqrt{2}}{\sqrt{2}}$$
$$= \frac{\sqrt{6}}{2}$$

d $\quad 2\sqrt{3} - 4\sqrt{27} = 2\sqrt{3} - 4\sqrt{9}\sqrt{3}$
$$= 2\sqrt{3} - 4 \cdot 3\sqrt{3}$$
$$= 2\sqrt{3} - 12\sqrt{3}$$
$$= (2 - 12)\sqrt{3}$$
$$= -10\sqrt{3}$$

Writing an expression in simplest form is important for approximating expressions if a calculator is not available. For example:

$$\frac{1}{\sqrt{10}} = \frac{1}{3.1622776\ldots} = ?$$

$$\frac{1}{\sqrt{10}} = \frac{\sqrt{10}}{10} = \frac{3.1622776\ldots}{10} = 0.31622776\ldots$$

When a calculator is available, simplest form is not as important except as guidelines for writing radical expressions in a standard way. Thus the process of simplifying an expression is sometimes called **standardizing an expression** or writing the expression in **standard form**.

Problem Set **A**

ASSIGNMENT GUIDE

Basic (2 days)
(1) 2–26 (even)
(2) 1–21 (odd), 28–36 (even)

Average (2 days)
(1) 2–36 (even)
(2) 1–35 (odd), 37–40

Advanced (2 days)
(1) 2–36 (even)
(2) 38–49

Write each expression in standard form.

1 $\left(\sqrt{7}\right)^2$
7

2 $\left(2\sqrt{5}\right)^2$
20

3 $\sqrt{9x^2}$
$3x$

4 $-\sqrt{100x^4}$
$-10x^2$

5 $\sqrt{50}$
$5\sqrt{2}$

6 $\sqrt{12}$
$2\sqrt{3}$

7 $\sqrt[3]{27}$
3

8 $\sqrt[3]{-8}$
-2

9 $\sqrt{3} \cdot \sqrt{7}$
$\sqrt{21}$

10 $\sqrt{5} \cdot \sqrt{2}$
$\sqrt{10}$

11 $\dfrac{\sqrt{18}}{\sqrt{2}}$
3

12 $\dfrac{\sqrt{20}}{\sqrt{10}}$
$\sqrt{2}$

13 $\sqrt{\dfrac{9}{16}}$
$\dfrac{3}{4}$

14 $-\sqrt{\dfrac{100}{49}}$
$-\dfrac{10}{7}$

15 $-\sqrt{40x^3}$
$-2x\sqrt{10x}$

16 $\sqrt{20x^3}$
$2x\sqrt{5x}$

17 $\sqrt{\dfrac{7}{4}}$
$\dfrac{\sqrt{7}}{2}$

18 $-\sqrt{\dfrac{5}{9}}$
$\dfrac{-\sqrt{5}}{3}$

19 $3\sqrt{3} + \sqrt{27}$
$6\sqrt{3}$

20 $\sqrt{24} - 3\sqrt{6}$
$-\sqrt{6}$

21 $\sqrt{x^5}$
$x^2\sqrt{x}$

Solve each equation. (Review: Section 3.7)

22 $3z - 5 = 16$
$z = 7$

25 $4 + 7a = 4$
$a = 0$

23 $5(y - 3) = 30$
$y = 9$

26 $2b + 9 = 17$
$b = 4$

24 $6x = x - 10$
$x = -2$

27 $-7 = 5 + 3c$
$c = -4$

Problem Set **B**

One of the three expressions is different from the other two. Write the one that is different in simplest exact form.

28 3^2 $\qquad$ $9\sqrt{2} - 2$ $\qquad$ $\sqrt{81}$
$9\sqrt{2} - 2$

29 $\sqrt{24}$ $\qquad$ $7\sqrt{6} - 3\sqrt{6}$ $\qquad$ $2\sqrt{6}$
$7\sqrt{6} - 3\sqrt{6} = 4\sqrt{6}$

30 $\sqrt{2} \cdot \sqrt{6}$ $\qquad$ $6\sqrt{\dfrac{1}{3}}$ $\qquad$ $\sqrt{144}$
$\sqrt{144} = 12$

31 $5\sqrt{8}$ $\qquad$ $\dfrac{1}{2}\sqrt{40}$ $\qquad$ $\sqrt{200}$
$\dfrac{1}{2}\sqrt{40} = \sqrt{10}$

32 $x\sqrt{x}$ $\qquad$ $\sqrt{x^3}$ $\qquad$ $\dfrac{1}{\sqrt{x}}$
$\dfrac{1}{\sqrt{x}} = \dfrac{\sqrt{x}}{x}$

33 $\sqrt{16x^2}$ $\qquad$ $\dfrac{x\sqrt{48}}{\sqrt{3}}$ $\qquad$ $4x\sqrt{x} - \sqrt{x}$
$4x\sqrt{x} - \sqrt{x} = (4x - 1)\sqrt{x}$

34 $\sqrt[3]{16x^2}$ $\qquad$ $4x$ $\qquad$ $\dfrac{2}{3}\sqrt[3]{54x^2}$
$4x$

35 $-4x\sqrt[3]{24}$ $\qquad$ $\sqrt[3]{-216x^3}$ $\qquad$ $-8x\sqrt[3]{\dfrac{27}{64}}$
$-4x\sqrt[3]{24} = -8x\sqrt[3]{2}$

36 $\left(\sqrt{x^{10}}\right)^2$ $\qquad$ $\left(\sqrt{x}\right)^{10}$ $\qquad$ $\sqrt{x^{10}}$
$x^{10} = \sqrt{x^{10}}^{\,2}$

37 $\dfrac{5\sqrt{3}}{\sqrt{81}}$ $\qquad$ $\dfrac{\sqrt{75}}{3}$ $\qquad$ $\sqrt{\dfrac{25}{27}}$
$\dfrac{\sqrt{75}}{3} = \dfrac{5\sqrt{3}}{3}$

Problem Set C

Write each expression in standard form.

38 $\dfrac{5x\sqrt{3x^2}}{6y\sqrt{6xy}}$

$\dfrac{5x\sqrt{2xy}}{12y^2}$

39 $\left(\sqrt{2x}-3\sqrt{y}\right)\left(3\sqrt{x}+\sqrt{y}\right)$

$3x\sqrt{2}+\sqrt{2xy}-9\sqrt{xy}-3y$

40 $\sqrt[3]{81x^5y}-x\sqrt[3]{24x^2y}$

$x\sqrt[3]{3x^2y}$

41 $3\sqrt{x^2y}+x\sqrt{y^3}-\dfrac{x}{3}\sqrt{81y}$

$xy\sqrt{x}$

42 $2\sqrt[3]{2x^3y^2}+\dfrac{1}{2}\sqrt[3]{128x^3y^2}-x\sqrt[3]{\dfrac{1}{4}y^2}$

$7x\sqrt[3]{2y^2}$

43 $\sqrt[3]{\dfrac{81}{x^2}}-\dfrac{3\sqrt[3]{x}}{x\sqrt[3]{9}}+\dfrac{4}{x}\sqrt[3]{-192x}$

$\dfrac{14\sqrt[3]{3x}}{x}$

Consider the following expression:

$$\frac{1}{5+\sqrt{3}}$$

The process of removing the radical from the denominator of the expression is called **rationalizing the denominator**. Multiply by:

$$\frac{5-\sqrt{3}}{5-\sqrt{3}}$$

The expression $5-\sqrt{3}$ is the **conjugate** of the denominator, $5+\sqrt{3}$.

■ $\dfrac{1}{5+\sqrt{3}}=\dfrac{1}{5+\sqrt{3}}\cdot\dfrac{5-\sqrt{3}}{5-\sqrt{3}}=\dfrac{5-\sqrt{3}}{5^2-\left(\sqrt{3}\right)^2}=\dfrac{5-\sqrt{3}}{25-3}$

$=\dfrac{5-\sqrt{3}}{22}$

Rationalize the denominator of each expression:

44 $\dfrac{3}{4+\sqrt{7}}$

$\dfrac{-12+3\sqrt{7}}{33}$

45 $\dfrac{2}{5-\sqrt{2}}$

$\dfrac{10+2\sqrt{2}}{23}$

46 $\dfrac{5}{-7+\sqrt{10}}$

$\dfrac{35+5\sqrt{10}}{39}$

47 $\dfrac{\sqrt{2}}{2+\sqrt{2}}$

$\sqrt{2}-1$

48 $\dfrac{2+\sqrt{3}}{2-\sqrt{3}}$

$7+4\sqrt{3}$

49 $\dfrac{1}{\sqrt{7}+\sqrt{8}}$

$-\sqrt{7}+\sqrt{8}$

Section 11.7   Solving Radical Equations

An equation that contains a radical is called a **radical equation**. Solving radical equations usually involves finding the square of each side of the equation.

EXAMPLES

■
$$\sqrt{x} = 5$$
$$\left(\sqrt{x}\right)^2 = \left(5\right)^2$$
$$x = 25$$

■
$$\sqrt{7y^2 - 12} = 2y$$
$$7y^2 - 12 = 4y^2$$
$$3y^2 = 12$$
$$y^2 = 4$$
$$y = 2 \quad \text{or} \quad y = -2$$

It is always necessary to check the solutions to radical equations.

■   *check* for $x = 25$:
$$\sqrt{x} = 5$$
$$\sqrt{25} \stackrel{?}{=} 5$$
$$5 \stackrel{?}{=} 5 ✓$$

■   *check* for $y = 2$:
$$\sqrt{7y^2 - 12} = 2y$$
$$\sqrt{7(2)^2 - 12} \stackrel{?}{=} 2(2)$$
$$\sqrt{28 - 12} \stackrel{?}{=} 4$$
$$\sqrt{16} \stackrel{?}{=} 4$$
$$4 \stackrel{?}{=} 4 ✓$$

■   *check* for $y = -2$:
$$\sqrt{7y^2 - 12} = 2y$$
$$\sqrt{7(-2)^2 - 12} \stackrel{?}{=} 2(-2)$$
$$\sqrt{7 \cdot 4 - 12} \stackrel{?}{=} -4$$
$$\sqrt{28 - 12} \stackrel{?}{=} -4$$
$$\sqrt{16} \stackrel{?}{=} -4$$
$$4 \stackrel{?}{=} -4 \quad \text{No.}$$

The value $y = -2$ does not check.

*Most extraneous solutions (also called **extraneous roots**) result from setting a radical equal to a negative number; the step of squaring both sides masks that contradictory equation.*

The process of finding the square of each side of an equation can sometimes produce **extraneous results**, or false solutions.

Sample Problems

1   Solve and check:

   a $\sqrt{3x + 4} = 5$ **b** $\sqrt{y} = -3$

PROCEDURE

   a $\sqrt{3x + 4} = 5$ *To check* $\sqrt{3x + 4} = 5$

                $3x + 4 = 25$ $\sqrt{3(7) + 4} \overset{?}{=} 5$

                    $3x = 21$ $\sqrt{21 + 4} \overset{?}{=} 5$

                      $x = 7$ $\sqrt{25} \overset{?}{=} 5$

                                                         $5 \overset{?}{=} 5 \checkmark$

   b   The equation $\sqrt{y} = -3$ asks for the principal square root of a real number to be negative three. Since the principal square root is always positive (or zero), the equation has no real number solution.

2   Solve and check:

   a $\sqrt{z} + 5 = 13$

   b $-8\sqrt{2w + 4} = 32$

   c $\dfrac{3}{\sqrt{x - 2}} = \dfrac{7}{1}$

Brighter students may enjoy the following extension of Section 11.5X. First, if $i = \sqrt{-1}$, then $i^2 = -1$. and $i^4 = (-1)(-1) = 1$. Then, from $2w + 4 = 16$:

$$2w + 4 = 16i^4$$
$$2w = 16i^4 - 4$$
$$w = 8i^4 - 2$$

Checking:

$$-8\sqrt{2w + 4} = 32$$
$$-8\sqrt{2(8i^4 - 2) + 4} \overset{?}{=} 32$$
$$-8\sqrt{16i^4 - 4 + 4} \overset{?}{=} 32$$
$$-8\sqrt{16i^4} \overset{?}{=} 32$$
$$(-8)(4i^2) \overset{?}{=} 32$$
$$(-8)(-4) \overset{?}{=} 32$$
$$32 \overset{?}{=} 32 \checkmark$$

Thus $w = 8i^4 - 2$ is a solution.

PROCEDURE   Isolate the radical before squaring each side of the equation:

   a $\sqrt{z} + 5 = 13$ *To check* $\sqrt{z} + 5 = 13$

                   $\sqrt{z} = 8$ $\sqrt{64} + 5 \overset{?}{=} 13$

                     $z = 64$ $8 + 5 \overset{?}{=} 13$

                                                        $13 \overset{?}{=} 13 \checkmark$

   b $-8\sqrt{2w + 4} = 32$ *To check* $-8\sqrt{2w + 4} = 32$

                 $\sqrt{2w + 4} = -4$ $-8\sqrt{(2)(6) + 4} \overset{?}{=} 32$

                   $2w + 4 = 16$ $-8\sqrt{16} \overset{?}{=} 32$

                        $2w = 12$ $(-8)(4) \overset{?}{=} 32$

                           $w = 6$ $-32 \overset{?}{=} 32$ No.

The value $w = 6$ does not check. The equation $-8\sqrt{2w + 4} = 32$ does not have any solution in the real number system.

c $\dfrac{3}{\sqrt{x-2}} = \dfrac{7}{1}$

$7\sqrt{x-2} = 3$

$\sqrt{x-2} = \dfrac{3}{7}$

$x - 2 = \dfrac{9}{49}$

$x = \dfrac{9}{49} + \dfrac{98}{49} = \dfrac{107}{49}$

To check $\dfrac{3}{\sqrt{x-2}} = \dfrac{7}{1}$

$\dfrac{3}{\sqrt{\dfrac{107}{49} - \dfrac{98}{49}}} \overset{?}{=} 7$

$\dfrac{3}{\sqrt{\dfrac{9}{49}}} \overset{?}{=} 7$

$\dfrac{3}{\dfrac{3}{7}} \overset{?}{=} 7$

$\dfrac{3}{1} \cdot \dfrac{7}{3} \overset{?}{=} 7$

$7 \overset{?}{=} 7 ✓$

ASSIGNMENT GUIDE

Basic (1 day)
2–24 (even)

Average (1 day)
8–36 (even)

Advanced (2 days)
(1) 8–36 (even)
(2) 11–35 (odd), 37–40

Problem Set   **A**

Solve for x and check.

1 $\sqrt{x} = 4$
    $x = 16$

2 $\sqrt{3x} = 6$
    $x = 12$

3 $\sqrt{2x} = 7$
    $x = \frac{49}{2}$

4 $\sqrt{5x} = -9$
    no solution

5 $\sqrt{x+4} = 7$
    $x = 45$

6 $\sqrt{2x-5} = 3$
    $x = 7$

7 $\sqrt{\dfrac{x}{3}} = 2$
    $x = 12$

8 $\sqrt{\dfrac{2x}{5}} = -3$
    no solution

9 $\sqrt{3x+2} = 5$
    $x = \frac{23}{3}$

10 $\sqrt{2x-1} = 7$
    $x = 25$

11 $\sqrt{4x+8} - 3 = 7$
    $x = 23$

12 $\sqrt{5x-5} + 4 = 9$
    $x = 6$

13 $\dfrac{4}{\sqrt{x}} = 2$
    $x = 4$

14 $\dfrac{-6}{\sqrt{x}} = -3$
    $x = 4$

15 $\sqrt{\dfrac{3x}{4}} - 1 = 8$
    $x = \frac{324}{3}$

16 $\sqrt{\dfrac{2x}{7}} + 5 = 3$
    no solution

17 $2\sqrt{x} = 6$
    $x = 9$

18 $4\sqrt{x+1} = 12$
    $x = 8$

19 $-3\sqrt{2x-7} = 9$
    no solution

Simplify each expression. (Review: Section 11.6)

20 $\sqrt{75} \div \sqrt{48}$

$\frac{5}{4}$

22 $\sqrt[3]{\frac{3}{8}}$

$\frac{\sqrt[3]{3}}{2}$

24 $\frac{3\sqrt{28}}{\sqrt{72}}$

$\frac{\sqrt{14}}{2}$

21 $12\sqrt[3]{128} - 3\sqrt[3]{54}$

$39\sqrt[3]{2}$

23 $4\sqrt{20} - 2\sqrt{40}$

$8\sqrt{5} - 2\sqrt{10}$

25 $\frac{1}{5}\sqrt{75}$

$\sqrt{3}$

Problem Set B

Solve and check.

26 $-4\sqrt{3x} = \sqrt{12}$

$x = \frac{1}{4}$

28 $\sqrt{\frac{18}{k-5}} = 3$

$k = 7$

30 $\sqrt{\frac{3c+1}{5}} = -7$

$c = 81\frac{1}{3}$

27 $\sqrt{\frac{2}{m+3}} = 1$

$m = -1$

29 $\sqrt{\frac{2t-5}{7}} = 3$

$t = 34$

31 $\sqrt{x^2 - 4} = x + 2$

$x = -2$

32 Eight less than the square root of a number is three. Find the number.

$x = 121$

32) $\sqrt{x} - 8 = 3$

33 One fourth the square root of a number is four. What is the number?

256

33) $\frac{\sqrt{x}}{4} = 4$

34 The square root of seven more than twice a number is five. What is the number?

9

34) $\sqrt{2x + 7} = 5$

35 The average of the square root of a number and nine is thirty-one. Find the number.

2809

35) $\frac{\sqrt{x} + 9}{2} = 31$

36 Use the electrical formula $I = \sqrt{P \div R}$ and find the value of P when R is twenty and I is eight.

1280

Problem Set C

Solve and check.

37 $\sqrt{2x} - \sqrt{3} = 5$

$x = 14 + 5\sqrt{3}$

39 $2\sqrt{5x + 1} + \sqrt{8} = 1$

$x = -\frac{11}{20} - \frac{\sqrt{2}}{5}$

38 $\sqrt{\frac{2x+3}{5}} = 6 - \sqrt{2}$

$x = \frac{187}{2} - 30\sqrt{2}$

40 $\sqrt{3x - 5} + \sqrt{5} = \sqrt{7}$

$x = \frac{7 - 2\sqrt{35}}{3}$

Chapter Study Guide

Vocabulary

As you study and review this chapter, be sure to learn the important mathematics vocabulary, including:

1   **Square root**

A square root of a number or expression is one of its two equal factors.

-   -4 and 4 are both square roots of 16

-   $-\frac{1}{2}$ and $\frac{1}{2}$ are square roots of $\frac{1}{4}$. The **principal square root** of $\frac{1}{4}$ is $\frac{1}{2}$.

Skills

Be sure you build the useful algebraic skills, including:

2   **Multiplying radicals**   Find the product: $\sqrt{2x} \cdot \sqrt{8x^3}$

PROCEDURE   If two nonnegative radicals have the same index, then the product of the radicals is the root of the product of the radicands.

$$\sqrt{2x} \cdot \sqrt{8x^3}$$
$$\sqrt{(2x)(8x^3)}$$
$$\sqrt{16x^4}$$
$$4x^2$$

3   **Dividing radicals**   Find the quotient: $\dfrac{\sqrt[3]{250y^5}}{\sqrt[3]{2y^2}}$

PROCEDURE   If two nonnegative radicals have the same index, then the quotient of the radicals is the root of the quotient of the radicands.

$$\frac{\sqrt[3]{250y^5}}{\sqrt[3]{2y^2}}$$
$$\sqrt[3]{\frac{250y^5}{2y^2}}$$
$$\sqrt[3]{125y^3}$$
$$5y$$

4   Adding and subtracting radicals   Find each sum or difference:

a $5\sqrt[3]{81} + 7\sqrt[3]{24}$

b $\sqrt{4x^2y^3} - 3x\sqrt{9y^3}$

PROCEDURE   If two radicals can be written so they have the same index and the same radicand, use the Distributive Property to combine them.

a
$$5\sqrt[3]{81} + 7\sqrt[3]{24}$$
$$5\sqrt[3]{27\cdot 3} + 7\sqrt[3]{8\cdot 3}$$
$$5\sqrt[3]{27}\cdot\sqrt[3]{3} + 7\sqrt[3]{8}\cdot\sqrt[3]{3}$$
$$5\cdot 3\sqrt[3]{3} + 7\cdot 2\sqrt[3]{3}$$
$$15\sqrt[3]{3} + 14\sqrt[3]{3}$$
$$(15 + 14)\sqrt[3]{3}$$
$$29\sqrt[3]{3}$$

b
$$\sqrt{4x^2y^3} - 3x\sqrt{9y^3}$$
$$\sqrt{4x^2y^2}\,\sqrt{y} - 3x\sqrt{9y^2}\,\sqrt{y}$$
$$2xy\sqrt{y} - 3x\cdot 3y\sqrt{y}$$
$$2xy\sqrt{y} - 9xy\sqrt{y}$$
$$(2 - 9)xy\sqrt{y}$$
$$-7xy\sqrt{y}$$

5   Writing radicals in simplest (standard) form
Simplify each expression:

a $\sqrt{\dfrac{32}{81}}$

b $\dfrac{m}{2\sqrt{p}}$

PROCEDURE   An expression is in simplest form (or standard form) if the following are true: no square root contains a perfect square, no cube root contains a perfect cube, etc.; the radicand is not a fraction; there are no radicals in the denominator; and all like radicals are combined.

a
$$\sqrt{\frac{32}{81}} = \frac{\sqrt{32}}{\sqrt{81}}$$
$$= \frac{\sqrt{16}\,\sqrt{2}}{9}$$
$$= \frac{4\sqrt{2}}{9}$$

b
$$\frac{m}{2\sqrt{p}} = \frac{m}{2\sqrt{p}}\cdot\frac{\sqrt{p}}{\sqrt{p}}$$
$$= \frac{m\sqrt{p}}{2p}$$

6   Solving radical equations

Solve and check:

a $3 - \sqrt{r} = -7$

b $\sqrt{4t^2 - 75} = t$

PROCEDURE   Isolate the radical and then square each side of the equation. The process may introduce **extraneous** solutions, so check each value.

a $3 - \sqrt{r} = -7$

$\quad\quad -\sqrt{r} = -10$

$\quad\quad\quad\quad r = 100$

To check $3 - \sqrt{r} = -7$

$\quad\quad\quad\quad 3 - \sqrt{100} \overset{?}{=} -7$

$\quad\quad\quad\quad\quad\quad 3 - 10 \overset{?}{=} -7$

$\quad\quad\quad\quad\quad\quad\quad -7 \overset{?}{=} -7 \checkmark$

b $\sqrt{4t^2 - 75} = t$

$\quad\quad 4t^2 - 75 = t^2$

$\quad\quad\quad 4t^2 = t^2 + 75$

$\quad\quad\quad 3t^2 = 75$

$\quad\quad\quad t^2 = 25$

$\quad\quad t = -5 \quad or \quad t = 5$

To check for $t = -5$:

$$\sqrt{4t^2 - 75} = t$$
$$\sqrt{(4)(-5)^2 - 75} \overset{?}{=} -5$$
$$\sqrt{(4)(25) - 75} \overset{?}{=} -5$$
$$\sqrt{100 - 75} \overset{?}{=} -5$$
$$\sqrt{25} \overset{?}{=} -5$$
$$5 \overset{?}{=} -5 \quad \text{No.}$$

The value $t = -5$ does not check.

To check for $t = 5$:

$$\sqrt{4t^2 - 75} = t$$
$$\sqrt{(4)(5)^2 - 75} \overset{?}{=} 5$$
$$\sqrt{(4)(25) - 75} \overset{?}{=} 5$$
$$\sqrt{100 - 75} \overset{?}{=} 5$$
$$\sqrt{25} \overset{?}{=} 5$$
$$5 \overset{?}{=} 5 \checkmark$$

The value $t = 5$ does check. The only solution is $t = 5$.

Chapter Test

Write each principal square root.

1 $\sqrt{3600}$
  60

3 $\sqrt{4x^2 - 24x + 36}$
  $2(x-3)$

2 $\sqrt{3^2 + 4^2}$
  5

4 $\sqrt{(-17)^2}$
  17

Write each expression without a radical sign.

5 $\sqrt[3]{\dfrac{-8}{343}}$
  $-\frac{2}{7}$

7 $\dfrac{1}{3}\sqrt[5]{\dfrac{3^{12}(x-2)^7}{9x^2 - 36x + 36}}$
  $3(x-2)$

6 $\dfrac{1}{2}\sqrt{\dfrac{256}{81}}$
  $\frac{8}{9}$

8 $\dfrac{1}{\sqrt[3]{\dfrac{-27}{64}}}$
  $-\frac{4}{3}$

Simplify each expression.

9 $\sqrt{75x^2}$
  $5x\sqrt{3}$

12 $8x\sqrt[3]{4x^2} \cdot \sqrt[3]{10x^4}$
  $16x^3\sqrt[3]{5}$

10 $-2\sqrt{5} \cdot 6\sqrt{15}$
  $-60\sqrt{3}$

13 $(x + y) \div \sqrt[3]{(x + y)^2}$
  $\sqrt[3]{x+y}$

11 $\dfrac{\sqrt{75}}{\sqrt{3}}$
  5

14 $\sqrt{\dfrac{5}{8x^3}}$
  $\frac{1}{4x^2}\sqrt{10x}$

Find each sum or difference.

15 $\sqrt{9x} - \sqrt{x}$
  $2\sqrt{x}$

17 $\sqrt{\dfrac{1}{3}} + \sqrt{\dfrac{1}{12}} - \sqrt{\dfrac{3}{4}}$
  0

16 $\sqrt{500} + \sqrt{125} - \sqrt{20}$
  $13\sqrt{5}$

18 $\sqrt[3]{32} - 5\sqrt[3]{-27} - 2\sqrt[3]{256}$
  $15 - 6\sqrt[3]{4}$

Write each expression in standard (simplest) form.

19 $-2x\sqrt[3]{\dfrac{-27}{64}}$
  $\frac{3}{2}x$

20 $\dfrac{1 + \sqrt{2}}{1 - \sqrt{2}}$
  $-(1+\sqrt{2})^2$

Solve and check.

21 $\sqrt{x - 4} = 6$
  $x = 40$

23 $-2\sqrt{x - 1} = 8$
  no solution

22 $\sqrt{y} - 3 = 7$
  $y = 100$

24 $\sqrt{15 \div (c + 3)} = 5$
  $c = -2\frac{2}{5}$

Problem Set: A Square Root Algorithm

There are several ways to find the square root of a number, without a calculator or a table. One way is to use a method of successive approximations. (See page 443 for successive approximations to a cube root.) Another **algorithm**, or step-by-step method, is a direct but complicated procedure for extracting a square root.

■ Find $\sqrt{73891}$ to the nearest whole number.

Step 1   Starting from the decimal point, rewrite the number in two-digit groups. (The last group may have one digit or two digits.)

$$\sqrt{7\ 38\ 91.00}$$

Step 2   Above the first group, write the square root of the greatest square in that group. Square the number and subtract. "Bring down" the next group.

$$\begin{array}{r} 2\quad\quad. \\ \sqrt{7\ 38\ 91.00} \\ \underline{4\quad\quad\quad\quad} \\ 3\ 38 \end{array}$$

Step 3   Multiply the digit in the square root by 20, and add a number n. That number n is the next digit in the square root, and $n(40 + n)$ cannot be greater than 338.

$$\begin{array}{r} 2\ \ 7\quad. \\ \sqrt{7\ 38\ 91.00} \\ \underline{4\quad\quad\quad\quad} \\ 3\ 38 \\ 47\quad\underline{3\ 29} \\ 9 \end{array}$$

Step 4   Subtract, and bring down the next group.

Step 5   Multiply the digits in the square root by 20, and add a number n. That number n is the next digit in the square root, and $n(540 + n) \le 991$. Subtract and bring down the next group.

$$\begin{array}{r} 2\ \ 7\ \ 1. \\ \sqrt{7\ 38\ 91.00} \\ \underline{4\quad\quad\quad\quad} \\ 3\ 38 \\ 47\quad\underline{3\ 29} \\ 9\ 91 \\ 541\quad\underline{5\ 41} \\ 4\ 50\ 00 \end{array}$$

Then repeat step 5 for as many digits as needed. To the nearest whole number, the square root of 73891 is 272.

$$\begin{array}{r} 2\ \ 7\ \ 1\ .\ 8 \\ \sqrt{7\ 38\ 91.00} \\ \underline{4\quad\quad\quad\quad} \\ 3\ 38 \\ 47\quad\underline{3\ 29} \\ 9\ 91 \\ 541\quad\underline{5\ 41} \\ 4\ 50\ 00 \\ 5428\quad\underline{4\ 34\ 24} \\ 15\ 76 \end{array}$$

7–8)

$$\begin{array}{r} 1.4\ \ 1\ \ 4\ \ 2\ \ 1\ \ 3\ \ 5\ \ 6\ \ 2\ \ 3\ 7 \\ \sqrt{2.00\ 00\ 00\ 00\ 00\ 00\ 00\ 00\ 00\ 00\ 00} \end{array}$$

9)

$$\begin{array}{r} 2.2\ \ 3\ \ 6\ \ 0\ \ 6\ \ 7\ \ 9 \\ \sqrt{5.00\ 00\ 00\ 00\ 00\ 00\ 00} \\ \underline{4} \\ 1\ 00 \\ 42\quad\underline{84} \\ 16\ 00 \\ 443\quad\underline{13\ 29} \\ 2\cdot71\ 00 \\ 4466\quad\underline{2\ 67\ 96} \\ 3\ 04\ 00 \\ 44720\quad\underline{0} \\ 3\ 04\ 00\ 00 \\ 447206\quad\underline{2\ 68\ 32\ 36} \\ 35\ 67\ 64\ 00 \\ 4472127\quad\underline{31\ 30\ 48\ 89} \\ 4\ 37\ 15\ 11\ 00 \\ 44721349\quad\underline{4\ 02\ 49\ 21\ 41} \\ 34\ 65\ 89\ 59 \end{array}$$

$$\frac{1 + \sqrt{5}}{2} = \frac{3.236068}{2}$$

$$= 1.618034$$

- Find $\sqrt{5539.881}$ to the nearest tenth.

Step 1   Form two-digit groups.

Step 2   The first digit is the square root of the greatest square in the first group.

Step 3   Multiply 7 times 20, and add 4. The number 4 is such that $4(140 + 4) \leq 639$.

Repeat the process in Step 3.

```
              7  4 . 4  3
          √ 55 39.88 10
            49
            ──────
            6 39
   144      5 76
            ──────
            63 88
  1484      59 36
            ──────
            4 52 10
 14883      4 46 49
            ──────────
              · 5 61
```

To the nearest tenth, the square root of 5539.881 is 74.4.

The following description for a three- or four-digit number may provide some explanation of this algorithm.

Consider the two-digit numeral **tu**, where t is the tens digit and u is the units digit. The value of **tu** is $(10t + u)$, and its square is the three- or four-digit number $100t^2 + 20tu + u^2$. Use the algorithm to find $\sqrt{100t^2 + 20tu + u^2}$ (the result should be $10t + u$, or the numeral **tu**).

As a first step, the square root of $100t^2$ is $10t$. By writing the digit **t** in the tens place, it has the value of $10t$. (This corresponds to Step 1 in the algorithm.)

$$\frac{\begin{array}{r} t \\ \hline \end{array}}{\sqrt{100t^2 + 20tu + u^2}}$$

$$\frac{100t^2}{}$$
$$20tu + u^2$$

Notice that $20tu + u^2 = u(20t + u)$. In words, $u(20t + u)$ is the product of the units digit and the value twenty times the tens digit plus the units digit. This corresponds to Step 3 in the algorithm.

Use the Square Root Algorithm to find each value.

1 $\sqrt{196}$ nearest unit

2 $\sqrt{2304}$ nearest unit

3 $\sqrt{3271.84}$ nearest tenth

4 $\sqrt{6807.54}$ nearest tenth

5 $\sqrt{8639.3}$ nearest tenth

6 $\sqrt{0.0018}$ to 4 decimal places

7 $\sqrt{2}$ to 5 decimal places

8 $\sqrt{2}$ to 10 decimal places

9 $\dfrac{1 + \sqrt{5}}{2}$ to 6 decimal places

(This is θ, the Golden Ratio)

1)
```
            1 4
          √ 1 96
            1
            ──
            96
   24       96
```

2)
```
            4 8
          √ 23 04
            16
            ──
            7 04
   88       7 04
```

3)
```
            5 7 . 2
          √ 32 71.84
            25
            ──
            7 71
  107       7 49
            ─────
            22 84
 1142       22 84
```

4)
```
            8 2 . 5 0
          √ 68 07.54 00
            64
            ──
            4 07
  162       3 24
            ─────
            83 54
 1645 .     82 25
            ──────
            1 29 00
16500            0
            ──────
            1 29 00
```

5)
```
            9 2 . 9 4
          √ 86 39.30 00
            81
            ──
            5 39
  182       3 64
            ──────
            1 75 30
 1849       1 66 41
            ──────
            8 89 00
18584       7 43 36
            ──────
            1 45 64
```

6)
```
            .0 4 2 4 2
          √ .00 18 00 00 00
            16
            ──
            2 00
   82       1 64
            ─────
            36 00
  844       33 76
            ──────
            2 24 00
 8482       1 69 64
            ──────
            54 36
```

Chapter 12

QUADRATIC EQUATIONS

For many Basic courses, this chapter will mark the end of the school year.

Section 12.1   Solving Equations with more than one Solution

The old map describes where the treasure was buried:

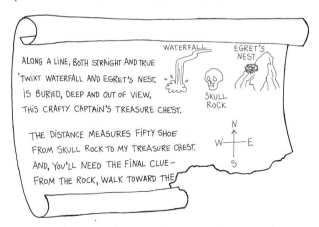

ALONG A LINE, BOTH STRAIGHT AND TRUE
'TWIXT WATERFALL AND EGRET'S NEST,
IS BURIED, DEEP AND OUT OF VIEW,
THIS CRAFTY CAPTAIN'S TREASURE CHEST.

THE DISTANCE MEASURES FIFTY SHOE
FROM SKULL ROCK TO MY TREASURE CHEST.
AND, YOU'LL NEED THE FINAL CLUE—
FROM THE ROCK, WALK TOWARD THE[

The corner is torn; the map doesn't describe whether the treasure is "toward the west" or "toward the nest." Thus there are two locations to dig for the treasure.

In mathematics, equations that have more than one solution are familiar. Most problems that involve absolute value can have two solutions. For example, the equation $|x| = 3$ has two solutions: $x = 3$ or $x = -3$. Other equations with two solutions involve the squares of numbers. The equation $y^2 = 25$ has two solutions: $y = 5$ or $y = -5$.

Sample Problems

1   Solve for all values of the variable:
   a $|3t| = 15$ b $|2w + 3| = 17$

   PROCEDURE   In part **a**, the expression inside the absolute value symbols can be 15 or -15. In part **b**, the expression inside the absolute value symbols can be 17 or -17.

   a $3t = 15$ or $3t = -15$
   $t = 5$ $t = -5$
   The solution is $t = \pm 5$

   b $2w + 3 = 17$ or $2w + 3 = -17$
   $2w = 14$ $2w = -20$
   $w = 7$ $w = -10$
   The solution is $w = 7$ or $w = -10$.

2   Solve for all values of the variable:
   a $n^2 = 4$ b $2m^2 = 20$

   PROCEDURE

   a $n^2 = 4$ b $2m^2 = 20$
   $n = 2$ or $n = -2$ $m^2 = 10$
                                   $m = \sqrt{10}$ or $m = -\sqrt{10}$

3   Solve for all values of the variable:
   a $x(x - 6) = 0$
   b $(2y + 5)(3y - 4) = 0$

   PROCEDURE   If a product equals zero, then at least one of its factors must be zero. This result is called the **Property of a zero product**.

Property

If a and b are real numbers, then the PROPERTY OF A ZERO PRODUCT is that if $ab = 0$, then $a = 0$ or $b = 0$.

In mathematics, the word *or* always includes the possibility of "both." Thus in the zero product property, if $ab = 0$, then a can be zero, b can be zero, or both a and b can be zero.

a $x(x - 6) = 0$
$$x = 0 \quad or \quad x - 6 = 0$$
$$x = 6$$
The solution is:
$$x = 0 \quad or \quad x = 6.$$

b $(2y + 5)(3y - 4) = 0$
$$2y + 5 = 0 \quad or \quad 3y - 4 = 0$$
$$2y = -5 \qquad\qquad 3y = 4$$
$$y = -\tfrac{5}{2} \qquad\qquad y = \tfrac{4}{3}$$
The solution is:
$$y = -\tfrac{5}{2} \quad or \quad y = \tfrac{4}{3}$$

*While **or** is generally used in the inclusive sense, brighter students should be aware that a single variable cannot have two values at the same time. Thus, in part **a**, **x** may have two values, 0 or 6, but **x** cannot equal both 0 and 6 simultaneously.*

Problem Set **A**

ASSIGNMENT GUIDE

Basic ($1\frac{1}{2}$ days)
(1) 2–30 (even)
(2) See p. 482.

Average (1 day)
16, 17, 26–30 (even),
40–56 (even), 58–60

Advanced (1 day)
16, 36, 38, 59–68, 70–76
(even)

1 For the equation $|m| = 11$, how many values can m have?

   2

2 What are the solutions to $|m| = 11$?

   11, −11

3 For the equation $ab = 0$, what must be true about a or b?

   $a = 0$, $b = 0$, or both a and b equal zero

4 If $ab = 0$, can both a and b equal zero?

   yes

Solve each equation.

5 $|x| = 6$
   $x = 6$ or $x = -6$

6 $|x| = 10$
   $x = 10$ or $x = -10$

7 $|2x| = 12$
   $x = 6$ or $x = -6$

8 $|3x| = 15$
   $x = 5$ or $x = -5$

9 $|5x| = 11$
   $x = \frac{11}{5}$ or $x = -\frac{11}{5}$

10 $|4x| = 13$
   $x = \frac{13}{4}$ or $x = -\frac{13}{4}$

11 $|8x| = 2$
   $x = \frac{1}{4}$ or $x = -\frac{1}{4}$

12 $|9x| = 3$
   $x = \frac{1}{3}$ or $x = -\frac{1}{3}$

13 $\left|\frac{1}{2}x\right| = 5$
   $x = 10$ or $x = -10$

14 $\left|\frac{1}{4}x\right| = 3$
   $x = 12$ or $x = -12$

15 $x(x - 4) = 0$
   $x = 0$ or $x = 4$

16 $x(x - 5) = 0$
   $x = 0$ or $x = 5$

17 $x(x + 2) = 0$
   $x = 0$ or $x = -2$

18 $(x - 2)(x - 3) = 0$
   $x = 2$ or $x = 3$

19 $(x + 8)(x + 3) = 0$
   $x = -8$ or $x = -3$

20 $(x + 1)(x + 9) = 0$
   $x = -1$ or $x = -9$

21 $(x - 4)(x + 5) = 0$
   $x = 4$ or $x = -5$

22 $(x + 3)(x - 5) = 0$
   $x = -3$ or $x = 5$

23 $\left(x + \frac{1}{4}\right)(x - 1) = 0$
   $x = -\frac{1}{4}$ or $x = 1$

24 $\left(x - \frac{1}{2}\right)(x + 3) = 0$
   $x = \frac{1}{2}$ or $x = -3$

Factor each trinomial. (Review: Section 6.5)

25 $x^2 + 5x + 6$
$(x + 3)(x + 2)$

26 $x^2 + 14x + 45$
$(x + 9)(x + 5)$

27 $x^2 + x - 6$
$(x + 3)(x - 2)$

28 $x^2 - x - 6$
$(x - 3)(x + 2)$

29 $2x^2 + 3x + 1$
$(2x + 1)(x + 1)$

30 $3x^2 + 5x + 2$
$(3x + 2)(x + 1)$

31 $6x^2 + 5x + 1$
$(3x + 1)(2x + 1)$

32 $2x^2 - 3x - 2$
$(2x + 1)(x - 2)$

33 $5x^2 - 7x + 2$
$(5x - 2)(x - 1)$

34 $6x^2 - 7x + 2$
$(2x - 1)(3x - 2)$

35 $12x^2 + 8x - 15$
$(2x + 3)(6x - 5)$

36 $12x^2 - 11x - 15$
$(3x - 5)(4x + 3)$

37 $12x^2 + 24x - 15$
$(6x - 2)(3x + 5)$

38 $12x^2 - 3x - 15$
$(4x - 5)(3x + 3)$

Problem Set B

Solve each equation.

39 $|y - 4| = 12$
$y = 16 \ or \ y = -6$

40 $|a - 2| = 10$
$a = 12 \ or \ a = -8$

41 $|b + 2| = 6$
$b = 4 \ or \ b = -8$

42 $|c + 3| = 8$
$c = 5 \ or \ c = -11$

43 $|r + 8| = 2$
$r = -6 \ or \ r = -10$

44 $|s + 7| = 3$
$s = -4 \ or \ s = -10$

45 $|x - 5| = 0$
$x = 5$

46 $|2v - 4| = 0$
$v = 2$

47 $|2y + 7| = 1$
$y = -3 \ or \ y = -4$

48 $|3x - 2| = 2$
$x = \frac{4}{3} \ or \ x = 0$

49 $(2x + 1)(x - 5) = 0$
$x = -\frac{1}{2} \ or \ x = 5$

50 $(5y - 1)(y + 3) = 0$
$y = \frac{1}{5} \ or \ y = -3$

51 $3(n - 5)^2 = 27$
$n = 8 \ or \ n = 2$

52 $2(x + 1)^2 = 8$
$x = 1 \ or \ x = -3$

53 $(3a + 4)(2a + 5) = 0$
$a = -\frac{4}{3} \ or \ a = -\frac{5}{2}$

54 $(7t - 4)(2t + 7) = 0$
$t = \frac{4}{7} \ or \ t = -\frac{7}{2}$

55 $(9u - 15)(4u + 12) = 0$
$u = \frac{5}{3} \ or \ u = -3$

56 $(6g + 21)(6g + 12) = 0$
$g = -\frac{1}{3} \ or \ g = -2$

57 $(r + 3)(r + 3) = 0$
$r = -3$

58 $(5p - 2)(5p - 2) = 0$
$p = \frac{2}{5}$

59 David and his cousin Larry have birthdays that are only 9 days apart. David's birthday is June 24. When is Larry's?

59   June 15 *or* July 3

60 Mike's house is on the straight road that goes through Hurleyville. Yesterday, he bicycled 2 miles along the road from his house to his friend's house, which is 3 miles from Hurleyville. Draw a picture showing where Mike's house might be located.

60)

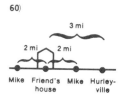

Mike   Friend's   Mike   Hurley-
      house   ville

Problem Set   C

Solve for x. If there is no solution, indicate why.

61 $(x + 7)\left(\dfrac{1}{4}x - 5\right) = 0$

     $x = -7 \; or \; x = 20$

62 $\left(\dfrac{1}{2}x + 8\right)(3x - 5) = 0$

     $x = -16 \; or \; x = \dfrac{5}{3}$

63 $|x + 2| = -6$
     no solution (the absolute value cannot be less than zero)

64 $|2x - 1| = |2x - 1|$
     all real numbers

65 $13 - |2x + 5| = 4$

     $x = 2 \; or \; x = -7$

66 $\dfrac{x + 7}{|x + 7|} = -1$

     all real numbers less than -7

67 $(x - |x|)\cdot\dfrac{1}{x} = |x|$

     $x = -2$

68 $(x - 2)\cdot|x - 2| = 0$
     $x = 2$

69 $|x - 3| + |x + 3| = 0$
     no solution (both $|x -3|$ and $|x +3|$ would have to be zero

70 $3x(x - 1)(x + 1) = 0$
     $x = 0 \; or \; x = -1 \; or \; x = 1$

Define the symbol $)x($,   where $x > 0$, as:

$$)x(= \begin{cases} x & \text{if } x \geq 1 \\ \dfrac{1}{x} & \text{if } 0 < x < 1 \end{cases}$$

Thus $)3(= 3$ and $)\dfrac{1}{2}(= 2.$ Using this information, solve the following:

71 $)x(= 5$

     $x = 5 \; or \; x = \dfrac{1}{5}$

72 $)x(= \dfrac{3}{2}$

     $x = \dfrac{3}{2} \; or \; x = \dfrac{2}{3}$

73 $)x(= 4x$

     $x = \dfrac{1}{2}$

74 $)x - 4(= 2$

     $x = 6 \; or \; x = \dfrac{9}{2}$

75 $)\dfrac{3x}{4}(= 6$

     $x = 8 \; or \; x = \dfrac{2}{9}$

76 $)3x(= 24$

     $x = 8 \; or \; x = \dfrac{1}{72}$

Section 12.2 Solving a Quadratic Equation by Factoring

The term **quadratic** refers to a second-degree expression. Examples of **quadratic terms** are y^2 and $-17z^2$; **quadratic expressions** are $x^2 - 2x + 1$ and $4x^2 + 2$. A **quadratic equation** is an equation, in one variable, with one quadratic term. Examples of quadratic equations in one variable are:

$$3m^2 = 5 \qquad 4y^2 + 2y = \frac{3}{4}y \qquad 6x^2 - 2x + 1 = 0$$

The third example is in the **standard form of a quadratic equation**:

Definition

Students should realize that the restriction $a \neq 0$ implicitly implies that b and c can be zero.

The STANDARD FORM OF A QUADRATIC EQUATION is $ax^2 + bx + c = 0$, where $a, b,$ and c are real numbers and $a \neq 0$.

EXAMPLES

- $3y^2 - 2y - 1 = 0$
- $1.7y^2 - 0.3y = 0$

- $4y^2 + 2 = 0$
- $-6y^2 = 0$

When it is possible to factor a quadratic equation that is in standard form, the equation is easily solved.

Sample Problems

1 Rewrite in standard form and solve:

    a $z^2 = 9$ b $2y^2 = 8y$ c $x^2 = 4x + 5$

PROCEDURE   After writing each equation in standard form, factor the equation, and then apply the property of a zero product.

$$
\begin{array}{rl}
\text{a} & z^2 = 9 \\
\text{ADD } -9: & z^2 - 9 = 0 \\
\text{factor:} & (z - 3)(z + 3) = 0 \\
\text{Therefore} & z - 3 = 0 \quad or \quad z + 3 = 0 \\
& z = 3 \qquad\qquad z = -3
\end{array}
$$

The solution is $z = \pm 3$.

b

$$2y^2 = 8y$$

ADD $-8y$: $\quad 2y^2 - 8y = 0$

MULTBY $\frac{1}{2}$: $\quad y^2 - 4y = 0$

factor: $\quad y(y - 4) = 0$

Therefore $\quad y = 0 \quad or \quad y - 4 = 0$

$$y = 4$$

The solution is $\quad y = 0 \quad or \quad y = 4.$

c

$$x^2 = 4x + 5$$

ADD $-4x$: $\quad x^2 - 4x = 5$

ADD -5: $\quad x^2 - 4x - 5 = 0$

factor: $\quad (x - 5)(x + 1) = 0$

Therefore $\quad x - 5 = 0 \quad or \quad x + 1 = 0$

$$x = 5 \qquad x = -1$$

The solution is $\quad x = 5 \quad or \quad x = -1.$

2 Solve and check: $\quad 11p + 15 = 12p^2$

PROCEDURE

$$11p + 15 = 12p^2$$

ADD $-11p$: $\quad 15 = 12p^2 - 11p$

ADD -15: $\quad 0 = 12p^2 - 11p - 15$

factor: $\quad 0 = (3p - 5)(4p + 3)$

Therefore $\quad 3p - 5 = 0 \quad or \quad 4p + 3 = 0$

$$3p = 5 \qquad\qquad 4p = -3$$

$$p = \frac{5}{3} \qquad\qquad p = -\frac{3}{4}$$

Check each solution:

$$11p + 15 = 12p^2 \qquad\qquad 11p + 15 = 12p^2$$

$$11\left(\frac{5}{3}\right) + 15 \overset{?}{=} 12\left(\frac{5}{3}\right)^2 \qquad 11\left(-\frac{3}{4}\right) + 15 \overset{?}{=} 12\left(-\frac{3}{4}\right)^2$$

$$\frac{55}{3} + \frac{45}{3} \overset{?}{=} 12\left(\frac{25}{9}\right) \qquad \frac{-33}{4} + \frac{60}{4} \overset{?}{=} 12\left(\frac{9}{16}\right)$$

$$\frac{100}{3} \overset{?}{=} \frac{3 \cdot 4 \cdot 25}{3 \cdot 3} \qquad\qquad \frac{27}{4} \overset{?}{=} \frac{4 \cdot 3 \cdot 9}{4 \cdot 4}$$

$$\frac{100}{3} \overset{?}{=} \frac{100}{3} \checkmark \qquad\qquad \frac{27}{4} \overset{?}{=} \frac{27}{4} \checkmark$$

Both solutions check.

3 Solve and check: $\frac{1}{4}x^2 + \frac{1}{4} = \frac{1}{2}x$

PROCEDURE Multiply both sides of the equation by 4, the least common denominator, to clear the equation of fractions. Then write the equation in standard form and solve it.

$$\frac{1}{4}x^2 + \frac{1}{4} = \frac{1}{2}x$$

MULTBY 4: $\quad x^2 + 1 = 2x$

ADD $-2x$: $\quad x^2 - 2x + 1 = 0$

factor: $\quad (x - 1)(x - 1) = 0$

Therefore $x - 1 = 0$ or $x - 1 = 0$

$\quad\quad\quad\quad x = 1 \quad\quad\quad\quad x = 1$

The only solution is $x = 1$.

ASSIGNMENT GUIDE

Basic ($2\frac{1}{2}$ days)
(1) 6–16 (even)
    477: 11–23 (odd)
(2) 17–22, 24, 26, 39, 40
(3) 487: 1–15

Average (3 days)
(1) 6–22 (even), 39, 40
(2) 42–60 (even)
(3) 487: 2–38 (even)

Advanced (3 days)
(1) 39, 40, 42–60 (even)
(2) 61–72
(3) 487: 2–38 (even)

Problem Set **A**

1 A second-degree expression is called a(n) __?__ expression.

    quadratic

2 An equation, in one variable, that has one quadratic term is called a(n) __?__ __?__ .

    quadratic equation

3 The equation $3x^2 - 22x + 5 = 0$ is said to be in __?__ form.

    standard

4 The standard form of a quadratic equation is __?__ .

    $ax^2 + bx + c = 0$

Change to standard form (where necessary) and solve:

5 $a^2 = 4$

    $a = 2 \ or \ a = -2$

6 $2b^2 - 6b = 0$

    $b = 0 \ or \ b = 3$

7 $b^2 + b - 6 = 0$

    $b = -3 \ or \ b = 2$

8 $t^2 - 7t + 6 = 0$

    $t = 6 \ or \ t = 1$

9 $d^2 = 16$

    $d = -4 \ or \ d = 4$

10 $w^2 = 25$

    $w = 5 \ or \ w = -5$

11 $4g^2 - 8g = 0$

    $g = 0 \ or \ g = 2$

12 $3h^2 - 15h = 0$

    $h = 0 \ or \ h = 5$

13 $10x^2 = 4x$

    $x = 0 \ or \ x = \frac{2}{5}$

14 $12y = 8y^2$

    $y = 0 \ or \ y = \frac{3}{2}$

15 $2q = 15 - q^2$

    $q = -5 \ or \ q = 3$

16 $v^2 + 2v = 8$

    $v = -4 \ or \ v = 2$

17 $49 = n^2$

    $n = 7 \ or \ n = -7$

18 $64 = m^2$

    $m = 8 \ or \ m = -8$

19 $b^2 + 12 = 7b$

    $b = 3 \ or \ b = 4$

20 $s^2 + 12s = 13$

    $s = -13 \ or \ s = 1$

21 $2y = 4y^2$

    $y = 0 \ or \ y = \frac{1}{2}$

22 $6x^2 = 2x$

    $x = 0 \ or \ x = \frac{1}{3}$

Solve and check:

23 $t^2 + t = 2$

$t = 1 \ or \ t = -2$

24 $3p = p^2 - 4$

$p = 4 \ or \ p = -1$

25 $6x^2 = 4x$

$x = 0 \ or \ x = \frac{2}{3}$

26 $6x^2 = 9x$

$x = 0 \ or \ x = \frac{3}{2}$

Factor each trinomial. (Review: Section 6.5)

These problems can be used to preview the work with perfect-square trinomials, Section 12.3.

27 $x^2 + 2x + 1$

$(x + 1)(x + 1)$

28 $x^2 - 6x + 9$

$(x - 3)(x - 3)$

29 $x^2 - 4x + 4$

$(x - 2)(x - 2)$

30 $y^2 + 14y + 49$

$(y + 7)(y + 7)$

31 $4x^2 + 4x + 1$

$(2x + 1)(2x + 1)$

32 $9w^2 - 12w + 4$

$(3w - 2)(3w - 2)$

33 $4t^2 + 12t + 9$

$(2t + 3)(2t + 3)$

34 $25a^2 - 70a + 49$

$(5a - 7)(5a - 7)$

35 $b^2 - 10b + 1$

cannot be factored over the integers

36 $d^2 - 5d - 6$

$(d - 6)(d + 1)$

37 $6m^2 + 5m - 6$

$(2m + 3)(3m - 2)$

38 $\frac{1}{4}r^2 - \frac{1}{2}r + \frac{1}{4}$

$(\frac{1}{2}r - \frac{1}{2})(\frac{1}{2}r - \frac{1}{2})$

Problem Set **B**

39 The square of an integer minus five times the integer is equal to negative six. What is the integer?

2 or 3

40 The square of an integer minus four times the integer is equal to five. What is the integer?

5 or −1

Solve for n.

41 $2n^2 - 9n = 5$

$n = -\frac{1}{2} \ or \ n = 5$

42 $6n^2 + n = 2$

$n = \frac{1}{2} \ or \ n = -\frac{2}{3}$

43 $4n^2 + 1 = 4n$

$n = \frac{1}{2}$

44 $9n^2 + 12n + 4 = 0$

$n = -\frac{2}{3}$

45 $4n^2 + 4 = 17n$

$n = \frac{1}{4} \ or \ n = 4$

46 $\frac{1}{3}n^2 + \frac{1}{3}n = \frac{2}{3}$

$n = 1 \ or \ n = -2$

47 $\frac{1}{4}n^2 + \frac{1}{2}n = 2$

$n = -4 \ or \ n = 2$

48 $2n^2 + 15 = 11n$

$n = \frac{5}{2} \ or \ n = 3$

49 $-6 = 24n^2 - 25n$

$n = \frac{3}{8} \ or \ n = \frac{2}{3}$

50 $-56n - 15 = 20n^2$

$n = -\frac{3}{10} \ or \ n = -\frac{5}{2}$

Solve for n.

51 $12n^2 = 29n + 21$

$n = 3 \text{ or } n = -\dfrac{7}{12}$

52 $2 = \dfrac{1}{3}n^2 + \dfrac{5}{6}n$

$n = \dfrac{3}{2} \text{ or } n = -4$

53 $18n^2 = -9n + 20$

$n = \dfrac{5}{6} \text{ or } n = -\dfrac{4}{3}$

54 $\dfrac{1}{4}n^2 - \dfrac{7}{12}n + \dfrac{1}{3} = 0$

$n = \dfrac{4}{3} \text{ or } n = 1$

Solve each equation.

55 $x^2 = 2$

$x = \pm\sqrt{2}$

56 $y^2 - 10 = 0$

$y = \pm\sqrt{10}$

57 $g^2 - 8 = 0$

$g = \pm 2\sqrt{2}$

58 $20 = k^2$

$k = \pm 2\sqrt{5}$

59 $3u^2 = 36$

$u = \pm 2\sqrt{3}$

60 $144 = 2m^2$

$m = \pm 6\sqrt{2}$

Problem Set C

Solve and check.

61 $x^2 + \sqrt{2} \cdot x = 4$

$x = \sqrt{2} \text{ or } x = -2\sqrt{2}$

62 $z^2 + 18 = 5\sqrt{3} \cdot z$

$z = 3\sqrt{3} \text{ or } z = 2\sqrt{3}$

63 $8p^3 = 4p^2$

$p = 0 \text{ or } p = \dfrac{1}{2}$

64 $3g^3 + 6g^2 = 24g$

$g = 0 \text{ or } g = 2 \text{ or } g = -4$

65 $y^3 = y$

$y = 0 \text{ or } y = 1 \text{ or } y = -1$

66 $4u = u^3$

$u = 0 \text{ or } u = 2 \text{ or } u = -2$

67 What two integers satisfy these conditions: its square plus itself equals seventy-two.

$8 \text{ or } -9$

68 Find three integers such that for each one, its cube minus itself equals its square plus itself.

$0, 2 \text{ or } -1$

68) $x^3 - x = x^2 + x$
$x^3 - x^2 - 2x = 0$
$x(x^2 - x - 2) = 0$
$x(x - 2)(x + 1) = 0$
$x = 0 \text{ or } x = 2$
$\text{or } x = -1$

69 For what value(s) of b does the equation $x^2 + 4 = bx$ have just one solution?

$4 \text{ or } -4$

70 Solve for x: $(ax + b)^2 = c^2$

$x = \dfrac{|c| - b}{a}$

71 Solve for a: $(ax + b)^2 = c^2$

$a = \dfrac{|c| - b}{x}$

72 Solve for b: $(ax + b)^2 = c^2$

$b = |c| - ax$

Project: Happy Birthday Two You

In a classroom of fifteen people, do you think it is likely that two people have the same birthday? Is it likely in a class of twenty-five people? How about a group of sixty people? The **probability** that someone else has the same birthday as you is $\frac{1}{365} = 0.00274$ (we won't consider February 29).

$$\text{probability} = \frac{\text{the number of "favorable" outcomes}}{\text{the number of possible outcomes}}$$

For three people, the probability that no two have the same birthday is:

$$1 \cdot \tfrac{364}{365} \cdot \tfrac{363}{365} = 0.99180$$

The probability that there are two people (out of the three) that **do** have the same birthday is $1 - 0.99180 = 0.00820$. If four people are together, the probability that no two have the same birthday is:

$$1 - 1 \cdot \tfrac{364}{365} \cdot \tfrac{363}{365} \cdot \tfrac{362}{365} = 1 - 0.98364 = 0.01636$$

1 For five people, the probability that no two have the same birthday is:

$$1 \cdot \tfrac{364}{365} \cdot \tfrac{363}{365} \cdot \tfrac{362}{365} \cdot \tfrac{361}{365}$$

and the probability that there are two people with the same birthday is 1 minus that value. Calculate these two values.

2 For ten people, the probability that there is at least one pair of identical birthdays is:

$$1 - 1 \cdot \tfrac{364}{365} \cdot \tfrac{363}{365} \cdot \tfrac{362}{365} \cdot \tfrac{361}{365} \cdot \tfrac{360}{365} \cdot \tfrac{359}{365} \cdot \tfrac{358}{365} \cdot \tfrac{357}{365} \cdot \tfrac{356}{365}$$

What is this value?

3 Use a calculator (or even better, a computer) to fill in this table:

number of people	3	5	8	10	15	18	20	22	24	26	28	30
probability that two have the same birthday												

4 When the probability in problem 3 is 0.5 or greater, then there is a 50-50 chance that there will be a birthday match. How many people are necessary in order to have at least a 50-50 chance for a match?

5 How many people are necessary for a 70% chance at a birthday match? How many for a 95% chance? For a 100% chance?

---

1) 0.973, 0.027

2) 0.117

3)
No. of people	Prob. of match
3	0.008
5	0.027
8	0.074
10	0.117
15	0.253
18	0.347
20	0.411
22	0.476
24	0.538
26	0.598
28	0.654
30	0.706

4) at least 23 people (probability of a match is 0.507)

5) 30 people: 0.706
47 people: 0.955

366 people would be needed for a 100% chance

Finding the product of the numerators and the product of the denominators will exceed the capacity of calculators and most computers. Students will have to "chain" their computions:

$364 \div 365 \times 363 \div 365$
$\times 362 \div 365 \times 361 \div \ldots$

485

Xtending the topic: Using Perfect Squares

If $a^2 = b^2$, then $a = \pm b$ (that is, $a = b$ or $a = -b$).

EXAMPLES

- $z^2 = 49$
  $z = \pm 7$

- $y^2 = (n + 5)^2$
  $y = \pm(n + 5)$
  That is, $y = n + 5$ or $y = -(n + 5) = -n - 5$.

- $r^2 = \dfrac{a^2}{b^2}$

  $r = \dfrac{\pm a}{\pm b} = \pm \dfrac{a}{b}$

*Students can substitute values for **a** and **b** to understand why there are only two values for **r** rather than four values.*

Sample Problem

1   Solve each equation:
   a $v^2 + 6v + 9 = 49$
   b $w^2 - 12w + 36 = 7$

PROCEDURE   Rewrite each equation in the form $a^2 = b^2$.

a $v^2 + 6v + 9 = 49$
           $(v + 3)(v + 3) = 49$
              $(v + 3)^2 = 7^2$

Thus $v + 3 = 7$ or $v + 3 = -7$
           $v = 4$ $v = -10$

The solution is $v = 4$ or $v = -10$.

b $w^2 - 12w + 36 = 7$
           $(w - 6)(w - 6) = 7$
              $(w - 6)^2 = 7$

Therefore $w - 6 = \sqrt{7}$ or $w - 6 = -\sqrt{7}$
                      $w = 6 + \sqrt{7}$ $w = 6 - \sqrt{7}$
The solution can be written $w = 6 \pm \sqrt{7}$.

Problem Set **X**

Solve the equations using perfect squares.

1 $y^2 - 4y + 4 = 16$

$y = 6 \text{ or } y = -2$

2 $a^2 - 6a + 9 = 4$

$a = 5 \text{ or } a = 1$

3 $g^2 + 2g + 1 = 9$

$g = 2 \text{ or } g = -4$

4 $x^2 + 10x + 25 = 1$

$x = -6 \text{ or } x = -4$

5 $t^2 + 8t + 16 = 25$

$t = 1 \text{ or } t = -9$

6 $w^2 + 4w + 4 = 9$

$w = 1 \text{ or } w = -5$

7 $r^2 - 6r + 9 = 6$

$r = 3 + \sqrt{6} \text{ or } r = 3 - \sqrt{6}$

8 $h^2 - 16h + 64 = 11$

$h = 8 \pm \sqrt{11}$

9 $z^2 + 10z + 25 = 15$

$z = -5 + \sqrt{15} \text{ or } z = -5 - \sqrt{15}$

10 $u^2 + 12u + 36 = 19$

$u = -6 + \sqrt{19} \text{ or } u = -6 - \sqrt{19}$

11 $4x^2 - 4x + 1 = 4$

$x = \frac{3}{2} \text{ or } x = -\frac{7}{2}$

12 $9y^2 - 6y + 1 = 9$

$y = \frac{4}{3} \text{ or } y = -\frac{2}{3}$

13 $25s^2 + 10s + 1 = 16$

$s = \frac{3}{5} \text{ or } s = -1$

14 $16m^2 + 8m + 1 = 4$

$m = \frac{1}{4} \text{ or } m = -\frac{3}{4}$

15 $49c^2 + 14c + 1 = 64$

$c = 1 \text{ or } c = -\frac{9}{7}$

16 $100d^2 + 20d + 1 = 16$

$d = \frac{3}{10} \text{ or } d = -\frac{1}{2}$

17 $36a^2 - 12a + 1 = 7$

$a = \frac{1 + \sqrt{7}}{6} \text{ or } a = \frac{1 - \sqrt{7}}{6}$

18 $25v^2 + 70v + 49 = 144$

$v = 1 \text{ or } v = -\frac{19}{5}$

19 $64x^2 - 112x + 49 = 36$

$x = \frac{13}{8} \text{ or } x = \frac{1}{8}$

20 $36r^2 - 60r + 25 = 49$

$r = 2 \text{ or } r = -\frac{1}{3}$

21 $16a^2 + 24a + 9 = 17$

$a = \frac{-3 + \sqrt{17}}{4} \text{ or } a = \frac{-3 - \sqrt{17}}{4}$

22 $4y^2 + 28y + 49 = 13$

$y = \frac{-7 + \sqrt{13}}{2} \text{ or } y = \frac{-7 - \sqrt{13}}{2}$

23 $49w^2 - 14w + 1 = 10$

$w = \frac{1 + \sqrt{10}}{7} \text{ or } w = \frac{1 - \sqrt{10}}{7}$

24 $64y^2 - 48y + 9 = 14$

$y = \frac{3 + \sqrt{14}}{8} \text{ or } y = \frac{3 - \sqrt{14}}{8}$

25 $4x + 4 + x^2 = 9$

$x = 1 \text{ or } x = -5$

26 $9 + x^2 - 6x = 64$

$x = 11 \text{ or } x = -5$

27 $1 + 25x^2 - 10x = 16$

$x = 1 \text{ or } x = -\frac{3}{5}$

28 $1 + 12x + 36x^2 = 36$

$x = \frac{5}{6} \text{ or } x = -\frac{7}{6}$

29 $9x^2 + 64 - 48x = 1$

$x = 3 \text{ or } x = \frac{7}{3}$

30 $64 = 20x + 25x^2 + 4$

$x = \frac{6}{5} \text{ or } x = -2$

31 $44r^2 - 132r + 99 = 44$

$r = \frac{5}{2} \text{ or } r = \frac{1}{2}$

32 $2c + 4 + \frac{1}{4}c^2 = 9$

$c = 2 \text{ or } c = -10$

33 $0.36r^2 - 0.6r + 0.25 = 4$

$r = \frac{5}{2} \text{ or } r = -\frac{25}{6}$

34 $0.64b^2 - 0.48b + 0.09 = 1$

$b = \frac{7}{8} \text{ or } b = -\frac{13}{8}$

35 $x^2 - 4x + 4 = 9x^2 - 6x + 1$

$x = -\frac{1}{2} \text{ or } x = \frac{3}{4}$

36 $25x^2 - 20x + 4 = x^2 + 4x + 4$

$x = 1 \text{ or } x = 0$

37 $3f^2 + 6f + 3 = 12f^2 - 12f + 3$

$f = 0 \text{ or } f = -\frac{2}{3}$

38 $2x^2 + 6x + \frac{9}{2} = \frac{1}{2} + 6x + 18x^2$

$x = \frac{1}{2} \text{ or } x = -\frac{1}{2}$

Section 12.3 Forming Perfect-Square Trinomials

Some quadratic equations that contain perfect-square trinomials are simple to solve:

The next sections use "completing the square" to build up to the quadratic formula, Section 12.5. This section is restricted to quadratics with $a = 1$, b even. Odd values for b are introduced in Section 12.3X and Section 12.4 considers quadratics with $a \neq 1$. (The phrase "completing the square" is used in Section 12.4.)

- $x^2 + 6x + 9 = 16$
  $(x + 3)^2 = 16$
  $x + 3 = 4$ or $x + 3 = -4$
  $x = 1$ $x = -7$

- $y^2 - 10y + 25 = 1$
  $(y - 5)^2 = 1$
  $y - 5 = 1$ or $y - 5 = -1$
  $y = 6$ $y = 4$

The quadratic equation $z^2 + 6z = 16$ can be rewritten with a perfect-square trinomial by adding 9 to each side of the equation

$$\begin{aligned} \text{equation:} \qquad & z^2 + 6z = 16 \\ \text{ADD 9:} \qquad & z^2 + 6z + 9 = 16 + 9 \\ \text{factor:} \qquad & (z + 3)^2 = 25 \end{aligned}$$

Thus $z + 3 = 5$ or $z + 3 = -5$
        $z = 2$ $z = -8$

Sample Problems

1 Solve for t:
$$t^2 - 14t = 32$$

PROCEDURE   The key to this expression is in the coefficient of t, which is the number -14. The only perfect-square trinomial that gives $t^2 - 14t$ is the expression $(t - 7)^2$:

$$(t - 7)^2 = t^2 - 14t + 49$$

Notice what happens when 49 is added to each side of the original equation:

$$\begin{aligned} & t^2 - 14t = 32 \\ \text{ADD 49:} \qquad & t^2 - 14t + 49 = 32 + 49 \\ \text{factor:} \qquad & (t - 7)^2 = 81 \end{aligned}$$

Thus $t - 7 = 9$ or $t - 7 = -9$
        $t = 16$ $t = -2$
The solution is $t = 16$ or $t = -2$.

2   Solve for q: $q^2 + 8q = 20$

PROCEDURE   Write a two-step **detour** to find a perfect-square trinomial with the middle term $8q$:

$$q^2 + 8q = 20$$

detour: $\begin{cases} q^2 + 8q + \square = 20 + \square \\ (q + 4)^2 = 20 + \square \end{cases}$

The $\square$ represents the number that makes the left-hand side a perfect-square trinomial.

ADD 16:
$$q^2 + 8q + 16 = 20 + 16$$
$$(q + 4)^2 = 36$$

The "detour" found that adding 16 will make the left-hand side a perfect-square trinomial.

$q + 4 = 6$ *or* $q + 4 = -6$
$q = 2$ $q = -10$

The solution is $q = 2$ *or* $q = -10$.

The steps of the detour show how to write the equation using a perfect-square trinomial. Note that 16 is the square of half the coefficient of q.

3   Solve for n: $n^2 + 10n + 5 = 0$

PROCEDURE   First rewrite the equation with only variables on one side, then rewrite that side as a perfect-square trinomial.

$$n^2 + 10n + 5 = 0$$
ADD -5:
$$n^2 + 10n = -5$$

detour: $\begin{cases} n^2 + 10n + \square = -5 + \square \\ (n + 5)^2 = -5 + \square \end{cases}$

ADD 25: $n^2 + 10n + 25 = -5 + 25$
factor: $(n + 5)^2 = 20$

$n + 5 = \sqrt{20}$ *or* $n + 5 = -\sqrt{20}$
$= \sqrt{4}\sqrt{5}$ $= -\sqrt{4}\sqrt{5}$
$= 2\sqrt{5}$ $= -2\sqrt{5}$
$n = -5 + 2\sqrt{5}$ $n = -5 - 2\sqrt{5}$

The solution is $n = -5 \pm 2\sqrt{5}$.

ASSIGNMENT GUIDE

Basic (optional 1 day)
1–4, 6–30 (even)

Average (3 days)
(1) 6–30 (even)
(2) 13–19 (odd), 31–39
(3) 493: 2–32 (even)

Advanced (3 days)
(1) 6–30 (even), 31–35
(2) 36–48
(3) 493: 2–32 (even), 34, 35

Problems 5–12 can be used as oral exercises by having students state the perfect-square trinomial that has the given quadratic and linear terms.

Problem Set **A**

1 The expression $x^2 + 6x + 9$ is called a(n) __?__ trinomial.

perfect-square

2 The expression $y^2 + 10y + 25$ can be written as $(y + \underline{\;?\;})^2$.

$y^2 + 10y + 25 = (y+5)^2$

3 The expression $z^2 - 12z + \underline{\;?\;}$ is a perfect-square trinomial.

36

4 In order to write the equation $n^2 + 2n = 5$ using a perfect-square trinomial, add the number __?__ to each side of the equation.

1

Solve and check.

5 $x^2 + 6x = 72$
$x = 6 \text{ or } x = -12$

6 $x^2 + 8x = 33$
$x = 3 \text{ or } x = -11$

7 $y^2 - 4y = 12$
$y = 6 \text{ or } y = -2$

8 $z^2 - 10z = 11$
$z = 11 \text{ or } z = -1$

9 $a^2 - 2a = 48$
$a = 8 \text{ or } a = -6$

10 $d^2 - 4d = 77$
$d = 11 \text{ or } d = -7$

11 $g^2 + 12g = 45$
$g = 3 \text{ or } g = -15$

12 $h^2 + 2h = 120$
$h = 10 \text{ or } h = -12$

13 $k^2 + 8k = 1$
$k = 4 + \sqrt{17} \text{ or } k = 4 - \sqrt{17}$

14 $y^2 + 12y = 7$
$y = -6 + \sqrt{43} \text{ or } y = -6 - \sqrt{43}$

15 $m^2 - 10m = 40$
$m = 5 + \sqrt{65} \text{ or } m = 5 - \sqrt{65}$

16 $n^2 - 6n = 7$
$n = 3 + \sqrt{43} \text{ or } n = 3 - \sqrt{43}$

17 $p^2 - 20p = 3$
$p = 10 + \sqrt{103} \text{ or } p = 10 - \sqrt{103}$

18 $r^2 - 14r = 2$
$r = 7 + \sqrt{51} \text{ or } r = 7 - \sqrt{51}$

19 $s^2 + 18s = -40$
$s = -9 + \sqrt{41} \text{ or } s = -9 - \sqrt{41}$

20 $t^2 + 16t = -45$
$t = -8 + \sqrt{19} \text{ or } t = -8 - \sqrt{19}$

Write each expression in standard form. (Review: Chapter 11)

21 $\sqrt{24}$
$2\sqrt{6}$

22 $\sqrt{60}$
$2\sqrt{15}$

23 $\sqrt{18}$
$3\sqrt{2}$

24 $\sqrt{72}$
$6\sqrt{2}$

25 $\dfrac{4 - 2\sqrt{8}}{2}$
$2 - 2\sqrt{2}$

26 $4\sqrt{48}$
$16\sqrt{3}$

27 $6\sqrt{45}$
$18\sqrt{5}$

28 $2\sqrt{27}$
$6\sqrt{3}$

29 $3\sqrt{20}$
$6\sqrt{5}$

30 $\dfrac{-10 + \sqrt{84}}{2}$
$-5 + \sqrt{21}$

Problem Set B

31 The product of two consecutive integers is seventy-two. What is the larger number?

9

32 The product of two consecutive even integers is forty-eight. What is the smaller number?

6

33 The product of a number and ten more than the number is thirty-nine. What is the number?

3 or −13

34 The square of an integer plus eight times the integer is equal to thirty-three. Find the integer.

3 or −11

35 Find one or more integers such that its square plus twelve times the integer is equal to twenty-eight.

2 or −14

36 Find one or more integers such that its square minus ten times the integer is equal to fifty-six.

14 or −4

37 Find one or more integers such that the square of the integer minus four times the integer is equal to six squared.

9 or −4

38 Find one or more integers whose square is equal to forty-five plus four times the integer.

9 or −5

39 Find one or more integers whose square is equal to nineteen minus eighteen times the integer.

−19 or 1

31) $x(x + 1) = 72$

32) $x(x + 2) = 40$

33) $x(x + 10) = 39$

34) $x^2 + 8x = 33$

35) $x^2 + 12x = 28$

36) $x^2 - 10x = 56$

37) $x^2 - 4x = 36$

38) $x^2 = 45 + 4x$

39) $x^2 = 19 - 18x$

Problem Set C

Solve each equation.

40 $\ell^2 + \dfrac{1}{2}\ell - 5 = 0$

$\ell = \dfrac{9}{4}$ or $\ell = -\dfrac{11}{4}$

41 $3y^2 - 36 = -3y$

$y = 3$ or $y = -4$

42 $15x - 3x^2 - 12 = 0$

$x = 4$ or $x = 1$

43 $2x^2 - 30 = 4x$

$x = 5$ or $x = -3$

44 $r^2 + \dfrac{2}{3}r = 7$

$r = \dfrac{7}{3}$ or $r = -3$

45 $15x - 3x^2 + 18 = 0$

$x = 6$ or $x = -1$

46 $e^2 - \dfrac{1}{3}e = 8$

$e = 3$ or $e = \dfrac{-8}{3}$

47 $x^2 = 2(3x - 4)$

$x = 4$ or $x = 2$

48 $z^2 = 3(2z - 3)$

$z = 3$

X tending the topic: Perfect-Square Trinomials with Odd Linear Coefficients

In the quadratic equation $x^2 - 10x = 6$, x^2 is the quadratic term and $-10x$ is the linear term. The equation can be rewritten using a perfect-square trinomial by adding 25 to each side of the equation:

$$x^2 - 10x + 25 = 6 + 25$$
$$(x - 5)^2 = 31$$
$$x - 5 = \sqrt{31} \quad or \quad x - 5 = -\sqrt{31}$$
$$x = 5 \pm \sqrt{31}$$

The number that was added, 25, was the square of half the coefficient of the linear term.

When the coefficient of the linear term is odd (and the coefficient of the quadratic term is 1), the same procedure is used.

Sample Problem

This problem could also be solved by factoring.

1 Solve each quadratic equation:

a $r^2 - 5r + 6 = 0$ **b** $k^2 + k - 7 = -2$

PROCEDURE Rewrite the equation with the variables isolated, and then use the "detour" technique:

a
$$r^2 - 5r + 6 = 0$$
ADD -6: $\qquad r^2 - 5r = -6$

detour:
$$r^2 - 5r + \square = -6 + \square$$
$$\left(r - \frac{5}{2}\right)^2 = -6 + \square$$

Some brighter students may enjoy expressing all their answers using the "±" sign:

$$r = \frac{5}{2} \pm \frac{1}{2}$$

In general, the form is "half the sum plus or minus half the difference"; i.e., the solution $x = a$ *or* $x = b$ *can be written as:*

$$x = \frac{a + b}{2} \pm \frac{a - b}{2}$$

ADD $\frac{25}{4}$: $\quad r^2 - 5r + \dfrac{25}{4} = -6 + \dfrac{25}{4}$

factor: $\qquad \left(r - \dfrac{5}{2}\right)^2 = -\dfrac{24}{4} + \dfrac{25}{4} = \dfrac{1}{4}$

$$r - \frac{5}{2} = \frac{1}{2} \quad or \quad r - \frac{5}{2} = -\frac{1}{2}$$
$$r = \frac{6}{2} \qquad\qquad r = \frac{4}{2}$$

Thus the solution is $r = 3$ or $r = 2$.

b This problem uses the " $\pm$ " sign:

$$k^2 + k - 7 = -2$$

ADD 7: $\qquad k^2 + k = 5$

detour: $\left\{ \begin{array}{l} k^2 + k + \square = 5 + \square \\[2mm] \left(k + \dfrac{1}{2}\right)^2 = 5 + \square \end{array} \right.$

ADD $\frac{1}{4}$: $\qquad k^2 + k + \dfrac{1}{4} = 5 + \dfrac{1}{4}$

factor: $\qquad \left(k + \dfrac{1}{2}\right)^2 = \dfrac{20}{4} + \dfrac{1}{4} = \dfrac{21}{4}$

$$k + \dfrac{1}{2} = \pm\sqrt{\dfrac{21}{4}} = \dfrac{\pm\sqrt{21}}{2}$$

ADD $-\frac{1}{2}$: $\qquad k = -\dfrac{1}{2} \pm \dfrac{\sqrt{21}}{2}$

$$= \dfrac{-1 \pm \sqrt{21}}{2}$$

Problem Set X

Solve each equation.

1 $d^2 + d - 30 = 0$

$d = 5 \text{ or } d = -6$

2 $g^2 - 5g = 14$

$g = 7 \text{ or } g = -2$

3 $r^2 - 3r = 10$

$r = 5 \text{ or } r = -2$

4 $m^2 - m = 20$

$m = 5 \text{ or } m = -4$

5 $j^2 - 7j = -12$

$j = 4 \text{ or } j = 3$

6 $b^2 + 7b = 6$

$b = \dfrac{-7 + \sqrt{73}}{2} \text{ or } b = \dfrac{-7 - \sqrt{73}}{2}$

7 $T^2 + 5T = 8$

$T = \dfrac{-5 + \sqrt{57}}{2} \text{ or } T = \dfrac{-5 - \sqrt{57}}{2}$

8 $a^2 - 11a + 7 = 0$

$a = \dfrac{11 + \sqrt{93}}{2} \text{ or } a = \dfrac{11 - \sqrt{93}}{2}$

9 $c^2 - 5c + 3 = 0$

$c = \dfrac{5 + \sqrt{13}}{2} \text{ or } c = \dfrac{5 - \sqrt{13}}{2}$

10 $L^2 + 5L = -5$

$L = \dfrac{-5 + \sqrt{5}}{2} \text{ or } L = \dfrac{-5 - \sqrt{5}}{2}$

11 $k^2 + 8k - 13 = 0$

$k = -4 + \sqrt{29} \text{ or } k = -4 - \sqrt{29}$

12 $\frac{1}{2}t^2 - 3t + 2 = 0$

$t = -3 + \sqrt{5} \text{ or } t = -3 - \sqrt{5}$

13 $\frac{1}{3}a^2 - a = \frac{10}{3}$

$a = 5 \text{ or } a = -2$

14 $\frac{1}{2}b^2 - \frac{1}{2}b = 10$

$b = 5 \text{ or } b = -4$

15 $3v^2 + 3v - 6 = 0$

$v = -2 \text{ or } v = 1$

16 $2w^2 + 4 = 6w$

$w = 1 \text{ or } w = 2$

17 $0.25s^2 + 1.25s = 2$

$s = \dfrac{5 + \sqrt{57}}{2} \text{ or } s = \dfrac{5 - \sqrt{57}}{2}$

18 $0.5b^2 - 5.5b = -3.5$

$b = \dfrac{11 + \sqrt{93}}{2} \text{ or } b = \dfrac{11 - \sqrt{93}}{2}$

19 $0.2a^2 + 2a + 1.4 = 0$

$a = -5 + 3\sqrt{2} \text{ or } a = -5 - 3\sqrt{2}$

20 $0.1y^2 + 1.6y = 1.4$

$y = -8 + \sqrt{78} \text{ or } y = -8 - \sqrt{78}$

21 $0.1g^2 - g = 1.25$
  $g = 5 + \sqrt{12.5} \text{ or } g = 5 - \sqrt{12.5}$

22 $0.3h^2 + 2.7 = 2.4h$
  $h = 4 + \sqrt{7} \text{ or } h = 4 - \sqrt{7}$

23 $2R^2 + 12R = 12$
  $R = -3 + \sqrt{15} \text{ or } R = -3 - \sqrt{15}$

24 $\dfrac{h^2}{4} + 1 = \dfrac{5h}{4}$
  $h = 4 \text{ or } h = 1$

25 $h^2 + 8h + 13 = 0$
  $h = -4 + \sqrt{3} \text{ or } h = -4 - \sqrt{3}$

26 $\frac{1}{3}J^2 - 2J + \frac{3}{2} = 0$
  $J = -3 + \dfrac{3\sqrt{2}}{2} \text{ or } J = -3 - \dfrac{3\sqrt{2}}{2}$

27 $5x^2 - 30x = 10$
  $x = 3 \pm \sqrt{11}$

28 $\dfrac{k^2}{4} - 5 = \dfrac{k}{4}$
  $k = 5 \text{ or } k = -4$

29) $x^2 + x = 2$

29 Find two integers such that the square of the integer plus itself is equal to two.
  1, −2

30) $x^2 + x = 12$

30 Find two integers such that the square of the integer plus itself is equal to twelve.
  −4, 3

31) $x^2 - 5x = 36$

31 What are two integers such that when five times the integer is subtracted from the square of the integer, the result is thirty-six?
  9, −4

32) $x^2 - 7x = 144$

32 What are two integers such that if seven times the integer is subtracted from the square of the integer, the result is one hundred forty-four?
  16, −9

33) $x^2 + 11x = 45$

33 Find two real numbers such that the sum of the square of the number plus eleven times the number is forty-five.
  $x = \dfrac{-11 + \sqrt{301}}{2} \text{ or } x = \dfrac{-11 - \sqrt{301}}{2}$

34a) $x(3 - x) = 2;$
  $x^2 - 3x + 2 = 0$

  b) $x(9 - x) = -10;$
  $x^2 - 9x - 10 = 0$

  c) $x(-5 - x) = -14;$
  $x^2 + 5x - 14 = 0$

  d) $x(-\frac{7}{2} - x) = -2;$
  $x^2 + \frac{7}{2}x - 2 = 0$

  e) $x(\frac{1}{5} - x) = -\frac{2}{25};$
  $x^2 - \frac{1}{5}x - \frac{2}{25} = 0$

  f) $x(-x) = 7;$
  $x^2 = -7$
  $(x = \pm\, i\sqrt{7})$

  g) $x(-6 - x) = 0;$
  $x^2 + 6x = 0$

  h) $x(-x) = 0;\ x^2 = 0$

  i) $x(1 - x) = -1;$
  $x^2 - x - 1 = 0$

34 Find two numbers such that:

  a their sum is 3 and their product is 2
   (Represent the numbers as x and $3 - x$.)
   2, 1

  b their sum is 9 and their product is −10
   10, −1

  c their sum is −5 and their product is −14
   −7, 2

  d their sum is −3½ and their product is −2
   4, $-\dfrac{1}{2}$

  e their sum is $\dfrac{1}{5}$ and their product is $-\dfrac{2}{25}$
   $\dfrac{2}{5}, -\dfrac{1}{5}$

  f their sum is zero and their product is 7
   no real numbers

  g their sum is −6 and their product is zero
   0, −6

  h their sum is 0 and their product is zero
   0, 0

  i their sum is 1 and their product is −1
   $\dfrac{1 \pm \sqrt{5}}{2}$

35 Compare the coefficients of $ax^2 + bx + c = 0$ and the equations for problem 34. Can you find any patterns?
  the sum of the numbers is $-\dfrac{b}{a}$ and the product is $\dfrac{c}{a}$

Section 12.4 Completing the Square

SECTION SCHEDULE

Basic (optional 1 day)

Average (optional 2 days)

Advanced (2 days)

The method of solving a quadratic equation using a perfect-square trinomial is called **completing the square**. If the coefficient of the quadratic term is not 1, the method can still be used, with one additional step. That step is to multiply both sides of the equation by the reciprocal of the coefficient of the quadratic term.

Sample Problems

1   Solve for x: $4x^2 - 8x = 1$

PROCEDURE   Multiply each side of the equation by the reciprocal of 4.

$$4x^2 - 8x = 1$$

MULTBY $\frac{1}{4}$: $$x^2 - 2x = \frac{1}{4}$$

Students should realize that after the first step, the problem has been "reduced" to a previously-solved problem.

detour:
$$x^2 - 2x + \square = \frac{1}{4} + \square$$
$$(x - 1)^2 = \frac{1}{4} + \square$$

ADD 1: $$x^2 - 2x + 1 = \frac{1}{4} + 1$$

factor: $$(x - 1)^2 = \frac{5}{4}$$

$$x - 1 = \sqrt{\frac{5}{4}} \qquad or \qquad x - 1 = -\sqrt{\frac{5}{4}}$$

$$= \frac{\sqrt{5}}{2} \qquad\qquad\qquad = \frac{-\sqrt{5}}{2}$$

$$x = 1 + \frac{\sqrt{5}}{2} \qquad\qquad x = 1 - \frac{\sqrt{5}}{2}$$

$$= \frac{2}{2} + \frac{\sqrt{5}}{2} \qquad\qquad = \frac{2}{2} - \frac{\sqrt{5}}{2}$$

$$= \frac{2 + \sqrt{5}}{2} \qquad\qquad = \frac{2 - \sqrt{5}}{2}$$

The solution can be written as $x = \dfrac{2 \pm \sqrt{5}}{2}$

2   Solve for y: $3y^2 + 8y = 9$

PROCEDURE   First, multiply each side of the equation by the reciprocal of 3.

$$3y^2 + 8y = 9$$

MULTBY $\frac{1}{3}$: $$y^2 + \frac{8}{3}y = 3$$

detour: $\Bigg\{$
$$y^2 + \frac{8}{3}y + \square = 3 + \square$$
$$\left(y + \frac{4}{3}\right)^2 = 3 + \square$$

ADD $\frac{16}{9}$: $$y^2 + \frac{8}{3}y + \frac{16}{9} = 3 + \frac{16}{9}$$

factor: $$\left(y + \frac{4}{3}\right)^2 = \frac{27}{9} + \frac{16}{9} = \frac{43}{9}$$

$$y + \frac{4}{3} = \pm\frac{\sqrt{43}}{3}$$

ADD $-\frac{4}{3}$: $$y = -\frac{4}{3} \pm \frac{\sqrt{43}}{3}$$

$$= \frac{-4 \pm \sqrt{43}}{3}$$

ASSIGNMENT GUIDE

Basic (optional 1 day)
1–6, 7–19 (odd)

Average (optional 2 days)
(1) 1–6, 7–19 (odd)
(2) 8–30 (even)

Advanced (2 days)
(1) 8–16 (even), 22, 26,
    32–42 (even)
(2) 31–43 (odd), 44–56 (even)

Problem Set **A**

For each quadratic equation, state the coefficient of the quadratic term and state the reciprocal of that coefficient.

1 $2x^2 + 2x = 1$
$2, \frac{1}{2}$

2 $3b^2 - 3b = 1$
$3, \frac{1}{3}$

3 $3a^2 - 4a = 6$
$3, \frac{1}{3}$

4 $\frac{1}{2}q^2 - 1 = -\frac{5}{4}q$
$\frac{1}{2}, 2$

5 $2x^2 + 2x = 1$
$2, \frac{1}{2}$

6 $3b^2 - 3b = 1$
$3, \frac{1}{3}$

Solve by completing the square.

7 $3a^2 - 4a = 6$
$a = \frac{2 \pm \sqrt{22}}{3}$

8 $2y^2 - 7y = 2$
$y = \frac{7 \pm \sqrt{65}}{4}$

9 $6c^2 + 2c = 3$
$c = \frac{-1 \pm \sqrt{19}}{6}$

10 $5T^2 + 6T = 1$
$T = \frac{-3 \pm \sqrt{14}}{5}$

11 $2g^2 + 9g = 2$
$g = \frac{-9 \pm \sqrt{97}}{16}$

12 $4h^2 - h = 4$
$h = \frac{1 \pm \sqrt{65}}{8}$

Solve using any method.

13 $3x^2 - 4 = -2x$
$x = \dfrac{1 \pm \sqrt{13}}{3}$

14 $2d^2 - 5 = -2d$
$d = \dfrac{-1 \pm \sqrt{21}}{2}$

15 $10 - 2x = 3x^2$
$x = \dfrac{-1 \pm \sqrt{31}}{3}$

16 $6 = 4t^2 - 7t$
$t = \dfrac{7 \pm \sqrt{145}}{8}$

17 $5r^2 = 2r$
$r = 0 \text{ or } r = \dfrac{2}{5}$

18 $4 - 6y^2 = 3y$
$y = \dfrac{-3 \pm \sqrt{105}}{12}$

19 $2Q^2 - 7Q + 5 = 0$
$Q = 1 \text{ or } Q = \dfrac{5}{2}$

20 $3h^2 + 2 = 9h$
$h = \dfrac{9 \pm \sqrt{57}}{6}$

Solve each equation for the indicated variable. (Review: Section 3.8)

21 $a = bh$ for h
$h = \dfrac{a}{b}$

22 $A = \dfrac{1}{2}h(B + b)$ for b
$b = \dfrac{2A}{h} - B$

23 $a^2 + b^2 = c^2$ for a
$a = \pm\sqrt{c^2 - b^2}$

24 $p_1v_1 = p_2v_2$ for v_2
$v_2 = \dfrac{p_1v_1}{p_2}$

25 $A = p(1 + rt)$ for r
$r = \dfrac{A - p}{pt}$

26 $e = mc^2$ for c
$c = \pm\sqrt{\dfrac{e}{m}}$

27 $a^2 + b^2 = c^2$ for c
$c = \pm\sqrt{a^2 + b^2}$

28 $V = \dfrac{Bh}{3}$ for B
$B = \dfrac{3V}{h}$

29 $k = mv^2$ for v
$v = \pm\sqrt{\dfrac{k}{m}}$

30 $F = ma$ for a
$a = \dfrac{F}{m}$

Problem Set **B**

Solve by completing the square.

31 $\frac{1}{3}w^2 = 2w - \frac{1}{3}$
$w = 3 \pm 2\sqrt{2}$

32 $\frac{3}{4}B^2 = B + 3$
$B = \dfrac{2 \pm 2\sqrt{10}}{3}$

33 $\frac{2}{5}m^2 - \frac{3}{5}m = 2$
$m = \dfrac{3 \pm \sqrt{89}}{4}$

34 $\frac{1}{2}x^2 - \frac{5}{4} = x$
$x = \dfrac{2 \pm \sqrt{14}}{2}$

35 $0.17t^2 + 0.03t = 0.14$
$t = \dfrac{14}{17} \text{ or } t = -1$

36 $0.8A^2 = 3 - 1.2A$
$A = \dfrac{-3 \pm \sqrt{69}}{4}$

37 $0.6r = 0.2r^2 + 0.3$
$r = \dfrac{-3 \pm \sqrt{3}}{2}$

38 $0.18w = 0.15w^2 - 0.03$
$w = \dfrac{3 \pm \sqrt{14}}{5}$

39 $2x^2 - 7x + 3 = 0$
$x = \dfrac{1}{2} \text{ or } x = 3$

40 $8y^2 + 2y = 3$
$y = \dfrac{1}{2} \text{ or } y = \dfrac{-3}{4}$

41 $0.3R^2 + 0.1R = 1$
$R = \dfrac{5}{3} \text{ or } R = -2$

42 $\frac{1}{2}q^2 - 1 = -\frac{5}{4}q$
$q = \dfrac{5 \pm \sqrt{57}}{4}$

Problem Set C

43) $2w^2 = 4(6w)$

43 The length of a rectangle is twice the width; the number of square units in its area is four times the number of units in its perimeter. What are the dimensions of the rectangle?

$\ell = 24,\ w = 12$

44) $20 = 76t - 16t^2$

44 The distance that a home run ball is above the ground is given approximately by the formula $h = 76t - 16t^2$, where h is the height in feet and t is the time in seconds. How long after the batter hit it does it clear the twenty-foot high fence in center field?

$t = 5$ seconds or less

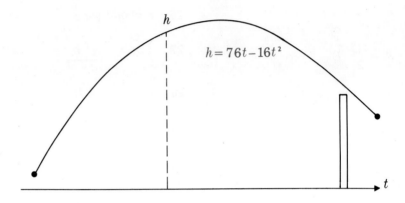

Solve each problem by two methods: completing the square and factoring. Show that the two methods produce the same answer.

45 $2x^2 = 8x$

$x = 0 \ or \ x = 4$

46 $3x^2 = 18x$

$x = 0 \ or \ x = 6$

47 $3y^2 = 48$

$y = 4 \ or \ y = -4$

48 $5a^2 = 45$

$a = 3 \ or \ a = -3$

49 $\frac{1}{3}g^2 + 2g + 3 = 0$

$g = -3$

50 $\frac{1}{8}h^2 + h + 2 = 0$

$h = -4$

51 $2J + 3 = 8J^2$

$J = \frac{3}{4} \ or \ J = \frac{-1}{2}$

52 $z^2 + z = \frac{3}{4}$

$z = \frac{1}{2} \ or \ z = \frac{-3}{2}$

53 $12x^2 - 11x - 15 = 0$

$x = \frac{-3}{4} \ or \ x = \frac{5}{3}$

54 $12x^2 + 8x - 15 = 0$

$x = \frac{5}{6} \ or \ x = -\frac{3}{2}$

55 $\frac{x^2}{a^2} + \frac{2bx}{a} + b^2 = 0$

$x = -ab$

56 $\frac{x^2}{a^2} = b^2$

$x = \pm\sqrt{ab}$

After-School Mathematics: Bakery Assistant

Vivian has an after-school job at a bakery. Several afternoons each week she helps close the store by putting away breads, cakes, and cookies and by cleaning the glass shelves. On Saturday mornings she helps out in the back room.

One Saturday, she was given the job of decorating a birthday cake. She was to put twenty-one yellow frosting roses around the circumference of the cake. The problem was to space them evenly along the circumference.

She solved the problem in this way. She knew that twenty-one was divisible by three, so she put three roses equally spaced around the circumference. She then had eighteen remaining roses to place between those already on the cake, or six roses in each of the three sections. For each section, she carefully noted the point that divided that section in half, and put three roses into that half. When she finished the cake, she counted the roses twice to be sure!

Students could be asked to suggest other "easy" ways to arrange the 21 roses, such as 16 on the circumference, 4 on a concentric circle halfway to the center, and 1 at the center.

Application: License Plates

License plates in state A have two letters followed by four numbers. To determine the number of different license plates that can be made, consider the number of choices for each position on the plates:

$$\left(\begin{matrix}26\\ \text{choices}\end{matrix}\right) \cdot \left(\begin{matrix}26\\ \text{choices}\end{matrix}\right) \cdot \left(\begin{matrix}10\\ \text{choices}\end{matrix}\right) \cdot \left(\begin{matrix}10\\ \text{choices}\end{matrix}\right) \cdot \left(\begin{matrix}10\\ \text{choices}\end{matrix}\right) \cdot \left(\begin{matrix}10\\ \text{choices}\end{matrix}\right)$$

There are 6,760,000 or 6.76×10^6 different license numbers.

License numbers in state B have three letters followed by three numbers, but no letter can be used more than once. License numbers in state C are three letters followed by three numbers, but no number can be used more than once. Which of the three states has the greatest number of different license plate numbers? Which state has the least number?

State A: 6.76×10^6
State B: $26 \cdot 25 \cdot 24 \cdot 10 \cdot 10 \cdot 10$
$\qquad = 1.56 \times 10^7$
State C: $26 \cdot 26 \cdot 26 \cdot 10 \cdot 9 \cdot 8$
$\qquad = 1.265472 \times 10^7$
State B has the greatest number of different plates; state A has the least.

Section 12.5   The Quadratic Formula

The previous 2 sections lead up to the quadratic formula. The steps of obtaining the result are usually called the derivation of the formula.

The problems in this section require students to apply the formula rather than to repeat its derivation.

A quadratic equation written in the form $ax^2 + bx + c = 0$, where a, b, and c are real numbers, $a \neq 0$, is said to be in **standard form**. The method of completing the square can be applied to the standard form equation. The solution, after about a dozen steps, is the following:

$$x = \frac{-b + \sqrt{b^2 - 4ac}}{2a} \quad \text{or} \quad x = \frac{-b - \sqrt{b^2 - 4ac}}{2a}$$

The steps toward the solution are the following:

$$ax^2 + bx + c = 0$$

$$\text{ADD } -c: \qquad ax^2 + bx = -c$$

$$\text{MULTBY } \frac{1}{a}: \qquad x^2 + \frac{b}{a}x = -\frac{c}{a}$$

detour:

$$x^2 + \frac{b}{a}x + \square = -\frac{c}{a} + \square$$

$$\left(x + \frac{b}{2a}\right)^2 = -\frac{c}{a} + \square$$

$$\text{ADD } \frac{b^2}{4a^2}: \qquad x^2 + \frac{b}{a}x + \frac{b^2}{4a^2} = -\frac{c}{a} + \frac{b^2}{4a^2}$$

$$\text{factor:} \qquad \left(x + \frac{b}{2a}\right)^2 = -\frac{4ac}{4a^2} + \frac{b^2}{4a^2} = \frac{b^2 - 4ac}{4a^2}$$

$$x + \frac{b}{2a} = \sqrt{\frac{b^2 - 4ac}{4a^2}} \quad \text{or} \quad x + \frac{b}{2a} = -\sqrt{\frac{b^2 - 4ac}{4a^2}}$$

$$= \frac{\sqrt{b^2 - 4ac}}{2a} \qquad\qquad = \frac{-\sqrt{b^2 - 4ac}}{2a}$$

$$x = -\frac{b}{2a} + \frac{\sqrt{b^2 - 4ac}}{2a} \qquad x = -\frac{b}{2a} + \frac{-\sqrt{b^2 - 4ac}}{2a}$$

$$= \frac{-b + \sqrt{b^2 - 4ac}}{2a} \qquad\qquad = \frac{-b - \sqrt{b^2 - 4ac}}{2a}$$

The solution can be written as:

$$x = \frac{-b \pm \sqrt{b^2 - 4ac}}{2a}$$

This expression is called the **quadratic formula**.

Sample Problems

These Sample Problems can also be solved by factoring. Section 12.5X uses the quadratic formula for expressions that cannot be factored over the integers.

1 Use the quadratic formula to solve $3x^2 + 7x - 6 = 0$.

PROCEDURE Comparing the equation to the standard form equation, $a = 3, b = 7, c = -6$. Substitute these values into the quadratic formula:

$$x = \frac{-b \pm \sqrt{b^2 - 4ac}}{2a}$$

$$= \frac{-(7) \pm \sqrt{(7)^2 - 4(3)(-6)}}{2(3)}$$

$$= \frac{-7 \pm \sqrt{49 - (-72)}}{6}$$

$$= \frac{-7 \pm \sqrt{121}}{6}$$

$$= \frac{-7 \pm 11}{6}$$

Thus $x = \dfrac{-7 + 11}{6} = \dfrac{4}{6} = \dfrac{2}{3}$ or $x = \dfrac{-7 - 11}{6} = \dfrac{-18}{6} = -3$

2 Solve using the quadratic formula:

a $20y^2 - 37y + 15 = 0$ **b** $9t = 5 - 2t^2$

PROCEDURE

a $20y^2 - 37y + 15 = 0$. Thus $a = 20, b = -37, c = 15$.

$$y = \frac{-b \pm \sqrt{b^2 - 4ac}}{2a}$$

$$= \frac{-(-37) \pm \sqrt{(-37)^2 - 4(20)(15)}}{2(20)}$$

$$= \frac{37 \pm \sqrt{1369 - 1200}}{40}$$

$$= \frac{37 \pm \sqrt{169}}{40}$$

$$= \frac{37 \pm 13}{40}$$

Thus $y = \dfrac{37 + 13}{40} = \dfrac{50}{40} = \dfrac{5}{4}$ or $y = \dfrac{37 - 13}{40} = \dfrac{24}{40} = \dfrac{3}{5}$

b Write the equation in standard form:

$$9t = 5 - 2t^2$$

ADD $2t^2$: $\qquad 2t^2 + 9t = 5$

ADD -5: $\quad 2t^2 + 9t - 5 = 0$

Thus $a = 2$, $b = 9$, $c = -5$.

$$t = \frac{-b \pm \sqrt{b^2 - 4ac}}{2a}$$

$$= \frac{-9 \pm \sqrt{9^2 - 4(2)(-5)}}{2(2)}$$

$$= \frac{-9 \pm \sqrt{81 + 40}}{4}$$

$$= \frac{-9 \pm \sqrt{121}}{4}$$

$$= \frac{-9 \pm 11}{4}$$

Then $\quad t = \dfrac{-9 + 11}{4} = \dfrac{2}{4} = \dfrac{1}{2}$ $\quad or \quad$ $t = \dfrac{-9 - 11}{4} = \dfrac{-20}{4} = -5$

ASSIGNMENT GUIDE

Basic (3 days)
(1) 5–25 (odd)
(2) 6–26 (even)
(3) 505: 1–8, 26

Average (3 days)
(1) 5–31 (odd)
(2) 6–30 (even)
(3) 505: 12–32 (even)

Advanced (3 days)
(1) 5–35 (odd)
(2) 6–34 (even)
(3) 505: 12–36 (even), 38–43

Problem Set **A**

1 The standard form of a quadratic equation is __?__, where a, b, and c are real numbers, $a \neq 0$.

$\quad ax^2 + bx + c = 0$

2 The expression $\quad x = \dfrac{-b \pm \sqrt{b^2 - 4ac}}{2a}$ is called the __?__ __?__.

$\quad$ quadratic formula

3 The denominator in the quadratic formula is __?__.

$\quad 2a$

4 The radicand in the quadratic formula is __?__.

$\quad b^2 - 4ac$

Solve each equation using the quadratic formula.

5 $2x^2 - 5x + 3 = 0$

$\quad x = \frac{3}{2} \text{ or } x = 1$

6 $3x^2 - 11x + 10 = 0$

$\quad x = 2 \text{ or } x = \frac{5}{3}$

7 $4x^2 + 13x - 12 = 0$

$\quad x = \dfrac{-13 \pm \sqrt{354}}{4}$

8 $4x^2 + 7x - 15 = 0$

$\quad x = \frac{5}{4} \text{ or } x = -3$

9 $2x^2 - 3x - 14 = 0$

$\quad x = \frac{7}{2} \text{ or } x = -2$

10 $2x^2 - x - 55 = 0$

$\quad x = \frac{11}{2} \text{ or } x = -5$

11 $3x^2 + 16 = 16x$

$\quad x = \frac{4}{3} \text{ or } x = 4$

12 $4x^2 + 9 = 15x$

$\quad x = \frac{3}{4} \text{ or } x = 3$

Solve each equation.

13 $4x^2 + 3 = 8x$
$x = \dfrac{3}{2}$ or $x = \dfrac{1}{2}$

14 $15x^2 + 15 = 34x$
$x = \dfrac{3}{5}$ or $x = \dfrac{5}{3}$

15 $3x^2 + 23x = -14$
$x = \dfrac{-2}{3}$ or $x = -7$

16 $2x^2 + 17x = -30$
$x = \dfrac{-5}{2}$ or $x = -6$

17 $6x^2 + 5x = 6$
$x = \dfrac{-3}{2}$ or $x = \dfrac{2}{3}$

18 $12 = 20x^2 + x$
$x = \dfrac{3}{4}$ or $x = \dfrac{-4}{5}$

19 $7 = 6x^2 - 19x$
$x = \dfrac{-1}{3}$ or $x = \dfrac{7}{2}$

20 $12x^2 - 23x = 24$
$x = \dfrac{-3}{4}$ or $x = \dfrac{8}{3}$

Write each radical in standard form. (Review: Section 11.6)

21 $\sqrt{180}$
$6\sqrt{5}$

22 $\sqrt{294}$
$7\sqrt{6}$

23 $\sqrt{112}$
$4\sqrt{7}$

24 $\sqrt{192}$
$8\sqrt{3}$

25 $\sqrt{324}$
18

26 $\sqrt{242}$
$11\sqrt{2}$

Problem Set **B**

Solve using the quadratic formula.

27   Six times the square of a number, plus the number, plus six, is equal to seven. Find two rational numbers for which this is true.
$x = \dfrac{1}{3}$ or $x = \dfrac{-1}{2}$

27) $6x^2 + x + 6 = 7$

28   Find two rational numbers such that four times the difference found by subtracting the number from its square is equal to thirty-five.
$x = \dfrac{-5}{2}$ or $x = \dfrac{7}{2}$

28) $4(x^2 - x) = 35$

29   The sum of twenty-four times the square of a rational number and thirty-five is the same as the product of the number and fifty-eight. What is the number?
$x = \dfrac{7}{6}$ or $x = \dfrac{5}{4}$

29) $24x^2 + 35 = 58x$

30   Find the positive rational number such that when twice the number is subtracted from ninety-nine times its square, the result is one hundred twenty.
$x = \dfrac{10}{9}$ or $x = \dfrac{-12}{11}$

30) $99x^2 - 2x = 120$

31   Find the negative rational number such that when twenty-nine times the number is added to two hundred eight times its square, the result is two hundred ten.
$\dfrac{-195}{208}$

31) $208x^2 + 29x = 210$

Problem Set C

Solve by any method.

32 $323x^2 + 964x + 713 = 0$
$$x = \frac{-437}{323} \; or \; x = \frac{-527}{323}$$

33 $1961x^2 - 3935x + 1724 = 0$
$$x = \frac{3935 \pm \sqrt{9161169}}{3922}$$

34 $\frac{1}{36}x^2 + \frac{5}{2}x + 36 = 0$
$$x = -72 \; or \; x = -18$$

35 $0.01x^2 + 0.207x + 0.014 = 0$
$$x = \frac{-207 \pm \sqrt{42289}}{20}$$

X tending the topic: Irrational Solutions from the Quadratic Formula

In the quadratic formula, the radicand $b^2 - 4ac$ is called the **discriminant**. When the discriminant $b^2 - 4ac$ is a positive number that is not a perfect square, the solutions to the original equation will be irrational numbers.

Sample Problem

1 Solve each equation:

  a $3x^2 + 5x + 1 = 0$ **b** $x^2 - 6x - 2 = 0$

  PROCEDURE   Both equations are already in standard form.

  a The values of the coefficients are $a = 3, b = 5, c = 1$:

$$x = \frac{-b \pm \sqrt{b^2 - 4ac}}{2a}$$

$$= \frac{-5 \pm \sqrt{5^2 - 4(3)(1)}}{2(3)}$$

$$= \frac{-5 \pm \sqrt{25 - 12}}{6}$$

$$= \frac{-5 \pm \sqrt{13}}{6}$$

The solution can be left as it is or it can be written as:

$$x = \frac{-5 + \sqrt{13}}{6} \quad or \quad x = \frac{-5 - \sqrt{13}}{6}$$

b $a = 1, b = -6, c = -2$

$$x = \frac{-b \pm \sqrt{b^2 - 4ac}}{2a}$$

$$= \frac{-(-6) \pm \sqrt{(-6)^2 - 4(1)(-2)}}{2(1)}$$

$$= \frac{6 \pm \sqrt{36 + 8}}{2}$$

$$= \frac{6 \pm \sqrt{44}}{2}$$

$$= \frac{6 \pm \sqrt{4 \cdot 11}}{2}$$

$$= \frac{6 \pm 2\sqrt{11}}{2}$$

$$= 3 \pm \sqrt{11}$$

In part **a**, notice that the two values of x can be written as:

$$\frac{-5 + \sqrt{13}}{6} = -\frac{5}{6} + \frac{\sqrt{13}}{6}$$

$$\frac{-5 - \sqrt{13}}{6} = -\frac{5}{6} - \frac{\sqrt{13}}{6}$$

In part **b**, the values of x are $3 + \sqrt{11}$ and $3 - \sqrt{11}$. Each pair of values are **conjugates**. In general, the two solutions to a quadratic equation will be conjugates.

Problem Set **X**

Solve each quadratic equation.

1 $2x^2 + 7x + 4 = 0$
$$x = \frac{-7 \pm \sqrt{17}}{4}$$

2 $x^2 - 3x - 5 = 0$
$$x = \frac{3 \pm \sqrt{29}}{2}$$

3 $x^2 + 5x - 2 = 0$
$$x = \frac{-5 \pm \sqrt{33}}{2}$$

4 $3n^2 + 7n + 3 = 0$
$$n = \frac{-7 \pm \sqrt{13}}{6}$$

5 $8e^2 - 3e - 1 = 0$
$$e = \frac{3 \pm \sqrt{41}}{6}$$

6 $5y^2 - 5y + 1 = 0$
$$y = \frac{5 \pm \sqrt{5}}{10}$$

7 $4p^2 - 5p - 2 = 0$
$$p = \frac{5 \pm \sqrt{57}}{8}$$

8 $3t^2 + 7t + 1 = 0$
$$t = \frac{-7 \pm \sqrt{37}}{6}$$

9 $7n^2 - n = 1$
$$n = \frac{1 \pm 5\sqrt{2}}{14}$$

10 $2r^2 = 2r + 2$
$$r = \frac{1 \pm \sqrt{5}}{2}$$

11 $3a^2 + 2a - 7 = 0$

$a = \dfrac{-1 \pm \sqrt{11}}{3}$

12 $b^2 + 8b + 2 = 0$

$b = -4 \pm \sqrt{14}$

13 $4k^2 + 8k + 1 = 0$

$k = \dfrac{-2 \pm \sqrt{3}}{2}$

14 $3h^2 - 6h + 1 = 0$

$h = \dfrac{3 \pm \sqrt{6}}{3}$

15 $3c^2 - 6c + 2 = 0$

$c = \dfrac{3 \pm \sqrt{3}}{3}$

16 $2M^2 - 10M + 5 = 0$

$M = \dfrac{5 \pm \sqrt{15}}{2}$

17 $5d^2 + 12d + 3 = 0$

$d = \dfrac{-6 \pm \sqrt{21}}{5}$

18 $3g^2 + 4g - 2 = 0$

$g = \dfrac{-2 \pm \sqrt{10}}{3}$

19 $6x^2 - 9x + 1 = 0$

$x = \dfrac{9 \pm \sqrt{57}}{12}$

20 $4T^2 + 7T - 3 = 0$

$T = \dfrac{-7 \pm \sqrt{97}}{8}$

21 $12x = 10x^2 + 1$

$x = \dfrac{6 \pm \sqrt{26}}{10}$

22 $11b = 8b^2 + 3$

$b = 1 \ or \ b = \dfrac{3}{8}$

23 $8K - 4 = 3K^2$

$K = -2 \ or \ K = \dfrac{-2}{3}$

24 $r - r^2 = 7r$

$r = 0 \ or \ r = -6$

25 $a^2 - 5 = 0$

$a = \pm \sqrt{5}$

26 $b^2 = 7$

$b = \pm \sqrt{7}$

27 $2c^2 = 9$

$c = \pm \dfrac{3\sqrt{2}}{2}$

28 $d^2 + d = 1$

$d = \dfrac{-1 \pm \sqrt{5}}{2}$

29 $5 - e^2 = 3e$

$e = \dfrac{-3 \pm \sqrt{29}}{2}$

30 $5f^2 + f = 1$

$f = \dfrac{-1 \pm \sqrt{21}}{10}$

31 $(g + 1)(g - 2) = 3$

$g = \dfrac{1 \pm \sqrt{21}}{2}$

32 $(h - 3)(h + 5) = 5$

$h = -1 \pm \sqrt{21}$

33 $(3 + k)(3 - k) = 1$

$k = \pm 2\sqrt{2}$

34 $(m - 7)(7 - m) - 1 = 0$

$m = \pm 4\sqrt{3}$

35 $(n - 2)n - 2 = 0$

$n = 1 \pm \sqrt{3}$

36 $(p - 3)p - 3 = 0$

$p = \dfrac{3 \pm \sqrt{21}}{2}$

37 $(q - 5)q - 5 = 0$

$q = \dfrac{5 \pm 3\sqrt{5}}{2}$

38 $(r - 6)r - 6 = 0$

$r = 3 \pm \sqrt{15}$

39 Find the sum of the two solutions of the equation $ax^2 + bx + c = 0$.

sum is $\dfrac{-b}{a}$

40 Find the product of the two solutions of the equation $ax^2 + bx + c = 0$.

$\dfrac{c}{a}$

41 If one of the solutions of a quadratic equation is a rational number, must the other solution be rational?

yes (if the coefficients are rational numbers)

42 If one of the solutions to a quadratic equation is an irrational number, must the other solution be irrational?

yes (if the coefficients are rational numbers)

43 If one of the solutions to a quadratic equation is an integer, must the other solution also be an integer?

no

Section 12.6 Equations that Yield Quadratics

SECTION SCHEDULE

Basic (optional 1 day)

Average (2 days)

Advanced (2 days)

To solve an equation that contains fractions, a useful first step is to multiply each side of the equation by the least common denominator (LCD). That step results in an equivalent equation with no fractions.

When an equation contains variables in the denominator of a fraction, multiplying each side of the equation by the LCD often results in a quadratic equation. The quadratic equation can be solved by factoring, by using the quadratic formula, or by any other appropriate method.

The process of eliminating a variable from a denominator may introduce an extraneous solution. (See Sample Problem 2, p. 509.)

EXAMPLE

- Find all numbers such that the sum of the number and its reciprocal is $2\frac{1}{6}$.

If n represents the number, then $\dfrac{1}{n}$ is its reciprocal.

$$n + \frac{1}{n} = 2\tfrac{1}{6}$$

$$n + \frac{1}{n} = \frac{13}{6}$$

MULTBY $6n$:
$$6n\left(n + \frac{1}{n}\right) = 6n\left(\frac{13}{6}\right)$$

$$6n^2 + 6 = 13n$$

ADD $-13n$:
$$6n^2 - 13n + 6 = 0$$

Use the quadratic formula with $a = 6$, $b = -13$, $c = 6$:

$$n = \frac{-b \pm \sqrt{b^2 - 4ac}}{2a}$$

$$= \frac{-(-13) \pm \sqrt{(-13)^2 - 4(6)(6)}}{2(6)}$$

$$= \frac{13 \pm \sqrt{169 - 144}}{12}$$

$$= \frac{13 \pm \sqrt{25}}{12}$$

$$= \frac{13 \pm 5}{12}$$

Thus $n = \dfrac{13 + 5}{12} = \dfrac{18}{12} = \dfrac{3}{2}$ or $n = \dfrac{13 - 5}{12} = \dfrac{8}{12} = \dfrac{2}{3}$

Sample Problems

1 Find the number(s), to the nearest thousandth, for which the reciprocal is one less than the number.

PROCEDURE   Let r represent the number, and $\dfrac{1}{r}$ be its reciprocal.

$$\frac{1}{r} = r - 1$$

MULTBY r: $r\left(\dfrac{1}{r}\right) = r(r - 1)$

$$1 = r^2 - r$$

ADD -1: $0 = r^2 - r - 1$

Use the quadratic formula with $a = 1, b = -1, c = -1$:

$$r = \frac{-b \pm \sqrt{b^2 - 4ac}}{2a}$$

$$= \frac{-(-1) \pm \sqrt{(-1)^2 - 4(1)(-1)}}{2(1)}$$

$$= \frac{1 \pm \sqrt{1 + 4}}{2}$$

$$= \frac{1 \pm \sqrt{5}}{2}$$

Using a calculator (or a table of square roots), the values, to the nearest thousandth, are 1.618 and -0.618.

2 Solve and check:

$$\frac{x}{x - 3} = \frac{x - 1}{2x - 6}$$

PROCEDURE   Find the cross-product of the proportion.

$$\frac{x}{x - 3} = \frac{x - 1}{2x - 6}$$

$$x(2x - 6) = (x - 1)(x - 3)$$

$$2x^2 - 6x = x^2 - 4x + 3$$

$$x^2 - 6x = -4x + 3$$

$$x^2 - 2x = 3$$

$$x^2 - 2x - 3 = 0$$

Use the quadratic formula with $a = 1, b = -2, c = -3$, or, for this problem, factor the trinomial:

$$(x - 3)(x + 1) = 0$$
$$x - 3 = 0 \quad or \quad x + 1 = 0$$
$$x = 3 \qquad\qquad x = -1$$

Check $x = 3$:

$$\frac{x}{x - 3} = \frac{x - 1}{2x - 6}$$

$$\frac{3}{3 - 3} \overset{?}{=} \frac{3 - 1}{2(3) - 6}$$

$$\frac{3}{0} \overset{?}{=} \frac{2}{0}$$

Does not check.

Check $x = -1$:

$$\frac{x}{x - 3} = \frac{x - 1}{2x - 6}$$

$$\frac{-1}{-1 - 3} \overset{?}{=} \frac{-1 - 1}{2(-1) - 6}$$

$$\frac{-1}{-4} \overset{?}{=} \frac{-2}{-8}$$

$$\frac{1}{4} \overset{?}{=} \frac{1}{4} \checkmark$$

The value of 3 for x does not check, but $x = -1$ does check. The "solution" $x = 3$ is called an **extraneous solution** to the equation; it seems to be a solution to an equation, but it does not satisfy the equation.

Problem Set **A**

Solve each equation. Be sure to check for extraneous solutions.

1 $\dfrac{x}{9} = \dfrac{1}{4x}$

$x = \pm \dfrac{3}{2}$

2 $y = \dfrac{4}{y}$

$y = \pm 2$

3 $\dfrac{g + 3}{2} = -\dfrac{1}{g}$

$g = -2 \text{ or } g = -1$

4 $\dfrac{-2}{2A} = \dfrac{A + 8}{-9}$

$A = -9 \text{ or } A = 1$

5 $\dfrac{r^2 - 12}{r} = 1$

$r = 4 \text{ or } r = -3$

6 $\dfrac{2}{t} = \dfrac{6 - t}{4}$

$t = 2 \text{ or } t = 4$

7 $\dfrac{d}{2} = \dfrac{1 - d}{4d}$

$d = \dfrac{1}{2} \text{ or } d = -1$

8 $\dfrac{k - 4}{3} = \dfrac{k - 4}{k}$

$k = 3 \text{ or } k = 4$

9 $\dfrac{25x}{2} = \dfrac{10x + 1}{x + 1}$

$x = \dfrac{1}{5} \text{ or } x = \dfrac{-2}{5}$

10 $\dfrac{2x}{-3} = \dfrac{x + 1}{x + 2}$

$x = \dfrac{-1}{2} \text{ or } x = -3$

11 $Q - 2 = \dfrac{3}{Q}$

$Q = 3 \text{ or } Q = -1$

12 $2b + 3 = \dfrac{2}{b}$

$b = \dfrac{1}{2} \text{ or } b = -2$

Solve each equation. Check for extraneous solutions.

13 $w - 2 = \dfrac{1}{w} - 2$

$w = \pm 1$

14 $16z = \dfrac{3}{z} + 2$

$z = \dfrac{1}{2} \text{ or } z = \dfrac{-3}{2}$

15 $2g - 6 = \dfrac{8}{g}$

$g = 4 \text{ or } g = -1$

16 $2c + \dfrac{12}{c} = 11$

$c = \dfrac{3}{2} \text{ or } c = 4$

17 $\dfrac{4}{m} = 6m + 10$

$m = \dfrac{1}{3} \text{ or } m = -2$

18 $x - 8 = \dfrac{-16}{x}$

$x = 4$

Solve each equation by factoring. (Review: Section 12.2)

19 $x^2 - 3x - 4 = 0$

$x = 4 \text{ or } x = -1$

20 $y^2 + 10y + 21 = 0$

$y = -7 \text{ or } y = -3$

21 $2z^2 + 5z + 3 = 0$

$z = \dfrac{-3}{2} \text{ or } z = -1$

22 $w^2 - 16 = 0$

$w = \pm 4$

23 $r^2 + 5 = 6r$

$r = 5 \text{ or } r = 1$

24 $s^2 + s = 6$

$s = -3 \text{ or } s = 2$

25 $4t^2 = -4t - 1$

$t = \dfrac{1}{2}$

26 $v^2 + 2v + \dfrac{3}{4} = 0$

$v = \dfrac{-3}{2} \text{ or } v = -\dfrac{1}{2}$

Problem Set **B**

Solve each equation. Check for extraneous solutions.

27 $a - 1 = \dfrac{a + 2}{3}$

$a = \dfrac{5}{2}$

28 $\dfrac{x - 1}{2} = \dfrac{2}{x} + \dfrac{x}{4}$

$x = 4 \text{ or } x = -2$

29 $\dfrac{h}{2} + \dfrac{1}{2h} = \dfrac{1 + h}{3h}$

$h = -\dfrac{1}{3} \text{ or } h = 1$

30 $\dfrac{y}{5} + \dfrac{2}{3} = \dfrac{2y}{15} - \dfrac{5}{3y}$

$y = -5$

31 $2 + \dfrac{8}{x^2} = \dfrac{17}{x}$

$x = \dfrac{1}{2} \text{ or } x = 8$

32 $\dfrac{b - 1}{15} = \dfrac{3 - b^2}{12b} + \dfrac{b - 1}{20}$

$b = 3 \text{ or } b = \dfrac{-5}{2}$

33 $\dfrac{L}{6} + \dfrac{L + 1}{L} = \dfrac{3 - L}{3L}$

$L = -8$

34 $5x = x + 4 - \dfrac{3}{x + 1}$

$x = \pm \dfrac{1}{2}$

35 $\dfrac{1}{3 + m} = \dfrac{m}{-1}$

$m = \dfrac{-3 \pm \sqrt{5}}{2}$

36 $\dfrac{c}{y^2} + \dfrac{b}{y} = -a$

$y = \dfrac{-b \pm \sqrt{b^2 - 4ac}}{2a}$

For each equation find a value of k so that the equation has only one solution.

37 $x^2 + kx + 1 = 0$
$k = 2$ or $k = -2$

42 $x^2 - 2kx + 5 = -4$
$k = 3$ or $k = -3$

38 $x^2 + 6x + k = 0$
$k = 9$

43 $x^2 + kx + 25 = 5x$
$k = 15$ or $k = -15$

39 $x^2 + kx + 49 = 0$
$k = 14$ or $k = -14$

44 $k^2x^2 + 1 = 6x$
$k = 9$

40 $x^2 - 12x = k$
$k = -36$

45 $kx^2 + 4x + 16 = 0$
$k = \frac{1}{4}$

41 $kx^2 + 12x + 9 = 0$
$k = 4$

46 $kx^2 + kx + 1 = 0$
$k = 4$

47 The sum of a number and its reciprocal is $2\frac{9}{10}$. What is the number?
$\frac{2}{5}$ or $\frac{5}{2}$

48 If $\dfrac{a}{b} = \dfrac{b}{c}$ and $c = a - b$, find the ratio $\dfrac{a}{b}$, which is known as the "Golden Section." $\dfrac{a}{b} = \dfrac{1 + \sqrt{5}}{2} = 1.618\ldots$

Problem Set C

Solve each equation. Check for extraneous solutions.

49 $\dfrac{x + 1}{x + 2} = \dfrac{2x + 6}{x + 3}$
$x = -3$

51 $\dfrac{x - 3}{x + 2} = \dfrac{x - 1}{2x + 4}$
$x = 1$ or $x = -1$

50 $\dfrac{x + 5}{4 - 2x} = \dfrac{x}{x - 2}$
$x = \dfrac{-3}{5}$

52 $\dfrac{x}{3x + 9} = \dfrac{x + 2}{x + 3}$
no solution

53 If the reciprocal of the quotient of two numbers equals the reciprocal of their product, what must be true about at least one of the numbers?
one number must be ± 1

54 One number is four larger than another. Find the two numbers if their quotient equals the reciprocal of their product minus the square root of their quotient.
see margin

55 Find two numbers such that the reciprocal of their quotient plus the reciprocal of their sum equals the opposite of their difference, which is negative one.
the numbers are $-\dfrac{1}{3}$ and $\dfrac{2}{3}$

53) $\dfrac{y}{x} = \dfrac{1}{xy}$
$x = xy^2$
$1 = y^2$
$y = \pm 1$ (also, $x \neq 0$, $y \neq 0$)

54) The problem is ambiguous. It can be translated several ways:

$\dfrac{x + 4}{x} = \dfrac{1}{x(x + 4)} - \sqrt{\dfrac{x + 4}{x}}$

$\dfrac{x}{x + 4} = \dfrac{1}{x(x + 4)} - \sqrt{\dfrac{x}{x + 4}}$

$\dfrac{x + 4}{x} = \dfrac{1}{x(x + 4) - \sqrt{\dfrac{x + 4}{x}}}$

$\dfrac{x}{x + 4} = \dfrac{1}{x(x + 4) - \sqrt{\dfrac{x}{x + 4}}}$

none of which is easily solved!

55) $\dfrac{1}{\frac{x}{y}} + \dfrac{1}{x + y} = -(x - y)$

$x - y = -1$ so
$x = y - 1$

$\dfrac{y}{x} + \dfrac{1}{x + y}$
$= y - x$

$\dfrac{y}{(y - 1)} + \dfrac{1}{(y - 1) + y}$
$= y - (y - 1)$

$\dfrac{y}{y - 1} + \dfrac{1}{2y - 1}$
$= 1$

$2y^2 - y + y - 1$
$= 2y^2 - 3y + 1$

$3y = 2$

$y = \dfrac{2}{3}$

$x = -\dfrac{1}{3}$

Chapter Study Guide

Vocabulary

As you study and review this chapter, be sure to learn the important mathematics vocabulary, including:

1   **Standard form of a quadratic equation**   The STANDARD FORM OF A QUADRATIC EQUATION is $ax^2 + bx + c = 0$, where a, b, and c are real numbers and $a \neq 0$.

- $3x^2 - 2x + 5 = 0$ is in standard form
$$(a = 3, b = -2, c = 5)$$

- $5x^2 - 13 = 0$ is in standard form
$$(a = 5, b = 0, c = -13)$$

- For the equation $2y^2 = y - 3$, the standard form is:
$2y^2 - y + 3 = 0$ $(a = 2, b = -1, c = 3)$

Skills

Be sure you build the useful algebraic skills, including:

2   **Using the property of a zero product**
Solve for y:
$$y(y + 2) = 0$$

PROCEDURE   The property of a zero product is that if the product of two numbers is zero, then one (or both) of the factors must equal zero.

$$y(y + 2) = 0$$
$$y = 0 \quad or \quad y + 2 = 0$$
$$y = -2$$

Thus the solution to $y(y + 2) = 0$ is $y = 0$ or $y = -2$.

3 **Using the method of Completing the Square**   Solve each equation:

a $x^2 + 2x = 8$ b $3y^2 + 24y = -45$ c $z^2 - 5z = 24$

PROCEDURE   Use a "detour" to find a perfect-square trinomial that gives the quadratic term and linear term.

a $x^2 + 2x = 8$

detour: $\Big\langle$
$$x^2 + 2x + \square = 8 + \square$$
$$(x + 1)^2 = 8 + \square$$

ADD 1: $x^2 + 2x + 1 = 8 + 1$
factor: $(x + 1)^2 = 9$
$$x + 1 = 3 \quad or \quad x + 1 = -3$$
$$x = 2 \qquad\qquad x = -4$$

b $3y^2 + 24y = -45$

MULTBY $\dfrac{1}{3}$: $y^2 + 8y = -15$

detour: $\Big\langle$
$$y^2 + 8y + \square = -15 + \square$$
$$(y + 4)^2 = -15 + \square$$

ADD 16: $y^2 + 8y + 16 = -15 + 16$
factor: $(y + 4)^2 = 1$
$$y + 4 = 1 \quad or \quad y + 4 = -1$$
$$y = -3 \qquad\qquad y = -5$$

c $z^2 - 5z = 24$

detour: $\Big\langle$
$$z^2 - 5z + \square = 24 + \square$$
$$\left(z - \frac{5}{2}\right)^2 = 24 + \square$$

ADD $\frac{25}{4}$: $z^2 - 5z + \dfrac{25}{4} = 24 + \dfrac{25}{4}$

factor: $\left(z - \dfrac{5}{2}\right)^2 = \dfrac{96}{4} + \dfrac{25}{4} = \dfrac{121}{4}$

$$z - \frac{5}{2} = \frac{11}{2} \quad or \quad z - \frac{5}{2} = -\frac{11}{2}$$

$$z = \frac{16}{2} \qquad\qquad z = -\frac{6}{2}$$

$$= 8 \qquad\qquad\quad = -3$$

4   **Using the quadratic formula**   Solve each equation:

a $3x^2 + 2x - 8 = 0$
b $9r^2 + 3r - 2 = 0$

PROCEDURE   Compare each equation to the standard form of a quadratic equation to find the values of a, b, and c.

a $a = 3, b = 2, c = -8$

$$x = \frac{-b \pm \sqrt{b^2 - 4ac}}{2a}$$

$$= \frac{-2 \pm \sqrt{2^2 - 4(3)(-8)}}{2(3)}$$

$$= \frac{-2 \pm \sqrt{4 + 96}}{6}$$

$$= \frac{-2 \pm \sqrt{100}}{6}$$

$$= \frac{-2 \pm 10}{6}$$

The solution is $x = \dfrac{-2 + 10}{6} = \dfrac{8}{6} = \dfrac{4}{3}$

or $x = \dfrac{-2 - 10}{6} = \dfrac{-12}{6} = -2$

b $a = 9, b = 3, c = -2$

$$r = \frac{-b \pm \sqrt{b^2 - 4ac}}{2a}$$

$$= \frac{-3 \pm \sqrt{3^2 - 4(9)(-2)}}{2(9)}$$

$$= \frac{-3 \pm \sqrt{9 + 72}}{18}$$

$$= \frac{-3 \pm \sqrt{81}}{18}$$

$$= \frac{-3 \pm 9}{18}$$

The solution is $r = \dfrac{-3 + 9}{18} = \dfrac{6}{18} = \dfrac{1}{3}$

or $r = \dfrac{-3 - 9}{18} = \dfrac{-12}{18} = -\dfrac{2}{3}$

5 Solving equations that yield quadratics   Solve for x: $\dfrac{x-4}{x+1} = \dfrac{x-2}{2x+2}$

PROCEDURE

$$\dfrac{x-4}{x+1} = \dfrac{x-2}{2x+2}$$

$$(x-4)(2x+2) = (x+1)(x-2) \qquad \text{(cross-product)}$$

$$2x^2 - 6x - 8 = x^2 - x - 2$$

$$x^2 - 6x - 8 = -x - 2$$

$$x^2 - 5x - 8 = -2$$

$$x^2 - 5x - 6 = 0$$

$$(x-6)(x+1) = 0$$

$$x - 6 = 0 \quad or \quad x + 1 = 0$$

$$x = 6 \qquad\qquad x = -1$$

Check $x = 6$:

$$\dfrac{x-4}{x+1} = \dfrac{x-2}{2x+2}$$

$$\dfrac{6-4}{6+1} \overset{?}{=} \dfrac{6-2}{2(6)+2}$$

$$\dfrac{2}{7} \overset{?}{=} \dfrac{4}{14}$$

$$\dfrac{2}{7} \overset{?}{=} \dfrac{2}{7} \checkmark$$

Check $x = -1$:

$$\dfrac{x-4}{x+1} = \dfrac{x-2}{2x+2}$$

$$\dfrac{-1-4}{-1+1} \overset{?}{=} \dfrac{-1-2}{2(-1)+2}$$

$$\dfrac{-5}{0} \overset{?}{=} \dfrac{-3}{0}$$

Does not check.

The only solution is $x = 6$; $x = -1$ is an extraneous solution.

Math History: Fermat's Last Theorem

Many great discoveries in mathematics have been made by amateur mathematicians. The French lawyer Pierre de Fermat is better known for his work in mathematics than for his work with the law.

Fermat's best-known result is known as *Fermat's Last Theorem*. It started with an edition of the problems of Diophantus that was published in 1621. As Fermat read Diophantus, he began to think about the Pythagorean Theorem, $x^2 + y^2 = z^2$. He realized that there are no similar equations for cubes or fourth powers. Fermat wrote in the margin of his copy of Diophantus that the equation $x^n + y^n = z^n$ has no solutions when x, y, and z are integers and n is greater than 2. Then he wrote that he had found a marvelous proof of this result, but that the margin was too small to contain the proof.

Ever since, people have been trying to show that Fermat's "last theorem" is either true or false. So far, no one has been able to prove or disprove it.

Chapter Test

Solve each equation.

1 $|3x| = 51$

$x = \pm 17$

2 $|2y - 5| = 9$

$y = 7 \ or \ y = -2$

3 $x^2 = 25$

$x = \pm 5$

4 $3y^2 = 15$

$y = \pm \sqrt{5}$

5 $3t(t + 4) = 0$

$t = 0 \ or \ t = -4$

6 $(2n + 5)(5n - 2) = 0$

$n = \frac{-5}{2} \ or \ n = \frac{2}{5}$

Change each equation to standard form and solve.

7 $16x^2 = 81$

$x = \pm \frac{9}{4}$

8 $x^2 = -11x$

$x = 0 \ or \ x = -11$

9 $x^2 = 15x - 50$

$x = 5 \ or \ x = 10$

10 $2x^2 + x = 3$

$x = \frac{-3}{2} \ or \ x = 1$

11 $\frac{1}{4}x^2 = \frac{1}{2}x + 2$

$x = 4 \ or \ x = -2$

12 $42x = 9 + 49x^2$

$x = \frac{3}{7}$

Solve by completing the square.

13 $x^2 - 8x = 9$

$x = 9 \ or \ x = -1$

14 $y^2 + 14y = -1$

$y = -7 \pm 4\sqrt{3}$

15 $2x^2 = 3x + 2$

$x = -\frac{1}{2} \ or \ x = 2$

16 State the quadratic formula.

$x = \frac{-b \pm \sqrt{b^2 - 4ac}}{2a}$

Use the quadratic formula to solve each equation.

17 $6x^2 + 17x + 5 = 0$

$x = -\frac{5}{2} \ or \ x = -\frac{1}{3}$

18 $2x^2 - 13x + 15 = 0$

$x = \frac{3}{2} \ or \ x = 5$

19 $10x^2 + 33x - 7 = 0$

$x = \frac{1}{5} \ or \ x = -\frac{7}{2}$

20 $12x^2 - 29x - 8 = 0$

$x = -\frac{1}{4} \ or \ x = \frac{8}{3}$

21 $48x^2 + 106x + 55 = 0$

$x = -\frac{5}{6} \ or \ x = -\frac{11}{8}$

22 $x^2 - 4x - 3 = 0$

$x = 2 \pm \sqrt{7}$

Solve each equation and check for extraneous solutions.

23 $\frac{x}{6} = \frac{1 - x}{5 + 2x}$

$x = \frac{1}{2} \ or \ x = -6$

24 $\frac{2x}{x - 2} = \frac{x - 3}{x - 2}$

$x = -3$

Solve.

25) $x(x + 4) = 117$

25 The length of a rectangle is four inches more than its width. Its area is one hundred seventeen square inches. Find the length and width of the rectangle.

length is 13, width is 9

26) $3(x + x + 2) + 15$
$= x(x + 2)$

26 Fifteen more than three times the sum of two consecutive odd integers is equal to the product of the integers. Find the integers.

7, 9

Problem Set: Cumulative Review 1–12

Problem Set   **A**

For classes that are approaching the end of the term, these 7 pages provide a comprehensive review of the first 12 chapters. Additional end-of-term review problems can be selected from the Cumulative Review for Chapters 1–14, pp. 606–609.

Multiple choice.

1 If $n = 1\frac{1}{2}$, then $3n = $ ___?___   *c*

  a $5\frac{1}{2}$ **c** $4\frac{1}{2}$

  b $1\frac{1}{10}$ **d** 5

2 The variable expression for MULTIPLYBY 31 (x) is: *b*

  a $x + 31$ **c** $31 \div x$

  b $31x$ **d** $x \div 31$

3 A verbal translation of the algebraic expression $2n$ is: *c*

  a half a number   **c** twice a number

  b a number increased by two   **d** two more than a number

4 The value $\left(\frac{1}{2}\right)^2$ is: *c*

  a $\dfrac{3}{2}$ **b** $\dfrac{1}{6}$ **c** $\dfrac{1}{4}$ **d** $\dfrac{1}{8}$

5 Solve for x: $-\frac{5}{8}x = -40$ *d*

  a $x = 25$ **c** $x = 5$

  b $x = 8$ **d** $x = 64$

6 Solve for ℓ: $V = \ell \cdot w \cdot h$ *b*

  a $\ell = V \cdot w \cdot h$ **c** $\ell = V - w \cdot h$

  b $\ell = \dfrac{V}{w \cdot h}$ **d** $\ell = V + w \cdot h$

7 The process of writing a trinomial as the product of two binomials is called: *c*

  a FOIL   **c** factoring

  b finding the GCF   **d** multiplying binomials

Perform the indicated operations.

8 Multiply: $(-3k^2)(2k^3)$

$-6k^5$

9 Solve for x: $\dfrac{18}{5} - x < \dfrac{23}{5}$

$x > -1$

10 Solve for x: $2x - 9 < 37$

$x < 23$

11 Factor: $f^2 - 4f - 45$

$(f-9)(f+5)$

12 Factor: $6z^2 + z - 15$

$(2z-3)(3z+5)$

13 Simplify: $\dfrac{y^2 - 16}{y} \div \dfrac{y+4}{y}$

$y - 4$

14 Simplify: $\dfrac{2x-3}{x-1} - \dfrac{x}{1-x}$

3

15 Solve for w: $\dfrac{4w}{w-3} = \dfrac{7}{2}$

$w = -21$

16 Solve for t: $\dfrac{2}{3t} + \dfrac{5}{4} = \dfrac{9}{4t}$

$t = \dfrac{19}{15}$

17 Simplify: $-6\sqrt[4]{81x^{12}}$

$-18x^3$

18 Simplify: $\sqrt{80}$

$4\sqrt{5}$

19 Solve for x: $\sqrt{x+3} + 5 = 0$

no solution

20 Solve for y: $|4y| = 17$

$\dfrac{17}{4}, -\dfrac{17}{4}$

21 Solve for m: $15m^2 = 9m$

$0, \dfrac{3}{5}$

22 Solve for s: $s^2 + s - 20 = 0$

$4, -5$

23 Six times the sum of a number and negative four is thirty. What is the number?

9

24 What is the equation of the line with slope $\frac{2}{3}$ and y-intercept 1?

$y = \frac{2}{3}x + 1$

25) $x + y = 82$
$y = 3x - 10$

25 The sum of two numbers is eighty-two. One number is ten less than three times the other. Find the larger number.

59

26 Solve the system of equations:

$5x - 3y = 2$
$4x + 2y = 6$

$(1,1)$

27 Write each verbal expression as a variable expression:

a a number increased by six

b the product of one third and a number

c the difference between a number and four

a $n + 6$ b $\frac{1}{3}n$ c $n - 4$

28 Solve and check each equation:

a $y + 3 = 17$ c $1 - n = -6$

b $14 = t - 11$ d $3m - 7 = 11$

a $y = 14$ b $t = 25$ c $n = 7$ d $m = 6$

29 Perform the indicated operations:

  a $(-9)(8)(-2)$ **c** $-15 \div 25$

  b $(-8)(-4)(0)(-5)$ **d** $3(2+3) - 2(-6-3)^2 + 16$

  a 144   b 0   c $-\frac{3}{5}$ d -131

30 Combine like terms:

  a $17a^2 - 19a + 12a^2 - 11$

  b $-(9n^2 - 11n) - 8n$

  a $29a^2 - 19a - 11$ b $-9n^2 + 3n$

31 The number of girls receiving A's in Ms. Addem's algebra class is one more than twice the number of boys receiving A's. If seven girls received A's, how many boys did?

  31) $2x + 1 = 7$

  3

32 Write as a monomial: the product of three x to the sixth power, four x to the fourth power, and x squared.

  $12x^{12}$

33 Solve for x:

  a $4(x-1) > 3(x-2)$ **c** $x+3 \geq 7$ *or* $x+1 < 1$

  b $-3x > 12$ **d** $-5x < -24$

  a $x > -2$ b $x < -4$ c $x \geq 4$ or $x < 0$ d $x > \frac{24}{5}$

34 Factor each expression:

  a $m^2 + 7m + 6$ **b** $a^2 - a - 20$

  a $(m+6)(m+1)$ b $(a-5)(a+4)$

35 Find the area of a rectangle if its length is $2x + 7$ and its width is $3x - 2$.

  $6x^2 + 17x - 14$

Perform each operation.

36 Multiply: $\dfrac{3ab}{4ac} \cdot \dfrac{8a^2b}{9c^2}$

  $\dfrac{2a^2b^2}{3c^3}$

37 Divide: $\dfrac{x^2 - 6x + 9}{x^2 - 9} \div \dfrac{5x}{x+3}$

  $\dfrac{x-3}{5x}$

38 Subtract: $\dfrac{16}{2-x} - \dfrac{8x}{2-x}$

  8

39 Add: $\dfrac{1}{x+3} + \dfrac{3}{x^2 + 6x + 9}$

  $\dfrac{x+6}{x^2 + 6x + 9}$

40 Solve for y: $\dfrac{3}{y} = \dfrac{9}{y+2}$

  $y = 1$

41 Solve for n: $\dfrac{3n-2}{n} = \dfrac{7}{3}$

  $n = 3$

42 Amanda can build a snow fort in two hours, and Leslie can build one in three hours. How long will it take (in hours and minutes) if they work together.

  42) $(\frac{1}{2} + \frac{1}{3})x = 1$

  1 hour, 12 minutes

43 Find the x-intercept and y-intercept of:

    a $x + y = 3$

    b $2y = 3x + 7$

         a x intercept is 3, y intercept is 3   b x intercept is $\frac{-7}{3}$, y intercept is $\frac{7}{2}$

44 Write each equation in slope-intercept form.

    a $3x + 2y = 8$

    b $4x + y = -1$

         a $y = -\frac{3}{2}x + 4$ b $y = -4x - 1$

45) $x + y = 40$
    $x - y = 8$

45 The sum of Lynne's age and Toni's age is forty, and the difference between their ages is eight. If Lynne is older, how old is each?

        Lynne is 24, Toni is 16

46 Solve the system of equations:

$$3x - 2y = -63$$
$$5x + y = -2$$

    $(-5\frac{2}{13}, 23\frac{10}{13})$

47 Evaluate each expression:

    a $-\sqrt{49}$ **c** $\sqrt{1\frac{11}{25}}$

    b $\sqrt{0.16}$ **d** $\sqrt{1.21}$

         a -7 b 0.4 c $\frac{6}{5}$ d 1.1

48 Perform the operations and write in standard form:

    a $\sqrt{125}\ \sqrt{40}$ **c** $\sqrt[3]{8} - \sqrt[3]{16} - 3\sqrt[3]{54}$

    b $\sqrt{98x^4} + 3\sqrt{50} - 8\sqrt{2}$ **d** $\sqrt[3]{-8} + \sqrt[5]{32}$

         a $50\sqrt{2}$ b $7x^2\sqrt{2} + 7\sqrt{2}$ c $2 - 11\sqrt[3]{2}$ d 0

49 Solve each equation:

    a $|x| = 3$ **c** $4x^2 + 13x = -3$

    b $x^2 - x - 6 = 0$ **d** $|x - 3| = 5$

         a $3, -3$ b $3, -2$ c $-\frac{1}{4}, -3$ d $8, -2$

Write an equation for each problem and solve the equation.

50 The product of three and x is equal to twenty.

    $3x = 20; x = \frac{20}{3}$

51 The sum of three consecutive integers is two hundred four.

    $x + x + 1 + x + 2 = 204; 67, 68, 69$

Solve and check.

52 $23 - (x + 2) = 2x - 8(3x + 4)$

    $x = \frac{-53}{21}$

53 $-3y + \frac{1}{2}(2y - 5) = 3 - (y + 6)$

    $y = \frac{1}{2}$

Problem Set **B**

Translate to algebraic symbols.

54 y is greater than six *and* y is less than or equal to ten

$6 < y \le 10$

55 w is less than or equal to fourteen *or* w is greater than twenty-three

$w \le 14 \text{ or } w > 21$

56 r is a positive number less than fifteen

$0 < r < 15$

57 t is a nonpositive number greater than negative twenty-seven

$-27 < t \le 0$

58 Solve: $2x - 7 < 3x - 1 < -5x - 9$

$-6 < x < -1$

59 A number decreased by six is at least twenty-one. Find the values for the number.

$x \ge 27$

59) $x - 6 \ge 21$

Perform the operations.

60 Factor: $5y^2 - 42y - 27$

$(5y + 3)(y - 9)$

61 Factor: $49 - n^2$

$(7 - n)(7 + n)$

62 Simplify: $\dfrac{7}{12x} - \dfrac{2}{3x} + 3x$

$\dfrac{36x^2 - 1}{12x}$

63 Subtract: $\dfrac{a^2 - 2a}{a - 3} - \dfrac{a - 3a^2 - 3}{3 - a}$

$\dfrac{-(2a^2 + a + 3)}{a - 3}$

64 Solve: $1.1 = 0.5x$

$x = 2.2$

65 Solve: $\dfrac{3}{8}x = 16$

$x = \dfrac{128}{3}$

66 Simplify: $\dfrac{3}{4} \div \dfrac{5}{16}$

$2\dfrac{2}{5}$

67 Simplify: $\dfrac{14}{a + b} \div \dfrac{7}{a^2 - b^2}$

$2(a - b)$

68 A horizontal line passes through $(5, -2)$ and $(0, x)$. Find x.

$x = -2$

69 Draw the graph of the equation $y = 3x - 2$. Then:

graph passes through $(0, -2)$ and $(1, 1)$

a Write the equation of a line parallel to it.

b Write the equation of a line perpendicular to it.

a answers may vary; slope = 3; y-intercept $\neq -2$ **b** answers may vary; slope $= -\dfrac{1}{3}$

70 Write the slope-intercept form and the standard form of the equation of a line with slope $\frac{2}{3}$ and x-intercept $(4, 0)$.

$y = \dfrac{2}{3}x - \dfrac{8}{3}$; $2x - 3y = 8$

71 Solve the system of equations: $9x - 4 = 2y$

$4 - 6x = \dfrac{1}{2}y$

$\left(\dfrac{20}{33}, \dfrac{8}{11}\right)$

Simplify each expression.

72 $\sqrt[3]{-8x^2y^{12}}$

$-2y\sqrt[4]{2x^2}$

73 $\sqrt[4]{48 - 4 \cdot 8}$

2

74 $\sqrt[3]{125 + 91}$

6

75 $-\sqrt[3]{-192x^4}$

$4x\sqrt[3]{3x}$

76 $3\sqrt{10} \cdot 2\sqrt{5}$

$30\sqrt{2}$

77 $\sqrt{50} \div \left(-\sqrt{10}\right)$

$-\sqrt{5}$

Solve and check.

78 $\sqrt{2x - 5} = 25$

$x = 315$

79 $\sqrt{7x + 1} = 8$

$x = 9$

80) $17 - \sqrt{x} = 12$

80 The difference between seventeen and the square root of a number is twelve. Find the number.

$x = 25$

81) $x(x + 2) = 59 + 4$

81 The product of two consecutive odd integers is four more than fifty-nine. Find the larger integer.

9

82) $2x^2 - 9x = 35$

82 Twice the square of a number minus nine times the number is thirty-five. Find the number.

$-\frac{5}{2}$ or 7

83) $3x + \frac{1}{x} = 2$

83 Find the number such that three times the number plus its reciprocal is two.

-1 or $\frac{1}{3}$

Evaluate for $a = -2$, $b = 6$, and $n = 4$.

84 The quotient found by dividing b by a.

-3

85 The product of a and the reciprocal of n.

$-\frac{1}{2}$

86 Find the GCF of $48x^3y$, $32xy^2$, and $60y^3$.

$4y$

Factor each trinomial.

87 $6x^2 - 29x - 5$

$(6x + 1)(x - 5)$

88 $4m^2 + 42m + 80$

$2(2m + 5)(m + 8)$

Solve.

89 $1\frac{5}{8}x = 9\frac{1}{10}$

$x = 5\frac{3}{5}$

90 $\frac{1}{8}x - 3 = -5$

$x = -16$

91 $-4(2x - 5) + 3x = x - 28$

$x = 8$

92 $-\frac{4}{5}x < \frac{1}{5}$

$x > -\frac{1}{4}$

Problem Set C

Solve by completing the square.

93 $2x^2 + 4x = 15$

$x = \dfrac{-2 \pm \sqrt{34}}{2}$

94 $0.12y^2 - 2y = 4.5$

$y = \dfrac{50 \pm 5\sqrt{154}}{6}$

95 $\frac{3}{4}x^2 + 3x - 9 = 0$

$x = 2, x = -6$

96 Factor: $2x^3 - 4x^2 - 8x + 16$

$2(x-2)^2(x+2)$

97 Write an equation that has the solution $x = -6$ or $x = 4$.

$x^2 + 2x - 24 = 0$

98 Solve: $\sqrt{y - 30} = \sqrt{y} - 2$

$y = 72\frac{1}{4}$

99 Solve for x: $\dfrac{3x}{3x^2 + 5x + 2} = \dfrac{2x}{2x^2 + 5x + 3} - \dfrac{3x + 1}{6x^2 + 13x + 6}$

$x = \dfrac{-9 \pm \sqrt{69}}{6}$

100 Write the equation of the line through $(-9,2)$ and perpendicular to the line with equation $\dfrac{3}{4}x + \dfrac{2}{5}y = -\dfrac{1}{3}$.

$-8x + 15y = 102$

101 The distance formula $d = \sqrt{(x_2 - x_1)^2 + (y_2 - y_1)^2}$ gives the distance between two points (x_1, y_1) and (x_2, y_2). Find the perimeter of the triangle whose vertices are $(-1, -2)$, $(2, -2)$, and $(-1, -6)$.

12

102 Find the area of the triangle in the previous problem.

6

103 A rectangular monument three meters by seven meters is surrounded by a paved sidewalk. If the outside perimeter of the sidewalk is three times the perimeter of the monument, find the width of the sidewalk.

5 meters

104 Find the area of the sidewalk in the previous problem.

200 sq meters

105 Write using algebraic symbols: A variable is greater than or equal to negative five *or* the variable is less than six.

$x \geq -5 \text{ or } x < 6$

106 What is the area of a square if the side is $3x + 2y$ meters long?

$9x^2 + 12xy + 4y^2$

107 Find a number such that the square of two fewer than the number equals the square of eight more than the number.

-3

---

101) The distance between $(-1, -2)$ and $(2, -2)$ is 3; between $(-1, -2)$ and $(-1, -6)$ is 4; between $(2, -2)$ and $(-1, -6)$ is 5. The perimeter is 12.

102) The triangle is a right triangle:

$A = \dfrac{1}{2} bh$

$ = \dfrac{1}{2} (3)(4)$

$ = 6$

103)

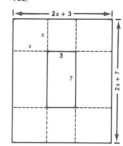

$2(2x+3) + 2(2x+7)$

$ = 3(20)$

$8x = 40$

$x = 5$

104) The area of the pavement is:

$(2x+3)(2x+7) - 21$

$ = (13)(17) - 21$

$ = 200$

106) $(3x + 2y)^2 =$

$ 9x^2 + 12xy + 4y^2$

107) $(x-2)^2 = (x+8)^2$

Chapter 13

FUNCTIONS

CHAPTER SCHEDULE

Basic (optional)
Problem Sets .4 Days
Review   0 Days
Test   0 Days

Average
Problem Sets 11 Days
Review   3 Days
Test   2 Days

Advanced
Problem Sets 13 Days
Review   1 Day
Test   1 Day

This chapter is optional for Basic courses. For Average courses, this chapter may mark the end of the term.

Section 13.1   Notation for Functions

The term **function** was defined in Section 1.5 as a rule that is applied to a number or variable and that results in a single value. "Function machines" were used to illustrate functions:

SECTION SCHEDULE

Basic (optional 1 day)

Average (1 day)

Advanced (2 days)

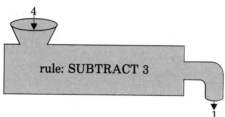

The machine starts with the number 4, applies the rule   SUBTRACT 3,   and the result is the number 1. This chapter borrows some vocabulary from computer users. The number 4 that goes into the machine is called the **input**, and the number 1 that is the result is called the **output**.

In general, these machine rules can be expressed in **function notation**. The rule   SUBTRACT 3   is written as:

$$f(x) = x - 3$$

The notation $f(x)$ is read "f of x." The input is x and the output is $x - 3$.

For the function $f(x) = x - 3$ and the particular input 4, replace x by 4 wherever x appears:

$$f(x) = x - 3$$
$$f(4) = 4 - 3 = 1$$

Other input and output values for $f(x) = x - 3$ are:

$$f(-2) = -2 - 3 = -5$$
$$f(-1) = -1 - 3 = -4$$
$$f(0) = 0 - 3 = -3$$
$$f(1) = 1 - 3 = -2$$
$$f(2) = 2 - 3 = -1$$
$$f(3) = 3 - 3 = 0$$

These values can be recorded in a table or on a graph:

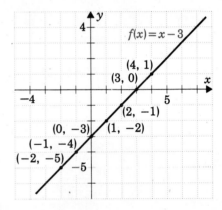

x	-2	-1	0	1	2	3	4
$f(x)$	-5	-4	-3	-2	-1	0	1

It is usual to label the vertical axis as the y-axis, even when using function notation. The graph of $f(x) = x - 3$ is a straight line with intercepts $(0, -3)$ and $(3, 0)$.

Sample Problems

1   If $f(x) = -x + 5$, find the following:
    a $f(2)$
    b $f(-6)$
    c $f(0)$
    d a such that $f(a) = 0$

PROCEDURE   In the expression $f(x) = -x + 5$, x represents the input number. For a particular value of the input number, substitute it for x on both sides of the equation.

a $f(2) = -(2) + 5 = -2 + 5 = 3$
b $f(-6) = -(-6) + 5 = 6 + 5 = 11$
c $f(0) = -(0) + 5 = 0 + 5 = 5$
d $f(a) = -a + 5$
   If $f(a) = 0$, then $0 = -a + 5$
$$-5 = -a$$
$$a = 5$$

   To check
$$f(5) = -(5) + 5 = 0 \checkmark$$

2   If $g(x) = x^2 - 16$,   find the following:
a $g(3)$
b $g(-3)$
c a such that $g(a) = 0$

PROCEDURE   The notation $g(x)$ is used the same way as $f(x)$.

a $g(3) = (3)^2 - 16 = 9 - 16 = -7$
b $g(-3) = (-3)^2 - 16 = 9 - 16 = -7$
c   If $g(a) = 0$, then:

$$0 = a^2 - 16$$
$$16 = a^2$$
$$a = 4 \quad or \quad a = -4$$

3   If $f(4) = 8$,   identify the function(s) that could be the rule:
a $f(x) = 2x$ d $f(x) = x^2 - 8$
b $f(x) = \frac{1}{2}x$ e $f(x) = 12 - x$
c $f(x) = x - 4$ f $f(x) = x$

PROCEDURE
Test each rule with the input value 4 to see if the output value is 8.

a $f(4) = 2(4) = 8$ Yes; $f(x) = 2x$ could be the rule.
b $f(4) = \frac{1}{2}(4) = 2$ No; $f(x) = \frac{1}{2}x$ could not be the rule.

c $f(4) = 4 - 4 = 0$ No.
d $f(4) = 4^2 - 8 = 16 - 8 = 8$ Yes.
e $f(4) = 12 - 4 = 8$ Yes.
f $f(4) = 4$ No.

4 For $h(x) = 8 - x$, fill in a table of values and draw the resulting graph.

PROCEDURE
Choose several values for x and find the corresponding $h(x)$ values:

x	−2	0	1	3	6
$h(x)$	10	8	7	5	2

Graph the points. (Note that the vertical axis is labeled as the y-axis.)

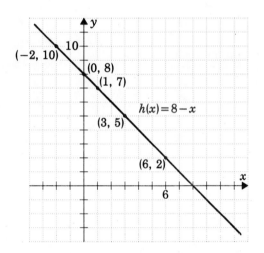

532: 1–11

Problem Set **A**

Find each value:

1 $f(8), f(1)$; $f(x) = x - 5$
$f(8) = 3, f(1) = -4$

2 $f(-7), f(1)$; $f(x) = x + 3$
$f(-7) = -4, f(1) = 4$

3 $g(-3), g(0)$; $g(x) = x + 6$
$g(-3) = 3, g(0) = 6$

4 $g(-1), g(5)$; $g(x) = x - 7$
$g(-1) = -8, g(5) = -2$

5 $h(4), h(12)$; $h(x) = 8 - x$
$h(4) = 4, h(12) = -4$

6 $h(9), h(2)$; $h(x) = 6 - x$
$h(9) = -3, h(2) = 4$

7 $f(7), f(-3)$; $f(t) = -1 + t$
$f(7) = 6, f(-3) = -4$

8 $f(-1), f(4)$; $f(r) = -4 + r$
$f(-1) = -5, f(4) = 0$

9 $f(-2), f(8)$; $f(p) = -3 - p$
$f(-2) = -1, f(8) = -11$

10 $f(-7); f(1)$; $f(q) = -5 - q$
$f(-7) = 2, f(1) = -6$

Which of the four rules can represent the given expression? (There may be more than one correct answer.)

11 $f(6) = 3$

   a $f(x) = x + 3$
   b $f(x) = \frac{1}{2}x$
   c $f(x) = 9 - x$
   d $f(x) = x - 3$
     b, c, d

12 $g(2) = 5$

   a $g(x) = 7 - x$
   b $g(x) = x - 3$
   c $g(x) = 2x + 1$
   d $g(x) = x + 3$
     a, c, d

13 $h(10) = 4$

   a $h(x) = 40 \div x$
   b $h(x) = x - 6$
   c $h(x) = 14 - x$
   d $h(x) = -x + 10$
     a, b, c

14 $f(0) = -2$

   a $f(r) = 2r$
   b $f(r) = -2 + r$
   c $f(r) = 3r - 2$
   d $f(r) = -r$
     b, c

15 $g(7) = 1$

   a $g(t) = t - 6$
   b $g(t) = 8 - t$
   c $g(t) = t - 8$
   d $g(t) = t \div 7$
     a, b, d

16 $h(3) = 3$

   a $h(s) = s$
   b $h(s) = s - 6$
   c $h(s) = 2s - 3$
   d $h(s) = 6 - s$
     a, c, d

17 $f(-4) = 12$

   a $f(x) = x + 16$
   b $f(x) = -3x$
   c $f(x) = -x + 8$
   d $f(x) = 2x + 20$
     a, b, c, d

18 $f(-2) = -1$

   a $f(x) = x - 3$
   b $f(x) = x + 1$
   c $f(x) = x \div 2$
   d $f(x) = -3 - x$
     b, c, d

For each table of values, find a rule that represents the table.

19

x	10	2	11	-1
$f(x)$	3	-5	4	-8

f(x) = x − 7

20

x	-3	0	$2\frac{1}{2}$	4
$g(x)$	1	4	$6\frac{1}{2}$	8

g(x) = x + 4

21

x	1	$-\frac{1}{2}$	-5	$3\frac{1}{2}$
$h(x)$	$4\frac{1}{2}$	3	$-1\frac{1}{2}$	7

h(x) = x + 7/2

22

r	$1\frac{1}{2}$	-1	4	$2\frac{1}{4}$
$f(r)$	$\frac{3}{4}$	$-1\frac{3}{4}$	$3\frac{1}{4}$	$1\frac{1}{2}$

f(r) = r − 3/4

Find the x-intercept and y-intercept for each line. (Review: Section 9.2)

23 $2x + 3y = 5$

x-intercept $= \frac{5}{2}$, y-intercept $= \frac{5}{3}$

24 $y = -2x - 1$

x-intercept $= \frac{3}{2}$, y-intercept $= -1$

25 $\dfrac{1 + y}{3} = \dfrac{x}{4}$

x-intercept $= \frac{4}{3}$, y-intercept $= -1$

26 $4x - y = 6$

x-intercept $= \frac{4}{3}$, y-intercept $= 4$

27 $y = -3x + 4$

x-intercept $= \frac{4}{3}$, y-intercept $= 4$

28 $\dfrac{2x - y}{3} = 5$

x-intercept $= \frac{15}{2}$, y-intercept $= -15$

Problem Set **B**

Which of the four rules can represent both given expressions? (There may be more than one correct answer.)

29 $f(2) = 5$ and $f(5) = 2$
  a $f(x) = x + 3$
  b $f(x) = 10 \div x$
  c $f(x) = -x - 3$
  d $f(x) = 7 - x$

    b, d

30 $g(0) = -4$ and $g(1) = -3$
  a $g(x) = x^2 - 4$
  b $g(x) = -x - 4$
  c $g(x) = -4 - x^2$
  d $g(x) = x - 4$

    a, b, d

31 $h(-2) = 0$ and $h(3) = 5$
  a $h(x) = 2 + x$
  b $h(x) = x - 2$
  c $h(x) = x^2 - 4$
  d $h(x) = 4 - x$

    a, c

32 $f(-2) = -6$ and $f(6) = 2$
  a $f(r) = r + 4$
  b $f(r) = 12 \div r$
  c $f(r) = r - 4$
  d $f(r) = 8 - r$

    b, c

33 $g(2) = 7$ and $g(-1) = 4$
  a $g(t) = t^2 + 3$
  b $g(t) = t - 5$
  c $g(t) = 4t + 1$
  d $g(t) = 5 - t$

    a

34 $h(8) = 2$ and $h(-4) = -4$
  a $h(q) = q \div 4$
  b $h(q) = q - 6$
  c $h(q) = 16 \div q$
  d $h(q) = q$

    c

For each function, make a table of ordered pairs and graph the function.

35 $f(x) = x - 6$
    some points are (0,6), (1,−5), (2,−4)

36 $f(x) = -x + 5$
    some points are (5,0), (4,1), (2,2)

37 $g(x) = \frac{1}{2}x$
    some points are (0,0), (2,1), (4,2), (6,3)

38 $g(x) = x + 4$
    some points are (0,4), (1,5), (2,6)

39 $h(x) = 7 - x$
    some points are (0,7), (1,6), (2,5)

40 $h(x) = -3x$
    some points are (0,0), (1,−3), (2,−6)

For each table, find a rule that represents all the ordered pairs. (Each rule is of the form $n \cdot x$, $n - x$, or $n \div x$.)

41

x	4	-3	-12	1
$f(x)$	6	-8	-2	24

$f(x) = 24 \div x$

42

x	-2	0	$3\frac{1}{2}$	8
$f(x)$	9	7	$3\frac{1}{2}$	-1

$f(x) = 7 - x$

43

x	0	$\frac{1}{2}$	2	-1
$f(x)$	0	3	12	-6

$f(x) = 6x$

44

x	-12	-6	0	3
$f(x)$	-4	-2	0	1

$f(x) = \frac{1}{3} \cdot x$

45

x	-9	-3	2	6
$f(x)$	-4	-12	18	6

$f(x) = 36 \div x$

46

x	-3	0	2	4
$f(x)$	5	2	0	-2

$f(x) = 2 - x$

Problem Set C

For each table, find two different rules that work for both ordered pairs. (Rules like $f(x) = x - 7$ and $f(x) = -7 + x$ are not considered different.)

47

x	2	6
$f(x)$	6	2

$f(x) = 12 \div x$, $f(x) = 8 - x$

48

x	-2	3
$g(x)$	1	6

$g(x) = x + 3$, $g(x) = x^2 - 3$

49

x	0	1
$h(x)$	1	2

$h(x) = x + 1$, $h(x) = x^2 + 1$

50

x	-3	4
$f(x)$	13	20

$f(x) = x^2 + 4$, $f(x) = x + 16$

51

t	-1	-4
$f(t)$	5	20

$f(t) = -5t$, $f(t) = t^2 + 4$

52

r	0	1
$g(r)$	-3	-2

$g(r) = r - 3$, $g(r) = r^2 - 3$

53

s	2	-5
$h(s)$	-5	2

$h(s) = -3 - s$, $h(s) = -10 \div s$

54

x	1	3
$f(x)$	4	12

$f(x) = x + 3$, $f(x) = x^2 + 3$

Xtending the topic: Set Notation for Functions

Sometimes **set notation** is used to describe a function. For example, the notation $\{(x,y): \; y = x - 7\}$, which is read "The set of ordered pairs (x,y) such that $y = x - 7$," means the set of input numbers x and output numbers y that are related by the rule $y = x - 7$ or $f(x) = x - 7$.

Problem Set   X

Graph the following sets of points:

1 $\{(x,y): \; y = x - 7\}$
some points are (0,−7), (1,−6)
(6,−1), (7,0)

2 $\{(x,y): \; y = 3x - 2\}$
some points are (0,−2), (1,1),
(2,4), (−1,−5)

3 $\{(x,y): \; y = \dfrac{12}{x} + 2\}$
some points are (1,14), (2,8),
(3,6), (4,5), (6,4)

4 $\{(x,y): \; y = x^2 - 7x + 1\}$
some points are (0,1), (1,−5),
(2,−9), (3,−11), (4,−11),
(5,−9), (6,−5)

Represent a rule for each table in set notation:

5

x	−2	0	2	4
y	0	2	4	6

$\{(x,y): y = x + 2\}$

6

x	−3	0	3	6
y	−1	0	1	2

$\{(x,y): y = \frac{1}{3}x\}$

7

x	−3	−1	2	6
$f(x)$	−4	−12	6	2

$\{(x, f(x)): f(x) = 12 \div x\}$

8

x	−2	1	3	5
$g(x)$	−6	3	9	15

$\{x, g(x)): g(x) = 3x\}$

Translate to set notation, and graph each set:

9 The set of ordered pairs (x,y) such that the product of x and y is the number thirty-six.
some points are (1,36), (2,18), (3,12), (4,9), (6,6), (9,4), (12,3), (18,2), (36,1)

10 The set of ordered pairs (x,y) such that five times the abscissa plus three times the ordinate is negative twenty.
some points are (0,$\frac{-20}{3}$), (1,$\frac{-25}{3}$), (−1,−5), (−4,0), (2,−10)

11 The set of ordered pairs (x,y) such that the absolute value of the product of the coordinates is twelve.
some points are (1,12), (2,6), (3,4), (4,3), (6,2), (12,1); also (1,−12), (2,−6), (3,−4) etc.;
(−1,12), (−2,6), (−3,4) etc.;
(−1,−12), (−2,−6), (−3,−4) etc.

9) $\{(x, y): xy = 36\}$

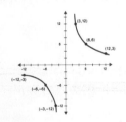

10) $\{(x, y): 5x + 3y = -20\}$

11) $\{(x, y): |xy| = 12\}$

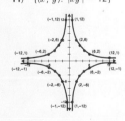

Section 13.2   Linear Functions

SECTION SCHEDULE

Basic (optional 2 days)

Average (2 days)

Advanced (2 days)

Chapter 9 presented the y-form of a linear equation, $y = mx + b$, where m is the slope and b is the y-intercept. Since the graph of $y = mx + b$ is a straight line, the graph of the function $L(x) = mx + b$ will also be a straight line. Thus the function $L(x) = mx + b$ is called a **linear function**.

Students may want to refer to Problem Set C of Section 9.6 (p. 383) which lists the conditions for a linear equation.

Definition

> A **LINEAR FUNCTION** is a function that can be written in the form $L(x) = mx + b$, where m and b are real numbers.

EXAMPLES

■   The following are all linear functions:

$$L(x) = x - 4 \qquad L(x) = -\tfrac{2}{3}x$$
$$L(x) = -5x - 17 \qquad L(x) = 7$$
$$L(x) = \tfrac{1}{2}x + 1 \qquad L(x) = x\sqrt{3} - \sqrt{5}$$

Consider the graphs of three examples:

$$L(x) = x - 4$$
$$L(x) = \tfrac{1}{2}x + 1$$
$$L(x) = 7$$

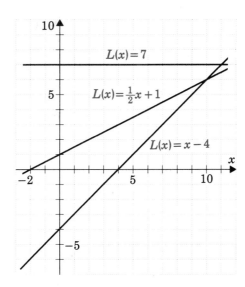

The graph of function $L(x) = 7$ is a horizontal line; the function is called a **constant function** because the value of $L(x)$ is constant. For other functions, when the graph of the function crosses the x-axis, the value of $L(x)$ must be zero. In general, if $L(x)$ is zero for a function, that value of x is called a **zero of the function**.

Definition

> **A ZERO OF A FUNCTION (or simply, a ZERO) is an input value that is associated with the output value 0.**

EXAMPLES

- For $L(x) = x - 4$
  $$0 = x - 4$$
  $$4 = x$$
  The value $x = 4$ is a zero of $L(x) = x - 4$.

- For $L(x) = \tfrac{1}{2}x + 1$
  $$0 = \tfrac{1}{2}x + 1$$
  $$-1 = \tfrac{1}{2}x$$
  $$-2 = x$$
  The value $x = -2$ is a zero of $L(x) = \tfrac{1}{2}x + 1$

Sample Problems

1   Find the zeros of $L(x) = -2x + 6$.

PROCEDURE   There are two methods: either graph the function and find where it crosses the x-axis, or set $L(x)$ equal to zero and solve for x.

Students should realize that the algebraic method is more accurate, especially for non-integral zeros.

Graphical

x	-2	0	2	4
$L(x)$	10	6	2	-2

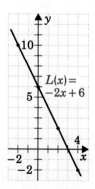

Algebraic

$$L(x) = -2x + 6$$
$$0 = -2x + 6$$
$$-6 = -2x$$
$$3 = x$$

The zero of $L(x)$ is the value $x = 3$.

The zero of $L(x)$ is the value $x = 3$.

2 For each graph, find the function rule and the zeros of the function.

a

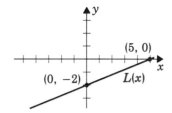

c

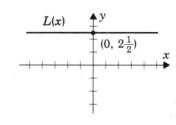

Students may want to write the slope as:

$$\frac{\Delta y}{\Delta x}$$

(where Δy is read "delta y" or "change in y").

b

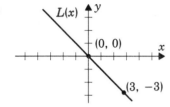

d

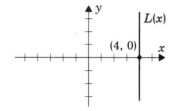

PROCEDURE Use the methods from Chapter 9 to write each equation.

a The line contains $(0,-2)$ and $(5,0)$. The slope is:

$$\frac{-2-0}{0-5} = \frac{2}{5}$$

Since the line contains $(0,-2)$, the y-intercept is -2. Thus the equation of the line is $y = \frac{2}{5}x - 2$, and the linear function is $L(x) = \frac{2}{5}x - 2$. The line contains $(5,0)$, so the zero of $L(x)$ is 5.

b The y-intercept and the x-intercept are both zero, and the slope is:

$$\frac{0-(-3)}{0-3} = \frac{3}{-3} = -1$$

The equation of the line is $y = -1x + 0$ or $y = -x$, so the linear function is $L(x) = -x$. The value $x = 0$ is a zero.

c The graph is a horizontal line; its equation is $y = 2\frac{1}{2}$. Thus the linear function is the constant function $L(x) = 2\frac{1}{2}$. Since the graph does not cross the x-axis, the function does not have a zero.

d The graph is a vertical line; its equation is $x = 4$. However, a vertical line cannot represent a function. When the function rule is applied to an input number, the result must be a single output number. But the two points $(4,1)$ and $(4,3)$ are both on the vertical line $x = 4$. The number 4 cannot represent an input number, since there would be more than one output number. Thus a vertical line (or any equation of the form $x = c$) cannot represent a function.

ASSIGNMENT GUIDE

Basic (optional 2 days)
(1) 2–18 (even), 27–29
(2) 19–26, 30–32

Average (2 days)
(1) 1–18, 27–32
(2) 19–26, 33–44

Advanced (2 days)
(1) 2–26 (even), 33–38
(2) 27–32, 39–49

Problem Set **A**

State whether each of these is a linear function. If it is not, state why it is not.

1 $f(x) = 3x - 2$
      linear

2 $h(x) = \dfrac{3}{x}$
      linear

3 $g(x) = -2x + 5$
      linear

4 $g(x) = \frac{1}{3}x - 1$
      linear

5 $h(x) = x^2 + 1$
      not linear (x^2)

6 $f(x) = -x - 1$
      not linear $\left(\frac{1}{x}\right)$

7 $f(t) = -\dfrac{4}{t}$
      not linear $\left(\frac{1}{t}\right)$

8 $f(r) = 2 - r^2$
      not linear (r^2)

9 $g(t) = 1 - 6t$
      linear

10 $g(r) = -3 - 2r$
      linear

For each linear function and the given input value for x, find $L(x)$.

11 $L(x) = 5x - 1;$ $x = 2$
      $L(2) = 9$

12 $L(x) = 2x + 3;$ $x = 4$
      $L(4) = 11$

13 $L(x) = 1 - 2x;$ $x = -3$
      $L(-3) = 7$

14 $L(x) = -7 + 3x;$ $x = -1$
      $L(-1) = -10$

15 $L(x) = 4x + 1;$ $x = 2\frac{1}{2}$
      $L(2\frac{1}{2}) = 11$

16 $L(x) = 6x - 3;$ $x = 1\frac{1}{3}$
      $L(1\frac{1}{3}) = 5$

17 $L(x) = -13 + 20x;$ $x = 1.2$
      $L(1.2) = 11$

18 $L(x) = 4 - 8x;$ $x = 1.5$
      $L(1.5) = -8$

Find the zeros for each linear function.

19 $L(x) = x - 6$
      $x = 6$

20 $L(x) = x + 9$
      $x = -9$

21 $L(x) = 2x + 8$
      $x = -4$

22 $L(x) = 4x - 12$
      $x = 3$

23 $L(r) = -2r + 1$
      $r = \dfrac{1}{2}$

24 $L(s) = 3s + 4$
      $s = -\dfrac{4}{3}$

25 $L(t) = \frac{1}{2}t - 6$
      $t = 12$

26 $L(q) = \frac{1}{3}q + 1$
      $q = -3$

Solve each equation. (Review: Section 12.2)

27 $m^2 - 7m + 12 = 0$
      $m = 3$ or $m = 4$

28 $n^2 - 4n - 5 = 0$
      $n = 5$ or $n = -1$

29 $p^2 - 25 = 0$
      $p = 5$ or $p = -5$

30 $4t^2 - 1 = 0$
      $t = \frac{1}{2}$ or $t = -\frac{1}{2}$

31 $144 - s^2 = 0$
      $s = 12$ or $s = -12$

32 $1.6 - 0.4\,w^2 = 0$
      $w = 2$ or $w = -2$

Problem Set **B**

For each graph, write the linear function that represents it, and find the zeros.

33

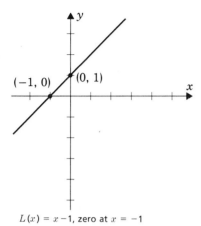

$L(x) = x - 1$, zero at $x = -1$

36

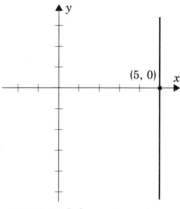

zero at $x = 5$ (not a function)

34

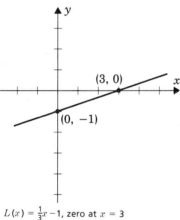

$L(x) = \frac{1}{3}x - 1$, zero at $x = 3$

37

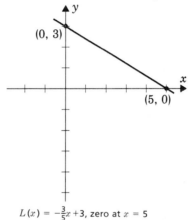

$L(x) = -\frac{3}{5}x + 3$, zero at $x = 5$

35

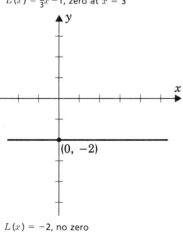

$L(x) = -2$, no zero

38

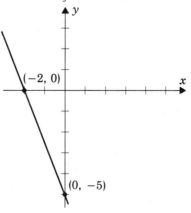

$L(x) = -\frac{5}{2}x + -5$, zero at $x = -2$

Use the Distributive Property to rewrite each of the following function rules in the form $L(x) = mx + b$.

39 $L(x) = 2(x - 1)$
$L(x) = 2x - 2$

40 $L(x) = 4(x - 3)$
$L(x) = 4x - 12$

41 $L(x) = \dfrac{4}{3}(6x - 9)$
$L(x) = 8x - 12$

42 $L(x) = -2(3x - 4)$
$L(x) = -6x + 8$

43 $L(x) = -3(2x + 1)$
$L(x) = -6x - 3$

44 $L(x) = -\dfrac{3}{2}(4x + 2)$
$L(x) = -6x - 3$

Problem Set C

Graphs and linear functions can help solve inequalities.

- To solve $2x < 6$, rewrite the inequality as $2x - 6 < 0$ and then consider the linear function $L(x) = 2x - 6$.

  The inequality $2x - 6 < 0$ is equivalent to $L(x) < 0$, and $L(x) < 0$ when the line is below the x-axis. Thus $L(x) < 0$ when $x < 3$, and the solution to the original inequality $2x < 6$ is $x < 3$.

- To solve $3x + 5 > -7$, rewrite the inequality as $3x + 12 > 0$ and let $L(x) = 3x + 12$. The zero of $L(x)$ is at $x = -4$, so $L(x) > 0$ when $x > -4$.

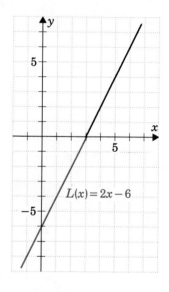

Use a linear function to solve each inequality.

45 $3x - 2 < 7$
$x < 3$

46 $7 - x > 3 + 3x$
$x < 1$

47 $4x + 1 > -11 + x$
$x > -4$

48 $6 < 5x + 16$
$x > -2$

49 $10x \le 2(2x - 9)$
$x \le -3$

50 $2x + 3(x + 3) < 2x + 24$
$x < 5$

51 $(10x + 10) \div 2 \ge -5$
$x \ge -2$

52 $3x + 8 < 2(x + 4)$
$x > 0$

Project: Polygonal Numbers

Polygonal numbers (pə lig′ ə n′l) are numbers that can be pictured geometrically as sets of dots forming a polygon.

square numbers:

triangular numbers:

Suppose $S(1)$ represents the first square number, $S(2)$ represents the second square number, and so on. Then:

$$S(1) = 1 \qquad S(2) = 4 \qquad S(3) = 9 \qquad S(4) = 16$$

In general, $S(n) = n^2$.

If the triangular numbers are $T(1), T(2), T(3), \ldots$, then:

$$T(1) = 1 \qquad T(3) = 6 \qquad T(5) = 15$$
$$T(2) = 3 \qquad T(4) = 10 \qquad T(6) = 21$$

1   What are the values of $S(5)$ through $S(15)$? What is $S(100)$?

2   Is 3249 a square number? Explain why or why not.

3   Is 654,321 a square number? Explain why or why not.

4   What are the values of the triangular numbers $T(9)$ through $T(15)$?

5   There is a formula for the nth triangular number. For each number, notice what happens when two triangular patterns are put together:

$$2 \cdot T(2) = 2 \cdot 3 \qquad 2 \cdot T(3) = 3 \cdot 4 \qquad 2 \cdot T(4) = 4 \cdot 5$$
$$T(2) = \frac{2 \cdot 3}{2} \qquad T(3) = \frac{3 \cdot 4}{2} \qquad T(4) = \frac{4 \cdot 5}{2}$$
$$= 3 \qquad\qquad = 12 \qquad\qquad = 10$$

a   Can use use this pattern to find $T(20)$? $T(25)$?
b   Can you use the pattern to find a general formula for $T(n)$?

6   If you found a formula for $T(n)$, use it to find:
a $T(55)$ 　　　　　　　**b** n, if $T(n) = 2926$

7   Is 6216 a triangular number? Explain why or why not.

1) $S(5) = 25$
　　 $S(6) = 36$
　　 $S(7) = 49$
　　 $S(8) = 64$
　　 $S(9) = 81$
　　 $S(10) = 100$
　　 $S(11) = 121$
　　 $S(12) = 144$
　　 $S(13) = 169$
　　 $S(14) = 196$
　　 $S(15) = 225$
　　 $S(100) = 10000$

2)   yes; $S(57) = 3249$

3)   no;   654,321 is not the square of a natural number

4) $T(9) = 45$
　　 $T(10) = 55$
　　 $T(11) = 66$
　　 $T(12) = 78$
　　 $T(13) = 91$
　　 $T(14) = 105$
　　 $T(15) = 120$

5a) $T(20) = \frac{(20)(21)}{2} = 210$

　　　 $T(25) = \frac{(25)(26)}{2} = 325$

b) $T(n) = \frac{n(n+1)}{2}$

6a) $T(55) = \frac{(55)(56)}{2} = 1540$

b)   If $T(n) = 2926$, then $n(n+1) = 5852$. Since $\sqrt{5852} = 76.5$, try $n = 76$:

$\frac{(76)(77)}{2} = 2926$

Thus $n = 76$.

7)   yes;

$T(111) = \frac{(111)(112)}{2} = 6216$

539

Section 13.3 The Quadratic Function
$$Q(x) = ax^2 + c$$

*The linear term is zero for each of the quadratic functions in this section. Thus the **y**-axis is an axis of symmetry for each of the parabolas in this section.*

Any function with a rule that can be written in the form $ax^2 + bx + c$, where a, b, and c are real numbers, $a \neq 0$, is a **quadratic function**. This section looks at quadratic functions such that $b = 0$; the resulting quadratic functions are of the form $Q(x) = ax^2 + c$, where a and c are real numbers, $a \neq 0$.

EXAMPLE

■ $Q(x) = x^2 - 9$

This function can be graphed by filling in a table of values for x and $Q(x)$, plotting the points, and connecting them with a smooth curve.

x	-4	-3	-2	-1	0	1	2	3	4
$Q(x)$	7	0	-5	-8	-9	-8	-5	0	7

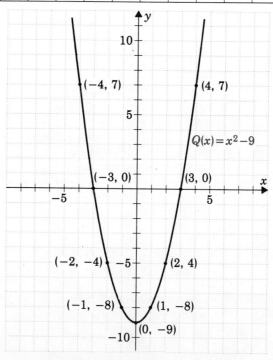

This curve is called a **parabola** (pə rab′ əl ə). This parabola crosses the x-axis at two points, $(-3, 0)$ and $(3, 0)$, and so $Q(x) = x^2 - 9$ has two zeros.

Also, there are no restrictions on the input numbers for the function, but the output numbers will always be greater than or equal to negative 9. Thus the function $Q(x) = x^2 - 9$ has a **minimum** at the point $(0, -9)$.

For every quadratic function, the output numbers are limited in that they have a minimum or a maximum. This limitation on output numbers is referred to as the **range**. (The limitation on the input numbers, which is referred to as the **domain**, is discussed in Section 13.5.)

Definition

The RANGE of a function is the set of possible output numbers.

EXAMPLES

- $R(x) = x^2 - 4$

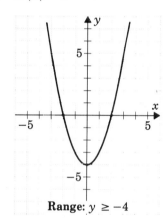

Range: $y \geq -4$

- $T(x) = -2x^2 - 1$

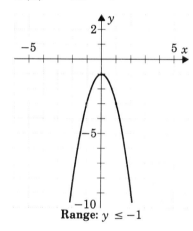

Range: $y \leq -1$

The range describes the possible values for the output numbers. Since the function symbols $R(x)$ and $T(x)$ also refer to the output numbers, those function symbols can be used to describe the range. Thus the range of the two examples can be described as $R(x) \geq -4$ and $T(x) \leq -1$, respectively.

Sample Problems

1. If $Q(x) = -2x^2 + 5$, find $Q(3)$ and $Q(\tfrac{1}{2})$.

   PROCEDURE   Replace x by each input number:

$$Q(3) = -2(3)^2 + 5 = -2(9) + 5$$
$$= -18 + 5$$
$$= -13$$

$$Q(\tfrac{1}{2}) = -2(\tfrac{1}{2})^2 + 5 = -2(\tfrac{1}{4}) + 5$$
$$= -\tfrac{1}{2} + 5$$
$$= 4\tfrac{1}{2}$$

2 Graph each function, describe the graph and find the range and the zeros.

a $Q(x) = -x^2 + 16$ **b** $T(x) = -4x^2$ **c** $R(x) = 2x^2 + 3$

PROCEDURE   Fill in a table of ordered pairs to graph each function.

a $Q(x) = -x^2 + 16$

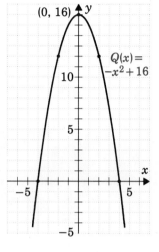

x	-4	-2	0	2	4
$Q(x)$	0	12	16	12	0

The graph opens downward. It has a maximum at $(0,16)$ and crosses the x-axis at $x = \pm 4$. The range of the function is $Q(x) \leq 16$ and the zeros are $x = \pm 4$.

b $T(x) = -4x^2$

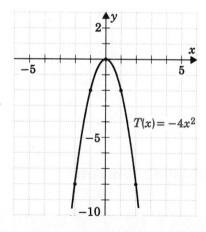

x	-2	-1	0	1	2
$T(x)$	-8	-4	0	-4	-8

The graph opens downward with a maximum at $(0,0)$; the range of the function is $T(x) \leq 0$. The function is **tangent** to the x-axis at $(0,0)$, which means that it touches but does not cross the x-axis. The function is said to have a "double zero" at $x = 0$.

c $R(x) = 2x^2 + 3$

x	-2	-1	0	1	2
$R(x)$	11	5	3	5	11

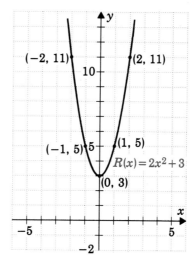

The graph opens upward with a minimum at $(0,3)$; the range is $R(x) \geq 3$. The graph does not cross the x-axis, so there are no zeros for the function $R(x) = 2x^2 + 3$.

3 Find the zeros of each quadratic function:

    a $Q(x) = x^2 - 9$ **b** $R(x) = x^2 + 3x - 10$ **c** $T(x) = x^2 + x - 5$

PROCEDURE In each case, set the function equal to zero and solve for x. Parts **a** and **b** can be solved by factoring; solve part **c** using the quadratic formula.

    a $Q(x) = x^2 - 9 = 0$

        $(x + 3)(x - 3) = 0$

          $x + 3 = 0$ or $x - 3 = 0$

            $x = -3$ $x = 3$

    b $R(x) = x^2 + 3x - 10 = 0$

         $(x + 5)(x - 2) = 0$

           $x + 5 = 0$ or $x - 2 = 0$

             $x = -5$ $x = 2$

    c $T(x) = x^2 + x - 5 = 0;$ $a = 1, b = 1, c = -5$

$$x = \frac{-b \pm \sqrt{b^2 - 4ac}}{2a}$$

$$= \frac{-1 \pm \sqrt{1^2 - 4(1)(-5)}}{2(1)}$$

$$= \frac{-1 \pm \sqrt{21}}{2}$$

ASSIGNMENT GUIDE

Basic (optional 1 day)
2–32 (even)

Average (2 days)
(1) 2–32 (even)
(2) 33–52

Advanced (2 days)
(1) 2–42 (even)
(2) 44–50 (even), 52–57

Problem Set A

1 The graph of a quadratic function is a curve that has a shape called a(n) __?__ .

parabola

2 The set of possible output values is called the __?__ .

range

3 The function $Q(x) = 2x^2 - 3$ has a minimum at (0, __?__).

−3

4 Does the function $Q(x) = 2x^2 - 3$ open upward or downward?

upward

5 The function $Q(x) = -2x^2 - 3$ has a maximum at (0, __?__).

−3

6 Does the function $Q(x) = -2x^2 - 3$ open upward or downward?

downward

Evaluate each function for the given input values.

7 $Q(x) = 2x^2 - 3$; use the values $x = 2, -2, 0$

5, 5, −3

8 $Q(x) = 3x^2 - 4$; use the values $x = 2, -2, 0$

8, 8, −4

9 $Q(r) = -3r^2 + 12$; use the values $r = -2, 1, 1\frac{1}{2}$

0, 9, 5.25

10 $Q(s) = -2s^2 + 8$; use the values $s = -2, 1, 1\frac{1}{2}$

0, 6, 3.5

11 $R(t) = 4t^2 + 1$; use the values $t = -\frac{1}{2}, 0, 3$

0, 1, 37

12 $R(x) = 6x^2 + 2$; use the values $x = -\frac{1}{3}, 4, 0$

$2\frac{2}{3}$, 98, 2

13 $R(x) = -x^2 - 5$; use the values $x = 1, -3, \sqrt{2}$

−6, −14, −7

14 $R(x) = -x^2 - 1$; use the values $x = -1, \sqrt{3}, 4$

−2, −4, −17

Find the given value for each function.

15 $R(x) = -3x^2 + 1$; find $R(-2)$

$R(-2) = -11$

16 $R(t) = t^2 + 7$; find $R(-3)$

$R(-3) = 16$

17 $R(t) = 2t^2 + 4$; find $R\left(\sqrt{3}\right)$

$R(\sqrt{3}) = 10$

18 $T(x) = -2x^2 - 6$; find $T\left(\sqrt{5}\right)$

$T(\sqrt{5}) = -16$

19 $T(x) = -8x^2$; find $T\left(\frac{1}{2}\right)$

$T(\frac{1}{2}) = -2$

20 $T(r) = 9r^2$; find $T\left(-\frac{1}{3}\right)$

$T(-\frac{1}{3}) = 1$

Graph each function, then list the minimum or maximum value, the zeros (if any), and the range.

21 $Q(x) = -2x^2$
some points are $(-1,-2)$, $(0,0)$, $(1,-2)$; maximum is zero, zero at $x = 0$

22 $R(x) = x^2 - 16$
some points are $(-4,0)$, $(0,-16)$, $(4,0)$, minimum is -16, zeros at $+4$, -4

23 $T(x) = x^2 - 5$
some points are $(-2,-1)$, $(0,-5)$, $(2,-1)$; minimum is -5, zeros at 5, -5

24 $Q(x) = 3x^2$
some points are $(0,0)$, $(1,3)$, $(-1,3)$, minimum is zero, zero at $x = 0$

25 $R(x) = -x^2 + 9$
points are $(1,8)$, $(0,9)$, $(-1,8)$; maximum is 9, zeros at $x = -3$, $x = 3$

26 $T(x) = 2x^2 + 1$
points are $(-1,3)$, $(0,1)$, $(1,3)$; minimum at $y = 1$, no zeros

Find all possible values for the variable. (Review: Section 12.1)

27 $|x| = 7$
$x = 7 \text{ or } x = -7$

28 $|y| + 1 = 3$
$y = 2 \text{ or } y = -2$

29 $|z + 3| = 5$
$z = 2 \text{ or } z = -8$

30 $|a - 2| = 4$
$a = 6 \text{ or } a = -2$

31 $|2c| = 6$
$c = 3 \text{ or } c = -3$

32 $|r + 1| = 0$
$r = -1$

Problem Set **B**

Solve by factoring.

33 $x^2 + x - 2 = 0$
$x = -2 \text{ or } x = 1$

34 $x^2 - 2x - 3 = 0$
$x = 3 \text{ or } x = -2$

35 $r^2 + 4r = 0$
$r = 0 \text{ or } r = -4$

36 $r^2 + 8r + 15 = 0$
$r = -5 \text{ or } r = -3$

37 $2t^2 - 9t + 4 = 0$
$t = \frac{1}{2} \text{ or } t = 4$

38 $3t^2 - 16t - 12 = 0$
$t = -\frac{2}{3} \text{ or } t = 6$

39 $6q^2 - q - 1 = 0$
$q = \frac{1}{2} \text{ or } q = -\frac{1}{3}$

40 $8q^2 + 10q + 3 = 0$
$q = -\frac{1}{2} \text{ or } q = -\frac{3}{4}$

41 $-m^2 + 4m + 12 = 0$
$m = 6 \text{ or } m = -2$

42 $-m^2 + m + 12 = 0$
$m = 4 \text{ or } m = -3$

Solve using the quadratic formula.

43 $x^2 - 10x + 16 = 0$
$x = 2 \text{ or } x = 8$

44 $y^2 + 6y - 7 = 0$
$y = -7 \text{ or } y = 1$

45 $z^2 + 5z = 0$
$z = 0 \text{ or } z = -5$

46 $w^2 - 4w = 0$
$w = 0 \text{ or } w = 4$

47 $3v^2 + 5v - 2 = 0$
$v = \frac{1}{3} \text{ or } v = -2$

48 $2h^2 - 3h - 2 = 0$
$h = -\frac{1}{2} \text{ or } h = 2$

49 $j^2 - 2 = 0$
$j = \pm\sqrt{2}$

50 $k^2 - 5 = 0$
$k = \pm\sqrt{5}$

51 $m^2 - 2m - 2 = 0$
$m = 1 \pm \sqrt{3}$

52 $n^2 - 6n + 7 = 0$
$n = 3 \pm \sqrt{2}$

Problem Set C

In problems 53–56, graph each family of curves on the same axes.

53 $Q(x) = -x^2 + 4$
$R(x) = -x^2 + 2$
$S(x) = -x^2$
$T(x) = -x^2 - 2$
$V(x) = -x^2 - 4$

55 $Q(x) = x^2 - 5$
$R(x) = x^2 - 3$
$S(x) = x^2 - 1$
$T(x) = x^2 + 1$
$V(x) = x^2 + 3$

54 $Q(x) = 2x^2 - 7$
$R(x) = 2x^2 - 4$
$S(x) = 2x^2 - 1$
$T(x) = 2x^2 + 2$
$V(x) = 2x^2 + 5$

56 $Q(x) = -3x^2 + 6$
$R(x) = -3x^2 + 3$
$S(x) = -3x^2$
$T(x) = -3x^2 - 3$
$V(x) = -3x^2 - 6$

57 For the quadratic function $Q(x) = ax^2 + c$:

a How does the sign of a affect the graph?

b How does the **magnitude** (size) of a affect the graph?

c How does the sign of c affect the graph?

d How does the magnitude of c affect the graph?

a   if $a > 0$, the graph has a minimum; if $a < 0$, the graph has a maximum

b   as a increases, the graph becomes narrower

c,d   the value of c is the maximum or minimum; it is the y-intercept

Section 13.4   Absolute Value Functions

The absolute value of an expression can be symbolized as ABSVAL (x) or $|x|$. It is also possible to consider absolute value as a function, with input numbers and output numbers.

EXAMPLES

- $F(x) = |x - 5|$

- $G(x) =$ ABSVAL $(2x - 1)$

x	-1	0	1	3	5	7	9
$f(x)$	6	5	4	2	0	2	4

x	-2	0	$\frac{1}{2}$	1	3	5
$G(x)$	5	1	0	1	5	9

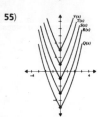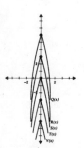

Sample Problems

1   Evaluate $F(x) = $ ABSVAL $(2x + 3)$ for $x = -4$, $x = -1$, and $x = 1$.

PROCEDURE   Replace x by its value on each side of the equation:

$$
\begin{aligned}
\text{If}\quad x = -4,\quad F(-4) &= \text{ABSVAL } (2(-4) + 3) \\
&= \text{ABSVAL } (-8 + 3) \\
&= \text{ABSVAL } (-5) \\
&= 5
\end{aligned}
$$

$$
\begin{aligned}
\text{If}\quad x = -1,\quad F(-1) &= \text{ABSVAL } (2(-1) + 3) \\
&= \text{ABSVAL } (-2 + 3) \\
&= \text{ABSVAL } (1) \\
&= 1
\end{aligned}
$$

$$
\begin{aligned}
\text{If}\quad x = 1,\quad F(1) &= \text{ABSVAL } (2(1) + 3) \\
&= \text{ABSVAL } (2 + 3) \\
&= \text{ABSVAL } (5) \\
&= 5
\end{aligned}
$$

2   Graph $G(x) = |3x - 6|$ and describe it.

PROCEDURE   Fill in a table with some values for $G(x)$ and graph the points.

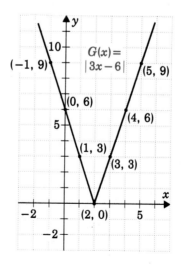

x	-1	0	1	2	3	4	5
$G(x)$	9	6	3	0	3	6	9

Graphs of absolute value functions, like graphs of quadratic functions, have an axis of symmetry. For absolute value functions, the graph is symmetric about a vertical line through its zero.

The graph of $G(x) = |3x - 6|$ is V-shaped and opens upward, with a minimum at (2,0). The range for the output values is $G(x) \geq 0$.   The function has a zero at $x = 2$.

Basic (omit)

Average (3 days)
(1) 1–20
(2) 21–36
(3) 551: 1–6

Advanced (2 days)
(1) 2–24 (even), 26–31
(2) 35–42
    551: 1–6

9) from (−6,0) through (0,6) and from (−6,0) through (−12,6). The graph is V-shaped, opens upward, minimum at $x = -6$, range is $F(x) \geq 0$

10) from (3,0) through (0,3) and from (3,0) through (3,3). The graph is V-shaped, opens upward, minimum at $x = 3$, range is $G(x) \geq 0$

11) from (2,0) through (0,2) and from (2,0) through (4,2). The graph is V-shaped, opens upward, minimum at $x = 2$, range is $H(x) \geq 0$

12) from (−1,0) through (0,1) and from (−1,0) through (−2,1). The graph is V-shaped, opens upward, minimum at $t = -1$, range is $F(t) \geq 0$

13) from ($\frac{1}{2}$,0) through (0,1) and from ($\frac{1}{2}$,0) through (1,1). The graph is V-shaped, opens upward, minimum at $r = \frac{1}{2}$, range is $F(r) \geq 0$

14) from (−$\frac{5}{3}$,0) through (−1,2) and from (−$\frac{5}{3}$,0) through (−$\frac{7}{3}$,2). The graph is V-shaped, opens upward, minimum at $s = -\frac{5}{3}$, range is $F(s) \geq 0$

15) from (−$\frac{1}{2}$,0) through (0,2) and from (−$\frac{1}{2}$,0) through (1,2). The graph is V-shaped, opens upward, minimum at $x = -\frac{1}{2}$, range is $G(x) \geq 0$

16) from (−$\frac{3}{2}$,0) through (−1,1) and from (−$\frac{3}{2}$,0) through (−2,1). The graph is V-shaped, opens upward, minimum at $x = -\frac{3}{2}$, range is $H(x) \geq 0$

3 Graph $H(x) = -|-2x + 5|$ and describe it.

PROCEDURE Graph $H(x)$ from a table of values:

x	−1	0	1	2	3	4	5	6	7
$H(x)$	−7	−5	−3	−1	−1	−3	−5	−7	−9

One other point is important: $H(2\frac{1}{2}) = -|-2(2\frac{1}{2}) + 5| = -|-5 + 5| = 0.$ Thus the graph contains $(2\frac{1}{2},0)$.

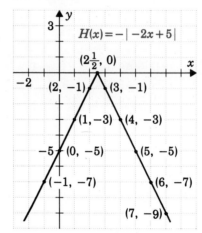

The V-shaped graph opens downward, with a maximum at $(2\frac{1}{2},0)$. The range for the function is $H(x) \leq 0$, and the function has a zero at $x = 2\frac{1}{2}$.

Problem Set **A**

Evaluate each function for the given input values.

1 $F(x) = |x + 6|$; $x = -8, -1$
    2, 5

2 $G(x) = |x - 3|$; $x = 5, -2$
    2, 5

3 $H(x) = $ ABSVAL $(x - 2)$;
$x = 3\frac{1}{2}, -5$
    $\frac{3}{2}$, 7

4 $F(t) = $ ABSVAL $(t + 1)$;
$t = -4, -\frac{1}{2}$
    3, $\frac{1}{2}$

5 $F(r) = |2r - 1|$; $r = -3, 2$
    7, 3

6 $F(s) = |3s + 5|$; $s = -1, 0$
    2, 5

7 $G(x) = $ ABSVAL $(4x + 2)$;
$x = -1, 0$
    2, 2

8 $H(x) = $ ABSVAL $(2x + 3)$;
$x = -5, 1$
    7, 5

For problems **9–16**, graph each function in problems 1–8 and describe the graph.

Find the maximum or minimum for each function:

17 $F(x) = |x + 4|$

minimum at $x = -4$

18 $G(x) = $ ABSVAL $(-x + 6)$

minimum at $x = 6$

19 $H(x) = $ ABSVAL $(3x - 1)$

minimum at $x = \frac{1}{3}$

20 $F(x) = |8x + 2|$

minimum at $x = -\frac{1}{4}$

Use the formula $x \cdot y = k$ (inverse variation) and find the value of y for the given values of x and k. (Review: Section 8.3)

21 $x = 4, k = 20$

$y = 5$

22 $x = -6, k = 24$

$y = -4$

23 $x = 25, k = 200$

$y = 8$

24 $x = 0.2, k = 1$

$y = 5$

25 $x = 1.5, k = 7.5$

$y = 5$

26 $x = 0.4, k = 0.016$

$y = 0.4$

Problem Set **B**

Graph each function and describe the graph.

27 $F(x) = |-x + 5|$

28 $F(x) = |-x - 3|$

29 $G(x) = |-3x - 8|$

30 $G(x) = |-2x + 5|$

31 $H(x) = |-2x + 6|$

32 $H(x) = |-3x - 12|$

33 $F(x) = |-8x|$

34 $F(x) = |4 - x|$

35 $F(x) = -|x + 2|$

36 $F(x) = -|2x - 4|$

Problem Set **C**

Graph each pair of functions on the same set of axes.

37 $F(x) = |2x - 5|$
   $G(x) = -|2x - 5|$

38 $F(x) = |2x + 3|$
   $G(x) = -|2x - 3|$

39 $F(x) = |3x - 1|$
   $G(x) = |-3x - 1|$

27) from (5,0) through (0,5) and through (10,5); V-shaped opens upward, minimum at $x = 5$, range is $F(x) \ge 0$

28) from (−3,0) through (0,3) and through (−6,3); V-shaped, opens upward minimum at (−3,0), range is $F(x) \ge 0$

29) from $(-\frac{8}{3}, 0)$ through (0,8) and through $(-\frac{16}{3}, 8)$; V-shaped, opens upward, minimum at $x = -\frac{8}{3}$, range is $G(x) \ge 0$

30) from $(\frac{5}{2}, 0)$ through (0,5) and through (5,5); V-shaped, opens upward, minimum at $x = \frac{5}{2}$, range is $G(x) \ge 0$

31) from (3,0) through (0,6) and through (6,6); V-shaped, opens upward, minimum at $x = 3$, range is $H(x) \ge 0$

32) from (−4,0) through (0,12) and through (−8,12); V-shaped opens upward, minimum at $x = -4$, range is $H(x) \ge 0$

33) from (0,0) through (−1,8) and through (1,8); V-shaped, opens upward, minimum at $x = 0$, range is $F(x) \ge 0$

34) from (4,0) through (0,4) and through (8,4); V-shaped, opens upward, minimum at (4,0), range is $F(x) \ge 0$

35) from (−2,0) through (0,−2) and through (−4,0); V-shaped, opens downward, maximum at (−2,0), range, $F(x) \le 0$

36) from (2,0) through (0,−4) and through (4,−4); V-shaped, opens downward, maximum at $x = 2$, range is $F(x) \le 0$

37) $F(x)$ has a minimum at $(\frac{5}{2},0)$; from there it passes through (0,5) and (5,5). $G(x)$ has a maximum at $(\frac{5}{2},0)$; from there it passes through (0,5) and (5,5).

38) $F(x)$ has a minimum at $(-\frac{3}{2},0)$; from there it passes through (0,3) and (−3,3). $G(x)$ has a maximum at $(\frac{3}{2},0)$; from there it passes through (0,−3) and (3,−3).

39) $F(x)$ has a minimum at $(\frac{1}{3},0)$; from there it passes through (0,1) and $(\frac{2}{3},1)$. $G(x)$ has a minimum at $(-\frac{1}{3},1)$; from there it passes through (0,1) and $(-\frac{2}{3},1)$.

40) $F(x)$ opens upward, $G(x)$ opens downward. The minimum for $F(x)$ is the maximum for $G(x)$. $G(x)$ is the reflection of $F(x)$ over the x-axis.

41) $F(x)$ and $G(x)$ are the same shape and both open upward; their minimums are $\dfrac{-b}{a}$ and $\dfrac{b}{a}$, respectively.

40 In general, how do the graphs differ for the functions
$F(x) = |ax + b|$ and $G(x) = -|ax + b|$? How are they the same?

41 In general, how do the graphs differ for the functions
$F(x) = |ax + b|$ and $G(x) = |-ax + b|$? How are they the same?

42 Find the point at which the function $F(x) = |ax + b|$ is a maximum or minimum.   minimum at $(-\dfrac{b}{a},0)$

X tending the topic: **Graphing Inequalities with Absolute Value**

To graph the inequality $y \le |x + 3|$, first graph the function $F(x) = |x + 3|$:

x	−5	−4	−3	−2	−1	0	1
$F(x)$	2	1	0	1	2	3	4

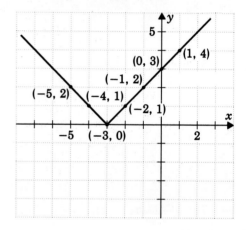

The inequality $y \le |x + 3|$ represents all the points on the V-shaped graph *and* all the points below the graph:

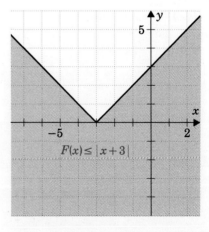

$F(x) \le |x+3|$

Problem Set X

Graph each inequality.

1 $y \geq |x - 2|$ **3** $y \leq -|-x + 4|$ **5** $y > |-x + 5| - 3$

2 $y \leq |2x + 1|$ **4** $y \geq -|-2x - 2|$ **6** $y < -|x - 1| + 4$

Section 13.5   Functions with a Variable in the Denominator

Evaluate the function $f(x) = \dfrac{30}{x - 2}$ for $x = 17$, $x = -4$, and $x = 2$:

If $x = 17$, $f(x) = f(17) = \dfrac{30}{17 - 2} = \dfrac{30}{15} = 2$

If $x = -4$, $f(x) = f(-4) = \dfrac{30}{-4 - 2} = \dfrac{30}{-6} = -5$

If $x = 2$, $f(x) = f(2) = \dfrac{30}{2 - 2} = \dfrac{30}{0} = ?$

Division by zero is not defined. Thus the value 2 cannot be considered as an input number for this function. A restriction on the input numbers for a function refers to the **domain**.

Definition

The DOMAIN of a function is the set of possible input numbers.

EXAMPLES

- $F(x) = \dfrac{1}{x}$

  The domain can be all real numbers except $x = 0$. This can be abbreviated as Domain: $x \neq 0$

- $G(x) = \dfrac{3x}{x^2 - 3x + 2}$

  The denominator factors as $(x - 2)(x - 1)$. Thus the domain of the function is all real numbers except $x = 2$ or $x = 1$. Domain: $x \neq 1, 2$

1) all points on or above the rays from (2,0) through (0,2) and from (2,0) through (4,2)

2) all points on or below the rays from $(-\frac{1}{2}, 0)$ through (0,1) and from $(-\frac{1}{2}, 0)$ through (-1,1).

3) all points on or below the rays from (4,0) through (0,-4) and from (4,0) through (8,-4)

4) all points on or above the rays from (-1,0) through (0,-2) and from (-1,0) through (-1,-2).

5) all points above the rays from (5,-3) through (0,2) and from (5,-3) through (10,2)

6) all points below the rays from (1,4) through (0,3) and from (1,4) through (2,3)

SECTION SCHEDULE

Basic (omit)

Average (1 day)

Advanced (3 days)

Sample Problems

1 Graph the function $f(x) = \dfrac{-12}{x}$ and describe it.

PROCEDURE   Fill in a table of ordered pairs:

x	-10	-6	-2	-1	1	2	6	10
$f(x)$	1.2	2	6	12	-12	-6	-2	-1.2

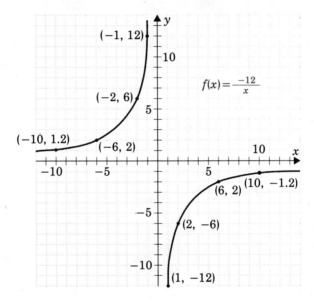

The graph has two **branches** or parts. There is no maximum or minimum, because $f(x)$ gets "very positive" (as x approaches zero from the left) and "very negative" (as x approaches zero from the right). The graph gets "increasingly closer" to the x-axis and the y-axis, but it does not cross or touch either axis. The domain of the function is all real numbers other than zero (Domain: $x \neq 0$) and the range is all real numbers other than zero (Range: $f(x) \neq 0$). The graph does not touch the x-axis, and so the function has no zeros.

The x-axis and y-axis are each called an **asymptote** (as'im tōt') to the curve, because the curve gets "increasingly closer" but does not touch or cross either axis. The shape of the curve, including both branches, is referred to as a **hyperbola** (hī pur'bə lə).

2 Graph the function $g(x) = \dfrac{16}{-3x + 4}$ and describe it.

PROCEDURE   Fill in a table of ordered pairs:

x	-6	-4	-2	0	2	4	6	8
$g(x)$	0.73	1	1.6	4	-8	-2	-1.14	-0.8

Addition values are helpful between $x = 0$ and $x = 2$ because $g(x)$ changes its sign in that interval:

x	0	$\frac{1}{3}$	$\frac{2}{3}$	1	$\frac{4}{3}$	$\frac{5}{3}$	2
$g(x)$	4	$5\frac{1}{3}$	8	16	—	-16	-8

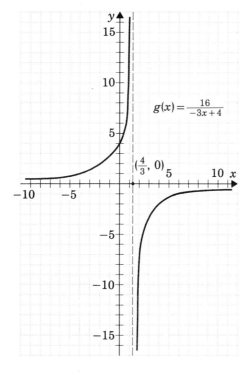

The graph of $g(x)$ is a hyperbola with asymptotes $x = \frac{4}{3}$ and $y = 0$ (the x-axis). The restrictions on the input and output values are:

Domain: $x \neq \dfrac{4}{3}$

Range: $g(x) \neq 0$

The graph crosses the y-axis at (0,4) and the function has no zeros, no maximum, and no minimum.

ASSIGNMENT GUIDE

Basic (omit)

Average (1 day)
1–10, 14–21

Advanced (3 days)
(1) 2–14 (even), 16–23
(2) 24–41
(3) 42–47
      558: 1–9

3 Suppose you have two dozen pens to distribute equally and completely among some friends.

  a How many pens would each of four friends receive? Each of eight friends? Each of nine friends?

  b Let x represent the number of friends and $P(x)$ the number of pens per friend. What is the function rule for $P(x)$?

  c What is the domain for $P(x)$? What is the range?

PROCEDURE   Start with a total of 24 pens.

  a Four friends would each receive 6 pens, and eight friends would each receive 3 pens. The 24 pens could not be equally and completely distributed among nine friends (unless they could be broken!).

  b The function rule is $P(x) = \dfrac{24}{x}$.

  c The domain for $P(x)$ refers to the possible numbers of friends. The domain consists of the integers 1, 2, 3, 4, 6, 8, 12, 24; other numbers will not distribute the pens equally and completely. The range, which refers to the number of pens per friend, consists of the same integers 1, 2, 3, 4, 6, 8, 12, 24.

7) one branch contains $(\frac{1}{10},1), (\frac{1}{3},3), (3,\frac{1}{3}), (10,\frac{1}{10})$; the other branch contains $(-\frac{1}{10},-1), (-\frac{1}{3},-3), (-3,-\frac{1}{3}), (-10,-\frac{1}{10})$. The asymptotes are $x=0$ and $y=0$

8) one branch contains $(2,-1), (3,-\frac{1}{2}), (4,-\frac{1}{3}), (10,-\frac{1}{9})$; the other branch contains $(-2,\frac{1}{3}), (-3,\frac{1}{4}), (-4,\frac{1}{5}), (-10,\frac{1}{11})$. The asymptotes are $x=1$ and $y=0$.

9) one branch contains $(1,6), (2,3), (3,2), (6,1)$; the other branch contains $(-1,-6), (-2,-3), (-3,-2), (-6,-1)$. The asymptotes are $x=0$ and $y=0$.

10) one branch contains $(1,10), (2,5), (5,2), (10,1)$; the other branch contains $(-1,-10), (-2,-5), (-5,-2), (-10,-1)$. The asymptotes are $x=0$ and $y=0$

11) one branch contains $(1,-16), (2,-8), (4,-4), (8,-2), (16,-1)$; the other branch contains $(-1,16), (-2,8), (-4,4), (-8,2), (-16,1)$. The asymptotes are $x=0$ and $y=0$.

Problem Set **A**

1 If $f(x) = \dfrac{36}{x}$ find $f(2), f(-4)$, and $f(8)$.

    18, −9, 4.5

2 If $g(x) = \dfrac{48}{x}$ find $g(16), g(-8)$, and $g(-10)$.

    3, 6, 4.8

3 If $h(t) = \dfrac{-40}{t}$ find $h(-5), h(16)$, and $h(-40)$.

    3, $\frac{-5}{2}$, 1

4 If $f(r) = \dfrac{-20}{r}$ find $f(20), f(-16)$, and $f(1)$.

    $-1, \frac{5}{4}, -20$

5 If $G(x) = \dfrac{-8}{x+2}$ find $G(6), G(-4)$, and $G(0)$.

    −1, 4, −4

6 If $G(r) = \dfrac{-9}{x-3}$ find $G(6), G(-6)$, and $G(-3)$.

    $-3, 1, \frac{3}{2}$

For each function, graph the function and describe the graph.

7 $F(x) = \dfrac{1}{x}$

8 $F(x) = \dfrac{-1}{x-1}$

9 $F(x) = \dfrac{6}{x}$

10 $F(x) = \dfrac{10}{x}$

11 $G(x) = \dfrac{-16}{x}$

12 $G(x) = \dfrac{-8}{x}$

13 $H(x) = \dfrac{2}{x-4}$

14 $H(x) = \dfrac{5}{x+1}$

15 $F(x) = \dfrac{-3}{x+6}$

12) one branch contains $(1,-8)$, $(2,-4)$, $(4,-2)$, $(8,-1)$; the other branch contains $(-1,8)$, $(-2,4)$, $(-4,2)$, $(-8,1)$. The asymptotes are $x=0$ and $y=0$.

13) one branch contains $(4.1,20)$, $(6,2)$, $(5,1)$, $(8,\frac{1}{2})$; the other branch contains $(0,-\frac{1}{2})$, $(1,-\frac{2}{3})$, $(2,1)$, $(3,-2)$, $(3.9,-20)$. The asymptotes are $x=4$ and $y=0$

14) one branch contains $(0,5)$, $(1,\frac{5}{2})$, $(4,1)$, $(9,\frac{1}{2})$; the other branch contains $(-2,-5)$, $(-3,-\frac{5}{2})$, $(-6,1)$, $(-11,\frac{1}{2})$. The asymptotes are $x=-1$ and $y=0$

15) one branch contains $(-12,\frac{1}{2})$, $(-7,3)$, $(-6.1,30)$; the other branch contains $(-5.9,-30)$, $(-5,-3)$, $(0,-\frac{1}{2})$. The asymptotes are $x=-6$ and $y=0$

Evaluate each function for the given input value. (Review: Sections 13.3, 13.4)

16 $f(x) = x^2 - 5;\quad x = -7$

$f(-7) = 44$

17 $g(x) = 2x^2 + 1;\quad x = -2$

$g(-2) = 9$

18 $h(x) = \dfrac{1}{4}x^2 - \dfrac{1}{4};\quad x = 5$

$h(5) = 6$

19 $f(x) = |x + 6|;\quad x = -7$

$f(-7) = 1$

20 $g(x) = -|x - 3|;\quad x = -3$

$g(-3) = -6$

21 $h(x) = \dfrac{-|x + 2|}{3};\quad x = -2$

$h(-2) = 0$

Problem Set **B**

22 If $f(x) = \dfrac{-8}{3x + 2}$ find $f(-2), f(2),$ and $f(0)$.

$2, -1, -4$

23 If $g(x) = \dfrac{10}{-2x + 5}$ find $g(2), g(0),$ and $g(3)$.

$10, 2, -10$

For each function, graph the function and describe the graph.

24 $F(x) = \dfrac{12}{2x + 3}$

25 $F(x) = \dfrac{14}{-3x - 5}$

26 $G(x) = \dfrac{-9}{-2x + 1}$

27 $G(x) = \dfrac{-8}{4x - 3}$

28 Sixty cups are to be packed in one layer of a rectangular box.

  a How many rows would there be if there are twelve columns?

5

  b Can there be ten full columns?

yes, 6 in each

  c Can there be eight full columns?

no

24) one branch contains $(-1,12)$, $(0,4)$, $(\frac{9}{2},1)$; the other branch contains $(-2,-12)$, $(-6,-\frac{4}{3})$, $(-\frac{15}{2},-1)$. The asymptotes are $x = -\frac{3}{2}$ and $y = 0$.

25) one branch contains $(-4,2)$ and $(-2,14)$; the other branch contains $(0,-\frac{14}{5})$ and $(2,-\frac{14}{11})$. The asymptotes are $x = -\frac{5}{3}$ and $y = 0$.

26) one branch contains $(1,9)$ and $(2,3)$; the other branch contains $(0,-9)$ and $(-1,-3)$. The asymptotes are $x = \frac{1}{2}$ and $y = 0$.

27) one branch contains $(-1,\frac{8}{7})$ and $(0,\frac{8}{3})$; the other branch contains $(1,-8)$, $(2,-\frac{8}{5})$, $(3,-\frac{8}{9})$. The asymptotes are $x = \frac{3}{4}$ and $y = 0$

Problem Set C

29 If the area of a rectangle has measure ten, express the length as a function of the width.

$\ell(w) = \dfrac{10}{w}$

30 If the area of a rectangle has measure forty, express the width as a function of the length.

$w(\ell) = \dfrac{40}{\ell}$

31 State the domain and range for problem 30.

domain: $\ell > 0$ range: $w > 0$

32 If the length of a classroom test period is forty-five minutes, express the average length of time per question as a function of the number of questions.

$t(n) = \dfrac{45}{n}$

33 State the domain and range for problem 32.

domain: n is a natural number   range: $t > 0$

34 Describe the asymptotes for the graph of the function $f(x) = \dfrac{k}{x + b}$

asymptotes at $x = -b$ and $y = 0$

35 Describe the asymptotes for the graph of the function $g(x) = \dfrac{k}{ax + b}$

asymptotes at $x = -\dfrac{b}{a}$ and $y = 0$

Find a value of k so that the two given points are on the graph of the function $F(x) = k \div x$.

36 (2,8) and (4,4)

$k = 16$

37 $(-5,2)$ and $(2,-5)$

$k = -10$

38 $(3\frac{1}{2},\frac{2}{7})$ and $(-\frac{1}{2},-2)$

$k = 1$

39 $(2a,\frac{1}{2})$ and $(-5a,-\frac{1}{5})$

$k = 1$

40 (4,4) and $\left(8\sqrt{2},\sqrt{2}\right)$

$k = 16$

41 $\left(\sqrt{17},\sqrt{17}\right)$ and $\left(2\sqrt{17},\frac{1}{2}\sqrt{17}\right)$

$k = 17$

Find a value of k so that the two given points are on the graph of the function $F(x) = k \div (2x - 1)$.

42 $(3,\frac{1}{5})$ and $(10,\frac{1}{19})$

$k = 1$

43 (3,3) and $(-7,-1)$

$k = 15$

44 (5,1) and $(14,\frac{1}{3})$

$k = 9$

45 $(3\frac{1}{2},-1)$ and $(-\frac{1}{2},3)$

$k = -6$

46 $(8,\frac{1}{3})$ and $(-9\frac{1}{2},-\frac{1}{4})$

$k = 5$

47 (1,2) and $(5,\frac{2}{9})$

$k = 2$

X tending the topic: Functions with a Variable as an Exponent

How long will it take to double your money if the money is left in an account that pays ten percent interest each year?

Start with Q dollars:

after the first year: $\quad Q + 0.1Q = Q(1 + 0.1) = Q(1.1)$

after the second year: $\quad Q(1.1) + 0.1(Q(1.1))$
$$\begin{aligned} &= Q(1.1)[1 + 0.1] \\ &= Q(1.1)[1.1] \\ &= Q(1.1)^2 \end{aligned}$$

after the third year: $\quad Q(1.1)^2 + 0.1(Q(1.1)^2)$
$$\begin{aligned} &= Q(1.1)^2[1 + 0.1] \\ &= Q(1.1)^2[1.1] \\ &= Q(1.1)^3 \end{aligned}$$

After x years, the total amount will be $\quad Q(1.1)^x$. For that to be double the original amount:

$$Q(1.1)^x = 2Q$$
$$(1.1)^x = 2$$

This equation cannot be solved by ordinary methods, because the variable appears as an exponent. An approximate answer can be found using a graph of the function $f(x) = (1.1)^x$. (The values for $F(x)$ in the table are rounded to two decimal places.)

x	1	2	3	4	5	6	7	8	9
$f(x)$	1.1	1.21	1.33	1.46	1.61	1.77	1.95	2.14	2.36

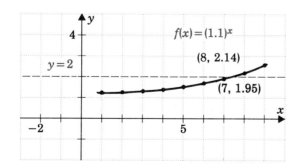

The line $y = 2$ indicates when the original investment has doubled. The graph of $f(x) = (1.1)^x$ crosses the line $y = 2$ between $x = 7$ and $x = 8$. Thus an investment at ten percent interest would double after seven years and before eight years.

A function such as $f(x) = (1.1)^x$, where x appears as a variable, is called an **exponential function**.

Note: The table of ordered pairs for $f(x) = (1.1)^x$ only used natural number values for x, but the function was graphed using a solid line. Later mathematics courses will use other sets of numbers for exponents, including integer, rational, and real values. The $f(x)$ values on the graph can be "checked" using a calculator with a y^x key.

Problem Set X

1   If $f(x) = 3^x$, for what value of x is $f(x) = 81$?

$x = 4$

2   If $g(x) = 2^x$, for what value of x is $g(x) = 64$?

6

7) The problem can be translated as: Where does the function $f(x) = (1.075)^x$ cross the line $y = 3$?

$f(15) = (1.075)^{15} = 2.96$
$f(16) = (1.075)^{16} = 3.18$

between 15 and 16 years.

3   Graph $F(x) = (1.06)^x$. Between what two integer values of x is $F(x) = 2$?
the graph contains (11,1.898) and (12,2.012);
between $x = 11$ and $x = 12$

4   Graph $G(x) = (1.09)^x$. Between what two integer values of x is $G(x) = 3$?
the graph contains (12,2.810) and (13,3.06);
between $x = 12$ and $x = 13$

8) For $g(x) = (1.094)^x$:

$g(7) = (1.094)^7 = 1.88$
$g(8) = (1.094)^8 = 2.05$

between 7 and 8 years.

5   If $h(x) = (0.9)^x$, between what two integer values of x is $h(x) = 0.45$?
the graph contains (7,0.478) and (8,0.430);
between $x = 7$ and $x = 8$

6   If $h(x) = \left(\dfrac{3}{4}\right)^x$, between what two integer values of x is $h(x) = 0.2$?
the graph contains (5,0.237) and (6,0.178);
between $x = 5$ and $x = 6$

9) For $p(x) = (10,000)(1.05)^x$

$p(10) = (10,000)(1.05)^{10}$
$= 16,288$
$p(14) = (10,000)(1.05)^{14}$
$= 19,799$
$p(15) = (10,000)(1.05)^{15}$
$= 20,789$

between 14 and 15 years.
(Students should realize that population figures should not be rounded up; rather, they should be expressed to the greatest whole integer.)

7   How long will it take to triple an investment if the interest rate is $7\frac{1}{2}\%$ per year?
$(1.075)^{15} = 2.959$; $(1.075)^{16} = 3.181$; sixteen years

8   How long will it take to double an investment at 9.4% per year?
between 7 and 8 years

9   The population of a city is increasing at the rate of five percent per year. If the population of the city is now 10,000, what would the estimated population be in ten years? In how many years would it be 20,000?
16,288; between 14 and 15 years

After-School Mathematics: Bridge

Melissa enjoyed playing cards, so one day she watched her mother's bridge group. Her mother tried to coach her on the fundamentals. The object is for one team to win two out of three games. It may take one or more hands to complete each game. To play a hand, one of the players wins a bid. Bidding is a special way of communicating to your partner how many points you have and what your strong suit is.

After explaining an overview of the game, Melissa's mother taught her how to count the points in her hand. The entire deck is dealt, so each player has thirteen cards. An ace is worth four points; a king, three; a queen, two; and a jack, one. The other cards have no point value. However, points are also given for distribution. A void (no cards in a suit) is worth three points, a singleton (one card in a suit) is worth two points, and doubleton (two cards in a suit) is worth one point. In order to open the bidding, a player must have at least thirteen points.

Melissa tried to remember all of the rules as she looked at the first hand she was dealt: A, K, 10, 7, and 2 of spades; K, Q, J, 8, and 3 of hearts; A, J, and 5 of clubs; and no diamonds. She counted 21 points with distribution! She knew that she had a good hand. If only she knew what to do with it!

Application: Watering Cycle

In the greenhouse, the carnations are watered every other day, and the seedlings are watered twice per day. The bonsai trees are watered every five days, and the cactus plants are watered only every fourteen days.

Suppose that on a certain day, all the plants were watered. How many days would it be until all the plants were again watered on the same day?

The least common multiple of 2, $\frac{1}{2}$, 5, and 14 is 70. All the plants will be watered together in 70 days.

559

Section 13.6   Describing Graphs

Functions that are the same type have graphs with similar features. For example, all linear functions of the form $f(x) = ax + b$ ($a \neq 0$) are graphed by straight lines. The graphs have no maximum or minimum, no asymptote, one zero, and unrestricted domain and range.

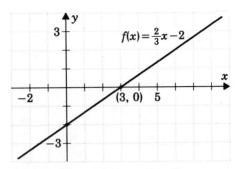

$$f(x) = \tfrac{2}{3}x - 2$$

(3, 0)

The absolute value function $g(x) = |ax + b|$, $a \neq 0$, has a V-shaped graph with a minimum on the x-axis. The function $h(x) = -|ax + b|$, $a \neq 0$, has a V shape with a maximum on the x-axis. Each function has a zero, unrestricted domain, and restricted range.

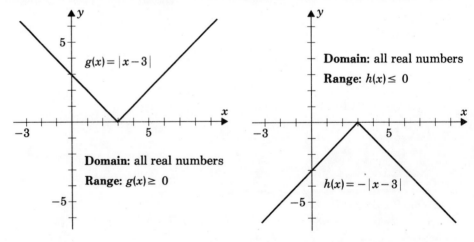

$g(x) = |x - 3|$

Domain: all real numbers

Range: $g(x) \geq 0$

Domain: all real numbers

Range: $h(x) \leq 0$

$h(x) = -|x - 3|$

Other features of a graph that could be described are whether it has an axis of symmetry, and whether it is continuous or discontinuous.

Other types of functions also have graphs that have many common features.

Sample Problems

1   Describe the general characteristics of the following types of functions:

    a   quadratic functions of the form $Q(x) = ax^2 + c$, $a \neq 0$

    b   functions of the form $F(x) = \dfrac{c}{ax - b}$ $a \neq 0, c \neq 0$

PROCEDURE

a These functions have graphs that are parabolas that open upward or open downward. The graph has either a maximum or a minimum (depending on the sign of a) and as many as two zeros. The domain is all real numbers; the range is restricted.

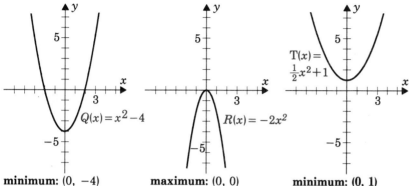

minimum: (0, −4)

2 zeros: $x = -2$, $x = 2$

Domain: all real numbers

Range: $Q(x) \geq -4$

maximum: (0, 0)

1 zero: $x = 0$

Domain: all real numbers

Range: $R(x) \leq 0$

minimum: (0, 1)

no zeros

Domain: all real numbers

Range: $T(x) \geq 1$

b These functions have graphs that are hyperbolas. The graphs, which have two branches, have no maximum or minimum and no zeros. The graphs have two asymptotes: $x = 0$ and $y = -b/a$. The domain and range are both restricted.

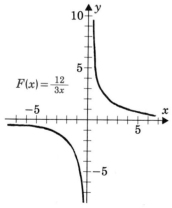
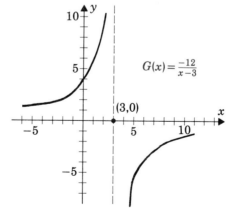

asymptotes: $x = 0$ (the y-axis)
$\quad\quad\quad\quad y = 0$ (the x-axis)

Domain: $x \neq 0$

Range: $y \neq 0$

asymptotes: $x = 3$
$\quad\quad\quad\quad y = 0$

Domain: $x \neq 3$

Range: $y \neq 0$

2   Graph the function $G(x) = x^3 + 3x^2 - 2x - 6$ and describe the graph.

PROCEDURE   Fill in a table of input and output values, and connect the points with a smooth curve.

x	-4	-3	-2	-1	0	1	2
$G(x)$	-14	0	2	-2	-6	-4	10

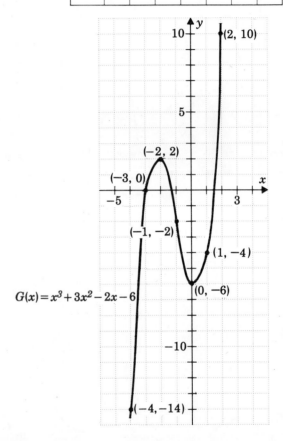

Since the variable does not appear in a denominator, there is no restriction on the domain. Also, there is no restriction on the range; $G(x)$ can be "very positive" or it can be "very negative." Thus the graph has no maximum or minimum and no asymptotes.

The function has three zeros, one at $x = -3$, one between $x = -2$ and $x = -1$, and one between $x = 1$ and $x = 2$. The function has a **local maximum** near the point $(-2,2)$ and the graph has a **local minimum** near the point $(0,-6)$. (These points are both approximated from the graph.)

Problem Set A

Describe each graph.

1

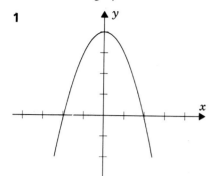

2

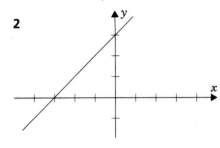

3

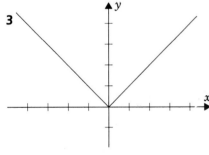

4

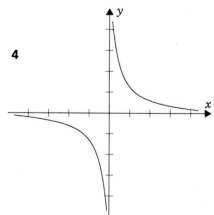

5

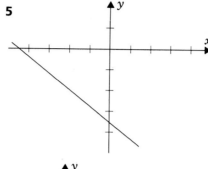

6

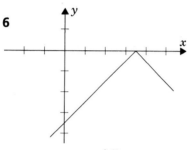

7

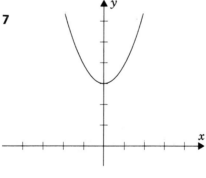

8

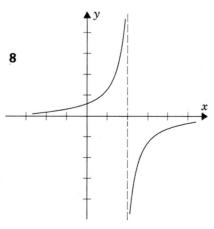

ASSIGNMENT GUIDE

Basic (omit)

Average (2 days)
(1) 1–26
(2) 28–52 (even)

Advanced (2 days)
(1) 9–20, 22–40 (even)
(2) 52–68 (even)

1) parabola, opens downward, maximum at (0,4), zeros at $x = -2$ and $x = 2$

2) straight line, x-intercept at $x = -3$, y-intercept at $y = 3$

3) V-shaped, opens upward, minimum at (0,0), zero at $x = 0$

4) hyperbola in upper right and lower left portions of the plane; asymptotes are $x = 0$ and $y = 0$

5) straight line, x-intercept between $x = -5$ and $x = -4$, y-intercept between $y = -4$ and $y = -3$

6) V-shaped, opens downward, maximum at $(3\frac{1}{2},0)$

7) parabola, opens up, minimum at (3,0)

8) hyperbola in lower right and upper left portions of the plane; asymptotes at $x = 2$ and $y = 0$

9) a line with slope 4; the x-intercept is $\frac{1}{4}$, and the y-intercept is -1

10) V-shaped, opens upward, minimum at $(\frac{1}{4},0)$

11) hyperbola in upper right and lower left portions of the plane; asymptotes at $x = \frac{1}{4}$ and at $y = 0$

12) a parabola, opens upward with minimum at $(0,-1)$

13) the zero of $f(x) = 4x - 1$ is at $x = \frac{1}{4}$

14) the zero of $g(x) = |4x - 1|$ is at $x = \frac{1}{4}$

15) $h(x)$ has no zeros

16) the zeros of $k(x) = 4x^2 - 1$ are at $x = \frac{1}{2}$ and at $x = -\frac{1}{2}$

17) $f(\frac{1}{2}) = 1$

18) $g(\frac{1}{2}) = 1$

19) $h(\frac{1}{2}) = 1$

20) $k(\frac{1}{2}) = 0$

27) a line with slope -3; the x-intercept is -2 and the y-intercept is -6

28) parabola, opens upward, minimum at $(0,-8)$, zeros at $x = 2$ and $x = -2$

29) V-shaped, opens upward, minimum at $(1,0)$

30) hyperbola in upper right and lower left portions of the plane, asymptotes at $x = -\frac{1}{2}$, $y = 0$

31) parabola, opens downward, maximum at $(-1,-2)$, no zeros

32) line with slope 2, y-intercept 1

33) V-shaped, opens downward, maximum at $(-1,0)$

34) horizontal line through $y = 5$, slope 0

35) parabola, opens downward, maximum at $(0,0)$

For each function, describe the shape of the graph.

9 $f(x) = 4x - 1$

11 $h(x) = \dfrac{1}{4x - 1}$

10 $g(x) = |4x - 1|$

12 $k(x) = 4x^2 - 1$

For problems **13–16**, find the zeros of each function in problems 9–12.

For problems **17–20**, find the output value for $x = \frac{1}{2}$ for each of the functions in problems 9–12.

Evaluate each function for the given input value. (Review: Sections 13.3, 13.4, 13.5)

21 $Q(x) = 3x^2 - 2; \quad x = -1$

1

24 $g(x) = -|\frac{2}{3}x + 8|; \quad x = -12$

0

22 $Q(r) = \dfrac{1}{2}r^2 + 3; \quad r = -6$

21

25 $h(x) = \dfrac{5}{2x - 9}; \quad x = -3$

$-\frac{1}{3}$

23 $f(x) = |3x - 7|; \quad x = -1$

10

26 $h(t) = \dfrac{-6}{3 - 4t}; \quad t = -2$

$\frac{-6}{11}$

Problem Set **B**

For each function, describe the shape of the graph.

27 $f(x) = -3x - 6$

34 $p(x) = 5$

28 $g(x) = 2x^2 - 8$

35 $q(x) = -5x^2$

29 $h(x) = |-x + 1|$

36 $r(x) = |3 - x|$

30 $k(x) = \dfrac{1}{2x + 1}$

37 $K(x) = \dfrac{4}{x - 2}$

31 $F(x) = -x^2 - 1$

38 $Q(x) = (x + 1)(x - 1)$

32 $G(x) = 2x + 1$

39 $R(x) = x$

33 $H(x) = -|2x + 2|$

40 $T(x) = $ ABSVAL $(3x)$

Find the input value for the given output value.

41 $f(x) = 3x + 2;$ $f(x) = 8$

$x = 2$

42 $F(x) = 3x^2 + 3;$ $F(x) = 6$

$x = 1$ or $x = -1$

43 $F(t) = \dfrac{1}{t - 3};$ $F(t) = 2$

$t = \dfrac{7}{2}$

44 $f(t) = -t + 4;$ $f(t) = -7$

$x = 11$

45 $G(s) = |2s - 1|;$ $G(s) = 0$

$s = \dfrac{1}{2}$

46 $G(r) = -2r^2 + 1;$ $G(r) = 2$

no real number

47 $g(m) = \dfrac{4}{m + 2};$ $g(m) = -\dfrac{1}{2}$

$m = -10$

48 $g(n) = |3n + 5|;$ $g(n) = -3$

no real number

49 $T(x) = \dfrac{|x + 3|}{|x - 3|};$ $T(x) = 0$

$x = -3$

50 $R(x) = (x + 1)(x - 1);$ $R(x) = 1$

$x = \sqrt{2}$ and $x = -\sqrt{2}$

51 $S(x) = |(x - 3)(x + 3)|;$ $S(x) = 5$

$x = 2, -2, \sqrt{14}$ and $-\sqrt{14}$

52 $Q(x) = 5(x - 3) + 5x^2;$ $Q(x) = 3$

$x = \dfrac{-5 \pm \sqrt{385}}{10}$

Problem Set **C**

For each function, sketch the graph and describe it.

53 $f(x) = \dfrac{x + 1}{x - 4}$

54 $g(x) = x^3 + 3x^2 - x - 3$

55 $h(x) = \dfrac{|x|}{x}$

56 $f(x) = \dfrac{x + 1}{x^2 - 4}$

57 $G(x) = x^3 + 3x^2 - 3x - 9$

58 $H(x) = \dfrac{1}{-|2x|}$

For each function, find the output values for $x = -3, -1, 0, 1, 3.$

59 $f(x) = (x - 1)^3$

59–61) $-64, -8, -1, 0, 8$

60 $g(x) = x^3 - 3x^2 + 3x - 1$

61 $h(x) = (x - 1)(x^2 - 2x + 1)$

62 $k(x) = \dfrac{(x^2 - 2x + 1)^2}{x - 1}$

63 $m(x) = (x - 1)^5 \div (x - 1)^2$

62–63) $-64, -8, -1,$ Und, 8

64 $f(x) = (x^2 - 1)(x^2 - 9)$

65 $g(x) = (x^2 - 4x + 3)(x^2 + 4x + 3)$

66 $h(x) = (x^3 - 3x^2 - x - 3)(x + 3)$

67 $k(x) = \dfrac{x^6 - 9x^4 - x^2 + 9}{x^2 + 1}$

68 $m(x) = x^4 - 10x^2 + 9$

64–68) $0, 0, 9, 0, 0$

36) V-shaped, opens upward, minimum at (3,0)

37) hyperbola in upper right and lower left portions of the plane; asymptotes are $x = 2$ and $y = 0$

38) parabola, opens upward, minimum at $(0, -1)$ zeros at $x = 1$ and $x = -1$

39) a line through the origin, slope is 1

40) V-shaped, opens upward, minimum at (0,0)

53) hyperbola: branches contain (5,6) and $(6, \frac{7}{2})$; $(1, -\frac{2}{3})$ and $(3, -1)$; asymptotes are $x = 4$ and $y = 1$

54) the graph has a relative maximum around $(-2, 3)$ and a relative minimum around $(0, -3)$. The zeros are near $x = -1 - \sqrt{2}$, $x = -1$ and $x = -1 + \sqrt{2}$

55) the graph is $y = 1$ for $x > 0$ and $y = -1$ for $x < 0$

56)

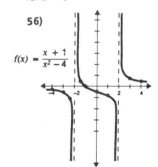

$f(x) = \dfrac{x + 1}{x^2 - 4}$

57) the graph has a relative maximum around $(-2, -1)$ and a relative minimum around (0,9). The zeros are near $x = -3$, $x = -2\frac{1}{2}$ and $x = 1\frac{3}{4}$

58) hyperbola in quadrants III and IV; asymptotes are the x-axis and the negative y-axis.

ASSIGNMENT GUIDE

Basic (omit)

Average (3 days)
(1) 531: 41, 43, 45
    564: 27, 29, 31, 37
(2) 570: 1–26
(3) 606: 1–4, 7–26
    608: 27–37

Advanced (1 day)
538: 50–52
564: 27, 29, 31, 37
570: 1–26

Chapter Study Guide

Vocabulary

As you study and review this chapter, be sure to learn the important mathematics vocabulary, including:

1 **Linear Function**   A LINEAR FUNCTION is a function that can be written in the form $L(x) = mx + b,$ where m and b are real numbers.

- $L(x) = 2x - 7$
- $P(x) = -6x$
- $L(y) = -5y + \frac{1}{2}$
- $L(x) = 3$

2 **Zero of a function**   A ZERO OF A FUNCTION (or simply, a ZERO) is an input value that is associated with the output value 0.

- For $f(x) = 3x - 1,$ $x = \frac{1}{3}$ is a zero:
  $f(\frac{1}{3}) = 3(\frac{1}{3}) - 1 = 1 - 1 = 0$

- For $Q(x) = 2x^2 - 32,$ $x = 4$ and $x = -4$ are zeros:
  $Q(4) = 2(4)^2 - 32 = 2 \cdot 16 - 32 = 32 - 32 = 0$
  $Q(-4) = 2(-4)^2 - 32 = 2 \cdot 16 - 32 = 32 - 32 = 0$

3 **Range**   The RANGE of a function is the set of possible output numbers.

- For $Q(x) = x^2 + 1$
  the range is $Q(x) \geq 1.$

- For $T(x) = -|x|$
  the range is $T(x) \leq 0.$

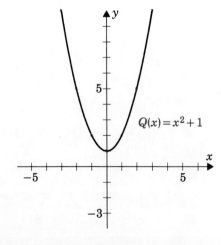

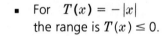

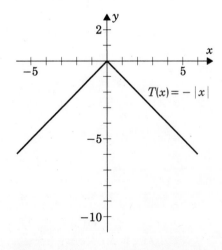

4   Domain
The DOMAIN of a function is the set of possible input numbers.

- For $f(x) = \dfrac{1}{x + 5}$ the domain is all real numbers except $x = -5$

  (Domain: $x \neq -5$)

- For $g(x) = x^2 + 3$ the domain is all real numbers.

Skills

Be sure you build the useful algebraic skills, including:

5   Using function notation   Find each input or output value:

a   For $f(x) = 3x^2 - 5$,   find $f(1), f(-3)$, and $f(0)$.

b   For $g(x) = x^2 - 7$,   find the value(s) of x if $g(x) = 9$.

c   For $h(x) = \dfrac{3}{|x|}$ find $h(3), h(-3)$, and $h(0)$.

d   For $k(x) = \dfrac{1}{|x|}$ find the value(s) of x if $k(x) = 2$.

PROCEDURE

a $f(1) = 3(1)^2 - 5 = 3 \cdot 1 - 5 = 3 - 5 = -2$
   $f(-3) = 3(-3)^2 - 5 = 3 \cdot 9 - 5 = 27 - 5 = 22$
   $f(0) = 3(0)^2 - 5 = 0 - 5 = -5$

b $g(x) = x^2 - 7 = 9$
   $$x^2 = 16$$
   $$x = 4 \quad or \quad x = -4$$

c $h(3) = \dfrac{3}{|3|} = \dfrac{3}{3} = 1$

   $h(-3) = \dfrac{3}{|-3|} = \dfrac{3}{3} = 1$

   $h(0) = \dfrac{3}{|0|} = \dfrac{3}{0} \qquad h(0)$ is undefined.

d $k(x) = \dfrac{1}{|x|} = 2$
   $$1 = 2|x|$$
   $$\dfrac{1}{2} = |x|$$
   $$x = \dfrac{1}{2} \quad or \quad x = -\dfrac{1}{2}$$

6 Graphing functions   Graph each function:

a $Q(x) = x^2 - 4$ **b** $F(x) = |2x + 3|$ **c** $G(x) = \dfrac{36}{x}$

PROCEDURE   Form a table of values for each function.

a

x	−2	−1	0	1	2
$Q(x)$	0	−3	−4	−3	0

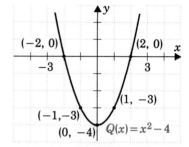

b

x	−4	−3	−2	$-\frac{3}{2}$	−1	0	1	2
$F(x)$	5	3	1	0	1	3	5	7

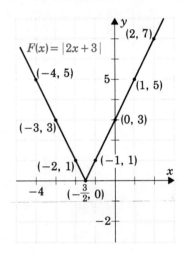

c

x	−9	−6	−3	0	3	6	9
$G(x)$	−4	−6	−12	−	12	6	4

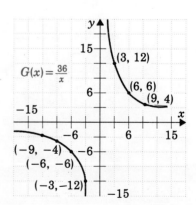

7   **Finding zeros of functions**
Find the zero(s) of each function in problem 6.

PROCEDURE   The function $Q(x) = x^2 - 4$ has two zeros, one at $x = -2$ and one at $x = 2$. The function $F(x) = |2x + 3|$ has a zero at $x = -\frac{3}{2}$. $G(x)$ has no zeros.

8   **Describing graphs**   Describe the graph of each function in problem 6.

PROCEDURE

a   The graph of $Q(x)$ is a parabola that opens upward. It has a minimum, at $(0, -4)$, and two zeros, at $x = -2$ and $x = 2$. The domain is all real numbers; the range is $Q(x) \geq -4$.

b   The graph of $F(x)$ is V-shaped and opens upward. It has a minimum at $\left(-\frac{3}{2}, 0\right)$ and a zero at $x = -\frac{3}{2}$. The domain is all real numbers; the range is $F(x) \geq 0$.

c   The graph of $G(x)$ is a hyperbola with asymptotes $x = 0$ and $y = 0$. The function has no zeros. The domain is all real numbers except $x = 0$; the range is all real numbers except $y = 0$.

Math History: The Conic Sections

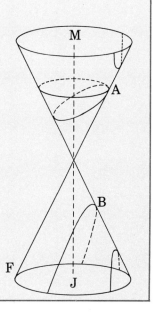

If a plane slices a cone, the intersection of the plane and the cone will be a curve. Depending on the angle of the slice, the curve may be a circle, an ellipse, a parabola, or a hyperbola. Thus the four curves are called the four **conic sections**.

Suppose a plane cuts a cone at point A. If the slice is perpendicular to line MJ (which is called the **axis** of the cone), then the curve is a circle. If the cut is at a slight angle, the curve is an ellipse.

Another plane cuts the cone at point B. If the slice is parallel to line AF (which is called an **element** of the cone), then the curve is a parabola. If the slice intersects both **nappes** of the cone, the curve is a hyperbola.

Chapter Test

State whether each function is a linear, quadratic, or absolute value function.

1 $f(x) = x^2 + 9$

   quadratic

2 $f(x) = -3(2x - 5)$

   linear

3 $f(x) = |6 - 2x|$

   absolute value function

4 $f(x) = -16$

   linear

5 $f(x) = 6 - \frac{1}{2}x^2$

   quadratic

6 $f(x) = |-4| + \frac{1}{3}x$

   linear

Find the output of each function for $f(-3)$, $f(2)$, and $f(0)$.

7 $f(x) = 7 - 2x$

   $f(-3) = 13; f(2) = 3; f(0) = 7$

8 $f(x) = \frac{2}{3}(2x - 9)$

   $f(-3) = -10; f(2) = \frac{-10}{3}; f(0) = -6$

9 $f(x) = \dfrac{18}{x}$

   $f(-3) = -6; f(2) = 9; f(0)$
   is undefined

10 $f(x) = 5 - 2x^2$

   $f(-3) = -13; f(2) = -3; f(0) = 5$

11 $f(x) = |3 - 2x|$

   $f(-3) = 9; f(2) = 1; f(0) = 3$

12 $f(x) = \dfrac{10}{2 - x}$

   $f(-3) = 2; f(2)$ is undefined;
   $f(0) = 5$

Find a rule that represents all the ordered pairs of each set $(x, f(x))$.

13 $(-5,-8)$, $(0,-3)$, $(2,-1)$, $(7,4)$

   $f(x) = x - 3$

14 $(2,9)$, $(\frac{1}{2},36)$, $(3,6)$, $(9,2)$

   $f(x) = \dfrac{18}{|x|}$

15 $(-8,-5)$, $(0,-1)$, $(2,0)$, $(10,4)$

   $f(x) = \frac{1}{2}x - 1$

16 $(-3,7)$, $(0,-2)$, $(3,7)$, $(5,23)$

   $f(x) = x^2 - 2$

Find the zeros of the graph represented by each function.

17 $f(x) = 0.2 + 0.5x$

   $(-\frac{2}{5},0)$

18 $f(x) = 3x^2 - 27$

   $(3,0)(-3,0)$

19 $f(x) = x^2 + 2x - 15$

   $(3,0)(-5,0)$

20 $f(x) = \frac{2}{5}x$

   $(0,0)$

For each function, make a table of ordered pairs, graph the function, and describe each graph.

21 $f(x) = \frac{3}{2}x - 5$

22 $f(x) = -2x + 3$

23 $f(x) = \frac{1}{2}x$

24 $f(x) = -\frac{1}{2}x^2 + 8$

25 $f(x) = |3x - 2|$

26 $f(x) = -|-2x + 3|$

21) straight line passing through points $(0,-5)$ and $(3,-3)$

22) straight line passing through points $(0,3)$ and $(1,1)$

23) straight line passing through points $(0,0)$ and $(2,1)$

24) parabola, opens downward, maximum at $(0,8)$ and zeros at $(4,0)$ and $(-4,0)$

25) V-shaped which opens upward, minimum at $(\frac{2}{3},0)$. The domain is all real numbers and the range is $f(x) \geq 0$

26) V-shaped, opens downward, maximum at $(\frac{3}{2},0)$. The domain is all real numbers and the range is $f(x) \leq 0$

Problem Set: Composite Functions

Sometimes one function is used as the input for another function.

- $f(x) = 3x + 2$
  $g(x) = x^2$

    Then $g(f(x)) = g(3x + 2) = (3x + 2)^2 = 9x^2 + 12x + 4$

Such functions are called **composite functions**.

Consider the following functions:

$$f(x) = 3x + 2 \qquad m(x) = x^2 - 3 \qquad g(x) = x^2$$
$$h(x) = -5 - 2x \qquad p(x) = x \qquad q(x) = \sqrt{x}$$

Evaluate each expression:

1 $g(f(7))$

$g(3(7)+2) = 23^2 = 529$

2 $f(g(7))$

$f(7^2) = 3(49) + 2 = 149$

3 $m(h(-3))$

$m(-5-2(-3)) = 1^2 - 3 = -2$

4 $h(m(-3))$

$h((-3)^2 - 3) = -5 - 2(6) = -17$

5 $g(q(x))$

$g(\sqrt{x}) = (\sqrt{x})^2 = x$

6 $q(g(x))$

$q(x^2) = \sqrt{x^2} = |x|$

7 $f(h(x) + p(x))$

$f(-5-2x+x) = 3(-5-x) + 2 = -13 - 3x$

8 $m(f(p(x)))$

$m(f(x)) = m(3x+2) = (3x+2)^2 - 3 = 9x^2 + 12x + 1$

9 $f(h(g(x)))$

$f(h(x^2)) = f(-5-2x^2) = 3(-5-2x^2) + 2 = -13 - 6x^2$

10 $g(m(x) \cdot g(x))$

$g((x^2-3)(x^2)) = (x^4 - 3x^2)^2 = x^8 - 6x^6 + 9x^4$

11   In general, is $f(g(x)) = g(f(x))$?

no

Consider these two functions: $f(x) = 3x$, $g(x) = \dfrac{1}{3}x$

Then $g(f(x)) = g(3x) = \dfrac{1}{3}(3x) = x$.   Notice that $g(x)$ "undoes" what $f(x)$ does. The function $g(x)$ is called the **inverse** of $f(x)$.

Find an inverse function for each function:

12 $h(x) = x - 5$

$H(x) = x + 5$

13 $k(x) = x + 7$

$K(x) = x - 7$

14 $t(x) = -x$

$T(x) = -x$

15 $m(x) = 3x - 2$

$M(x) = \dfrac{x + 2}{3}$

16 $n(x) = \frac{2}{3}x + 17$

$N(x) = \dfrac{3(x-17)}{2}$

17 $p(x) = (x^2 + 2) \div 5$

$P(x) = 5x - 2$

Chapter 14

INTRODUCTION TO TRIGONOMETRY

CHAPTER SCHEDULE

Basic (optional)
Problem Sets   3 Days
Review   0 Days
Test   0 Days

Average (optional)
Problem Sets   3 Days
Review   0 Days
Test   0 Days

Advanced
Problem Sets   9 Days
Review   3 Days
Test   1 Day

The term "trigonometry" originally meant the measurement of triangles, and that is still its application in navigation, architecture, and engineering. Algebraic treatment of trigonometry also considers the properties of the trigonometric functions.

Section 14.1   The Tangent Ratio

The slope of a line through the origin is $\dfrac{y - 0}{x - 0} = \dfrac{y}{x}$.

SECTION SCHEDULE

Basic (optional 1 day)

Average (optional 1 day)

Advanced (1 day)

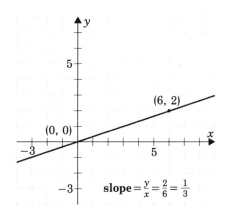

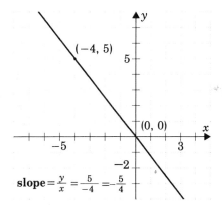

The slope of the line can also describe the angle determined by the line. Some vocabulary is necessary for a careful description of angles: A **ray** begins at a point called its **endpoint** and extends in one direction. An **angle** is made up of two rays that have a common endpoint. If the nonnegative x-axis is the **initial side** of an angle (the other ray is the **terminal side**), the angle is in **standard position**.

For an angle in standard position, the slope of the terminal side is called the **tangent of the angle**.

Definition

If an angle A is in standard position, and if the terminal side contains the point (x,y), then the TANGENT OF THE ANGLE is the ratio $y \div x$. In symbols:

$$\tan A = \frac{y}{x}$$

EXAMPLES

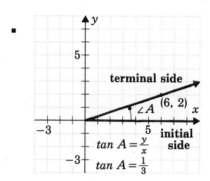

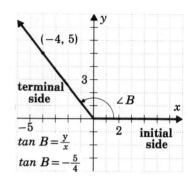

Sample Problems

1   An angle A is in standard position. Find $\tan A$ if the terminal side of the angle contains the point:

    a   (2,5)   c $(-2,0)$ e   (0,2)
    b $(-3,3)$ d   (2,300)   f $(5,-3)$

PROCEDURE   Draw the angles determined by the six points:

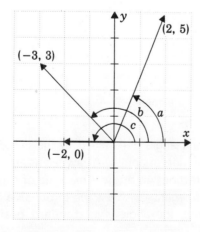

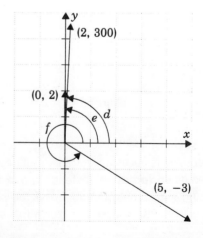

a $\tan A = \dfrac{5}{2} = 2.5$ **d** $\tan A = \dfrac{300}{2} = 150.0$

b $\tan A = \dfrac{3}{-3} = -1.0$ **e** $\tan A = \dfrac{2}{0}$ Undefined

c $\tan A = \dfrac{0}{-2} = 0$ **f** $\tan A = -\dfrac{3}{5} = -0.6$

In part **f**, notice that the angle is greater than 180°. In studying trigonometry, angles may be greater than 180° (or even greater than 360°). Angles may also be negative (when they are measured **clockwise** from the initial side). In part **e**, notice that the tangent ratio is undefined for an angle of 90°. It is also undefined for an angle of 270°.

2   Find the tangent ratio for each angle:
- **a**   10°
- **b**   58°
- **c**   78.35°
- **d**   45°

PROCEDURE   The rest of this chapter requires a **calculator** with a $TAN\,x$ key to determine the values of tangent ratios. (A **table of trigonometric ratios** could also be used for most of the problems.) Most trigonometric ratios are approximations, and the text will generally round off the values to three decimal places (most calculators give six- or eight-digit accuracy; most tables give four- or five-digit accuracy). The equal sign will be used, rather than " $\doteq$ " ("is approximately equal to"), throughout the chapter.

- **a** $\tan 10° = 0.176$
- **b** $\tan 58° = 1.600$
- **c** $\tan 78.35° = 4.850$
- **d** $\tan 45° = 1.$
  The value for $\tan 45°$ is an exact value:

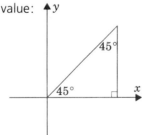

The triangle must be isosceles (the two legs are the same length) and so $y \div x = 1$.

3 Find the length BC:

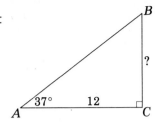

PROCEDURE The tangent ratio can be interpreted as the ratio of two sides of a right triangle:

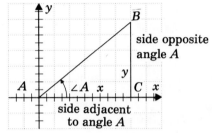

The ratio $\dfrac{y}{x}$ is the ratio $\dfrac{\text{side opposite angle } A}{\text{side adjacent to angle } A}$ so:

$$\tan A = \frac{\text{OPP}}{\text{ADJ}}$$

Thus $\tan 37° = \dfrac{BC}{AC}$

$$0.754 = \frac{BC}{12}$$

$$9.048 = BC$$

4 Find the measurement of angle R (to the nearest degree):

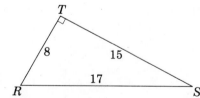

PROCEDURE

$$\tan R = \frac{\text{OPP}}{\text{ADJ}} = \frac{15}{8} = 1.875$$

Use a calculator (or a table) to find the angle that has 1.875 as its tangent ratio:

$$R = 62°$$

Problem Set A

ASSIGNMENT GUIDE

Basic (optional 1 day)
1–22

Average (optional 1 day)
2–20 (even), 22–30

Advanced (1 day)
17–22, 24, 26–30,
32–38 (even)

1 For an angle in standard position, the initial side of the angle is the nonnegative ___?___ .

   x-axis

2 The terminal side of an angle, in standard position, contains the point (x,y). The tangent of the angle is the ratio ___?___ .

   $\frac{y}{x}$

3 In a right triangle, the tangent of either **acute** angle (less than 90°) is the following ratio:

   $$\frac{\text{the length of the side } \underline{\ ?\ } \text{ the angle}}{\text{the length of the side } \underline{\ ?\ } \text{ the angle}}$$

   opposite (over) adjacent

4 State each tangent ratio:

a $tan\ A$ $\frac{BC}{AC}$

b $tan\ B$

   $\frac{AC}{BC}$

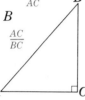

c $tan\ X$ $\frac{x}{y}$

d $tan\ Y$

   $\frac{y}{x}$

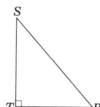

e $tan\ R$ $\frac{ST}{RT}$

f $tan\ S$

   $\frac{RT}{ST}$

g $tan\ N$ $\frac{MP}{MN}$

h $tan\ P$

   $\frac{MN}{MP}$

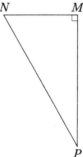

As stated in Sample Problem 2 (p. 575), many of the problems require a calculator with trigonometric functions.

State the tangent ratio for each angle (to 3 decimal places).

5 25°

   0.466

6 73°

   3.271

7 115.7°

   −2.078

8 168.5°

   −0.203

9 0.15°

   0.003

10 89.86°

   409.255

Find the measurement of each angle (to the nearest tenth of a degree), given its tangent ratio. (Each measure is greater than 0 and less than 180.)

11 $tan\ P = 0.618$

31.7°

14 $tan\ Q = 1.618$

58.3°

12 $tan\ T = 0.915$

42.5°

15 $tan\ S = -3.414$

106.3°

13 $tan\ R = 1.332$

53.1°

16 $tan\ M = -8.715$

96.5°

The **Pythagorean Theorem** (pi thag'ə rē' ən) states that if the sides of a right triangle have lengths a, b, and c, where c represents the **hypotenuse**, then:

$$c^2 = a^2 + b^2$$

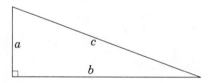

Find the length of each hypotenuse, given the other two sides. (Review: 11.1)

17 $a = 3, b = 7$

7.616

20 $a = 3.5, b = 2.7$

4.42

18 $a = 12, b = 10$

15.62

21 $a = 30, b = 40$

50

19 $a = 8, b = 15$

17

22 $a = 0.132, b = 0.431$

0.451

Problem Set **B**

For each triangle, find $tan\ Q$ and the measurement of angle Q.

23

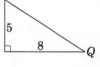

$tan\ Q = 0.625, \angle Q = 32.0°$

25

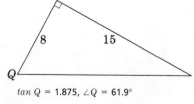

$tan\ Q = 1.875, \angle Q = 61.9°$

24

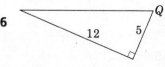

$tan\ Q = 0.444, \angle Q = 24°$

26

$tan\ Q = 2.4, \angle Q = 67.4°$

In problems 27–30, use the property that in any triangle, the sum of the three angle measurements is 180°.

27 In $\triangle RST$, $tan\ R = 0.869$ and $tan\ S = 3.078$. Find $\angle T$ (to the nearest degree).

$\angle T = 67°$

28 In $\triangle TAC$, find $\angle A$ (to the nearest tenth of a degree) if $tan\ T = 0.425$ and $tan\ C = 19.081$.

$\angle A = 70°$

29 In $\triangle ABC$, find $\angle B$ (to the nearest degree) if $tan\ A = \sqrt{3}$ and $\angle C = 90°$.

$\angle B = 30°$

30 In $\triangle PQR$, find $\angle P$ (to the nearest tenth of a degree) if $tan\ R = -1.428$ and $tan\ Q = 0.839$.

$\angle P = 15°$

Problem Set C

31 If $tan\ B = 0.466$, what is $tan\ 2B$?

$tan\ 2B = 1.192$

32 If $tan\ 3C = 1.376$, what is $\angle C$?

$\angle C = 18°$

33 If $tan\ 2D = 0.715$, what is $tan\ 3D$?

$tan\ 3D = 1.344$

34 If $tan\ 2E = 3.618$, what is $\angle E$?

$\angle E = 37.27°$

35 What is the exact value for $tan\ 30°$?

$tan\ 30 = \dfrac{\sqrt{3}}{3}$

36 What is the exact value for $tan\ 60°$?

$tan\ 60° = \sqrt{3}$

37 Find $\angle BAC$, $\angle BAD$, and $\angle CAD$.

$\angle BAC = 21.8°$, $\angle BAD = 58.0°$, $\angle CAD = 36.2°$

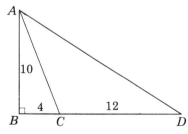

38 Points F, G, and H have coordinates (4,6), (12,0), and (12,12), respectively. What is the measurement of $\angle GFH$?

$\angle GFH = 73.7°$

31) $tan\ B = 0.466$
$B = 25°$
$2B = 50°$
$tan\ 2B = 1.19$

32) $tan\ 3C = 1.376$
$3C = 54$
$C = 18°$

33) $tan\ 2D = 0.715$
$2D = 35.6$
$D = 17.8$
$3D = 53.4$
$tan\ 3D = 1.35$

34) $tan\ 2E = 3.618$
$2E = 74.5$
$E = 37.3$

38)

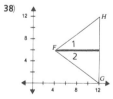

$tan\ \theta_1 = \dfrac{6}{8} = 0.75$
$\theta_1 = 36.9$
$\theta_1 = \theta_2$
$\angle HFG = 73.8°$

Section 14.2 The Sine Ratio and the Cosine Ratio

Suppose an angle θ (Greek letter "theta") is in standard position and its terminal side contains the point (x,y).

Students will see additional trigonometric functions in later algebra courses:

$$secant\ \boldsymbol{\theta} = \frac{1}{\cos\ \boldsymbol{\theta}}$$

$$cosecant\ \boldsymbol{\theta} = \frac{1}{\sin\ \boldsymbol{\theta}}$$

$$cotangent\ \boldsymbol{\theta} = \frac{1}{\tan\ \boldsymbol{\theta}}$$

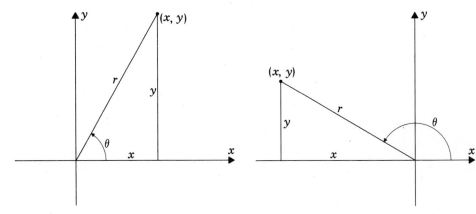

*The measure of **r** is derived by the Pythagorean Theorem.*

The distance r from the point (x,y) to the origin is $\sqrt{x^2 + y^2}$.

The ratio $y \div r$ is called the **sine of the angle** and the ratio $x \div r$ is called the **cosine of the angle**.

Definition

> If the terminal side of an angle θ, in standard position, contains the point (x,y), and if r represents the distance from (x,y) to the origin, then the SINE OF THE ANGLE is the ratio $y \div r$ and the COSINE OF THE ANGLE is $x \div r$.
>
> $$\sin\ \theta = \frac{y}{r} \qquad \cos\ \theta = \frac{x}{r} \qquad r = \sqrt{x^2 + y^2}$$

EXAMPLES

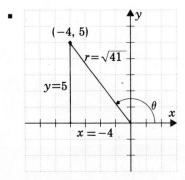

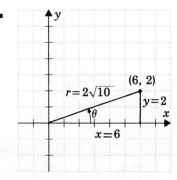

Notice that x and y may have positive or negative values (or zero), but r is never negative.

$$sin\theta = \frac{5}{\sqrt{41}} = 0.781 \qquad sin\theta = \frac{2}{2\sqrt{10}} = 0.316$$

$$cos\theta = \frac{-4}{\sqrt{41}} = -0.645 \qquad cos\theta = \frac{6}{2\sqrt{10}} = 0.949$$

A calculator with a **SIN x** key and a **COS x** key can be used to find values of the trigonometric ratios for specific angles.

Sample Problems

1   Find the sine ratio, the cosine ratio, and the tangent ratio for each angle.
   a   45°   c   0°
   b   115°   d   90°

PROCEDURE
   a sin 45° = 0.707
       cos 45° = 0.707
       tan 45° = 1
   b sin 115° = 0.906
       cos 115° = −0.423
       tan 115° = −2.145
   c sin 0° = 0
       cos 0° = 1
       tan 0° = 0
   d sin 90° = 1
       cos 90° = 0
       tan 90° is undefined

2   Find the lengths RQ and SQ.

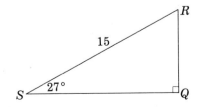

PROCEDURE

The sine and cosine ratios can each be interpreted as a ratio of two sides of a right triangle.

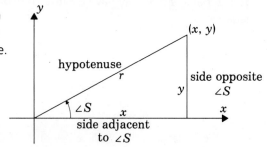

The ratio $\dfrac{y}{r}$ is the ratio: $\dfrac{\text{side opposite angle } S}{\text{hypotenuse}}$

and the ratio $\dfrac{x}{r}$ is the ratio: $\dfrac{\text{side adjacent to angle } S}{\text{hypotenuse}}$

$$sin\ S = \frac{\text{OPP}}{\text{HYP}} \qquad\qquad cos\ S = \frac{\text{ADJ}}{\text{HYP}}$$

Thus $\quad sin\ 27° = \dfrac{RQ}{RS} \qquad\qquad\qquad cos\ 27° = \dfrac{SQ}{RS}$

$$0.454 = \frac{RQ}{15} \qquad\qquad\qquad 0.891 = \frac{SQ}{15}$$

$$6.810 = RQ \qquad\qquad\qquad 13.365 = SQ$$

3 Find the measurement of angle A (to the nearest degree):

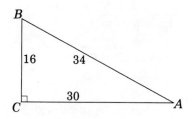

PROCEDURE   Use any one of the three trigonometric ratios.

$sin\ A = \dfrac{\text{OPP}}{\text{HYP}} = \dfrac{16}{34} = 0.471 \qquad\qquad cos\ A = \dfrac{\text{ADJ}}{\text{HYP}} = \dfrac{30}{34} = 0.882$

$\angle A = 28° \qquad\qquad\qquad\qquad\qquad\quad \angle A = 28°$

$$tan\ A = \frac{\text{OPP}}{\text{ADJ}} = \frac{16}{30} = 0.533$$

$$\angle A = 28°$$

Problem Set A

ASSIGNMENT GUIDE

Basic (optional 1 day)
1–18, 22

Average (optional 1 day)
1–19, 22, 23

Advanced (3 days)
(1) 6–20, 23–29
(2) 3–40
(3) 587: 10–12, 14–28
    (even), 31–35

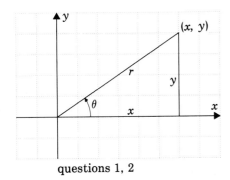

questions 1, 2

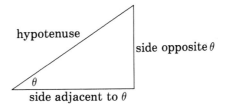

questions 3, 4

1   The distance r between the point (x,y) and the origin, is ___?___.
$\sqrt{x^2 + y^2}$

2   The sine ratio is ___?___; the cosine ratio is ___?___.
$\frac{y}{r}, \frac{x}{r}$

3   In a right triangle, $sin\ \theta$ is the ratio ___?___.
opposite over hypotenuse

4   In a right triangle, $cos\ \theta$ is the ratio ___?___.
$\frac{\text{ADJACENT}}{\text{HYPOTENUSE}}$

5   State each trigonometric ratio.

a $sin\ A$ $\frac{BC}{AB}$

b $cos\ B$ $\frac{BC}{AB}$

c $tan\ A$ $\frac{BC}{AC}$

d $cos\ A$ $\frac{AC}{AB}$

e $tan\ B$ $\frac{AC}{BC}$

f $sin\ B$ $\frac{AC}{AB}$

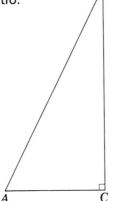

Find the sine, cosine, and tangent ratios for each angle (to 3 decimal places).

6   7°
$sin\ 7° = 0.122,\ cos\ 7° = 0.993,$
$tan\ 7° = 0.123$

7   86°
$sin\ 86° = 0.998,\ cos\ 86° = 0.070,$
$tan\ 86° = 14.301$

8   165°
$sin\ 165° = 0.259,\ cos\ 165° = -0.966,$
$tan\ 165° = -0.268$

9   13.32°
$sin\ 13.32° = 0.230,\ cos\ 13.32° = 0.973,$
$tan\ 13.32° = 0.237$

10   0.015°
$sin\ 0.015° = 0.000°,\ cos\ 0.015° = 1.00,$
$tan\ 0.015° = 0.000$

11   95.59°
$sin\ 95.59° = 0.995,\ cos\ 95.59° = -0.097,$
$tan\ 95.59° = -10.217$

Find the measurement of each angle (to the nearest tenth of a degree), given its sine ratio or cosine ratio. (Each measure is between 0° and 90°.)

12 $sin\ \theta = 0.628$
      38.9°

13 $cos\ \theta = 0.372$
      68.2°

14 $sin\ A = 0.112$
      6.4°

15 $sin\ B = 0.801$
      53.2°

16 $cos\ C = 0.714$
      44.4°

17 $cos\ D = 0.444$
      63.6°

Graph each function and describe the graph. (Review: Section 13.6)

18 $f(x) = -4x + 3$

19 $g(x) = |x|$

20 $Q(x) = \frac{1}{2}x^2 - 3$

21 $h(x) = -|x + 5|$

22 $R(x) = -3x^2 - 5$

23 $T(x) = \dfrac{6}{x - 1}$

Problem Set   B

For problems 24–27, find $sin\ \theta$ and the measurement of $\angle \theta$ (to the nearest tenth of a degree).

24

$sin\ \theta = 0.429$,
$\theta = 25.3°$

25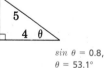

$sin\ \theta = 0.8$,
$\theta = 53.1°$

26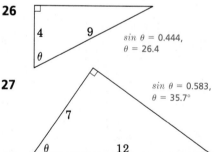

$sin\ \theta = 0.444$,
$\theta = 26.4$

27

$sin\ \theta = 0.583$,
$\theta = 35.7°$

28)
25 ft

$sin\ 67 = \dfrac{25}{x}$

$x = \dfrac{25}{sin\ 67} = 27.16$

29)

$tan\ 47 = \dfrac{12}{x}$

$x = \dfrac{12}{tan\ 47} = 11.19$

$OP = \sqrt{12^2 + (11.19)^2} = 16.4$

28   How long must a ladder be to reach twenty-five feet up the vertical face of a building if the ladder forms an angle of sixty-seven degrees with the ground?

     27.2 ft; a thirty-foot ladder

29   The ray from the origin O to a point P in Quadrant I forms an angle of forty-seven degrees with the nonnegative x-axis. If the ordinate of P is 12, find the abscissa and the length OP.

     $tan\ 47° = \dfrac{12}{x}$ so x, the abscissa, is 11.2; $OP = 16.4$

For problems 30–33, find *cos Q* and the measurement of ∠*Q* (to the nearest hundredth of a degree).

30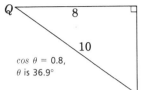

$cos \theta = 0.8$,
θ is 36.9°

31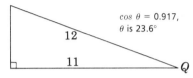

$cos \theta = 0.917$,
θ is 23.6°

32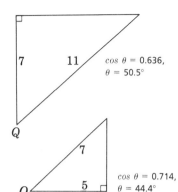

$cos \theta = 0.636$,
$\theta = 50.5°$

33

$cos \theta = 0.714$,
$\theta = 44.4°$

34 Find the length of side *BC*.

$BC = 14.3$

$cos \theta = \dfrac{15}{45} = 0.333$
$\theta = 70.5°$
Vertex angle is
$180 - 2(70.5) = 39°$

36) $A = \frac{1}{2}bh$
$sin\ 70.5 = \dfrac{h}{75}$.
$h = 45\ sin\ 70.5 = 42.4$
$A = (\frac{1}{2})(30)(42.4) = 636$

37) $sin\ \theta = 0.521$
$\theta = 31.4°$
$2\ \theta = 62.8$
$sin\ 2\ \theta = 0.889$

38) $cos\ 2\ \theta = 0.664$
$2\ \theta = 48.4$
$\theta = 24.2$

39) $sin\ 2\ \theta = 0.861$
$2\ \theta = 59.4$
$\theta = 29.7$
$3\ \theta = 89.1$
$cos\ 3\ \theta = 0.016$

40) $tan\ \theta = 3.25$
$\theta = 72.9$
$sin\ \theta = 0.956$
$cos\ \theta = 0.294$

Problem Set C

35 The sides of an isosceles triangle are thirty cm, forty-five cm, and forty-five cm. Find the measurement of each angle of the triangle.

70.5°, 70.5°, 39.0°

36 Find the area of the triangle in problem 35.

636.39 sq. cm

37 If *sin* θ = 0.521, what is *sin* 2θ?

$sin\ 2\theta = 0.889$

38 If *cos* 2θ = 0.664, what is ∠θ?

θ is 24.2°

39 If *sin* 2θ = 0.861, what is *cos* 3θ?

$cos\ 3\theta = 0.015$

40 If *tan* θ = 3.25, find *sin* θ and *cos* θ.

$sin\ \theta = 0.956, cos\ \theta = 0.294$

Xtending the topic: Graphing the Sine Function

The sine function, $S(x) = \sin x$, can be graphed with measurements for the angle along the x-axis and values for the sine ratio along the y-axis. A calculator can be used to fill in a table of input and output values:

x	-10	10	30	50	70	90	110	130	150	170	180	190	210
$S(x)$	$-.17$	.17	.5	.77	.94	1.	.94	.77	.5	.17	0	$-.17$	.17

x	240	270	310	360	450	540	630	720	730
$S(x)$	$-.87$	$-1.$	$-.77$	0	1	0	$-1.$	0	.17

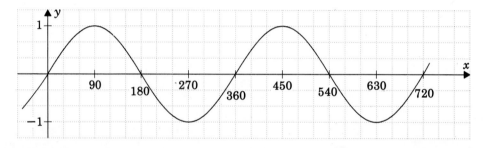

The graph illustrates that the sine function is periodic: the period is 2π, the range is $-1 \le \sin x \le 1$, the zeros are 0, 180, 360, etc.

The graph is called a **sine curve**. The domain of x-values is all real numbers, and the range is $-1 \le S(x) \le 1$. The graph reaches maximums at the points (90,1), (450,1), (810,1), etc., and reaches minimums at (270,-1), (630,-1), (990,-1), etc. The zeros of the function are at $x = 0$, $x = 180$, $x = 360$, etc.

Sample Problem

1   Express the value of each sine ratio in terms of an angle in Quadrant I.
   a $\sin 95°$
   b $\sin 160°$
   c $\sin 240°$
   d $\sin 330°$

PROCEDURE

Use the sine curve to find the
appropriate angle in Quadrant I.

a $sin\ 95° = sin\ 85°$

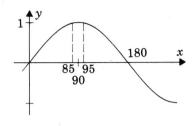

b $sin\ 160° = sin\ 20°$

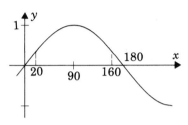

c $sin\ 240° = -\ sin\ 60°$

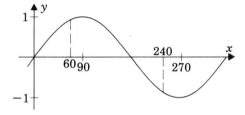

d $sin\ 330° = -\ sin\ 30°$

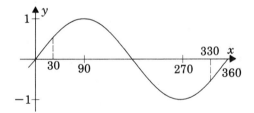

Problem Set X

Express the value of each sine ratio in terms of an angle in Quadrant I.

1 $sin\ 130°$

$sin\ 130° = sin\ 50°$

2 $sin\ 205°$

$sin\ 205° = -sin\ 25°$

3 $sin\ 275°$

$sin\ 275° = -sin\ 85°$

4 $sin\ 185°$

$sin\ 185° = -sin\ 5°$

5 $sin\ 225°$

$sin\ 225° = -sin\ 45°$

6 $sin\ 315°$

$sin\ 315° = -sin\ 45$

7 $sin\ -25°$

$sin\ -25° = sin\ 25°$

8 $sin\ -190°$

$sin\ -\ 190° = sin\ 10°$

9 $sin\ 125°$

$sin\ 125° = sin\ 55°$

10 Fill in a table of input and output values for the function $C(x) = \cos x$, and graph the function (graph the function from $x = -90$ to $x = 540$).

11 Describe the curve $C(x) = \cos x$.

Use the graph of $C(x) = \cos x$ to express the value of each cosine ratio in terms of an angle in Quadrant I.

12 $\cos 300°$

$\cos 300° = \cos 60°$

13 $\cos 340°$

$\cos 340° = \cos 20°$

14 $\cos 325°$

$\cos 325° = \cos 35°$

15 $\cos 105°$

$\cos 105° = -\cos 75°$

16 $\cos 160°$

$\cos 160° = -\cos 20°$

17 $\cos 230°$

$\cos 230° = -\cos 50°$

18 $\cos -30°$

$\cos -30° = \cos 30°$

19 $\cos -50°$

$\cos -50° = \cos 50°$

20 $\cos -86°$

$\cos -86° = \cos 86°$

21 $\cos (30 - 120)°$

$\cos (-90°) = \cos 90°$

22 $\cos (3 \cdot 120)°$

$\cos (360°) = \cos 0°$

23 $\cos (60 + 45)°$

$\cos (105°) = -\cos 75°$

24 $\cos (30 + 120)°$

$\cos (150°) = -\cos 30°$

25 $\cos (45 - 120)°$

$\cos (-75°) = \cos 75°$

26 $\cos (5 \cdot 150)°$

$\cos (750°) = \cos 30°$

27 $\cos (-3 \cdot 45)°$

$\cos (-135°) = -\cos 45°$

28 $\cos ((3 + 4) \cdot 75)°$

$\cos (525°) = -\cos 15°$

29 $\cos (0 - 6 \cdot 45)°$

$\cos (-270°) = \cos 90°$

30 Fill in a table of input and output values for the function $T(x) = \tan x$. Then graph the function from $x = -60$ to $x = 420$ and describe the curve $T(x) = \tan x$.

Use a calculator (or a table) for each problem:

31 Find $\tan 27° + \tan 58°$.

0.454 + 0.848 = 1.302

32 Find $\tan 85°$.

11.43

33 Is $\tan 27° + \tan 58° = \tan 85°$?

no

34 Find $\sin 10° + \sin 40°$.

0.174 + 0.766 = 0.940

35 Is $\sin 10° + \sin 40° = \sin 50°$?

no

36 Find $\cos 15° + \cos 12°$.

0.966 + 0.978 = 1.944

37 Find $\cos 27°$.

0.891

38 Is $\cos 15° + \cos 12° = \cos 27°$?

no

39 Find $\cos 38° + \cos 12°$.

0.788 + 0.978 = 1.766

40 Is $\cos 38° + \cos 12° = \cos 50°$?

no

Section 14.3 Applying the Three Trigonometric Ratios

SECTION SCHEDULE

Basic (optional 1 day)

Average (optional 1 day)

Advanced (3 days)

The trigonometric ratios can be applied when measurement problems involve right triangles. One type of problem involves rectangles and isosceles triangles.

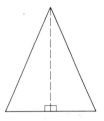

Another type of problem involves **indirect measurement**, such as measuring distance across water.

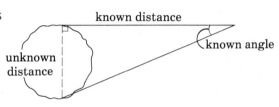

A third type of problem involves vertical distances and an **angle of depression** or an **angle of elevation** formed between a horizontal line and a line of sight.

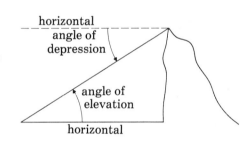

This section provides several examples of each type of problem.

Problem Set A

ASSIGNMENT GUIDE

Basic (optional 1 day)
594: 1–11

Average (optional 1 day)
594: 1–11

Advanced (3 days)
(1) 1–9, 16–20
(2) 22–26 (even), 28, 29
(3) 32–36
594: 1–11

1 From a point fifty-two feet from the foot of a flagpole, the angle of elevation of the top of the pole is sixty-three degrees. How high is the flagpole?

    102 feet

2 A beacon shines vertically onto the base of a cloud. From an observation tower twelve hundred meters from the searchlight, the angle of elevation of the base of the cloud is eighty-two degrees. How high is the cloud above the observation tower?

    8538.4 meters

1) $x = 52 \tan 63 = 102$

2) $x = 1200 \tan 82 = 8538.4$

3 From a point seventy-five feet from the base of a tree, the angle of elevation of the top of the tree is fifty degrees. Find the height of the tree.

89.4 feet

4 From a point eighty meters from the foot of a building, the angle of elevation of the top of the building is thirty-four degrees. Find the height of the building.

54 meters

5 A surveyor sighted across a canyon from a marker at M to a cactus at C. Then she marked off fifty meters from M, perpendicular to segment MC. From the new spot S, the angle to the cactus was seventy-five degrees. What is the distance across the canyon?

186.6 meters

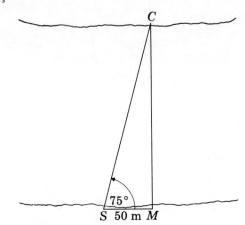

3) $x = 75\ tan\ 50 = 89.4$

4) $x = 80\ tan\ 34 = 54$

5) $x = 50\ tan\ 75 = 186.6$

6) $x = \dfrac{185}{tan\ 15} = 690.4$

7) $x = 125\ tan\ 49 = 143.8$

8)

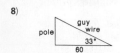

$x = \dfrac{60}{cos\ 33} = 71.5$

$y = 60\ tan\ 33 = 38.96$

9)

$x = \dfrac{170}{sin\ 40} = 264.5$

6 A forestry lookout tower sights a campsite at an angle of depression of fifteen degrees. If the height of the tower is one hundred eighty-five feet, how far from the campsite is the base of the lookout tower?

49.57 feet

7 Two buildings are one hundred twenty-five feet apart. How high is a window in one of the buildings if the angle of depression from that window, to the base of the other building, is forty-nine degrees?

143.8 feet

8 A guy wire that supports a telephone pole is anchored sixty meters from the base of the pole and forms an angle of thirty-three degrees with the ground. How long is the wire, and at what height does it meet the pole?

wire is 71.5 meters, meets pole at 38.9 meters

9 A smokestack two hundred feet tall is supported by a guy wire fastened thirty feet from the top of the stack. If the wire forms an angle of forty degrees with the ground, find the length of the wire.

264.5 feet

Represent each sum of signed numbers with arrows, and use the arrows to find that sum. (Review: Section 2.2)

10 $4 + -7$
      -3

12 $-8 + 5$
      -3

14 $-5 + 9$
      4

11 $-3 + -5$
      -8

13 $6 + -1$
      5

15 $7 + 2$
      9

Problem Set **B**

16 Figure $RECT$ is a rectangle and segment RC is a diagonal.

   a If $RE = 16$ and $EC = 12$, find $\angle ERC$.
                       $\angle ERC = 37°$

   b If $TC = 30$ and $EC = 16$, find $\angle TCR$.
                    $\angle TCR = 28°$

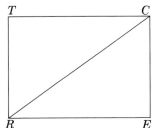

16a) $tan\ \angle ERC = \dfrac{CE}{RE} = 0.75$
         $\angle ERC = 37°$

b) $tan\ \angle TCR = \dfrac{TR}{TC} = 0.533$
        $\angle TCR = 28°$

17)

$cos\ C = \dfrac{5}{13} = 0.385$
     $C = 67.4°$

17 In isosceles triangle SCE, $SE = CE = 13$ and $SC = 10$. Find $\angle C$.

    $\angle C = 67.4°$

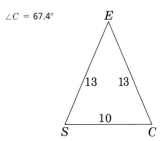
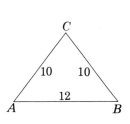

18 If $AC = BC = 10$ and $AB = 12$, find $\angle ACB$.

    $\angle ACB = 37°$

18)

$sin\ \angle ACD = \dfrac{6}{10} = 0.6$
   $\angle ACD = 36.9°$
   $\angle ACB = (2)(36.9) = 73.8°$

19 From one side of a river, the angle of elevation of a cliff on the other side is twelve degrees. If the cliff is four hundred meters high, how wide is the river at that point?

    1877.9 m

19)

$x = \dfrac{400}{tan\ 12} = 1878$

20 When the angle of elevation of the sun is forty-two degrees, how long is the shadow cast by a vertical pole twelve and two tenths meters tall?

    13.56 m

20)
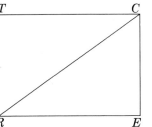

$x = \dfrac{12.2}{tan\ 42} = 13.6$

21)

$x = .4 \div tan\ 37$

21 A line is drawn from one corner of a sheet of notebook paper. It meets the longer edge of the paper ten inches from the shorter edge, and forms an angle of thirty-seven degrees with the shorter edge. How wide is the paper if it is fourteen inches long?

5.3 in

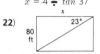

22)

$x = \dfrac{80}{tan\ 23} = 188.47$

$A = \ell w = (80)(188.47)$
$\quad = 15077.46$

22 In a rectangular garden that is eighty feet wide, a diagonal path forms an angle of twenty-three degrees with the longer edge. How long is the garden, and what is the area of the garden?

length = 188.47 ft, area = 15077.46 sq. ft.

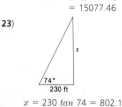

23)

$x = 230\ tan\ 74 = 802.1$

23 From a street corner two hundred thirty feet from the base of the Sears Tower Building, the angle of elevation of the window-washing carriage is seventy-four degrees. How high up the building is the carriage?

802.1 ft

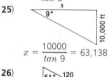

24)

$x = \dfrac{260}{tan\ 8} = 1850$

24 The angle of depression from the top of the Transamerica Pyramid to a ship in San Francisco Bay is eight degrees. How far is the ship from the base of the building if the building is two hundred sixty meters high?

36.54 m

25)

$x = \dfrac{10000}{tan\ 9} = 63,138$

25 An airplane is cruising at ten thousand feet above the ocean. When the plane is directly above a ship, the angle of depression from the plane to the shore is nine degrees. How far is the ship from the shore?

1583.8 ft

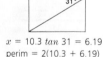

26)

$x = 120\ sin\ 51 = 93.26$

26 When the sun is directly overhead, find the length of the shadow cast by a pipe, one hundred twenty feet long, that rests against a wall forming an angle of fifty-one degrees with the wall.

93.26 ft.

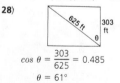

27)

$x = 10.3\ tan\ 31 = 6.19$
perim $= 2(10.3 + 6.19)$
$\quad = 32.98$
area $= (10.3)(6.19) = 63.8$

27 A rectangle is ten and three tenths centimeters long. If its diagonals form an angle of thirty-one degrees with the longer side, find the dimensions, perimeter, and area of the rectangle.

$\ell = 10.3,\ w = 61.9,\ p = 144,\ A = 638$

28)

$cos\ \theta = \dfrac{303}{625} = 0.485$

$\theta = 61°$

28 A path six hundred twenty-five feet long diagonally crosses a rectangular field. If the width of the field is three hundred three feet, find the angle formed by the path and the width.

61°

29) $x = 303\ tan\ 61 = 547$
need: $(2)(547 + 303$
$+ 625) = 2950$

29 How many feet of fencing would be needed to enclose both triangular fields in problem 28?

2950

30)

$x = \dfrac{22}{sin\ 63} = 24.69$

30 A ladder reaches twenty-two feet up the face of a building and forms an angle of sixty-three degrees with the ground. How long is the ladder?

24.69 ft

31 The base of an isosceles triangle is twenty centimeters and the two base angles are each fifty-three degrees. What is the perimeter?

$p = 43.2$ cm

Problem Set C

32 In equilateral triangle ABC, the altitude segment CH **bisects** (divides equally) the base and is perpendicular to the base. If each side of the triangle has length $2s$, find the lengths of AH and CH and find $tan\ A$.

  $AH = 5,\ CH = 5\sqrt{3},\ tan\ A = 1.732$

33 Two diagonals are drawn on a five-by-seven inch sheet of paper. Find the smaller angle formed by the diagonals.

  $35.7°$

34 Two ships are observed in the same line from the top of an eighty-meter high lighthouse. If the angles of depression of the ships are twenty degrees and forty degrees, find the distance between the ships (to the nearest meter).

  38 m

35 A canyon is thirty-six meters deep. From one rim of the canyon, the bottom is sighted at an angle of depression of fifty-two degrees. From the other rim, the angle of depression to the same spot is seventy degrees. Find the width of the canyon (to the nearest meter).

  145 m

36 A **quadrilateral** (a four-sided figure) $QUAD$ has right angles at Q and A, with $QU = 7$, $UA = 15$, and $DQ = 24$. Find $\angle D$ to the nearest tenth of a degree.

  $\angle D = 53.1°$

Xtending the topic: **A Formula for the Area of a Triangle**

A familiar formula for the area of a triangle is $A = \frac{1}{2}bh$ (the area is one half the product of the base and its altitude).

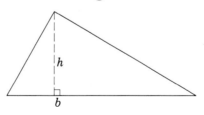

The sine ratio can be used to derive another formula for the area of a triangle without directly computing the length of the altitude. Consider $\triangle ABC$ (a capital letter represents the measure of an angle and a corresponding lower case letter represents the measure of the side opposite the angle):

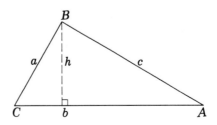

---

31)
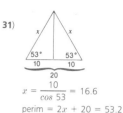

$x = \dfrac{10}{cos\ 53} = 16.6$

perim $= 2x + 20 = 53.2$

32)

$AH = s$

$CH = \sqrt{(2s)^2 - s^2}$

  $= s\sqrt{3}$

$tan\ A = \dfrac{s\sqrt{3}}{s} = \sqrt{3}$

33)

$tan\ \angle 1 = \dfrac{5}{7} = 35.5$

$\theta = 180 - 2\ \angle 1 = 109°$

34)

$x = 80\ tan\ 70 = 219.8$

$y = 80\ tan\ 50 = 95.3$

$y - x = 124.5$

35)
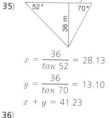

$x = \dfrac{36}{tan\ 52} = 28.13$

$y = \dfrac{36}{tan\ 70} = 13.10$

$x + y = 41.23$

36)
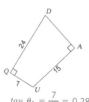

$tan\ \theta_1 = \dfrac{7}{24} = 0.282$

$\theta_1 = 16.3°$

$DU = \sqrt{7^2 + 24^2} = 25$

$sin\ \theta_2 = \dfrac{15}{25} = 0.6$

$\theta_2 = 36.9°$

$\angle QDA = \theta_1 + \theta_2 = 53.2°$

First, use the sine ratio to find an expression for the altitude h:

$$\sin C = \frac{h}{a}$$

$$a \sin C = h$$

Then, substitute this value for h into the formula $A = \frac{1}{2}bh$:

$$A = \frac{1}{2}bh$$

$$A = \frac{1}{2}ba \sin C$$

Property

The area of a triangle is one half the product of the lengths of two sides and the sine ratio of the angle formed by those sides.

Problem Set X

Find the area of each triangle.

1 $\triangle ABC$
3 A 4
5.33 B 6 C

5 $\triangle MNO$
M 12
4
17.68 O 15 N

2 $\triangle DEF$
D 6 E
4 4
7.93 F

6 $\triangle PQR$
14
4
22.25 P 12 R Q

3 $\triangle GHI$
G
2 6
7
5.56 H I

7 $\triangle STU$
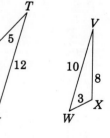
T
S 5
14.50 8 12
U

4 $\triangle JKL$
J 7 K
5 3
6.50 L

8 $\triangle VWX$
V
10
8
9.95 W 3 X

In each problem, find the area of triangle XYZ.

9 $XY = 7.1$, $YZ = 11.3$, $\angle Y = 32°$
21.26

10 $x = 17$, $z = 17$, $\angle Y = 42°$
96.69

11 $XZ = 6$, $\angle Z = 150°$, $YZ = 11.5$
17.25

Project: Open or Shut

Each year the students at Function High School perform a ritual as part of the school graduation ceremony. To start, the n students are assigned natural numbers 1 to n. (The n student lockers are already labeled 1 to n.)

Step 1 Student number 1 opens all the lockers.

Step 2 Student number 2 closes all the lockers whose numbers are divisible by 2.

Step 3 Student number 3 changes the state of each locker whose number is divisible by 3 (student 3 opens it if it is closed, or closes it if it is open).

Step 4 Each student, in order, takes a turn changing the state of the lockers whose numbers are divisible by that student's number.

1 For warm-up: If there are 10 students in the school, which lockers are open at the end of the ritual? What about 11 students? 12 students?

2 Which lockers are open if there are 25 students in the school?

3 Copy and fill in the following chart for the natural numbers from 1 to 25:

Number	Factors	Number of Factors
1	1	1
2	1,2	2
3	.	.
.	.	.
.	.	.

4 Can you use the table in problem 3 to describe whether a locker will be left open or shut?

5 Which lockers are left open at the end of the ritual if there are 1000 students in the school?

6 Each year the students at Mathtech High School follow a ritual similar to the one at FHS, with one difference: no student may touch the locker that has the student's own number. Answer problems 1–5 for the MHS ritual.

---

1) ten students:
1, 4, 9 are left open
eleven students:
1, 4, 9 are left open
twelve students:
1, 4, 9 are left open

2) twenty-five students:
1, 4, 9, 16, 25 are left open

3)

Number	Factors	Number of factors
1	1	1
2	1,2	2
3	1,3	2
4	1,2,4	3
5	1,5	2
6	1,2,3,6	4
7	1,7	2
8	1,2,4,8	4
9	1,3,9	3
10	1,2,5,10	4
11	1,11	2
12	1,2,3,4,6,12	6
13	1,13	2
14	1,2,7,14	4
15	1,3,5,15	4
16	1,2,4,8,16	5
17	1,17	2
18	1,2,3,6,9,18	6
19	1,19	2
20	1,2,4,5,10,20	6
21	1,3,7,21	4
22	1,2,11,22	4
23	1,23	2
24	1,2,3,4,6,8,12,24	8
25	1,5,25	3

4) When a locker has an odd number of factors (including 1) the locker will be left open. Only the square numbers have an odd number of factors.

5) The square numbers ≤ 1000 are 1,4,9,16,25, 36,49,64,81,100,121,144, 169,196,225,256,289,324, 361,400,441,484,529,576, 625,676,729,784,841,900, 961.

6) The difference is that every locker is touched by one fewer person. Thus the lockers that were left open at FHS will be left closed at MHS, and vice versa.

Section 14.4   Vectors

A physical **force** has both a direction and a magnitude; some examples would be a push to the right of twenty pounds, a wind toward the southeast at five kilometers per hour, or a river current downstream at twenty feet per minute.

A **vector** is a directed line segment that is used to represent the direction and magnitude of a force. The angle formed by the vector represents the direction, and the length of the vector represents the magnitude.

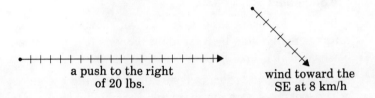

a push to the right
of 20 lbs.

wind toward the
SE at 8 km/h

When two vectors start from the same point and work together, the effect of the two vectors can be found by finding the diagonal of the **parallelogram** determined by the two vectors.

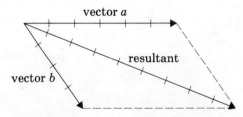

vector *a*

resultant

vector *b*

The diagonal of the parallelogram is called the **resultant** or the **sum** of the two vectors. The original vectors are called the **components**.

Sample Problem

1   Two forces act on a point: one is an eastward push of one hundred ten pounds and the other is a southern push at seventy pounds. What single force (to the nearest pound and tenth of a degree) would produce the same effect?

PROCEDURE   Use trigonometric ratios to find the magnitude and direction of the resultant force. First find the angle of the resultant and then find its magnitude.

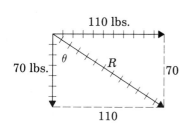

110 lbs.

70 lbs.

θ R

70

110

$$\tan\theta = \frac{110}{70} = 1.571$$

$$\theta = 57.6°$$

$$\sin\theta = \frac{110}{R}$$

$$\sin 57.6 = \frac{110}{R}$$

$$0.844 = \frac{110}{R}$$

$$0.844\,R = 110$$

$$R = 130$$

Students can check answers by measuring the magnitudes and directions on carefully drawn diagrams.

ASSIGNMENT GUIDE

Basic (omit)

Average (omit)

Advanced (2 days)
(1) 3–7, 16–20
(2) 22–24, 26

A single force of 130 pounds at an angle of 57.6° from due south would produce the same effect as the two forces.

Problem Set A

1 A directed line segment that represents a magnitude and a direction is called a(n) __?__ .

vector

2 A single force equivalent to two component vectors is called the __?__ of the components.

resultant or sum

In problems 3–7, state magnitudes and angle measures to the nearest tenth.

3 A helium-filled balloon rises vertically at a speed of 7 m/s in a wind that blows to the north at 3 m/s. What is the angle to the ground taken by the balloon?

66.8° (the magnitude is 7.62 m/s)

4 Two tractors pull an object across a field. One pulls due south with a force of 3500 kg and the other pulls due west at 4700 kg. Describe the force that acts on the object.

a force of magnitude 5861 at an angle of 53.3°

5 A cable from a crane to a weight forms an angle of sixty-five degrees with the ground. When the crane exerts a pull on the cable of five hundred kilograms, what is the vertical force acting on the weight?

453.15 kg

6 A student drove to school by driving seven blocks north and then three blocks west. If she walked home by the shortest path, how long was her walk, and what was its direction?

7.6 blocks southeast, angle of 23.2°

7 A boat sails due east at 12 km/h across a river that has a current of 2 km/h toward the south. Describe the speed and direction of the boat.

12.17 km/h at 9.4° from the south

3)

$$\tan\theta = \frac{7}{3} = 2.333$$

$$\theta = 66.8°$$

$$R = \sqrt{3^2 + 7^2} = 7.6$$

4)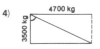

$$\tan\theta = \frac{4700}{3500} = 1.343$$

$$\theta = 53.3$$

$$R = \sqrt{(3500)^2 + (4700)^2} = 5862$$

5)

$$x = 500\,\sin 65 = 453.2$$

6)

$$R = \sqrt{7^2 + 3^2} = 7.62$$

$$\tan\theta = \frac{3}{7} = 0.429$$

$$\theta = 23.2$$

7)

$$\tan\theta = \frac{2}{12} = 0.167$$

$$\theta = 9.5$$

$$R = \sqrt{12^2 + 2^2} = 12.2$$

14.4 Vectors **597**

8–15)

$sin\ A$ = 0.8, A is 53.1°

$tan\ B$ = 0.75, B is 36.9°

$cos\ Y$ = 0.923, Y is 22.6°

$cos\ X$ = 0.385, X is 67.4

$tan\ R$ = 0.533, R is 28.1°

$sin\ S$ = 0.882, S is 61.9°

$sin\ Q$ = 0.742, Q is 47.9°

$cos\ E$ = 0.742, E is 42.1°

Find each trigonometric ratio and the measurement of each angle. (Review: Sections 14.1, 14.2)

8 $sin\ A$

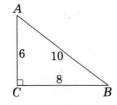

9 $tan\ B$

10 $cos\ Y$

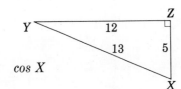

11 $cos\ X$

12 $tan\ R$

13 $sin\ S$

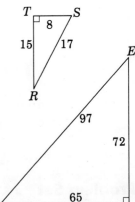

14 $sin\ Q$

15 $cos\ E$

16)

$tan\ \theta = \dfrac{23}{8} = 2.875$

$\theta = 70.8$

$R = \sqrt{23^2 + 8^2} = 24.4$

17)

$x = \dfrac{27}{sin\ 42} = 40.4$

18)

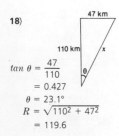

$tan\ \theta = \dfrac{47}{110}$

$= 0.427$

$\theta = 23.1°$

$R = \sqrt{110^2 + 47^2}$

$= 119.6$

19)

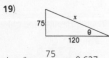

$tan\ \theta = \dfrac{75}{119.6} = 0.627$

$\theta = 32.1°$

Problem Set **B**

In problems 16–20, state magnitudes to the nearest hundredth and directions to the nearest tenth.

16 A ship sails north at twenty-three knots against an eastward current of eight knots. What is the actual speed of the ship?

24.36

17 A sign that weighs fifty-four kilograms is supported from its center by two ropes. If each rope forms an angle of forty-two degrees from the horizontal, what is the pull on each rope?

36.34

18 A ship sails one hundred ten kilometers due north from a lighthouse and then sails due east for forty-seven kilometers. How far is the ship from the lighthouse, and what is the angle to the lighthouse?

119.90, angle of 23.1°

19 If the lighthouse in problem 18 is seventy-five meters tall, what is the angle of depression from the lighthouse to the ship?

89.9°

20 A stone is dragged by a rope that forms an angle of thirty-six degrees with the horizontal. If the tension on the rope is thirty-nine kilograms, what is the horizontal force applied to the stone, and what is the vertical force?

horizontal force, 31.55 kg; vertical force, 22.92 kg.

Problem Set **C**

21   Two forces act on an object as shown. Find the magnitude and direction of the resultant.

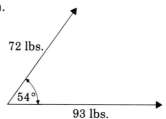

72 lbs.

54°

93 lbs.

PROCEDURE   Use the parallelogram method to represent the resultant. To find the magnitude and direction of the resultant, first find the lengths x and y:

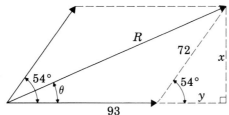

$$\sin 54° = \frac{OPP}{HYP} \qquad \cos 54° = \frac{ADJ}{HYP}$$

$$0.809 = \frac{x}{72} \qquad\qquad 0.588 = \frac{y}{72}$$

$$58.2 = x \qquad\qquad\quad 42.3 = y$$

$$\tan \theta = \frac{OPP}{ADJ} = \frac{x}{93 + y} = \frac{58.2}{93 + 42.3} = \frac{58.2}{135.3} = 0.430$$

$$\theta = 23.3°$$

$$\sin \theta = \frac{OPP}{HYP}$$

$$\sin 23.3° = \frac{x}{R}$$

$$0.396 = \frac{58.2}{R}$$

$$0.396\,R = 58.2$$

$$R = 147.0$$

The resultant is a force of 147.0 pounds that forms an angle of 23.3° with the 93-pound component.

20)

$x = 39 \cos 36 = 31.6$
$y = 39 \sin 36 = 22.9$

22)

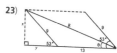

$x = 12 \sin 40 = 7.7$
$y = 12 \cos 40 = 9.2$
$R = \sqrt{x^2 + (y + 17)^2}$
$\quad = 27.3$
$\tan \theta = \dfrac{x}{17 + y} = 0.293$
$\quad \theta = 16.3°$

23)

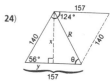

$x = 9 \sin 53 = 7.2$
$y = 9 \cos 53 = 5.4$
$R = \sqrt{x^2 + (y + 13)^2}$
$\quad = 19.8$
$\tan \theta = \dfrac{x}{y + 13} = 0.391$
$\quad \theta = 21.4°$

24)

$x = 140 \sin 56 = 116$
$y = 140 \cos 56 = 78.3$
$R = \sqrt{x^2 + (157 - y)^2}$
$\quad = 140$
$\tan \theta = \dfrac{x}{157 - y} = 1.474$
$\quad \theta = 55.8°$

25)

$x = 16.3 \sin 20 = 5.57$
$y = 16.3 \cos 20 = 15.3$
$R = \sqrt{x^2 + (22.1 - y)^2}$
$\quad = 8.79$
$\tan \theta = \dfrac{x}{22.1 - y} = 0.819$
$\quad \theta = 39.3°$

Describe the resultant for each set of components.

22–25) see p. 599

22

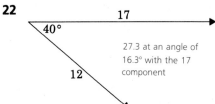

27.3 at an angle of
16.3° with the 17
component

24

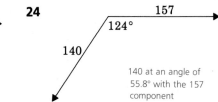

140 at an angle of
55.8° with the 157
component

26)

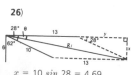

$x = 10 \sin 28 = 4.69$
$y = 10 \cos 28 = 8.83$
$R_1 = \sqrt{x^2 + (y + 13)^2}$
   $= 22.3$

$\tan \theta = \dfrac{x}{13 + y} = 0.215$

$\theta = 12.1°$

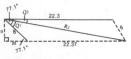

$n = 6 \sin 77.1 = 5.85$
$m = 6 \cos 77.1 = 1.34$
$R_2 = \sqrt{n^2 + (R_1 + m)^2}$
   $= 24.4$

$\tan Q_1 = \dfrac{n}{R_1 + m} = 0.247$

$Q_1 = 13.9°$
$Q_2 = 63.2°$

23

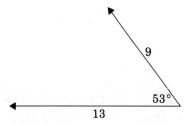

19.8 at an angle of
21.4° with the 13
component

25

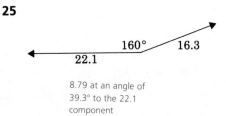

8.79 at an angle of
39.3° to the 22.1
component

Describe the resultant for the three component vectors. (First replace any pair of vectors by the resultant of that pair.)

27)

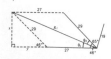

$x = 29 \sin 46 = 20.9$
$y = 29 \cos 46 = 20.1$
$R_1 = \sqrt{x^2 + (y + 27)^2}$
   $= 51.5$

$\tan \theta_1 = \dfrac{x}{y + 27} = 0.444$

$\theta_1 = 23.9°$
$\theta_2 = 46 - 23.9 = 22.1°$

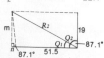

$m = 19 \sin 87.1 = 19.0$
$n = 19 \cos 87.1 = 0.96$
$R_2 = \sqrt{m^2 + (R_1 + n)^2}$
   $= 55.8$

$\tan Q_1 = \dfrac{m}{n + R_1} = 0.362$

$Q_1 = 19.9°$
$Q_2 = 87.1 - Q_1 = 67.2°$

26

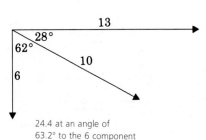

24.4 at an angle of
63.2° to the 6 component

28

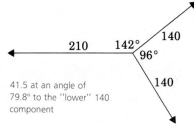

41.5 at an angle of
79.8° to the "lower" 140
component

27

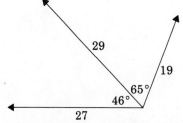

55.8 at an angle of
67.2° to the 19 component

29

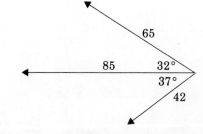

155.9 at an angle of
48.0° to the 42 component

After-School Mathematics: Garden Fence

Chris does gardening during the summer to earn extra money. Mrs. Mac-Gregor hired Chris to build a fence around her vegetable garden to keep the rabbits out.

Chris wanted to mark off good square corners for the fence. She knew that a triangle with sides 3, 4, and 5 must be a right triangle, and a right triangle has a right angle.

Chris took a long rope. She measured off three meters of rope and tied a knot. Then she measured off four meters from the knot and tied another knot. Then after measuring out five more meters, she cut the rope. When she tied the two ends of the rope and staked the knots of the rope into a triangle, she had a right angle!

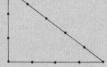

After Chris built one part of the fence, she put the four-meter side of the triangle on one edge of the fence line and used the three-meter side to line up the new fence posts. She used her triangle rope for all four corners, and ended up with four good square corners.

There are an infinite number of "Pythagorean triples" like 3,4,5. Some others are:	5,12,13	11,60,61
	7,24,25	20,21,29
	8,15,17	12,35,37
	9,40,41	

Application: Tassels

The students were told that it is a tradition to hang your tassel over the left front edge of your mortarboard cap. Then, when you receive your diploma, switch the tassel to the right side.

There were four hundred seniors in the graduating class. Twenty percent hung their tassels randomly, because they forgot the tradition. Five percent deliberately hung their tassels in back, because they didn't like the tradition. Of the seventy-five percent of the students who purposefully hung their tassels in the traditional way, four percent of them had the wind blow their tassels out of position.

How many students found their tassels hanging over the left front of their cap as they received a diploma?

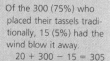

Of the 400 students: 80 students (20%) placed their tassels at random.

One fourth of the 80 placed them on the left: 20 students.

Of the 300 (75%) who placed their tassels traditionally, 15 (5%) had the wind blow it away.
20 + 300 − 15 = 305

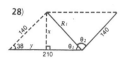

28)

$x = 140 \sin 38 = 86.2$
$y = 140 \cos 138 = 110.3$
$R_1 = \sqrt{x^2 + (210 - y)^2}$
$\quad = 131.8$

$\tan \theta_1 = \dfrac{x}{210 - y} = 0.865$

$\theta_1 = 40.9°$
$\theta_2 = 142 - \theta_1 = 101.1°$

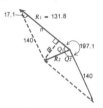

$m = 140 \sin 17.1 = 41.2$
$n = 140 \cos 17.1 = 133.8$
$R_2 = \sqrt{m^2 + (R_1 - n)^2}$
$\quad = 41.5$

$\tan Q_1 = \dfrac{m}{R_1 - n} = 8.24$
$Q_1 = 83.0$
$Q_2 = 162.9 - Q_1 = 79.8$

29)

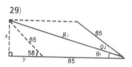

$x = 65 \sin 58 = 55.1$
$y = 65 \cos 58 = 34.4$
$R_1 = \sqrt{x^2 + (y + 85)^2}$
$\quad = 131.5$

$\tan \theta_1 = \dfrac{x}{y + 85} = 0.461$
$\theta_1 = 24.7°$
$\theta_2 = 32 - \theta_1 = 7.3°$

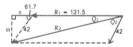

$m = 42 \sin 61.7 = 37.0$
$n = 42 \cos 61.7 = 19.9$
$R_2 = \sqrt{m^2 + (R_1 + n)^2}$
$\quad = 155.9$

$\tan Q_1 = \dfrac{m}{R_1 + n} = 0.244$

$Q_1 = 13.7$
$Q_2 = 61.7 - Q_1 = 48.0°$

ASSIGNMENT GUIDE

Basic (omit)

Average (omit)

Advanced (3 days)
(1) 1–24
      592: 21–25 (odd)
      598: 8–15
(2) 606: 1–30
(3) 608: 31–47

Chapter Study Guide

Vocabulary

As you study and review this chapter, be sure to learn the important mathematics vocabulary, including:

1   **sine of an angle, cosine of an angle, tangent of an angle**
    If an angle is in standard position, with its terminal side through the point (x,y), and if r represents the distance from (x,y) to the origin, then:

the SINE OF THE ANGLE is $\dfrac{y}{r}$

the COSINE OF THE ANGLE is $\dfrac{x}{r}$

the TANGENT OF THE ANGLE is $\dfrac{y}{x}$

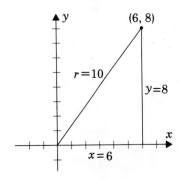 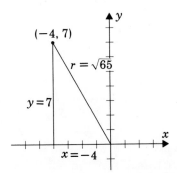

Skills

Be sure you build the useful algebraic skills, including:

2   **Finding a value for a trigonometric ratio given an angle**
    Find the value of the ratio to three decimal places.
    a   *sin* 57°   c   *tan* 23°
    b   *cos* 60°   d   *sin* 88°

      PROCEDURE   Use a calculator (or a table) and find the values.

        a   *sin* 57° = 0.839   c   *tan* 23° = 0.424
        b   *cos* 60° = 0.5   d   *sin* 88° = 0.999

3 **Finding a value for an angle given a trigonometric ratio**

Find the measurement of each angle to the nearest tenth.

a $\sin A = 0.614$ c $\tan C = 1.057$
b $\cos B = 0.013$ d $\cos D = 1.0$

PROCEDURE   Use a calculator (or a table).

a $\sin A = 0.614$ c $\tan C = 1.057$
    $A = 37.9°$ $C = 46.6°$
b $\cos B = 0.013$ d $\cos D = 1.0$
    $B = 89.3°$ $D = 0°$

4 **Using the trigonometric ratios in right triangles**

Find the missing parts of each triangle (to the nearest tenth).

a

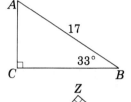

b

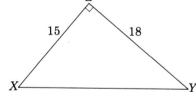

PROCEDURE

In a right triangle, the trigonometric ratios can be interpreted as:

$$\sin \theta = \frac{\text{OPPOSITE SIDE}}{\text{HYPOTENUSE}}$$

$$\cos \theta = \frac{\text{ADJACENT SIDE}}{\text{HYPOTENUSE}}$$

$$\tan \theta = \frac{\text{OPPOSITE SIDE}}{\text{ADJACENT SIDE}}$$

a $\sin B = \dfrac{\text{OPP}}{\text{HYP}}$ $\cos B = \dfrac{\text{ADJ}}{\text{HYP}}$ $\angle C = 90°$

   $\sin 33° = \dfrac{AC}{AB}$ $\cos 33° = \dfrac{BC}{AB}$ $\angle A = 90° - \angle B$
                                                              $= 90° - 33°$
   $0.545 = \dfrac{AC}{17}$ $0.839 = \dfrac{BC}{17}$ $= 57°$

   $9.3 = AC$ $14.3 = BC$

b $\tan X = \dfrac{\text{OPP}}{\text{ADJ}} = \dfrac{YZ}{XZ} = \dfrac{18}{15} = 1.2$

$X = 50.2°$

$\tan Y = \dfrac{\text{OPP}}{\text{ADJ}} = \dfrac{XZ}{YZ} = \dfrac{15}{18} = 0.833$

$Y = 39.8°$

$$\sin X = \dfrac{\text{OPP}}{\text{HYP}}$$

$$\sin 50.2 = \dfrac{YZ}{XY}$$

$$0.786 = \dfrac{18}{XY}$$

$$0.768 XY = 18$$

$$XY = 23.4$$

5 Finding resultants of vectors

Describe the length and direction of the resultant of these two vectors:

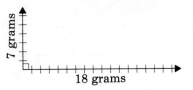

PROCEDURE   Use the parallelogram method to represent the resultant vector, and then use trigonometric ratios.

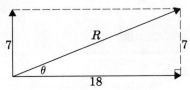

$\tan \theta = \dfrac{\text{OPP}}{\text{ADJ}} = \dfrac{7}{18} = 0.389$ $\qquad$ $\sin \theta = \dfrac{\text{OPP}}{\text{HYP}}$

$\theta = 21.3°$ $\qquad\qquad\qquad\qquad$ $\sin 21.3° = \dfrac{7}{R}$

$$0.363 = \dfrac{7}{R}$$

$$0.363R = 7$$

$$R = 19.3$$

The resultant is a vector with magnitude 19.3 grams. It forms an angle of 21.3° with the 18-gram vector.

Chapter Test

An angle θ is in standard position, and the terminal side contains the point (x,y). If $r = \sqrt{x^2 + y^2}$, state each ratio.

1 $tan\ \theta$ $\dfrac{y}{x}$

2 $sin\ \theta$ $\dfrac{y}{r}$

3 $cos\ \theta$ $\dfrac{x}{r}$

An angle A is in standard position. Find $tan\ A$, $sin\ A$, and $cos\ A$ if the terminal side contains the point:

4 (4,3)
  tan A = 0.75, sin A = 0.6
  cos A = 0.8

6 (5,−12)
  tan A = −2.4,
  sin A = −0.923, cos A = 0.385

8 (0,5)
  tan A is undefined,
  sin A = 1.0, cos A = 0

5 (−6,8)
  tan A = −1.33̄, sin A = 0.8,
  cos A = −0.6

7 (6,0)
  tan A = 0, sin A = 0,
  cos A = 1.0

9 (−15,−8)
  tan A = 0.53̄,
  sin A = −0.471,
  cos A = −0.882

Triangle TRG has a right angle at R. State each ratio of sides.

10 $tan\ G$
  $\dfrac{TR}{RG}$

11 $sin\ T$
  $\dfrac{RG}{GT}$

12 $cos\ G$
  $\dfrac{RG}{GT}$

Find the sine, cosine, and tangent ratios for each angle (to 3 decimal places).

13 62° *sin 62° = 0.883,*
  cos 62° = 0.924,
  tan 62° = 1.881

14 22.5° *sin 22.5° = 0.383,*
  cos 22.5° = 0.924,
  tan 22.5° = 0.414

15 100° *sin 100° = 0.985,*
  cos 100° = −0.174,
  tan 100° = −5.671

Find the measurement of each angle (to the nearest tenth of a degree). Each measure is greater than 0° and less than 180°.

16 $tan\ R = 0.5354$
  R = 28.7°

19 $sin\ A = 0.5783$
  A = 35.3°

17 $tan\ T = 6.691$
  T = 81.5°

20 $cos\ B = 0.7071$
  B = 45°

18 $tan\ G = -0.7400$
  G = 143.5°

21 $sin\ \theta = 0.884$
  θ = 62.1

22 From a chair at the top of a ferris wheel, Mac can see Jay at the entrance to the fairgrounds. If the forty-foot-high wheel is three hundred feet from the entrance, what is the angle of depression from Mac to Jay?
  θ = 7.59°

23 The resultant of two perpendicular forces is a 250 kg force that acts at an angle of 68.5° with one of the forces. Find the two component forces.
  92 kg, 233 kg

24 Each leg of an isosceles triangle is 13.4 cm, and each base angle is 62°. What is the perimeter of the triangle?
  39.4

Problem Set: Cumulative Review 1–14

Problem Set   **A**

Multiple choice

1   If $a = 7$ and $b = 10$, the value of $2a - \frac{1}{2}b$ is:

   a   4   **c**   24

   b   19   **d**   9

   d

2   The product of $5x^2$ and the quantity $7x - 2$ is:

   a $35x^2 - 14x$ **c** $25x^2$

   b $35x^3 - 10x^2$ **d** $35x^2 - 2$

    b

3   The trinomial $x^2 - 5x + 6$ can be factored as:

   a $(x + 3)(x + 2)$ **c** $(x - 6)(x + 1)$

   b $(x - 5)(x + 6)$ **d** $(x - 3)(x - 2)$

    d

4   The slope of the line through $(-1,6)$ and $(-4,2)$ is:

   a $\dfrac{4}{3}$ **c** $\dfrac{4}{5}$

   b $\dfrac{3}{4}$ **d** $\dfrac{5}{4}$

    a

5   For an angle in standard position, the initial side is:

   a   the x-axis   **c**   the y-axis

   b   the nonnegative x-axis   **d**   the nonpositive y-axis

    b

6   In a right triangle, the sine ratio for an acute angle is:

   a $\dfrac{\text{hypotenuse}}{\text{opposite side}}$ **c** $\dfrac{\text{adjacent side}}{\text{hypotenuse}}$

   b $\dfrac{\text{opposite side}}{\text{hypotenuse}}$ **d** $\dfrac{\text{opposite side}}{\text{adjacent side}}$

    b

7   Solve for z: $-8 = 2 + 5z$

   a $z = -2$ **c** $-\frac{5}{6}$

   b $z = -\frac{6}{5}$ **d** $z = -50$

    a

Perform the indicated operation(s).

8 Solve: $-2(3 - y) = 4(y + 1)$

-5

9 Solve: $\dfrac{x}{-3} \leq -18$

$x \leq 54$

10 Simplify: $\dfrac{(x - 4)(x - 7)}{(7 - x)(4 - x)}$

1

11 Solve: $6x - 7x \geq 12 + 3x$

$x \leq -3$

12 Solve: $24k^2 = 15k$

$k = 0, k = \dfrac{5}{8}$

13 Solve: $2x^2 - 7x = -6$

$x = \dfrac{3}{2}, x = 2$

14 Solve: $\dfrac{5t}{t - 2} = \dfrac{14}{3}$

$t = -28$

15 Solve: $\dfrac{3a}{2} + \dfrac{5}{4} = \dfrac{5a}{2}$

$a = \dfrac{5}{4}$

16 Simplify: $\sqrt{72}$

$6\sqrt{2}$

17 Solve: $\sqrt{x + 2} = 6$

$x = 34$

18 Find the zeros of the linear function $L(x) = 5x - 7$.

$x = \dfrac{7}{5}$

19 Find the x-intercept of the graph of $3x - 2y = 6$.

$(2,0)$

20 The sum of two numbers is one hundred thirty-four. One number is five more than twice the other. Find the larger number.

43

21 Evaluate each expression:

a $3k^3t^2$ for $k = 2, t = 5$

600

b $p^3 \div 4$ for $p = -4$

-16

22 Find the perimeter of a rectangle with length $9x^2$ and width $7y^2$.

$18x^2 + 14y^2$

23 Solve for x:

a $3x - 7 \leq 2x + 1$

$x \leq 8$

b $\frac{3}{4} + x \geq -\frac{3}{8}$

$x \geq -1\frac{1}{8}$

24 Factor:

a $y^2 + y - 2$

$(y + 2)(y - 1)$

b $s^2 - 17s + 30$

$(s - 15)(s - 2)$

25 Solve for x:

a $\dfrac{x - 3}{8} = \dfrac{x}{4}$

$x = -3$

b $\dfrac{6}{3 + 2x} = \dfrac{5}{6}$

$x = 2\frac{1}{10}$

26 Simplify:

a $\sqrt{2} - \sqrt{8}$

$-\sqrt{2}$

b $\sqrt[3]{16} \cdot \sqrt[3]{108}$

12

c $\sqrt{75} + 3\sqrt{48}$

$17\sqrt{3}$

d $\sqrt{500} \div \sqrt{20}$

5

Problem Set B

27 Write a verbal problem that can be represented by each equation:

a $12 + a = 12$ **c** $7 + x - 3 = -2$

b $E - 8 = 6$ **d** $n \div 3 = 7$

answers may vary

28 Evaluate each expression:

a $3y^4$ for $y = 3$ 243   **c** $(2w)^3$ for $w = 4$ 512

b x^5 for $x = 10$ 100,000   **d** $2(m + 3)$ for $m = -5$ -4

29 Find three consecutive odd integers with sum one hundred twenty-nine.

41, 43, 45

30 Write each expression as a product of a common factor (the GCF) and a polynomial.

a $153mn^3 - 68m^2n + 204m^4n^2$ $17mn(9n^2 - 4m + 12m^3n)$

b $75x^3y^2 + 15xy - 225y + 105x^2y$ $15y(5x^3y + x - 15 + 7x^2)$

31 Replace each blank with $<$, $=$, or $>$:

a $(14)(-3)$ __?__ $-53 + 8$ **b** $(-5)(7 + 3)$ __?__ $-2 \cdot 5^2$

$>$ $=$

32 Solve for x: $x + 2 \geq 3$ and $x - 3 \leq 2$

$1 \leq x \leq 5$

33 Factor completely:

a $72y - 50y^2$ **b** $3x^2 - 30x + 63$

$2y(36 - 25y)$ $3(x - 7)(x - 3)$

34 Multiply $3y + 2$ and $6y^2 - 2y^3 + 6 - 3y$ and write the product in descending powers of y.

$-6y^4 + 14y^3 + 9y^2 + 12y + 12$

35 Perform the operations and simplify:

a $\dfrac{x - 7}{xy + y} - \dfrac{x + 3}{x + 1} + x$ **b** $\dfrac{5}{x^2 - 9} + \dfrac{3}{3 - x}$

$\dfrac{x^2y + x - 3y - 7}{y(x + 1)}$ $\dfrac{3x + 4}{9 - x^2}$

36 Solve each equation:

a $\frac{4}{5} + \frac{9}{10}x = \frac{17}{20}$ **b** $0.614 - 3.4y = 2.63$

$x = \frac{1}{18}$ $y = -0.593$

37 A line with slope -3 passes through the points $(-5, 2)$ and $(x, -1)$. Find the value of x.

$x = -4$

Problem Set C

38 Solve for d: $\quad s = \frac{n}{2}(2a + (n-1)d)$

$d = \frac{2s - 2an}{n(n-1)}$

39 Solve for x: $\quad 9x^3 = x^5$

$x = -3, 0, 3$

40 Solve for y: $\quad \sqrt{y+25} = \sqrt{y} + 3$

$y = \frac{64}{9}$

41 State a function rule for the following pairs of points:

$$(2,-4), (1,-1), (0,2), (-1,5)$$

Then use the rule to find output values for the input values $x = -2$
and $x = 3$.

$f(x) = -3x + 2; f(-2) = 8; f(3) = -7$

42 Graph the family of curves on a single set of axes:

$F(x) = x^2 + 3x$

$G(x) = x^2 - 2x$

$H(x) = x^2$ $\quad$ congruent parabolas, open upward, with
minimums $F(x)$ at $(-\frac{3}{2}, -\frac{9}{4})$, $G(x)$ at $(1,-1)$, $H(x)$ at $(0,0)$

43 Angle A is in standard position. Find $\tan A$ if the terminal side of the
angle contains the point:

a $(1,4)$ $\quad$ 4.0 $\qquad\qquad$ **c** $(-2,3)$ $\quad$ −1.5

b $(2,7)$ $\quad$ 3.5 $\qquad\qquad$ **d** $(-3,1)$ $\quad$ −0.333

44 Graph the two curves on a single set of axes:

$f(x) = 2^x$

$g(x) = 3^x$ $\quad$ Graph of $f(x) = 2^x$ will pass through $(0,1)$, $(1,2)$,
$(2,4)$, $(3,8)$, $(-1,\frac{1}{2})$, $(-2,\frac{1}{4})$, $(-3,\frac{1}{8})$. Graph of $g(x) = 3^x$
will pass through $(0,1)$, $(1,3)$, $(2,9)$, $(3,27)$, $(-1,\frac{1}{3})$, $(-2,\frac{1}{9})$, $(-3,\frac{1}{27})$

45 The sides of a triangle have measures six, eight, and ten. Find the
tangent ratio for the angle opposite the shortest side, and find the
measure of that angle (to three decimal places).

tangent is 0.75, angle = 36.870°

46 A rectangle is forty centimeters wide. Its diagonal forms an angle of
thirty-seven degrees with the longer side. What is the length of the
diagonal?

66.5 cm

47 An airplane travels 175 mph in still air. If it heads west, flying against a
wind from the north at 30 mph, what is the direction and speed of the
airplane?

angle of 9.7° SW with speed 178 mph

Answers to Odd–Numbered Problems

Pages 3–4 (Section 1.1)

Set A **1)** sequence, ADD 3 **3)** ADD 4, 19 **5)** 20 **7)** ADD 6, 34 **9)** SUBTRACT 7, 11
11) MULTIPLYBY 2, 4 **13)** DIVIDEBY 3, 6 **15)** 4.28 **17)** 2.69 **19)** 9.51 **21)** 9.09
Set B **23)** 7, 13, 19, 25, 31, 37 **25)** 4, 12, 36, 108, 324, 972 **27)** 21, $18\frac{1}{2}$, 16, $13\frac{1}{2}$, 11, $8\frac{1}{2}$
29) 170, 17, 1.7, 0.17, 0.017, 0.0017 **31)** ADD 7, ADD 6, ADD 5, . . . mystery numbers: 23, 26
Set C **33)** MULTIPLYBY 2; MULTIPLYBY 3; MULTIPLYBY 4; . . . $a = 30$ **35)** 12
37) ADD 1; ADD 2; ADD 4; . . . $y = 18$; $3\frac{1}{2}$, $4\frac{1}{2}$, $6\frac{1}{2}$, $10\frac{1}{2}$, $18\frac{1}{2}$

Pages 7–10 (Section 1.2)

Set A **1)** variable **3)** raised dot **5)** $x + 8$ **7)** $5 \cdot k$ **9)** $8c + 4$ **11)** $q \cdot q + 9 \cdot q + 5$
13) $(3 - n) \cdot (4 \cdot n)$ **15)** 36 **17)** 14.6 **19)** 2.7 **21)** 0 **23)** 10, 6, 16, 4 **25)** 0.8, 0.4, 0.12, 3
27) 110, 90, 1000, 10 **Set B** **29)** 22 **31)** 4 **33)** 6.0 **35)** 1.05 **Set C** **37)** $p = 36$ cm
39) $d = 330$ mi. **41)** $A = 27$ square units **43)** $C = 628$ **45)** $\ell = 41$ **47)** $A = 105$ square units
49) $V = 8$ cubic units **51)** $S = 320.28$ **53)** $S = 5154\frac{2}{7}$ **55)** $S = 12.56$

Pages 14–19 (Section 1.3)

Set A **1)** a, d **3)** c, d **5)** a, c **7)** c, d **9)** b, c **11)** b, d **13)** b **15)** b, d
17) b, c, d **19)** all **21)** $15 - n$ **23)** $p = 17.4$ units **Set B** **25)** $n - 8$ **27)** $11 + k$
29) $J - 3$ **31)** $\dfrac{B}{2}$ **33)** $x \cdot 5, 5x$ **35–39)** answers may vary **41)** d **43)** b **45)** $n - 5$

47) $7 + 1 - 3$ **49)** $4 \div y$ **51)** $9 - 5x$ **53)** $7m - 4m$ **Set C** **55)** $5 + 4n$ **57)** $3n - \dfrac{n}{4}$
Set X **1)** $7y + 14$, $y \cdot 7 + 14$, yes **3)** $x \cdot 12 - 17$, no **5)** $(c + b) + (b + a)$, yes **7)** $(c + b) \cdot a$, yes
9) $c + b \cdot a$, yes

Pages 20–24 (Section 1.4)

Set A **1)** $2x - 7$ **3)** $n + 6 + 5$ **5)** $\dfrac{x}{5} + 6$ **7)** $x + 16$ **9)** $x + 17 - 10$ **11)** $\frac{1}{3}x + x$
13–19) answers may vary **21)** 8 **23)** 30 **25)** 21 **27)** 17 **29)** $\frac{3}{2}$ **31)** 39 **33)** 9
Set B **35–37)** answers may vary **39)** $2\frac{7}{8}$ **41)** 0.9 **43)** 24 **Set C** **45)** 17 **47)** -3
49) 42

Set X **1)** $\left(4 \cdot \frac{1}{4}\right) \cdot 7 = 1 \cdot 7$ **3)** $14 \cdot (5 \cdot 2) = 14 \cdot 10$ **5)** $\frac{1}{9} \cdot \left(\frac{1}{6} \cdot 6\right) = \frac{1}{9} \cdot 1$
7) $(3.2 \cdot 10) \cdot \frac{1}{2} = 32 \cdot \frac{1}{2}$ **9)** $1.71523 \cdot (2.51432 \cdot 0) = 1.71523 \cdot 0$

Pages 26–28 (Section 1.5)

Set A **1)** 10 **3)** 27 **5)** 5 **7)** 64 **9)** 7 **11)** 3 **13)** 20 **15)** 15 **17)** 28 **19)** $6x$

21) $3p$ **23)** $\dfrac{x}{2}$ **25)** $2x$ **27)** $k - 11$ **29)** $2y$ **31)** $n + 8$ **33)** $2r$ **35)** $12 - n$ **37)** $7q$

Set B **39)** ADD 3 (x) **41)** MULTIPLYBY 4 (x) **43)** SUBTRACT 11 (c)
45) DIVIDEBY 2 (b) or HALF (b) **47)** $n + 12$, ADD 12 (n) **49)** $2n$, DOUBLE (n) **51)** $M = 4\frac{1}{2}$
53) $P = 3$ **Set C** **55)** c **57)** b **59)** $N = 3$ **61)**) $S = 11$

Pages 33–40 (Section 1.6)

Set A **1)** x-axis, y-axis **3)** $(4, -2)$, origin **5** Berkeley, Richmond, $3000 **7)** $7000
9) profit of $1000 **11)** $p = 7m$ **13)** $\ell = 5\,m$ **15)** 54 **17)** 10 **19)** 8
Set B **21)** 14.8 ft., 0.8 sec. **23–25)** see graphs

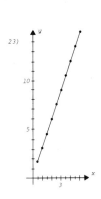

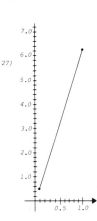

Set C **27)** see graph
Set X **1)** FREQ $(a) = 9$ **3)** FREQ $(e) = 10$ **5)** FREQ $(o) = 8$ **7)** FREQ $(s) = 3$ **9)** RELFREQ $(k) = 0$

11) FREQ (Red) = 34 **13)** FREQ (Red or Green) = 52 **15)** RELFREQ (Green) = $\dfrac{18}{100}$ = 18%

17) RELFREQ (Red or Green) = $\dfrac{52}{100}$ = 52% **19)** RELFREQ (not Red) = $\dfrac{66}{100}$ = 66%

21) answers will vary; the chart will need 11 entries (2 through 12)
23) If there are more combinations to produce a sum, then that sum will have a greater frequency.

Pages 44–45 (1/Chapter Test)

1) 21 **3)** 16 **5)** 13 **7)** 6 **9)** 11 **11)** 0 **13)** 30 **15)** 50 **17)** f **19)** c **21)** b
23) $\dfrac{n}{4} + 7$ **25)** c **27)** 6 **29)** 18

Pages 51–55 (Section 2.1)

Set A **1)** yes, 1 **3)** yes **5)** no **7–17)** see graphs **19)** 0,1,2,3 **21)** $\dfrac{2}{5}$ **23)** A = 15

25) $p = 22$ **27)** F = 77 **Set B** **29)** graph: solid dots at 1,2,3 **31)** graph: solid dots at 1,2,3, . . .

33) open dot at 4, solid line from 4 in the negative direction **35)** $\dfrac{2}{10}$ or $\dfrac{1}{5}$ **37)** $-\dfrac{151}{13}$ **39)** $\dfrac{0}{1}, \dfrac{0}{2}$, etc.

Set C **41)** A = 70.370158 **43)** 2.3 < 2.33 < 2.333...
Set X **1)** Answers may vary. Reading across the chart, examples are: Natural Numbers: none, 5, none, none, none, none. Whole Numbers: none, 5, none, none, none, 0. Integers: none, 5, none, none, −1, −1. Rational Numbers: none, 5, none, $\dfrac{2}{3}, \dfrac{2}{3}, \dfrac{2}{3}$. Irrational Numbers: none, none, π, π, π, π. Real Numbers: none, 5, π, π, π, π.
3) Real Numbers **5)** Rational Numbers **7)** Whole Numbers **9)** Natural Numbers **11)** Rational Numbers

Pages 59–62   (Section 2.2)

Set A   **1)** direction   **3)** $-7, 5, 0$ **5)** $5, 2\frac{1}{2}, 0$ **7)** arrow starts at origin, arrowhead at -3

9) solid dot at origin   **11)** $+2.50$ **13)** $+12$ **15)** $+7990$ **17)** -15 **19)** $+5$ **21)** tenth floor
23) 8   **25)** 14   **27)** 0   **29)** 5   **31)** 21   **33)** 1.16   **35)** -1 **Set B**   **37)** -2 **39)** $+104$
41) $+23$ **43)** -12 **45)** -3 **47)** 8   **49)** 2.32   **51)** 4.2   **Set C**   **53)** -0.0015927
55) $+0.0000838$ **57)** Gaston Chevrolet, -38.084; Billy Arnold, -25.764, A. J. Foyt, $+12.886$,
Al Unser, $+35.119$ **59)** -10 **61)** $+1\frac{31}{60}$ **63)** $-13\frac{29}{30}$

Pages 65–67   (Section 2.3)

Set A   **1)** -2 **3)** positive, negative   **5)** $+5$ **7)** -10 **9)** 0   **11)** 0   **13)** -7 **15)** $+2$
17) $-5 + (-1) = -6$ **19)** $3 + (-2) = 1$ **21)** $-5 + 3 = -2$ **23)** $3 + (-1) = 2$ **25)** $-2 + (-5) = -7$
27) $-1 + (-2) = -3$ **29)** 2   **31)** 5   **33)** 6   **Set B**   **35)** -10 **37)** -3 **39)** -16 **41)** $78°$
43) $\$4.50$ **Set C**   **45)** 1   **47)** $-\frac{11}{12}$ **49)** -0.2 **51)** 0.02   **53)** 6   **55)** 9   **57)** 0
59) -116 **61)** 11

Pages 69–72   (Section 2.4)

Set A   **1)** $-b$, OPP (b)   **3)** negative   **5)** $9 + (-5) = 4$ **7)** $8 + (-6) = 2$
9) $(+3) + (-9) = -6$ **11)** $5 + (-7) = -2$ **13)** $-14 + (+6) = -8$
15) $-2 - 8 = -2 + (-8) = -10$ **17)** $-3 - 2 = -3 + (-2) = -5$

19) $4\left(\frac{1}{2}\right) - (-2) = 2 + (+2) = 4$ **21)** $n + 9$ **23)** $p - 5$ **25)** $w - 14$ **27–29)** answers may vary

Set B   **31)** -9 **33)** -42 **35)** 6.93   **37)** 5   **Set C**   **39)** one solution is: $H = 9, A = 1, I = 6$,
$R = 0, C = 5, O = 7, M = 3, B = 8, E = 4, S = 2$
Set X   **1)** 60   **3)** -31 **5)** 15   **7)** -7 **9)** -35 **11)** 17   **13)** 1111   **15)** -591
17) -5

Pages 74–77   (Section 2.5)

Set A   **1)** -24, ADD 24 $(a - 24)$ **3)** $+13.2$, SUBTRACT 13.2 $(b + 13.2)$
5) $+75$, SUBTRACT 75 $(75 + e)$ **7)** -14, ADD 14 $(-14 + f)$ **9)** -2, ADD 2 $(-2 + x)$ **11)** 8   **13)** n
15) -4 **17)** -9 **Set B**   **19)** $g + 3$, SUBTRACT $3(g + 3)$ **21)** $w - 5$, ADD 5 $(w - 5)$
23) $p + 12$, SUBTRACT 12 $(p + 12)$ **Set C**   **25)** b   **27)** a   **29)** $x + 7 = 4$ **31)** $y - 6 = 15$
33–37) answers may vary

Pages 79–80   (Section 2.6)

Set A   **1)** $t = 3$ **3)** equivalent   **5)** $a = 4$ **7)** $y = 79$ **9)** $c = 22$ **11)** $R = 15$ **13)** $\ell = 5$
15) $D = -2$ **17)** $a = -6$ **19)** $V = -18$ **21)** $m = -3$ **23)** $x = 12$ **25)** $V = -13$
27) $T = 1$ **29)** $2 + N$ **31)** $8 + t$ **33)** $19 + A$ **Set B**   **35)** $r = 1.93$ **37)** $t = 1$
39) $h = -2.2$ **41)** $x = -0.6$ **43)** $R = 3.29$ **Set C**   **45)** $x = -1$ **47)** $m = -3$
49) $y = 6$ **51)** $w = 13$ **53)** $v = 2$

Pages 83–86   (Section 2.7)

Set A   **1)** b   **3)** a   **5)** b   **7)** b   **9)** $n + 24 = 50, n = 26$ **11)** $x - 38 = -20, x = 18$
13) $y - (-4) = 13, y = 9$ **15)** $29 - t = 15, t = 14$ **17)** $x + 6 = 23, x = 17$ **19)** 8   **21)** n
23) 10   **25)** 0   **Set B**   **27)** $\$9$ **29)** 1894 kW hrs   **31)** $\$589$ **33)** $\$150$ **35)** $\$389$
Set C   **37)** 56.1   **39)** $\frac{7}{8}$ **41)** $5\frac{3}{4}$ min.   **43)** $1\frac{1}{4}$ yds.   **45)** 15,105

Page 90   (2/Chapter Test)

1) Graph of 0, 1, 2, 3   **3)** open circle at 2, solid line in the negative direction from 2   **5)** yes, yes, no   **7)** -2
9) -13 **11)** 8   **13)** 8   **15)** 13   **17)** SUBTRACT 8   **19)** ADD 4   **21)** $x = 2$
23) $x + 12 = -3, x = -15$

Pages 95–99   (Section 3.1)

Set A   **1)** exponent, 3   **3)** 4, y, xt **5)** $a \cdot a \cdot a \cdot a \cdot a$ **7)** $2x \cdot x \cdot x \cdot x$ **9)** $4d \cdot d \cdot d \cdot k \cdot k$
11) a^3 **13)** $2x^2$ **15)** x^3y^2 **17)** a^4b^3 **19)** 2.345×10^3 **21)** 6.2×10^4 **23)** 1.0×10^{100}
25) 4.0×10^6 **27)** 3.249×10^2 **29)** 25   **31)** 16   **33)** $\frac{1}{4}$ **35)** 100,000   **37)** 130   **39)** 327,000
41) -4 **43)** 14   **45)** -14 **47)** 21   **49)** 18   **Set B**   **51)** 125   **53)** 96   **55)** 36   **57)** 288
59) 1200   **61)** 2^3 **63)** 3^4 **65)** 25^2 **67)** y^6 **Set C**   **69)** 9^{10} **71)** 11^{10} **73)** yes, $2^4 = 4^2$
75) 65536

Set X   **1)** r^{30} **3)** q^{2t} **5)** $81\,m^4n^4$ **7)** m^4 **9)** $\dfrac{1}{m^{q-h}}$ **11)** 2^6 **13)** 5^4 **15)** $\left(\dfrac{1}{2}\right)^6$ **17)** $(0.1)^{10}$

Pages 102–104   (Section 3.2)

Set A   **1)** positive   **3)** zero   **5)** $-\frac{1}{4}$ **7)** -48 **9)** -35 **11)** -27 **13)** -34 **15)** -25
17) -49 **19)** 12   **21)** 30   **23)** 0   **25)** 0   **27)** -24 **29)** 12   **31)** -14 **33)** 2   **35)** 9
37) 4   **39)** -27 **41)** -1 **43)** 216   **45)** a $\frac{2}{5}$ b $\frac{2}{5}$ **47)** a 27   b 27   **Set B**   **49)** 110
51) 700   **53)** 1680   **55)** 600   **57)** 0   **59)** $\frac{1}{5}$ **61)** $\frac{3}{2}$ **63)** $\frac{1}{y}$ **Set C**   **65)** 26   **67)** $\frac{3}{2}$
69) -39.24 **71)** 65,256   **73)** X: $-2\frac{2}{3}$ per minute, Y: -4 per minute

Pages 108–113   (Section 3.3)

Set A   **1)** positive   **3)** negative   **5)** positive   **7)** -2 **9)** -5 **11)** 3   **13)** $\frac{3}{4}$ **15)** -2
17) 3   **19)** -6 **21)** $-\frac{1}{2}$ **23)** $-\frac{1}{2}$ **25)** 3   **27)** d **29)** $\frac{7}{2}$ **31)** $-\frac{4}{3}$ **33)** $\frac{1}{2}$
35) no reciprocal   **37)** 3   **39)** -6 **41)** $-\frac{1}{3}$ **Set B**   **43)** $\frac{2}{5}$ **45)** -1 **47)** -9
49) 75   **Set C**   **51)** -2.368 **53)** $-\frac{10}{13}$ **55)** $-\frac{8}{5}$ or $-\frac{1}{40}$ **57)** 76%   **59)** 37

Set X   **1)** $\frac{8}{15}$ **3)** $\frac{9}{5}$ **5)** $\frac{26}{21}$ **7)** $\frac{4}{3}$ **9)** 2   **11)** $\dfrac{a^3b^2}{c^2d^3}$ **13)** 1

Pages 115–117   (Section 3.4)

Set A   **1)** multiplication   **3)** as they occur from left to right   **5)** innermost parentheses   **7)** 20
9) -1 **11)** 28   **13)** -16 **15)** 0   **17)** 24   **19)** -8 **21)** 0   **23)** -27 **25)** 9
27) -2 **29)** -59 **31)** $3 + f$, ADD $-3(3 + f)$ **33)** $w + 3$, ADD $-3(w + 3)$ **Set B**   **35)** 13
37) -3 **39)** -12 **41)** -73 **43)** -1 **Set C**   **45)** $C = -20.72$ **47)** $S = 657.00$
49) $4(2^3 - 5) \div ((-6) + 5)$

Pages 121–123   (Section 3.5)

Set A   **1)** 1   **3)** $\frac{1}{6}$ **5)** MULTIPLY BY $\frac{1}{8}$ **7)** MULTIPLY BY 4   **9)** MULTIPLY BY $\dfrac{1}{6.8}$ **11)** MULTIPLY BY 6
13) MULTIPLY BY $\frac{5}{3}$ **15)** $2x$, MULTIPLY BY $\frac{1}{2}$ **17)** $\frac{n}{5}$, MULTIPLY BY 5   **19)** $0.75 \cdot S$, MULTIPLY BY $\dfrac{1}{0.75}$
21) $\frac{2}{3}s$, MULTIPLY BY $\frac{3}{2}$ **23)** $\frac{1}{4}c$, MULTIPLY BY 4   **25)** b **27)** a **29)** $8k = 34$ **31)** $\frac{1}{3}n = 19$
33–35) answers may vary   **37)** $h = 23$ **39)** $G = 11$ **41)** $q = -4$ **43)** $x = -34$ **45)** $n = 17$
Set B   **47)** $\frac{96}{3} = f$ **49)** $3 \cdot 13 = J$ **Set C**   **51)** between 6075 and 9075

Pages 125–128   (Section 3.6)

Set A   **1)** equivalent   **3)** $\frac{3}{4}$ **5)** $n = 10$ **7)** $m = 40$ **9)** $y = \frac{11}{2}$ **11)** $y = -100$ **13)** $a = \frac{1}{2}$
15) $w = 10$ **17)** $w = -15$ **19)** $x = 2$ **21)** $k = 34$ **23)** $k = -17$ **25)** $k = 5.2$ **27)** $x = 49$
29) $n = 22$ **31)** $i = -5$ **Set B**   **33)** $n = 10$ **35)** $\ell = 16$ **37)** $a = -5$ **39)** $v = 144$
41) $y = 2$ **Set C**   **43)** $n = 12$ **45)** $x = -52$ **47)** $m = 9$ **49)** $h = 400$ **51)** $y = 342$
53) $x = 37$ **55)** $p = 63,000,000$ **57)** $r = 86\frac{4}{11}$ **59)** $x = 1066.67$
61) $s = 230.77$ miles/day (9.6 miles per hour)

Pages 131–138 (Section 3.7)

Set A   **1)** ADD 7, MULTBY $\frac{1}{3}$ **3)** ADD 5, MULTBY $\frac{1}{8}$ **5)** ADD -5, MULTBY $\frac{1}{4}$ **7)** ADD 10, MULTBY 3
9) ADD -6, MULTBY $\frac{1}{7}$ **11)** ADD $\frac{4}{19}$, MULTBY 7   **13)** ADD -11, MULTBY $\frac{4}{3}$
15) ADD -5, MULTBY $\frac{1}{3}$, $x = 5$ **17)** ADD 9, MULTBY $\frac{1}{6}$, $r = 4$ **19)** ADD -11, MULTBY $\frac{1}{3}$, $x = -3$
21) ADD 23, MULTBY $\frac{1}{3}$, $b = 9$ **23)** ADD -4, MULTBY $\frac{1}{2}$, $x = \frac{7}{2}$ **25)** ADD -24, MULTBY $\frac{1}{5}$, $r = 3$
27) ADD 7, MULTBY $\frac{1}{2}$, $x = 10$ **29)** ADD -18, MULTBY $-\frac{1}{3}$, $x = 2$ **31)** ADD -34, MULTBY $-\frac{1}{7}$, $x = 2$
33) ADD 5, MULTBY $-\frac{1}{2}$, $x = 7$ **35)** 108°   **37)** \$50   **39)** 6.00   **Set B**   **41)** $4n + 5 = 29$, $n = 6$

43) $2x + 15 = -13$, $x = -14$ **45)** $5 - \frac{m}{2} = -10$, $m = 30$ **47)** $x = -\frac{25}{3}$ **49)** $x = 12$

51) $t = 10$ **53)** $n = -66$ **Set C**   **55)** 172 chirps   **57)** 42 cards   **59)** 10 Capricorns
61) 10 hours   **63)** \$150,000   **65)** \$73 76   **67)** 11 nickels   **69)** 93.33°C   **71)** 58 pounds

73) $\frac{4}{9}$ **75)** 6.25%   **77)** 291.18   **79)** 280: $\frac{1}{22}$, 4.5%; 284: $\frac{1}{22}$, 4.5%; 287: $\frac{1}{11}$, 9%; 288: $\frac{1}{22}$, 4.5%;

289: $\frac{3}{22}$, 13.6%; 290: $\frac{3}{22}$, 13.6%; 291: $\frac{1}{22}$, 4.5%; 292: $\frac{1}{11}$, 9%; 293: $\frac{1}{22}$, 4.5%; 294: $\frac{1}{11}$, 9%; 295: $\frac{1}{11}$, 9%;

297: $\frac{1}{22}$, 4.5%; 299: $\frac{1}{22}$, 4.5%; 301: $\frac{1}{22}$, 4.5%   **81)** 1 hour, 28 minutes   **83)** longest: Brand Y, 1400;
shortest: Brand Y, 900   **85)** Brand Y
Set X   **1)** 3   **3)** 18   **5)** 6   **7)** 16   **9)** 12   **11)** 20   **13)** 68   **15)** 73   **17)** 18
19) answers will vary

Pages 140–142 (Section 3.8)

Set A   **1)** p **3)** $d - t$ **5)** pr **7)** $a + b$ **9)** $\frac{z}{w}$ **11)** $\frac{4a + b}{3}$ **13)** $t = \frac{d}{r}$ **15)** $c = s - e$

17) $B = C + A$ **19)** $z = w - x$ **21)** $B = \frac{c}{h}$ **23)** $p = \frac{i}{rt}$ **25)** 4.039×10^5 **27)** -16

29) $\frac{n}{4}$, MULTBY 4   **31)** 120°   **33)** \$9300   **Set B**   **35)** MULTBY 3, MULTBY $\frac{1}{h}$ **37)** ADD $-3y$,

MULTBY $\frac{1}{2}$ **39)** ADD $-r$, MULTBY $-\frac{1}{ax^2}$ **41)** $h = \frac{V}{\pi r^2}$ **43)** $a = \frac{2A}{p}$ **Set C**   **45)** $\ell = \frac{p - b}{2}$

47) $w = \frac{p - 2\ell}{2}$ **49)** $h = \frac{2A}{B + b}$ **51)** $b = \frac{2A - hB}{h}$ **53)** $h = \frac{SA - 2\pi r^2}{2\pi r}$ **55)** $a = \frac{bf}{b - f}$
57) $y = m(x - r) + s$

Page 146 (3/Chapter Test)

1) -9 **3)** $-\frac{1}{8}$ **5)** -2 **7)** 48   **9)** 71   **11)** -4 **13)** 100   **15)** $\frac{b}{a}$ **17)** MULTIPLYBY $\frac{5}{2}$

19) MULTIPLYBY $\frac{3b}{a}$ **21)** $x = \frac{5}{2}$ **23)** $x = \frac{m^2}{p}$ **25)** $x = 6$ **27)** \$0.40

Pages 147–149 (Cumulative Review 1–3)

Set A   **1)** sequence   **3)** origin, end   **5)** x, coefficient, exponent   **7)** positive, negative   **9)** c
11) a **13)** d **15)** d **17)** a **19)** 0   **21)** -108 **23)** 27   **25)** $1\frac{13}{18}$ **27)** 6
29) 0.0473   **Set B**   **31)** 4,5,6,7,8, ...   **33)** 1,2,3,4,5, ...   **35)** -7 **37)** $\frac{6}{5}$ **39)** 16
41) $m = -7$ **43)** $x = -21$ **45)** $t = 2$ **Set C**   **47)** $\frac{1369}{4}$ or $342\frac{1}{4}$ **49)** a 3   b 9   c 1   d 3   e 0
49) f $\frac{3}{52}$, 6%   g $\frac{9}{52}$, 17%   h $\frac{1}{52}$, 2%   i $\frac{3}{52}$, 6%

Pages 153–157 (Section 4.1)

Set A   **1)** yes, product of (constants and) variables   **3)** yes, product of a constant $\left(\frac{1}{3}\right)$ and a variable (v)

5) a factor that is a constant   **7)** $3x^3$, 3   **9)** $5n^2$, 5   **11)** $18x^7$, 18   **13)** $6x^4$, 6   **15)** y^8, 1
17) $20n^2p$, 20   **19)** $-w^7$, -1 **21)** $25x^2$, 25   **23)** $8x^6y^3$, 8   **25)** $3x^2$ **27)** $4y^2 \cdot 2y^3 = 8y^5$ **29)** 28, 28
31) 15, 15   **Set B**   **33)** $18x^3y^2$ **35)** $4a^5b^2$ **37)** $180y^7$ **39)** $8 \cdot 10^5$ **41)** 432   **43)** $36x^5$

45) 1.23×10^5　　**47)** 8.534085×10^2　　**Set C**　　**49)** 6.527578×10^{13}　　**51)** 4.02781×10^{20}
53) 7.0×10^3
Set X　　**1)** $2^3 \cdot 3$　　**3)** $2 \cdot 3^2 \cdot 5^2 \cdot x^2 \cdot y^5$　　**5)** $2^6 \cdot 5^6$　　**7)** $2^3 \cdot 3$　　**9)** $2 \cdot 3^2 \cdot 5^2 \cdot x^2 \cdot y^5$　　**11)** $2^6 \cdot 5^6$
13) $3^6 \cdot 5^2$　　**15)** $7 \cdot 11 \cdot 13$

Pages 161–163 (Section 4.2)

Set A　**1)** same variables, corresponding variables have same exponents　　**3)** multiplication and addition (or multiplication and subtraction)　　**5)** 3,8　　**7)** 1,7a　　**9)** x, 13x　　**11)** 13x　　**13)** $2b^2$　　**15)** 7y　　**17)** 7n
19) 0　　**21)** 9x　　**23)** 25x　　**25)** $x = 2$　　**27)** $x = 9$　　**29)** $x = 11$　　**Set B**　　**31)** $11a + 3b$
33) $8x + 16$　　**35)** $3x - 5$　　**37)** $3x^2 - x$　　**39)** $3x^3 + 2x - 6$　　**41)** $x^2 - 9$　　**43) a** $x + 8$　**b** $2x + 8$
Set C　　**45)** 12s　　**47)** $S = 2h\ell + 2wh + \ell w$　　**49)** $S = 5e^2$

Pages 165–167 (Section 4.3)

Set A　　**1)** $3x + 4x$, $(3 + 4)x$, $7x$　　**3)** 12, 14, 16, 18; x, $x + 2$, $x + 4$, $x + 6$　　**5)** $n = 6$　　**7)** $n = 4$
9) $x = 2$　　**11)** $n = 11$　　**13)** $n = 4$　　**15)** $w = 5$　　**17)** $x = \frac{15}{2}$　　**19)** $n = -2$　　**21)** $x = -1$
23) 46, 47　　**25)** 18 wood, 6 slate　　**27)** 18,18, same　　**29)** 15, 15, same　　**Set B**　　**31)** $n = 3$
33) $p = 5$　　**35)** $n = -4$　　**37)** $x = -\frac{7}{3}$　　**39)** 87,89　　**41)** $\ell = 21\frac{1}{2}$, $w = 12\frac{1}{2}$　　**Set C**　　**43)** 18 green, 90 blue

Pages 170–172 (Section 4.4)

Set A　　**1)** combining like terms, removing parentheses　　**3)** 3　　**5)** 7x　　**7)** m　　**9)** 3x　　**11)** 1
13) $6x + 18$　　**15)** $8x^2 + 24x - 16$　　**17)** $4x(2x - 5y) = 8x^2 - 20xy$　　**19)** $(5 + 11x)\,3x = 15x + 33x^2$
21) $12x + (-30)$　　**23)** $5x^2 + (-12x)$　　**Set B**　　**25)** $9x + 18$　　**27)** $x - 5$　　**29)** 80x　　**31)** $2x - 13$
Set C　　**33)** 408　　**35)** 82　　**37)** 82　　**39)** $24x - 16$
Set X　　**1–3)** programs may vary

Pages 174–176 (Section 4.5)

Set A　　**1)** remove parentheses, combine like terms　　**3)** $n = 6$　　**5)** $t = 6$　　**7)** $n = 3$　　**9)** $v = 15$
11) $w = 7$　　**13)** $r = 3$　　**15)** $x = -22$　　**17)** $p = -\frac{7}{5}$　　**19)** $d = 11$　　**21)** $-2, -1$　　**23)** 5, 7
25) $2(3x + 7) = 6x + 14$　　**27)** $5(m + h) = 5m + 5h$　　**Set B**　　**29)** $x = 2$　　**31)** $x = 2$　　**33)** $x = 26$
35) $x = 8$　　**37)** answers may vary　　**39)** 4, 5　　**Set C**　　**41)** $2\frac{1}{2}$　　**43)** 35 at \$1, 40 at 50¢
45) 66 tomato, 33 pepper

Pages 180–182 (Section 4.6)

Set A　　**1)** plus, minus　　**3)** two　　**5)** $2y + 3$　　**7)** $14x^2 - 7$　　**9)** $15n^2 + 3n$　　**11)** $-x^2 - x + 8$
13) $13x^2 + 13x + 17$　　**15)** $2x + 10$　　**17)** $x = 1$　　**19)** $n = -\frac{17}{2}$　　**Set B**　　**21)** $12x - 1$
23) $4x^2 + 12x - 12$　　**25)** $6x^3 + 10x^2 - 14x$　　**27)** $6x + 6$　　**Set C**　　**29)** $1000 + 1000r$
31) $1000 + 3000r + 3000r^2 + 1000r^3$　　**33)** \$1097.50, \$1204.51, \$1321.95, \$1450.84
Set X　　**1)** 3　　**3)** 0　　**5)** 4　　**7)** 3　　**9)** 4

Pages 184–188 (Section 4.7)

Set A　　**1)** the GCF is the greatest integer that is a factor of each integer　　**3)** ab^2　　**5)** c　　**7)** b
9) a　　**11)** b　　**13)** a　　**15)** a　　**17)** a　　**19)** $2(x + 3)$　　**21)** $7x(4 - x)$　　**23)** $4(x + 1)$
25) $4x(2x - 5)$　　**27)** $x^3(7x + 5)$　　**29)** $6x - 1$　　**31)** $2x^2 + 6x$　　**33)** $2x^2 - 7x$　　**35)** $-x^2 + 2x$
37) $-40x + 8$　　**Set B**　　**39)** 6　　**41)** 3　　**43)** xy　　**45)** $4b$　　**47)** $2(x + y - z)$
49) $3(6a^2 + 3a - 1)$　　**51)** $ab(a - b)$　　**53)** $4x^2(3x^2 - x + 2)$　　**55)** $7y(3y - 2 + 5y^2)$
Set C　　**57)** $20x^2y^4(10x - 7y)$　　**59)** $14x^2(5 - 7x^5 - 40x^2)$　　**61)** $21rs(5r + 7s)$　　**63)** $a(x^2 + x + 1)$
65) $\frac{1}{8}p^2\left(\frac{1}{3} - p + \frac{1}{6}p^2\right)$　　**67)** $\frac{a}{b}x\left(\frac{a}{b}x^4 - \frac{1}{b}x^2 + a\right)$

Set X　　**1)** 24　　**3)** 175　　**5)** $45x^2y$　　**7)** 36　　**9)** 18　　**11)** $14x^3z^2$

Page 192 (4/Chapter Test)

1) -6　　**3)** 9　　**5)** 3　　**7)** $10x$　　**9)** $-2xy - xy^2$　　**11)** $-18x + 12$　　**13)** $8y^2 - y + 17$
15) $x = -10$　　**17)** $p = 4$　　**19)** false　　**21)** $x + x + 1 = 121$; 60, 61

Pages 199–203   (Section 5.1)

Set A   **1)** nine is greater than five   **3)** five is greater than zero   **5)** negative twenty is less than negative seven   **7)** $13 > -18$ **9)** $-18 < -13$ **11)** $9 > -13$ **13)** $10 > 2$ **15)** $-12 > -15$
17) $14 > -13$ **19)** $x > 1, 1 < x$ **21)** $x < -3, -3 > x$ **23)** $x > 0, 0 < x$ **25)** $x < 5, 5 > x$
27) $1, 2, 3, \ldots, 9$ **29)** $1, 2, 3, 4$ **Set B**   **31)** $8 > 4 + 3$ **33)** $-12 > (2)(-10)$ **35)** $-8 > 0 - 9$
37) arrow in positive direction from an open dot at 3   **39)** arrow in positive direction from an open dot at -6
41) arrow in negative direction from an open dot at 5   **43)** closed dot at -2 **45)** arrow in positive direction from an open dot at -2 **Set C**   **47)** closed dots at 1, 2, 3, 4, 5   **49)** closed dots at 3, 4, 5, . . . , 9
51) arrow in positive direction from an open dot at 5   **53)** closed dots at 0, 1, 2, 3, 4, . . .   **55) a** $m < n$
55 b $n > p$ **c** $q < p$ **d** $p > m$ **e** $p > q$ **f** $q < n$ **57)** arrows in negative and positive directions from an open dot at 2

Set X   **1)** $\{1, 2\}$ **3)** $\{2, 4\}$ **5)** $\{3, 4, 5\}$ **7)** $\{x : 3 \leq x \leq 7\}$ **9)** $\left\{x : 13 < x < \dfrac{37}{2}\right\}$
11) $\{1, 2, 3, 4, 5, 6, 7, 8\}$

Pages 207–209   (Section 5.2)

Set A   **1)** n is less than or equal to four   **3)** n is greater than or equal to negative two   **5)** n is greater than or equal to negative one   **7)** arrow in the negative direction from a closed dot at 4   **9)** arrow in the positive direction from a closed dot at -2 **11)** arrow in the positive direction from a closed dot at -1
13) closed dots at $-5, -4, -3, -2, -1$ **15)** $x > 3$ **17)** $x < -3$ **19)** $x \geq -5$ **21)** $x \leq 6$
23) $x < 0$ **25)** $x \geq 0$ **27)** $x = -4$ **29)** $z = -1$ **Set B**   **31)** G **33)** B **35)** A
37) F **39)** $x > 1$ or $x < -2$ **41)** $1 \leq z < 4$ **43)** $n \geq 2$ or $n < 1$ **45)** $-3 < q \leq 0$ **47)** arrow in $-$ direction from open dot at -2, arrow in $+$ direction from open dot at 1   **49)** heavy line from closed dot at 1 to open dot at 4   **51)** arrow in $-$ direction from open dot at 1, arrow in $+$ direction from closed dot at 2
53) heavy line from open dot at -3 to closed dot at 0   **55)** $x = 4$ **57)** $x = 0$ **Set C**   **59)** closed dot at 1   **61)** no values   **63)** $-$ from open dot at -3, $+$ from open dot at 2   **65)** closed dot at 6
67) heavy line between open dots at -1 and 1   **69)** heavy line from open dot at -3 to closed dot at 0
71) heavy line from closed dot at -8 to open dot at -5 **73) a** $40 \leq s \leq 55$ **b** $s > 55$ **c** $s < 40$
75) $\dfrac{1}{2} \leq c \leq 12$

Pages 211–213   (Section 5.3)

Set A   **1)** $x < y, y > x$ **3)** $x + k < y + k$ **5)** $0 > -8$ **7)** $x < 5$ **9)** $a > 5$ **11)** $a < 15.2$
13) $c > 8$ **15)** $-2 < x$ **17)** $-11 < y$ **19)** $28.9 < x$ **21)** $d > -3$ **23)** $x = \dfrac{17}{3}$ **25)** $w = 0$
Set B   **27)** $x \leq 8$ **29)** $x \geq 6$ **31)** $x \geq 4.1$ **33)** $x > 5$ **35)** $-2 < x$ **37)** $x \geq -5$
39) $x > -8$ **41)** $x \geq 8$ **43)** $x \leq -1$ or $x \geq 1$ **45)** $x \geq 1$ and $x \leq 3, 1 \leq x \leq 3$ **47)** $n + 8 \geq 20$, $n \geq 12$ **49)** $w + 6 \leq 10, w \leq 4$ **Set C**   **51)** $1 \leq x \leq 3$ **53)** $x = -1$ or $x = -2$ or $x \geq 1$

Pages 216–220   (Section 5.4)

Set A   **1)** $-36 < -9 < 18$ **3)** $4 > 1 > -2$ **5)** $\dfrac{p}{10} < \dfrac{q}{10}$ **7)** $-10p > -10q$ **9)** $x > 4$
11) $x < -3$ **13)** $x > 8$ **15)** $x < -3$ **17)** $x > -9$ **19)** $x < -\dfrac{1}{2}$ **21)** $x \leq -11$ **23)** $x \geq 50$
25) $x \geq 12$ **27)** $x = \dfrac{7}{2}$ **29)** $z = \dfrac{5}{2}$ **Set B**   **31)** $x > -\dfrac{1}{9}$ **33)** $x \leq 9$ **35)** $x \geq \dfrac{1}{2}$ **37)** $x \geq -60$
39) $x \geq \dfrac{3}{4}$ **41)** $x < 14$ **43)** $x \geq 60$ **Set C**   **45)** $x \geq -\dfrac{1}{6}$ **47)** $x \geq -60$ **49)** $-4 < x \leq -2$
51) $7 < x < 9$ **53)** $x \geq 3$ **55)** $x \geq 6$
Set X   **1)** yes   **3)** yes   **5)** yes   **7)** yes

Pages 222–225   (Section 5.5)

Set A   **1)** $x > 4$ **3)** $x \geq -6$ **5)** $x < -14$ **7)** $x > 4$ **9)** $x > -1$ **11)** $x > \dfrac{3}{2}$ **13)** $x \leq 19$
15) $z \leq -\dfrac{7}{3}$ **Set B**   **17)** $x > 2$ **19)** $x < 6$ **21)** $x > \dfrac{9}{7}$ **23)** $x < \dfrac{9}{4}$ **25)** $x \geq 12$ **27)** $x \leq 9$
29) $2x - 5 \leq 13, x \leq 9$ **31)** $x \leq 4$ **Set C**   **33)** $x \geq -\dfrac{3}{2}$ **35)** no values for x **37)** $-1 < x < 3$
39) $-2 \geq x \geq 5$ **41)** $-17 < x < 8$ **43)** $5h - 4 + 2(h + 11) < 207, h < 27$, base < 135.

Set X **1)** $x = 5$ or $x = -5$ **3)** $z > 5$ or $z < -5$ **5)** $-1 \le q \le 7$ **7)** $-3 < n < 1$
9) $s \le 1$ or $s \ge 3$ **11)** $3 \le x \le 7$ **13)** $p \le 0$ or $p \ge 4$ **15)** $-1 < r < 11$ **17)** $t = -1.4$ or $t = 1.9\overline{3}$
19) $-0.6 \le x \le 1.6$

Page 230 (5/Chapter Test)

1) $>$ **3)** $>$ **5)** $>$ **7)** $<$ **9)** $<$ **11)** Negative nine is less than four. **13)** x is greater than or equal
to zero and less than or equal to one. **15)** x is greater than or equal to negative five and less than two.
17) Open circle at -2, solid line in the negative direction from -2 **19)** Solid dot at 2; solid line in the negative
direction from a solid dot at -4 **21)** solid line between a solid dot at -4 and a solid dot at 2
23) $x < 2$ **25)** $y \ge -6$ **27)** $-1 \le y \le 3$ **29)** $30 \le x \le 75$

Pages 235–238 (Section 6.1)

Set A **1)** four **3)** $a^2 + 9a + 18$ **5)** $x^2 + 4x - 21$ **7)** $a^2 - 9a + 14$ **9)** $2x^2 + 7x + 3$
11) $2ax + 8a - 24x - 32$ **13)** $35x^2 - 130x + 120$ **15)** $16 - a^2$ **17)** $100a^2 - 121$
19) $25x^2 + 20x + 4$ **21)** x^2 **23)** 18 **25)** $15y^3$ **27)** $3a^3b^3c$ **29)** $x^3y^4z^5$ **31)** $a^3x^3y^3$
Set B **33)** $3x^2 + xy - 14y^2$ **35)** $16 - a^2b^2$ **37)** $x^3 + 4x^2 + 4x + 1$ **39)** $2y^3 + 7y^2 - 34y - 24$
41) $-2x^2 - 8x - xy + 8y + 3y$ **43)** $12x^2 - 4x - 40$ **45)** $w = 19$, $\ell = 31$ **47)** 6, 8
Set C **49)** $8a^2x + 4bx - 2cx + 4a^2y + 2by - cy$ **51)** $9x^4 + 42x^3 + 19x^2 - 70x + 25$, 441
53) $2z^5 - z^4 + 4z^3 - 10z^2 + 6z - 1$, 51 **55)** $6x^5 + 2x^4 - 13x^3 + 7x - 2$, 132
Set X **1)** $x^3 + 8x^2 + 16x + 5$ **3)** $4z^4 - 7z^3 + 5z^2 - 7z + 5$ **5)** $4s^4 + 4s^3 - 19s^2 - 10s + 25$
7) $v^4 - 4v^3 - 6v^2 - 4v + 1$

Pages 240–242 (Section 6.2)

Set A **1)** Distributive Property, Vertical Form, FOIL **3)** No. FOIL is not a property, just a summary of the
pattern for multiplying binomials. **5)** $+11x$ **7)** $-7x$ **9)** $+4x$ **11)** $+7x$ **13)** $+5a$ **15)** $+0x$
17) $x^2 + 12x + 35$ **19)** $y^2 - 11y + 18$ **21)** $x^2 + 6x - 27$ **23)** $10x^2 + 27x + 18$
25) $14y^2 - 31y + 15$ **27)** $33y^2 + 5y - 18$ **29)** $9y^2 - 6y + 1$ **31)** $25r^2 - 1$ **33)** $8n^2 - 67n + 24$
35) 5 **37)** 4 **39)** 7, 4 **Set B** **41)** $2x^2 + 5xy + 3y^2$ **43)** $15 + 2x - x^2$ **45)** $4x^2 - 16y^2$
47) $64y^2 - 16y + 1$ **49)** $81 + 180y + 100y^2$ **Set C** **51)** $x^2 + 2x + 1$ **53)** $x^2 - 4x + 4$
55) $4a^2 + 4a + 1$ **57)** $49a^2 - 70a + 25$ **59)** 484 **61)** 6241

Pages 246–249 (Section 6.3)

Set A **1)** factoring **3)** no (the last term is negative) **5)** $+$, $+$ **7)** $+$, $-$ **9)** $-$, $+$
11) $+$, $-$ **13)** $-$, $+$ **15)** $x^2 - 4$ **17)** $a^2 - 81$ **19)** $4x^2 - 1$ **Set B** **21)** b **23)** a **25)** b
27) $(x + 5)(x + 1)$ **29)** $(x + 4)(x + 2)$ **31)** $(x - 5)(x - 4)$ **33)** $(x - 5)(x + 3)$ **35)** $(x - 3)(x + 2)$
37) $(x + 7)(x - 4)$ **39)** $(x + 9)(x - 4)$ **41)** $(x + 5)(x - 4)$ **43)** $(x - 20)(x - 2)$ **45)** $(x - 5)(x + 2)$

Set C **47)** $(a + 5)^2$ **49)** $(2x - 3)^2$ **51)** $(5c + 6d)^2$ **53)** $(11 - y)^2$ **55)** $\left(2x + \dfrac{1}{2}\right)^2$ **57)** $(ax + b)^2$

Set X **1)** $x = 9$ or $x = 4$ **3)** $x = 6$ or $x = -5$ **5)** $x = -8$ or $x = 1$ **7)** $x = 1$ **9)** $x = 3$ or $x = -1$
11) $x = 5$ or $x = -4$ **13)** $x = 3$ or $x = -2$ **15)** $x = 36$ or $x = -1$

Pages 251–253 (Section 6.4)

Set A **1)** $x^8 - 81 = (x^4)^2 - (9)^2$ **3)** $+$, $-$ **5)** $(x + 2)(x - 2)$ **7)** $(8 + a)(8 - a)$ **9)** $(x + 9)(x - 9)$
11) $(x^2 + 3y)(x^2 - 3y)$ **13)** $(k + m^4)(k - m^4)$ **15)** $(ab^3 + 10y^4)(ab^3 - 10y^4)$ **17)** $(b + a^2)(b - a^2)$
19) $(x^3 + 0.1)(x^3 - 0.1)$ **21)** 50 is not a perfect square **23)** exponent of y is odd **25)** exponent of x is
odd **27)** $5x^2 - 38x + 21$ **29)** $12x^2 - 16x - 3$ **31)** $7x^2 - 33x - 10$ **Set B** **33)** $2(x + 3)(x - 3)$
35) $5(x + 7)(x - 7)$ **37)** $y^2(1 + 6y)(1 - 6y)$ **39)** $3x^3(x + 3)(x - 3)$ **41)** $4(y + 4)(y - 4)$
Set C **43)** $(x + 2)(x - 6)$ **45)** $(4x + 3)(-2x - 5)$ **47)** $(x^2 + x + 9)(x^2 - 7x - 7)$
Set X **1)** $x^3 - a^3$ **3)** **a** $x^4 - 1$ **b** $x^5 - 1$ **5)** **a** $x^5 + 1$ **b** $x^7 + 1$
7) $x^{15} - 1 = (x - 1)(x^{14} + x^{13} + x^{12} + \cdots + x^2 + x + 1)$,
$x^{15} + 1 = (x + 1)(x^{14} - x^{13} + x^{12} - x^{11} + x^{10} - x^9 + x^8 - x^7 + x^6 - x^5 + x^4 - x^3 + x^2 - x + 1)$

Pages 256–258 (Section 6.5)

Set A **1)** $3x, 4x; 6x, 2x; 12x, x$ **3)** $6x^2, 5$ **5)** -3 **7)** $x+1$ **9)** $3x-5$ **11)** $(5x+1)(x+2)$
13) $(2x-1)(x-5)$ **15)** $(3x-5)(x-1)$ **17)** $(3x-1)(x+7)$ **19)** $(3x+2)(x+2)$
21) $(10x+1)(x+2)$ **23)** $(2x-5)(x-2)$ **25)** $5(2y+3)$ **27)** $6(1-3a^3)$ **29)** $xy(4x-7y)$
31) $8a^3(2a-3)$ **Set B** **33)** $(4x+5)(2x+3)$ **35)** $(4x-3)(3x+2)$ **37)** $(5x-4)(2x+5)$
39) $3(3x-4)(x-1)$ **41)** $y(5x-6)(3x+1)$ **Set C** **43)** $(x-4)(x+4)$ **45)** cannot be factored

Pages 260–262 (Section 6.6)

Set A **1)** common factor (other than 1) **3)** $3m$ **5)** 1 **7)** 3 **9)** 1 **11)** 2 **13)** x^3 **15)** 1
17) 1 **19)** $4y$ **21)** 5 **23)** $3m(m-3n)$ **25)** $(x-9)(x+9)$ **27)** $3(2a^2-5a+6)$
29) $(2x-3y)(2x+3y)$ **31)** $2(x^2+5x+1)$ **33)** $x^3(x-9)$ **35)** $(7a-10b)(7a+10b)$
37) $(3x-2)(3x-2)$ **39)** $4y(4+3x)(4-3x)$ **41)** $5(3x+2)(3x+2)$ **43)** $x=-4$ **45)** 23, 25
Set B **47)** $(3a-b)(2a+b)$ **49)** $(4x-9)(5x-2)$ **51)** $7y(x-1)(x+1)$ **53)** $2(6y-5)(3y+2)$
55) $(x^2+4y^2)(x+2y)(x-2y)$ **57)** $(2a^2+b)(9a^2-b)$ **Set C** **59)** $3t+7$ **61)** $7x+6$
63) $3(y+2)$
Set X **1)** $(x+3-y)(x+3+y)$ **3)** $(b^3+5)(a+1)(a-1)$ **5)** $(5a+3)(5a-3+2b)$

Page 266 (6/ Chapter Test)

1) $x^2-8x+12$ **3)** $9x^2-12x+4$ **5)** $4x^2-12xy+9y^2$ **7)** $3x^3+19x^2+15x-25$
9) $x^4-12x^3+46x^2-60x+25$ **11)** $4x^2-20x+25$ **13)** $9a^4-25$ **15)** $2x^2+11x-40$
17) $(x-8)(x+8)$ **19)** $(2y-3)(y-1)$ **21)** $(z^2-3)(z^2+4)$ **23)** $(4x+7)(x+2)$
25) $3(z+6)(z+4)$ **27)** $5a^2(2a+3)(2a-1)$ **29)** $(a^2+4)(a-2)(a+2)$

Pages 271–273 (Section 7.1)

Set A **1)** none **3)** $a\neq 0$ **5)** $d\neq 0$ **7)** $x\neq 0, y\neq 0$ **9)** $a\neq 0, c\neq 0$ **11)** $a\neq -b$ **13)** $\dfrac{a}{5}$
15) $\dfrac{3}{2a}$ **17)** $\dfrac{1}{d}$ **19)** $-\dfrac{y}{x}$ **21)** $\dfrac{5b}{3a}$ **23)** $\dfrac{3}{a+b}$ **25)** $\dfrac{2x}{3a}$ **27)** $\dfrac{x-2y}{3x+4y}$ **29)** $\dfrac{2a-1}{b}$
31) $\dfrac{a-1}{b(a+1)}$ **33)** $\dfrac{x-3}{x+4}$ **35)** $\dfrac{27}{20}$ **37)** $\dfrac{5}{72}$ **39)** $\dfrac{42}{5}$ **41)** $\dfrac{5}{72}$ **Set B** **43)** $\dfrac{x^2+4}{x^2+5}$ **45)** $\dfrac{3x-2}{3x+2}$
47) $\dfrac{a^2+a+2}{2(a^2-3a-4)}$ **49)** $\dfrac{x-5}{x+5}$ **51)** $\dfrac{a^2+1}{a+1}$ **53)** $\dfrac{5}{24}$ **55)** $\dfrac{15}{32}$ **57)** $\dfrac{3}{2}$ **59)** $r=\dfrac{4b}{a+3}$ **61)** $c=\dfrac{a-1}{2b}$
Set C **63)** $\dfrac{(2k+y)^2(k-y)}{(2k-y)^2}$ **65)** $\dfrac{3a+5}{3a-2}$ **67)** $\dfrac{3(t-2)}{2(t+2)}$ **69)** $\dfrac{a-3}{a-6}$ **71)** $\dfrac{2r+1}{2r-1}$ **73)** $\dfrac{6}{z}$

Pages 276–279 (Section 7.2)

Set A **1)** $\dfrac{a^3}{b^3}$ **3)** $\dfrac{2}{3y}$ **5)** 1 **7)** $\dfrac{x(x^2-5)}{x+5}$ **9)** $\dfrac{3}{2m}$ **11)** $\dfrac{x^2}{(x+4)(x-5)}$ **13)** 3 **15)** $\dfrac{y^2}{2}$
17) $\dfrac{1}{24ab}$ **19)** 17 **21)** $15\dfrac{5}{13}$ **23)** $1720\dfrac{2}{17}$ **Set B** **25)** $\dfrac{m(4+m)}{4-m}$ **27)** $\dfrac{(a^2+b^2)^2}{3a^2}$
29) $\dfrac{x(x-4)^2}{a}$ **31)** $\dfrac{2}{3}$ **33)** $\dfrac{x-4}{5-y}$ **35)** 9.78×10^5 **37)** $-43, -41, -39, -37, -35$
Set C **39)** 1 **41)** $\dfrac{3x^2-10}{3x^2+10}$ **43)** $-\dfrac{25}{96}$ **45)** $\dfrac{1}{m-2}$ **47)** $\dfrac{x+2}{x+3}$
Set X **1)** $\dfrac{x(x-2)}{(x-2y)(x-y)}$ $x\neq 0, 1, 2; y\neq 0$ **3)** $\dfrac{b(a+b)}{a(a-b)}$ $a\neq -b, b\neq 0$ **5)** $\dfrac{3b^3(4a+b)}{5a^3}$ $a\neq -2b$

Pages 282–283 (Section 7.3)

Set A **1)** $x-7$ **3)** $a-3b+\dfrac{-35b^2}{a-b}$ **5)** $2x-5$ **7)** x^2-x+1 **9)** $x+12+\dfrac{51}{x-3}$ **11)** $-\dfrac{4}{9}$
13) $-\dfrac{16}{13}$ **15)** $-\dfrac{39}{5}$ **Set B** **17)** $x=\dfrac{34}{15}$ **19)** $2(2a+3)$ **21)** $a-2b+\dfrac{-b^2}{a-b}$
23) $x^2-x+1+\dfrac{-2}{x+1}$ **25)** $2y^2+2y+3+\dfrac{7y+11}{y^2-y-2}$

27) $32y^5 - 16y^4 + 8y^3 - 4y^2 + 2y - 1 + \dfrac{2}{2y+1}$ **29)** $x^2 + 2x + 1 + \dfrac{3}{3x+2}$

31) $-4y^2 + 12y - 36 + \dfrac{108y - 31}{y^2 + 3y - 1}$

Pages 284–288   (Section 7.4)

Set A   **1)** $\dfrac{7}{8}$ **3)** $\dfrac{a}{2}$ **5)** $\dfrac{8}{a}$ **7)** $\dfrac{3}{c}$ **9)** $\dfrac{1}{x}$ **11)** $\dfrac{3a}{b}$ **13)** $\dfrac{3a+4}{3}$ **15)** $\dfrac{21-14a}{b}$ **17)** $-x-2$

19) $\dfrac{a+b}{x-y}$ **21)** 0   **23)** $\dfrac{41}{10}$ **25)** $-5\dfrac{19}{40}$ **Set B**   **27)** $\dfrac{y+x}{y-x}$ **29)** $\dfrac{7}{y}$ **31)** $\dfrac{3x^2}{3x^2-1}$ **33)** $a+b$

35) $b-5$ **37)** 1   **39)** $\dfrac{a}{5}$ **41)** $\dfrac{5}{2a-3}$ **43)** $-x^3+2x$ **45)** $55\dfrac{5}{9}$ **47)** 18.27 per cylinder,

109.61 for 6 cylinders   **Set C**   **49)** $\dfrac{5}{a-b}$ **51)** $-(x+y)$ **53)** $r-4$

Set X   **1)** 0.25   **3)** 1.4   **5)** $0.\overline{01}$ **7)** -1.03125 **9)** $-0.\overline{076923}$ **11)** $0.\overline{18}$ **13)** $-10.\overline{09}$
15) $0.\overline{956521739130434782608}$ **17)** $0.\overline{869565217391304347826}$ **19)** $0.\overline{782608695652173913043}$
21) $0.\overline{695652173913043478260}$

Pages 292–296   (Section 7.5)

Set A   **1)** $\dfrac{13}{15}$ **3)** $\dfrac{59}{120}$ **5)** $\dfrac{1}{35}$ **7)** $\dfrac{3b}{10}$ **9)** $\dfrac{11}{2a}$ **11)** $\dfrac{bc+ac+ab}{abc}$ **13)** $\dfrac{a-1}{4m}$ **15)** $\dfrac{7a-4c}{10b}$

17) $\dfrac{6a-8b}{a^2b}$ **19)** $\dfrac{5ab-2}{2b^2}$ **21)** $\dfrac{3b+1}{b}$ **23)** $\dfrac{5-x}{x}$ **25)** $\dfrac{2-5a}{a}$ **27)** 2   **29)** $\dfrac{9x-2}{10}$

31) $\dfrac{a-2b}{3a+4b}$ **33)** $\dfrac{2m}{3q}$ **35)** $\dfrac{2c-1}{b}$ **Set B**   **37)** $\dfrac{-2x+3y}{x-y}$ **39)** $\dfrac{3a-b}{(a-b)^2}$ **41)** $\dfrac{3}{4(a-b)}$

43) $\dfrac{12x-21}{x^2-9}$ **45)** $\dfrac{7x^2-5x-1}{x^2(x+1)}$ **47)** $\dfrac{-5a^2+5ab-3b^2}{ab(a-b)}$ **49)** $\dfrac{3x-5}{2x+1}$ **51)** $\dfrac{37}{90}$ **53)** $x=-12$

55) \$189   **Set C**   **57)** $\dfrac{-2y^3}{(x+y)(x-y)}$ **59)** $\dfrac{5x^2+10x+2}{(x+3)(x+2)}$ **61)** $\dfrac{12x-7y}{x(x-y)(x+y)}$

63) $\dfrac{3x^2+14x-10}{(x+3)(x-2)^2}$ **65)** $\dfrac{7x^2+42x+63-4y^2-4y}{y^2(x+3)}$ **67)** $\dfrac{-4a^3+2a^2+2a+1}{8a^3-1}$

69) $\dfrac{6x^2+129x+285}{(x-2)^2(x+7)^2}$ **71)** $\dfrac{(4x+3)(3x-1)}{x(2x+1)}$ **73)** $\dfrac{3}{2}$ **75)** $\dfrac{25}{24}$

Set X   **1)** $\dfrac{-7}{3}$ **3)** $\dfrac{169}{33}$ **5)** $\dfrac{208}{99}$ **7)** $\dfrac{-785}{999}$ **9)** $\dfrac{601}{999}$

Pages 298–300   (Section 7.6)

Set A   **1)** $\dfrac{1}{a-b}$ **3)** $\dfrac{14}{3-x}$ **5)** $\dfrac{11x}{3y-1}$ **7)** $\dfrac{x-1}{x-3}$ **9)** $\dfrac{9x}{2b-1}$ **11)** $\dfrac{3}{2a}$ **13)** $\dfrac{3}{5y}$

Set B   **15)** $\dfrac{6x-10}{x^2-4}$ **17)** $\dfrac{2x+1}{x^2-1}$ **19)** $\dfrac{2(a+b)}{a-b}$ **21)** -1 **23)** 1   **25)** $\dfrac{-1}{3+a}$ **27)** $\dfrac{13}{4}$ **29)** $\dfrac{3}{8}$

31) $\dfrac{17}{6}$ **33)** $\dfrac{25}{16}$ **35)** $16\dfrac{2}{3}$ minutes   **37)** 1531.25 sq. ft. of plywood; 48 sheets   **Set C**   **39)** $\dfrac{5x+6}{6}$

41) $\dfrac{4x}{(x-4)(x+4)}$ **43)** $\dfrac{(x+7)(-x-1)}{(x-3)^2}$

Set X   Since $a=b$, MULTBY $\left(\dfrac{1}{a-b}\right)$ is equivalent to dividing by zero.

Page 303   (7/Chapter Test)

1) $y \neq 0$ **3)** $x \neq 2, -2$ **5)** $a \neq b$ **7)** $\dfrac{(x+y)^2}{x-y}$ **9)** $\dfrac{2(y-2)}{y+2}$ **11)** $x^2+4x+16$ **13)** 4

15) 1   **17)** $\dfrac{a-4}{2}$ **19)** $\dfrac{3x+1}{6}$ **21)** $\dfrac{1}{2(x+3)}$ **23)** 2

Pages 304–307 (Cumulative Review 1–7)

Set A   **1)** $n - 5$ **3)** positive, negative   **5)** 9   **7)** FOIL   **9)** reciprocal   **11)** $>$ **13)** $<$

15) $<$ **17)** c **19)** c **21)** $n + 18 = 27$; $n = 9$ **23)** $12 - n = 9$; $n = 3$ **25)** $17 + q = 53$;

$q = 36$ **27)** $3n - 10 = -1$; $n = 3$ **Set B**   **29)** $x = -\frac{13}{17}$ **31)** $z > -\frac{5}{2}$ **33)** $3n^2 + 7n - 10$

35) $x + 1$ **37)** $\dfrac{5x(2x - y)}{y(x - y)}$ **39)** $(b - 6)(b + 6)$ **41)** $4(r - 1)(r + 1)$ **43)** $6(2y + 1)(y - 7)$

45) 225   **47)** 5   **49)** $\frac{20}{73}$ **51)** $80x^5$ **53)** $4a + 3$, $R24$ **55)** $\dfrac{4a^2 - 29a - 4}{(a - 2)(a + 2)(a - 3)}$

57) $d = 16$ **Set C**   **59)** $x > -\frac{9}{10}$ or $x < \frac{1}{2}$; all real numbers   **61)** $\dfrac{-14a + 7b + 6}{(2a - b)(2a - b)}$ **63)** 54,56

Pages 311–313 (Section 8.1)

Set A   **1)** $\frac{4}{1}$ **3)** $\frac{20}{1}$ **5)** $\frac{w}{1}$ **7)** $\frac{h}{2}$ **9)** $\frac{t - 5}{1}$ **11)** $r = -1$ **13)** $t = -5$ **15)** $n = -2$

Set B   **17)** $b = 186\frac{2}{3}$ **19)** $p = \frac{17}{135}$ **21)** $\frac{5}{3a}$ **23)** $\dfrac{1}{2w^2 - 7w + 3}$ **Set C**   **25)** 56.16

27) 56.96   **29)** 67.84   **31)** 90.24   **33)** 8.32

Set X   **1)** increased from 5.0% to 5.60%; 0.6%   **3)** b, c

Pages 317–320 (Section 8.2)

Set A   **1)** $n = 12$ **3)** $x = 6$ **5)** $m = \frac{15}{4}$ **7)** $t = \frac{105}{8}$ **9)** $x = \frac{18}{5}$ **11)** $w = \frac{96}{35}$ **13)** $x = \frac{1}{25}$

15) $n = \frac{765}{28}$ **17)** $n = \frac{18}{5}$ **19)** $\frac{16}{5}$kg   **21)** 17.75 cm   **23–27)** see graphs   **Set B**   **29)** $x = \frac{35}{26}$

31) $x = -\frac{31}{5}$ **33)** $t = 27$ **35)** $x = -\frac{13}{6}$ **37)** $w = \frac{1}{19}$ **39)** $\frac{5}{6}$cup   **41)** 36.45 lbs.   **43)** 64

45) 54   **47)** $\frac{192}{448}$ **49)** $4x^3$ **51)** $\dfrac{125x + 375}{512 - 1536x}$ **Set C**   **53)** $x = \frac{24}{25}$ **55)** $x = \frac{25}{4}$

57) $x = 0.0171365$

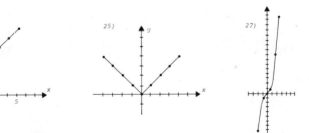

Pages 322–324 (Section 8.3)

Set A   **1)** yes, $xy = 18$ **3)** no   **5)** yes, $bh = 22$ **7)** no   **9)** yes, $ab = 20$ **11)** yes, $xy = 7$

13) $w = 1.5$ m   **15)** $\ell w = 88$ **17)** $gs = 373.5$ **19)** the graph contains the points (1,36), (2,18) (3,12),

(4,9), (6,6), (9,4), (12,3), (18,2), (36,1)   **21)** $17 + 2n$ **23)** $21 + 21y$ **25)** $\frac{x}{10} - 7$

Set B   **27)** the force is halved (divided by two)   **29)** S is multiplied by $\frac{1}{c}$ **31)** yes $(bh = 2A)$

33) no $\left(hr = \frac{v}{\pi}r\right)$ **35)** $h = \frac{14}{5}$ **37)** $x = -\frac{15}{7}$ **39)** $x = -4$ **41)** $m = 4$ **43)** $t = 9$

Set C   **45)** 0   **47)** $x = \dfrac{bc - ad}{d - c}$ **49)** $x = \dfrac{de - bf}{ab - ce}$ **51)** 0.09796

Pages 328–330 (Section 8.4)

Set A **1)** Becky: 2 miles, Elise: 3 miles **3)** $PQ = 9$, $SR = \frac{5}{3}$ **5)** Maria: 14%, Adelle: 12% **7)** 12, $\frac{13}{12}$

9) x^2, $\dfrac{ax + b}{x^2}$ **11)** $x^2 - 25$, $\dfrac{7x}{x^2 - 25}$ **Set B** **13)** 12:00 noon **15)** \$75

Set C **17)** 92.8 ounces **19)** $n = -7$ **21)** $t = -\dfrac{2}{25}$ **23)** $w = -\dfrac{28}{17}$ **25)** $xy(3y - 52x)$

27) $(7w + 4)(2w - 5)$ **29)** $(ax + b)(bx + d)$

Pages 333–336 (Section 8.5)

Set A **1)** $b = \frac{17}{5}$ **3)** $x = -\frac{9}{4}$ **5)** $t = 2$ **7)** $x = \frac{16}{3}$ **9)** $n = -28$ **11)** $a = \frac{6}{5}$ **13)** $x = \frac{1}{3}$
15) $x = -13$ **17)** $\frac{6}{5}$ hrs. **19)** 5 mi. **21)** 25.71 min. **23)** 21 **25)** n **27)** s
Set B **29)** $t = \frac{39}{2}$ **31)** $v = -2$ **33)** $r = -\frac{5}{2}$ **35)** $x = -9$ **37)** $t = -\frac{1}{10}$ **39)** $\frac{1}{8}$ pint **41)** 10
43) 30 red tiles, 50 blue tiles **45)** $2566\frac{2}{3}$ miles **Set C** **47)** $\frac{9}{5}$ hrs. **49)** $x = \frac{139}{75}$ **51)** $n = \frac{12}{5}$
53) $a = -\frac{19}{5}$ **55)** $x = \frac{16}{3}$ **57)** $x = \dfrac{a}{c - b}$

Pages 338–339 (Section 8.6)

Set A **1)** $h = \dfrac{2A}{b}$ **3)** $A = \dfrac{h(B + b)}{2}$ **5)** $E = IR$ **7)** $r = \dfrac{Mv^2}{Fg}$ **9)** $n = 3$ **11)** $x = 3$

13) $r = \dfrac{1}{2}$ **Set B** **15)** $b = \dfrac{2A - Bh}{h}$ **17)** $f = \dfrac{pq}{q + p}$ **19)** $m = \dfrac{t}{g - f}$

Set C **21)** $a = s - \dfrac{A^2}{s(s - b)(s - c)}$ **23)** $\dfrac{a}{b} = \dfrac{c}{d}$ **25)** $\dfrac{a}{c} = \dfrac{b}{d}$ **27)** $\dfrac{10}{11}$ mile, 4800 feet **29)** 2, 4

Page 342 (8/Chapter Test)

1) $\frac{4}{5}$ **3)** $\frac{6}{5}$ **5)** $x = -3$ **7)** no **9)** $x = -3$ **11)** $f = \dfrac{t - Mg}{-M}$ *or* $\dfrac{Mg - t}{M}$ **13)** 12

Pages 348–349 (Section 9.1)

Set A **1)** 2 **3)** D **5)** C **7)** 10 **9)** 10 **11)** (2,7), (0,5), (−3,2) **13)** (4,11), (0,3), (−2,−1)
15) (0,5), (−2,7), (5,0) **17)** (3,8), (0,7), (−6,5) **19)** $F = 32$ **21)** $y = 0$ **Set B** **23)** some points
are (−2,0), (−1,1), (2,0) **25)** some points are (0,10), (1,9), (2,8), (8,2), (9,1), (10,0) **27)** some points are
(0,9), (1,5), (2,1), $\left(\frac{9}{2},0\right)$ **29)** some points are (2,16), (1,14), (0,12), (−1,10), (−2,8), (−6,0) **31)** some
points are (0,0), (1,4), (2,8), (3,12) **33)** 3 points are (−2,−8), (0,−4), (2,0) **35)** 3 points are (−2,7), (0,8),
(2,9) **37)** 3 points are $\left(-2,\frac{2}{3}\right)$, (0,0), $\left(2,-\frac{2}{3}\right)$ **39)** 3 points are (−2,6), (0,5), (2,4)
Set C **41)** 3 points are (−2,5), (0,4), (2,3) **43)** 3 points are (−2,−10), (0,−6), (2,−2) **45)** points are
(0,16), (1,18), (2,20), (3,22), (14,44), (15,46)

Pages 353–357 (Section 9.2)

Set A **1)** 0 **3)** x-intercept is 3, y-intercept is 6 **5)** x-intercept is −3, y-intercept is 9
7) x-intercept is 4, y-intercept is −5 **9)** x-intercept is 5, y-intercept is 5 **11)** x-intercept is 9,
y-intercept is 3 **13)** x-intercept is 4, y-intercept is −3 **15)** x-intercept is 3, y-intercept is −15
17) x-intercept is 12, y-intercept is −3 **19)** x-intercept is −3, y-intercept is $\frac{1}{2}$ **21)** points are (4,0), (2,2),
(0,4) **23)** points are (8,0), (2,−3), (0,−4) **25)** points are (2,0), (−2,−10), (0,−5) **27)** 1 **29)** 0
31) −1 **Set B** **33)** 3 points are (−2,0), (1,9), (0,6) **35)** 3 points are (10,0), (0,5), (2,4) **37)** 3 points
are (5,0), (0,5), (2,3) **39)** 3 points are (−3,0), (0,−2), $\left(2,-\frac{10}{3}\right)$ **41)** 3 points are (4,0), (0,4), (2,2)

43) $\left(\frac{9}{2},0\right)$, $\left(0,3\right)$, $\left(2,\frac{5}{3}\right)$ **45)** 5 cents **Set C** **47)** x-intercepts are 7, −2; y-intercept is −14
49) x-intercepts are 3, −3; y-intercepts are $+\sqrt{3}$, $-\sqrt{3}$ **51)** x-intercepts are 5, −2; no y-intercepts
Set X **1)** (0,−5) **3)** $x_3 = 5$, $y_3 = -1$ **5)** (−3,2) **7)** (2,−1) **9)** (−5,1) **11)** (x_8, y_8) **13** (x_t, y_t)

Pages 360–364   (Sections 9.3)

Set A   **1)** $\frac{5}{4}$ **3)** -3 **5)** $-\frac{5}{4}$ **7)** $-\frac{4}{5}$ **9)** 1 **11)** $\frac{5}{4}$ **13)** $\frac{1}{25}$ **15)** $\frac{1}{2}$ **17)** $\frac{1}{2}$ **19)** -3
21) -3 **23)** The slope is the same, no matter what pair of points is used.   **25)** $r = 49$ **27)** $t = 4$
29) $a = -2$ **31)** $b = -3$ **Set B**   **33)** 3 points are $(0,1)$, $(3,0)$, $(6,-1)$, slope is $-\frac{1}{3}$

35) 3 points are $(-5,0)$, $(0,5)$, $(5,10)$, slope is 1 **37)** 3 points are $(0,1)$, $\left(\frac{1}{2},0\right)$, $(1,-1)$, slope is -2

39) 3 points are $(0,0)$, $(1,3)$, $(2,6)$, slope is 3 **41)** 2 other points are $(0,2)$ $(4,4)$

43) 2 other points are $(1,-4)$, $(3,2)$ **45)** 2 other points are $(0,-2)$, $(5,-2)$ **Set C**   **47)** 3 points are

$\left(0,\frac{5}{2}\right)$, $\left(2,-\frac{3}{2}\right)$, $\left(\frac{5}{4},0\right)$, slope is -2 **49)** 3 points are $(0,1)$, $\left(\frac{3}{2},0\right)$, $(3,-1)$, slope is $-\frac{2}{3}$ **51)** 3 points are $\left(0,\frac{3}{2}\right)$,

$\left(\frac{3}{5},0\right)$, $\left(4,\frac{17}{2}\right)$, slope is $-\frac{5}{2}$ **53)** -2 **55)** 1
Set X   **1)** 3 **3)** $\frac{1}{2}$ **5)** $-\frac{5}{3}$ **7)** $2\frac{1}{2}$ **9)** -3 **11)** 4

Pages 367–369   (Section 9.4)

Set A   **1)** y-intercept   **3)** horizontal   **5)** $m = 2$, $b = 5$ **7)** $m = -\frac{1}{2}$, $b = -1$ **9)** $m = 4$, $b = -\frac{1}{3}$
11) $m = -2$, $b = \frac{3}{5}$ **13)** $m = 2$, $b = 0$ **15)** $y = x + 11$, $m = 1$, $b = 11$ **17)** $y = x - 5$, $m = 1$, $b = -5$
19) $y = 4x - 2$, $m = 4$, $b = -2$ **21)** $y = \frac{1}{3}x - 2$, $m = \frac{1}{3}$, $b = -2$ **23)** 2 other points are $(-1,-1)$, $(1,5)$
25) 2 other points are $(-1,5)$, $(1,1)$ **Set B**   **27)** neither, $m = 1$ **29)** vertical, slope is undefined
31) horizontal, $m = 0$ **33)** neither, $m = -1$ **35)** vertical, slope is undefined   **37)** neither, $m = 1$
39) $y = \frac{3}{4}x + \frac{5}{4}$, $m = \frac{3}{4}$, $b = \frac{5}{4}$ **41)** $y = 2x + 6$, $m = 2$, $b = 6$ **43)** $y = \frac{2}{3}x + \frac{5}{3}$, $m = \frac{2}{3}$, $b = \frac{5}{3}$
45) $y = -\frac{2}{3}x - \frac{1}{3}$, $m = -\frac{2}{3}$, $b = -\frac{1}{3}$ **Set C**   **47)** 2 points are $(0,2)$, $(2,3)$ **49)** 2 points are $(0,-5)$,
$(1,-3)$ **51)** 2 points are $(0,0)$, $(1,-5)$ **53)** 2 points are $(0,2)$, $(4,-1)$ **55)** 2 points are $(0,-2)$, $(2,-2)$
57) 2 points are $(0,2)$, $(1,1)$ **59)** $y = 5$ when $x = 1$ **61)** 37

Pages 374–377   (Section 9.5)

Set A   **1)** parallel   **3)** negative reciprocals   **5)** parallel   **7)** perpendicular   **9)** perpendicular
11) perpendicular   **15)** parallel   **15)** parallel: $K = 2$, perpendicular: $K = -\frac{1}{2}$ **17)** parallel: $K = -\frac{1}{5}$,
perpendicular: $K = 5$ **19)** parallel: $K = -\frac{2}{7}$, perpendicular: $K = \frac{7}{2}$ **21)** $b = -12$ **23)** $b = -4$
25) $b = -17$ **27)** $b = 3$ **Set B**   **29)** parallel   **31)** parallel   **33)** perpendicular   **35)** parallel
37) $y = 2x + b$ **39)** $y = 4x + b$ **41)** $x = a$ **Set C**   **43)** 3 points are $(0,0)$, $(1,1)$, $(2,2)$
45) 3 points are $(0,-8)$, $(4,-6)$, $(8,-4)$ **47)** $3n + 5e = 30$ **49)** noncollinear   **51)** collinear   **53)** $K = 1$
55) $K = 11$ **57)** $K = \frac{39}{4}$ **59)** $K = -7$ **61)** $\frac{23}{8}$
Set X   **1)** $m = -\frac{1}{5}$ **3)** $m = 0$ **5)** $m = -1$ **7)** slope is undefined

Pages 380–385   (Section 9.6)

Set A   **1)** $Ax + By = C$ **3)** $-2x + y = -5$ **5)** $2x - y = -3$, $A = 2$, $B = -1$, $C = -3$
7) $4x + 6y = -7$, $A = 4$, $B = 6$, $C = -7$ **9)** $y = x + 3$, $x - y = 3$ **11)** $y = 5x - 2$, $-5x + y = -2$
13) $y = \frac{1}{2}x - 8$, $-x + 2y = -16$ **15)** $y = x + 2$, $-x + y = 2$ **17)** $y = 3$, $y = 3$ **19)** $m = \frac{5}{2}$
21) $m = \frac{2}{5}$ **23)** slope is undefined   **Set B**   **25)** $y = 2x - 2$ **27)** $y = 5x + 9$ **29)** $y = \frac{1}{2}x - 8$
31) $y = 2$ **33)** $y = 2x + 10$ **35)** $y = -3x - 13$ **37)** $y = -\frac{2}{3}x - \frac{8}{3}$ **39)** $y = -2$
Set C   **41)** $y = 3x + 2$ **43)** $y = x$ **45)** $y = 4$ **47)** $y = -\frac{2}{3}x + \frac{13}{3}$ **49)** $y = -\frac{1}{2}x + \frac{1}{2}$ **51)** linear
53) not linear: contains the product of variables   **55)** linear   **57)** not linear: contains the product of
variables and variables with exponent 2
Set X   **1)** $y = 2x - 1$ **3)** $y = -\frac{2}{3}x + 7$ **5)** $y = -\frac{3}{10}x + 2$ **7)** $y = -x$ **9)** $y = \frac{3}{2}x - \frac{1}{2}$
11) $y = -4x - 4$ **13)** $y = -4x$ **15)** $x = 7$

Page 390   (9/Chapter Test)

1) false   **3)** false   **5)** true   **7)** false   **9)** true   **11)** no slope (vertical line)   **13)** $y = 3x + 2$;
$-3x + y = 2$ **15)** $y = \frac{4}{5}x + \frac{3}{5}$; $4x - 5y = -3$ **17)** neither

Pages 394–396 (Section 10.1)

Set A **1)** (2,4) **3)** (3,2) **5)** (4,3) **7)** (2,3) **9)** (3,2) **11)** (4,1) **13)** (3,5) **15)** Sally guessed 6, Fred guessed 3 **17)** trapezoid PMNO **19)** grocery store and Ice Cream Parlor **21)** 3 points (0,10), (10,0), (5,5) **23)** 3 points are (0,6), (3,0), (1,4) **25)** 3 points are (0,4), (5,0), (3,2) **27)** 3 points are (0,−4), (5,0), (10,4) **29)** 3 points are (5,0), $\left(\frac{5}{2},0\right)$, (1,3) **Set B** **31)** (7,4) **33)** (−2,3) **35)** $\left(\frac{1}{3},-\frac{2}{3}\right)$

37) (−1,−7) **39)** Mark is 10, Meredith is 4 **Set C** **41)** $\left(\frac{1}{2},1\right)$ **43)** $\left(\frac{1}{2},\frac{1}{4}\right)$ **45)** (0,1)

47) no solution: lines are parallel

Pages 399–404 (Section 10.2)

Set A **1)** (5,3) **3)** (2,3) **5)** (−4,2) **7)** (4,−5) **9)** (−3,−2) **11)** 7,−4 **13)** 5,7
15) 1 km **17)** $m = \frac{1}{3}$ **19)** $m = -\frac{1}{2}$ **21)** $m = \frac{1}{2}$ **23)** $m = 3$ **Set B** **25)** (4,8) **27)** (−2,5)

29) (4,0) **31)** approx. (2.7,−1.6) **33)** (−1,5) **35)** $\left(8,\frac{9}{2}\right)$ **37)** (6t + 5) meters

Set C **39)** perpendicular **41)** parallel **43)** neither **45)** neither **47)** perpendicular
Set X **1)** dependent **3)** neither **5)** inconsistent **7)** inconsistent **9)** neither **11)** neither
13) the equations are dependent; there is not a unique solution

Pages 407–410 (Section 10.3)

Set A **1)** (6,3) **3)** (9,−7) **5)** (3,11) **7)** (−3,8) **9)** (5,2) **11)** $\left(\frac{3}{2},-\frac{9}{2}\right)$ **13)** (3,5)

15) (1,−3) **17)** Manny is 5 feet tall, Jack is 4 feet tall **19)** $250 in one account, $100 in the other account **21)** $4x - 3y = 6$ **23)** $y = 20$ **25)** $x - 20y = -12$ **27)** $3x - y = -7$

Set B **29)** (8.4,11.2) **31** $\left(\frac{5}{6},\frac{2}{3}\right)$ **33)** $\left(-\frac{3}{8},-\frac{9}{4}\right)$ **35)** $\left(-\frac{1}{3},\frac{7}{6}\right)$ **37)** $1750 in savings, $2750 in

NOW **39)** $10x - 30y$ **41)** $-24x + 56y$ **43)** $67x$ **Set C** **45)** (3,2), (−3,2)

47) $\left(\frac{21}{4},\frac{\sqrt{62}}{2}\right)$, $\left(\frac{21}{4},\frac{-\sqrt{62}}{2}\right)$

Pages 412–414 (Section 10.4)

Set A **1)** (3,1) **3)** (2,3) **5)** (4,8) **7)** (−1,2) **9)** (5,−3) **11)** (2,6) **13)** white: 10 sq m, blue: 15 sq m **15)** tin: 24 oz., bottle: 9 oz. **17)** $t = 5$ **19)** $n = 5$ **21)** $q = \frac{5}{2}$
Set B **23)** (13.44,34.08) **25)** (100,500) **27)** (16,8) **29)** 8 apples, 18 oranges **31)** −3
Set C **33)** (2,5), (−2,5) **35)** (3,4), (3,−4), (−3,4), (−3,−4) **37)** $\left(\frac{2}{9},\frac{5}{8}\right)$ **39)** (200,100)

Pages 417–419 (Section 10.5)

Set A **1)** (4,3) **3)** (−3,1) **5)** (4,7) **7)** (−4,−2) **9)** (7,−2) **11)** $v = 7$ **13)** $x = 8$

15) $z = -6$ **Set B** **17)** $\left(3,\frac{1}{4}\right)$ **19)** $\left(\frac{2}{3},-\frac{1}{4}\right)$ **21)** (2,6) **23)** (10,−5) **25)** (3,−6) **27)** (2,6)

29) (6,4) **31)** 15,23 **33)** 8 **Set C** **35)** (4,1) **37)** (−5,−3) **39)** (6,−3) **41)** $m = -31$, $n = -70$ **43)** $p = -3$, $q = -\frac{100}{23}$ **45)** (31,54)

Pages 422–423 (Section 10.6)

Set A **1)** 89 **3)** 37 **5)** (1,−3) **7)** (0,1) **9)** (−2,−3) **Set B** **11)** $x = 5$ **13)** $y = 1$
15) $x = -2$ **17)** $2000 at 6%, $5000 at 9% **19)** average air speed: 400 mph, average wind velocity: 50 mph **Set C** **21)** $9(t - u)$ **23)** the sum of the digits in the original number

Page 427 (10/Chapter Test)

1) (1,2) **3)** (7,9) **5)** (8,5) **7)** (3,2) **9)** (12,3) **11)** (1,3) **13)** 56 **15)** 80 pounds hamburger 20 pounds soy protein

Pages 428–431   (Cumulative Review 1–10)

Set A   **1)** d **3)** c **5)** c **7)** d **9)** answers will vary   **11)** answers will vary   **13)** $d = \dfrac{bc}{a}$

15) $10m^2 + 11m + 1$ **17)** $(c + 4)(c + 5)$ **19)** $\dfrac{3}{2y}$ **21)** $\dfrac{2x}{3}$ **23)** -3 **25)** $3x + 7$

27) $\dfrac{x}{7} + (3 \cdot \tfrac{1}{2}x)$ **Set B**   **29) a** $k = 121$ **b** $x = 4$ **31) a** $9a(8ab^3 + 2b^2 - 3)$ **b** $100y(x^4 + 10x + 100)$

33) a $0 \le k < 3;$ **b** $y > 6$ or $y < -6$ **35)** $(5x - 3)(5x + 3)$ **37)** $\dfrac{b^2 + ab + 3 - 2ab^2}{ab^2}$ **39)** $2(c - 7)^2$

41) $\dfrac{6 - 2y}{x - 7}$ **Set C**   **43) a** $\left(-\tfrac{4}{5}, -9\tfrac{3}{5}\right)$ **b** $x = \tfrac{2}{3},\ y = -\tfrac{2}{3}$ **45)** $11,5$ **47)** $(-4,2,-1)$

49) $3(x + 2)(x + 3)(x - 3)$ **51)** \$119.99

Pages 436–438   (Section 11.1)

Set A   **1)** 8   **3)** -10 **5)** 4   **7)** $-\dfrac{5}{4}$ **9)** 0.2   **11)** -20 **13)** 15   **15)** $\dfrac{5}{2}$ **17)** 12
19) -16 **21)** 64   **23)** $\dfrac{1}{243}$ **25)** $\dfrac{1}{8}$ **27)** 643   **29)** $\dfrac{49}{16}$ **Set B**   **31)** 9   **33)** $x + 4$

35) 61   **37)** 10   **39)** 8   **41)** 10   **Set C**   **43)** $\dfrac{2}{3}$ **45)** x^2 **47)** $x + 5$ **49)** $\dfrac{2x}{5}$ **51)** $\dfrac{b}{a}$

53) $a + b$

Set X   **1)** $|x|$ **3)** $a^2|bc^3|$ **5)** $-2|x|$ **7)** $-\dfrac{5|x^3|}{3|y|}$ **9)** $q^2|p|$ **11)** $-25|mn|$ **13)** $0.2|rt|$

15) $\dfrac{1}{0.3|t|}$

Pages 441–442   (Section 11.2)

Set A   **1)** 4   **3)** -2 **5)** 6   **7)** $\dfrac{3}{5}$ **9)** 1   **11)** 6   **13)** 16   **15)** $-x^{10}$ **17)** 6   **19)** -1

21) $5\sqrt{5} + 6$ **23)** $\dfrac{5\sqrt{5}}{6}$ **Set B**   **25)** xy^2 **27)** 2   **29)** $10x$ **31)** x **33)** $-a^{10}$ **35)** $\dfrac{a^2}{b}$

37) 8   **Set C**   **39)** $\dfrac{a^3}{b}$ **41)** $12x + 4$ **43)** x^2y **45)** $2x^2$ **47)** -20

Pages 445–450   (Section 11.3)

Set A   **1)** 5   **3)** 6   **5)** 36   **7)** $-28\sqrt{7}$ **9)** $2x$ **11)** $2x$ **13)** $2\sqrt{6}$ **15)** $2\sqrt{3}$
17 $-7\sqrt{2}$ **19)** -6 **21)** $\sqrt{13}$ **23)** $a^2 - 4b^2$ **25)** $16m^2 - n^2$ **27)** $4q^2 - 1$ **Set B**   **29)** $2\sqrt[3]{2}$
31) $2x\sqrt[3]{3x^2}$ **33)** $8\sqrt{10}$ **35)** $15\sqrt{6}$ **37)** $-120\sqrt{5}$ **39)** $x^5y\sqrt{x}$ **41)** 26.8
Set C   **43)** $a = 13.2$ **45)** $-48xy^3\sqrt{3}$ **47)** $12a^4\sqrt[3]{3a}$ **49)** $-10x^6y^5$
Set X   **1)** $3 < \sqrt{10} < 4$ **3)** $9 < \sqrt{89} < 10$ **5)** $-5 < -\sqrt{23} < -4$ **7)** $1 < \sqrt{3.6} < 2$

9) $-1 < -\sqrt{\dfrac{15}{22}} < 0$ **11)** $\sqrt{2} < \sqrt[3]{3} < 1.5$ **13)** $1.9 < \sqrt{4} < \sqrt[3]{9}$ **15)** $\sqrt[3]{5} < 3.5 < \sqrt[5]{3}$

17) 1.9   **19)** 6.8   **21)** 5.9   **23)** $(1.5)^2$ **25)** $7\sqrt{6}$ **27)** equal   **29)** $\sqrt{2} \cdot \sqrt{8}$ **31)** $2\sqrt{5}$
33) 1.414   **35)** 3.61   **37)** 2.8

Pages 453–454   (Section 11.4)

Set A   **1)** 2   **3)** 3   **5)** $2x$ **7)** -2 **9)** 8   **11)** $\dfrac{\sqrt{15}}{5}$ **13)** $\dfrac{\sqrt{30}}{10}$ **15)** $\dfrac{\sqrt{6}}{2}$ **17)** $-\dfrac{\sqrt{30x}}{6}$

19) $\dfrac{\sqrt{xy}}{x}$ **21)** $\dfrac{\sqrt{6}}{3}$ **23)** $\dfrac{4\sqrt{3}}{3}$ **25)** $-4x + 8xy$ **27)** $7ab - a$ **29)** $-x^2 - 6xy$

Set B   **31)** $\dfrac{3\sqrt{5x}}{5x^2}$ **33)** $\dfrac{3\sqrt{5}}{2}$ **35)** $-25\sqrt[3]{2}$ **37)** 15.5   **39)** 0.3   **Set C**   **41)** $2x^2\sqrt{15x}$

43) $\dfrac{\sqrt{x + y}}{x + y}$ **45)** $\dfrac{\sqrt{x}}{x + 7}$ **47)** $a + 1$ **49)** 1

624   *Answers*

Pages 457–459 (Section 11.5)

Set A   **1)** $5\sqrt{7}$ **3)** $7\sqrt{2}$ **5)** $-4\sqrt[3]{3}$ **7)** $\sqrt[3]{2x} - 10\sqrt[3]{6}$ **9)** $5\sqrt{2}$ **11)** $9\sqrt{2}$ **13)** 0

15) $x^2 - 4x - 21$ **17)** $6z^2 + 10z - 4$ **19)** $12 - t - t^2$ **Set B**   **21)** $-3x\sqrt{5x}$ **23)** $10\sqrt{2} - \sqrt{3}$

25) $-3\sqrt{7}$ **27)** $2\sqrt{3} + 3\sqrt{2}$ **29)** $6\sqrt{7} + 5\sqrt{14}$ **Set C**   **31)** $24x^2\sqrt{2x}$ **33)** $18x - 4\sqrt{x} - \dfrac{7\sqrt{x}}{3x}$

Set X   **1)** $15i$ **3)** $\frac{1}{4}r^2 i$ **5)** $-4t^4 i$ **7)** $6m\sqrt{ni}$ **9)** 1

Pages 461–463 (Section 11.6)

Set A   **1)** 7 **3)** $3x$ **5)** $5\sqrt{2}$ **7)** 3 **9)** $\sqrt{21}$ **11)** 3 **13)** $\dfrac{3}{4}$ **15)** $-2x\sqrt{10x}$

17) $\dfrac{\sqrt{7}}{2}$ **19)** $6\sqrt{3}$ **21)** $x^2\sqrt{x}$ **23)** $y = 9$ **25)** $a = 0$ **27)** $c = -4$ **Set B**   **29)** $4\sqrt{6}$

31) $\sqrt{10}$ **33)** $(4x - 1)\sqrt{x}$ **35)** $8x\sqrt[3]{6}$ **37)** $\dfrac{5\sqrt{3}}{3}$ **Set C**   **39)** $3x\sqrt{2} + \sqrt{2xy} - 9\sqrt{xy} - 3y$

41) $xy\sqrt{y}$ **43)** $\dfrac{-14\sqrt[3]{3x}}{x}$ **45)** $\dfrac{10 + 2\sqrt{2}}{23}$ **47)** $\sqrt{2} - 1$ **49)** $-\sqrt{7} + \sqrt{8}$

Pages 466–467 (Section 11.7)

Set A   **1)** $x = 16$ **3)** $x = \dfrac{49}{2}$ **5)** $x = 45$ **7)** $x = 12$ **9)** $x = \dfrac{23}{3}$ **11)** $x = 23$ **13)** $x = 4$

15) $x = 108$ **17)** $x = 9$ **19)** no solution   **21)** $39\sqrt[3]{2}$ **23)** $8\sqrt{5} - 2\sqrt{10}$ **25)** $\sqrt{3}$

Set B   **27)** $m = -1$ **29)** $t = 34$ **31)** $x = -2$ **33)** 256 **35)** 2809

Set C   **37)** $x = 4 + 5\sqrt{3}$ **39)** $x = -\dfrac{11}{20} - \dfrac{\sqrt{2}}{5}$

Page 471 (11/Chapter Test)

1) 60 **3)** $2(x - 3)$ **5)** $-\dfrac{2}{7}$ **7)** $3(x - 2)$ **9)** $5x\sqrt{3}$ **11)** 5 **13)** $\sqrt[3]{x + y}$ **15)** $2\sqrt{x}$

17) 0 **19)** $\frac{3}{2}x$ **21)** $x = 40$ **23)** no solution

Pages 477–479 (Section 12.1)

Set A   **1)** two   **3)** $a = 0$ or $b = 0$ (or both)   **5)** $x = 6$ or $x = -6$ **7)** $x = 6$ or $x = -6$

9) $x = \dfrac{11}{5}$ or $x = -\dfrac{11}{5}$ **11)** $x = \dfrac{1}{4}$ or $x = -\dfrac{1}{4}$ **13)** $x = 10$ or $x = -10$ **15)** $x = 0$ or $x = 4$

17) $x = 0$ or $x = -2$ **19)** $x = -8$ or $x = -3$ **21)** $x = 4$ or $x = -5$ **23)** $x = -\dfrac{1}{4}$ or $x = 1$

25) $(x + 3)(x + 2)$ **27)** $(x + 3)(x - 2)$ **29)** $(2x + 1)(x + 1)$ **31)** $(3x + 1)(2x + 1)$

33) $(5x - 2)(x - 1)$ **35)** $(6x - 5)(2x + 3)$ **37)** $3(2x - 1)(2x + 5)$ **Set B**   **39)** $y = 16$ or $y = -8$

41) $b = 4$ or $b = -8$ **43)** $r = -6$ or $r = -10$ **45)** $x = 5$ **47)** $y = -3$ or $y = -4$

49) $x = -\dfrac{1}{2}$ or $x = 5$ **51)** $n = 8$ or $n = 2$ **53)** $a = -\dfrac{4}{3}$ or $a = -\dfrac{5}{2}$ **55)** $u = \dfrac{5}{3}$ or $u = -3$

57) $r = -3$ **59)** June 15 or July 3   **Set C**   **61)** $x = -7$ or $x = 20$ **63)** no solution (the absolute value cannot be less than zero)   **65)** $x = 2$ or $x = -7$ **67)** $x = -2$ **69)** no solution (both $|x - 3|$ and $|x + 3|$ would have to be zero)   **71)** $x = 5$ or $x = \dfrac{1}{5}$ **73)** $x = \dfrac{1}{2}$ **75)** $x = 8$ or $x = \dfrac{2}{9}$

Pages 482–487 (Section 12.2)

Set A   **1)** quadratic   **3)** standard   **5)** $a = 2$ or $a = -2$ **7)** $b = -3$ or $b = 2$ **9)** $d = 4$ or $d = -4$

11) $g = 0$ or $g = 2$ **13)** $x = 0$ or $x = 2$ **15)** $q = -5$ or $q = 3$ **17)** $n = 7$ or $n = -7$

19) $b = 3$ or $b = 4$ **21)** $y = \dfrac{1}{2}$ or $y = 0$ **23)** $t = 1$ or $t = -2$ **25)** $x = 0$ or $x = \dfrac{2}{3}$

27) $(x + 1)(x + 1)$ **29)** $(x - 2)(x - 2)$ **31)** $(2x + 1)(2x + 1)$ **33)** $(2t + 3)(2t + 3)$ **35)** cannot be factored over the integers   **37)** $(2m + 3)(3m - 2)$ **Set B**   **39)** 2 or 3 **41)** $n = -\dfrac{1}{2}$ or $n = 5$

43) $n = \dfrac{1}{2}$ **45)** $n = \dfrac{1}{4}$ or $n = 4$ **47)** $n = -4$ or $n = 2$ **49)** $n = \dfrac{3}{8}$ or $n = \dfrac{2}{3}$

51) $n = 3$ or $n = -\dfrac{7}{12}$ **53)** $n = \dfrac{7}{12}$ or $-\dfrac{19}{12}$ **55)** $x = \pm\sqrt{2}$ **57)** $g = \pm 2\sqrt{2}$ **59)** $u = \pm 2\sqrt{3}$

Set C   **61)** $x = \sqrt{2}$ or $x = -2\sqrt{2}$ **63)** $p = 0$ or $p = \dfrac{1}{2}$ **65)** $y = 0$ or $y = 1$ or $y = -1$

67) 8 or -9 **69)** 4 or -4 **71)** $a = \dfrac{|c| - b}{x}$

Set X   **1)** $y = 6 \ or \ y = -2$ **3)** $g = 2 \ or \ g = -4$ **5)** $t = 1 \ or \ t = -9$ **7)** $r = 3 + \sqrt{6} \ or \ r = 3 - \sqrt{6}$
9) $z = -5 + \sqrt{15} \ or \ z = -5 - \sqrt{15}$ **11)** $x = \frac{3}{2} \ or \ x = -\frac{7}{2}$ **13)** $s = \frac{3}{5} \ or \ s = -1$ **15)** $c = 1 \ or \ c = -\frac{9}{7}$
17) $a = \frac{1 + \sqrt{7}}{6} \ or \ a = \frac{1 - \sqrt{7}}{6}$ **19)** $x = \frac{13}{8} \ or \ x = \frac{1}{8}$ **21)** $a = \frac{-3 + \sqrt{17}}{4} \ or \ a = \frac{-3 - \sqrt{17}}{4}$
23) $w = \frac{1 + \sqrt{10}}{7} \ or \ w = \frac{1 - \sqrt{10}}{7}$ **25)** $x = 1 \ or \ x = -5$ **27)** $x = 1 \ or \ x = -\frac{3}{5}$ **29)** $x = 3 \ or \ x = \frac{7}{3}$
31) $r = \frac{5}{2} \ or \ r = \frac{1}{2}$ **33)** $r = \frac{5}{2} \ or \ r = \frac{-25}{6}$ **35)** $x = -\frac{1}{2} \ or \ x = \frac{3}{4}$ **37)** $f = 0 \ or \ f = -\frac{2}{3}$

Pages 490–494   (Section 12.3)

Set A   **1)** perfect-square   **3)** 36   **5)** $x = 6 \ or \ x = -12$ **7)** $y = 6 \ or \ y = -2$ **9)** $a = 8 \ or \ a = -6$
11) $g = 3 \ or \ g = -15$ **13)** $k = -4 + \sqrt{17} \ or \ k = -4 - \sqrt{17}$ **15)** $m = 5 + \sqrt{65} \ or \ m = 5 - \sqrt{65}$
17) $p = 10 + \sqrt{103} \ or \ p = 10 - \sqrt{103}$ **19)** $s = -9 + \sqrt{41} \ or \ s = -9 - \sqrt{41}$ **21)** $2\sqrt{6}$
23) $3\sqrt{2}$ **25)** $2 - 2\sqrt{2}$ **27)** $18\sqrt{5}$ **29)** $6\sqrt{5}$ **Set B**   **31)** 9   **33)** $3 \ or \ -13$
35) $2 \ or \ -14$ **37)** $9 \ or \ -4$ **39)** $-19 \ or \ 1$ **Set C**   **41)** $y = 3 \ or \ y = -4$
43) $x = 5 \ or \ x = -3$ **45)** $x = 6 \ or \ x = -1$ **47)** $x = 4 \ or \ x = 2$

Set X   **1)** $d = 5 \ or \ d = -6$ **3)** $r = 5 \ or \ r = -2$ **5)** $j = 4 \ or \ j = 3$ **7)** $T = \frac{-5 \pm \sqrt{57}}{2}$
9) $c = \frac{5 \pm \sqrt{13}}{2}$ **11)** $k = -4 \pm \sqrt{29}$ **13)** $a = 5 \ or \ a = -2$ **15)** $v = -2 \ or \ v = 1$ **17)** $s = \frac{5 \pm \sqrt{57}}{2}$
19) $a = -5 \pm 3\sqrt{2}$ **21)** $g = 5 \pm \sqrt{12.5}$ **23)** $R = -3 \pm \sqrt{15}$ **25)** $h = -4 \pm \sqrt{3}$ **27)** $h = 3 \pm \sqrt{11}$
29) $1, -2$ **31)** $9, -4$ **33)** $\frac{-11 \pm \sqrt{301}}{2}$ **35)** the sum of the numbers is $-\frac{b}{a}$ and the product is $\frac{c}{a}$

Pages 496–498   (Section 12.4)

Set A   **1)** $2, \frac{1}{2}$ **3)** $3, \frac{1}{3}$ **5)** $2, \frac{1}{2}$ **7)** $a = \frac{2 \pm \sqrt{22}}{3}$ **9)** $c = \frac{-1 \pm \sqrt{19}}{6}$ **11)** $g = \frac{-9 \pm \sqrt{97}}{16}$
13) $x = \frac{1 \pm \sqrt{13}}{3}$ **15)** $x = \frac{-1 \pm \sqrt{31}}{9}$ **17)** $r = 0 \ or \ r = -\frac{2}{5}$ **19)** $Q = 1 \ or \ Q = \frac{5}{2}$ **21)** $h = \frac{a}{b}$
23) $a = \pm\sqrt{c^2 - b^2}$ **25)** $r = \frac{A - p}{pt}$ **27)** $c = \pm\sqrt{a^2 + b^2}$ **29)** $v = \pm\sqrt{\frac{k}{m}}$
Set B   **31)** $w = 3 \pm 2\sqrt{2}$ **33)** $m = \frac{3 \pm \sqrt{89}}{4}$ **35)** $t = \frac{14}{17} \ or \ t = -1$ **37)** $r = \frac{-3 \pm \sqrt{3}}{2}$
39) $x = \frac{1}{2} \ or \ x = 3$ **41)** $R = \frac{5}{3} \ or \ R = -2$ **Set C**   **43)** $\ell = 24, \ w = 12$ **45)** $x = 0 \ or \ x = 4$
47) $y = 4 \ or \ y = -4$ **49)** $g = -3$ **51)** $J = \frac{3}{4} \ or \ J = -\frac{1}{2}$ **53)** $x = -\frac{3}{4} \ or \ x = \frac{5}{3}$ **55)** $x = -ab$

Pages 502–506   (Section 12.5)

Set A   **1)** $ax^2 + bx + c = 0$ **3)** $2a$ **5)** $x = \frac{3}{2} \ or \ x = 1$ **7)** $x = \frac{-13 \pm \sqrt{354}}{4}$
9) $x = \frac{7}{2} \ or \ x = -2$ **11)** $x = \frac{4}{3} \ or \ x = 4$ **13)** $x = \frac{3}{2} \ or \ x = \frac{1}{2}$ **15)** $x = -\frac{2}{3} \ or \ x = -7$
17) $x = -\frac{3}{2} \ or \ x = \frac{2}{3}$ **19)** $x = -\frac{1}{3} \ or \ x = \frac{7}{2}$ **21)** $6\sqrt{5}$ **23)** $4\sqrt{7}$ **25)** 18
Set B   **27)** $x = \frac{1}{3} \ or \ x = -\frac{1}{2}$ **29)** $x = \frac{7}{6} \ or \ x = \frac{5}{4}$ **31)** $-\frac{195}{208}$
Set C   **33)** $\frac{3935 \pm \sqrt{1961169}}{3922}$ **35)** $x = \frac{-207 \pm \sqrt{42289}}{20}$
Set X   **1)** $x = \frac{-7 \pm \sqrt{17}}{4}$ **3)** $x = \frac{-5 \pm \sqrt{33}}{2}$ **5)** $e = \frac{3 \pm \sqrt{41}}{6}$ **7)** $p = \frac{5 \pm \sqrt{57}}{8}$ **9)** $n = \frac{1 \pm 5\sqrt{2}}{14}$
11) $a = \frac{-1 \pm \sqrt{11}}{3}$ **13)** $k = \frac{-2 \pm \sqrt{3}}{2}$ **15)** $c = \frac{3 \pm \sqrt{3}}{3}$ **17)** $d = \frac{-6 \pm \sqrt{21}}{5}$ **19)** $x = \frac{9 \pm \sqrt{57}}{12}$
21) $x = \frac{6 \pm \sqrt{26}}{10}$ **23)** $K = -2 \ or \ K = -\frac{2}{3}$ **25)** $a = \pm\sqrt{5}$ **27)** $c = \pm\frac{3\sqrt{2}}{2}$
29) $e = \frac{-3 \pm \sqrt{29}}{2}$ **31)** $g = \frac{1 \pm \sqrt{21}}{2}$ **33)** $k = \pm 2\sqrt{2}$ **35)** $n = 1 \pm \sqrt{3}$ **37)** $q = \frac{5 \pm 3\sqrt{5}}{2}$
39) sum is $-\frac{b}{a}$ **41)** yes (if the coefficients are rational numbers)   **43)** no

Pages 509–511 (Section 12.6)

Set A   **1)** $x = \pm\frac{3}{2}$ **3)** $g = -2 \text{ or } g = -1$ **5)** $r = 4 \text{ or } r = -3$ **7)** $d = \frac{1}{2} \text{ or } d = -1$
9) $x = \frac{1}{5} \text{ or } x = -\frac{2}{5}$ **11)** $Q = 3 \text{ or } Q = -1$ **13)** $w = \pm 1$ **15)** $g = 4 \text{ or } g = -1$
17) $m = \frac{1}{3} \text{ or } m = -2$ **19)** $x = 4 \text{ or } x = -1$ **21)** $z = -\frac{3}{2} \text{ or } z = -1$ **23)** $r = 5 \text{ or } r = 1$
25) $t = \frac{1}{2}$ **Set B**   **27)** $a = \frac{5}{2}$ **29)** $h = -\frac{1}{3} \text{ or } h = 1$ **31)** $x = \frac{1}{2} \text{ or } x = 8$ **33)** $L = -8$
35) $m = \dfrac{-3 \pm \sqrt{5}}{2}$ **37)** $k = 2 \text{ or } k = -2$ **39)** $k = 14 \text{ or } k = -14$ **41)** $k = 4$
43) $k = 15 \text{ or } k = -5$ **45)** $k = \frac{1}{4}$ **47)** $\frac{2}{5} \text{ or } \frac{5}{2}$ **Set C**   **49)** $x = -3$ **51)** $x = 1 \text{ or } x = -1$
53) one number must be ± 1 **55)** the numbers are $-\frac{1}{3}$ and $\frac{2}{3}$

Page 516 (12/Chapter Test)

1) $x = \pm 17$ **3)** $x = \pm 5$ **5)** $t = 0, -4$ **7)** $x = \pm\frac{9}{4}$ **9)** $x = 5, 10$ **11)** $x = 4, -2$
13) $x = 9, -1$ **15)** $x = -\frac{1}{2}, 2$ **17)** $x = -\frac{5}{2}, -\frac{1}{3}$ **19)** $x = \frac{1}{5}, -\frac{7}{2}$ **21)** $x = -\frac{5}{6}, -\frac{11}{8}$
23) $x = \frac{1}{2}, -6$ **25)** length is 13, width is 9

Pages 517–523 (Cumulative Review 1–12)

Set A   **1)** c **3)** c **5)** d **7)** c **9)** $x > -1$ **11)** $(f - 9)(f + 5)$ **13)** $y - 4$ **15)** $w = -21$
17) $-18x^3$ **19)** no solution   **21)** $0, \frac{3}{5}$ **23)** 9   **25)** 59   **27)** **a** $n + 6$ **b** $\frac{1}{3}n$ **c** $n - 4$
29) **a** 144   **b** 0   **c** $-\frac{3}{5}$ **d** -131 **31)** 3   **33)** **a** $x > -2$ **b** $x < -4$ **c** $x \geq 4 \text{ or } x < 0$ **d** $x > \frac{24}{5}$
35) $6x^2 + 17x - 14$ **37)** $\dfrac{x - 3}{5x}$ **39)** $\dfrac{x + 6}{x^2 + 6x + 9}$ **41)** $n = 3$ **43)** **a** x-intercept is 3, y-intercept is 3
43) **b** x-intercept is $-\frac{7}{3}$, y-intercept is $\frac{7}{2}$ **45)** Lynne is 24, Toni is 16   **47)** **a** -7 **b** 0.4   **c** $\frac{6}{5}$ **d** 1.1
49) **a** $3, -3$ **b** $3, -2$ **c** $-\frac{1}{4}, -3$ **d** $8, 2$ **51)** $x + x + 1 + x + 2 = 204$; 67,68,69   **53)** $y = \frac{1}{2}$
Set B   **55)** $w \leq 14 \text{ or } w > 21$ **57)** $-27 < t \leq 0$ **59)** $x \geq 27$ **61)** $(7 - n)(7 + n)$
63) $\dfrac{-(2a^2 + a + 3)}{a - 3} \text{ or } \dfrac{2a^2 + a + 3}{3 - a}$ **65)** $x = \frac{128}{3}$ **67)** $2(a - b)$ **69)** graph passes through $(0, -2)$ and
$(1,1)$ **a** answers may vary; slope = 3, y-intercept $\neq -2$ **b** answers may vary; slope $= -\frac{1}{3}$ **71)** $\left(\frac{20}{33}, \frac{8}{11}\right)$
73) 2   **75)** $4x\sqrt[3]{3x}$ **77)** $-\sqrt{5}$ **79)** $x = 9$ **81)** 9   **83)** $-1 \text{ or } \frac{1}{3}$ **85)** $-\frac{1}{2}$ **87)** $(6x + 1)(x - 5)$
89) $x = 5\frac{3}{5}$ **91)** $x = 8$
Set C   **93)** $x = \dfrac{-2 \pm \sqrt{34}}{2}$ **95)** $x = 2, x = -6$ **97)** $x^2 + 2x - 24 = 0$ **99)** $x = \dfrac{-9 \pm \sqrt{69}}{6}$
101) 12   **103)** 5 meters   **105)** $x \geq -5 \text{ or } x < 6$ **107)** -3

Pages 528–532 (Section 13.1)

Set A   **1)** $f(8) = 3, f(1) = -4$ **3)** $g(-3) = 3, g(0) = 6$ **5)** $h(4) = 4, h(12) = -4$ **7)** $f(7) = 6$,
$f(-3) = -4$ **9)** $f(-2) = -1, f(8) = -11$ **11)** b, c, d **13)** a, b, c **15)** a, b, d **17)** a, b, c, d
19) $f(x) = x - 7$ **21)** $h(x) = x + \frac{7}{2}$ **23)** x-intercept $= \frac{5}{2}$, y-intercept $= \frac{5}{3}$ **25)** x-intercept $= \frac{4}{3}$,
y-intercept $= -1$ **27)** x-intercept $= \frac{4}{3}$, y-intercept $= 4$ **Set B**   **29)** b, d **31)** a, c **33)** a
35) some points are $(0,-6), (1,-5), (2,-4), (6,0)$ **37)** some points are $(0,0), (2,1), (4,2), (6,3)$
39) some points are $(0,7), (1,6), (2,5)$ **41)** $f(x) = 24 \div x$ **43)** $f(x) = 6x$ **45)** $f(x) = 36 \div x$
Set C   **47)** $f(x) = 12 \div x, f(x) = 8 - x$ **49)** $h(x) = x + 1, h(x) = x^2 + 1$ **51)** $f(t) = -5t, f(t) = t^2 + 4$
53) $h(s) = -3 - s, h(s) = -10 \div s$
Set X   **1)** some points are $(0,-7), (1,-6), (6,-1), (7,0)$ **3)** some points are $(1,14), (2,8), (3,6), (4,5), (6,4)$,
$(12,3)$ and $(-1,-10), (-2,-4), (-3,-2), (-4,-1), (-6,0), (-12,1)$ **5)** $\{(x,y): y = x + 2\}$
7) $\{(x,f(x)): f(x) = 12 \div x\}$ **9)** some points are $(1,36), (2,18), (3,12), (4,9), (6,6), (9,4), (12,3), (18,2), (36,1)$;
also $(-1,-36), (-2,-18),$ etc.   **11)** some points are $(1,12), (2,6), (3,4), (4,3), (6,2), (12,1)$; also $(1,-12), (2,-6),$
$(3,-4),$ etc.; also $(-1,12), (-2,6), (-3,4),$ etc.; also $(-1,-12), (-2,-6), (-3,-4),$ etc.

Pages 536–538 (Section 13.2)

Set A　**1)** linear　**3)** linear　**5)** not linear (x^2)　**7)** not linear $\left(\frac{1}{t}\right)$　**9)** linear　**11)** $L(2) = 9$
13) $L(-3) = 7$　**15)** $L\left(\frac{5}{2}\right) = 11$　**17)** $L(1.2) = 11$　**19)** $x = 6$　**21)** $x = -4$　**23)** $r = \frac{1}{2}$
25) $t = 12$　**27)** $m = 3$ or $m = 4$　**29)** $p = 5$ or $p = -5$　**31)** $s = 12$ or $s = -12$
Set B　**33)** $L(x) = x + 1$, zero at $x = -1$　**35)** $L(x) = -2$, no zero　**37)** $L(x) = -\frac{3}{5}x + 3$, zero at $x = 5$
39) $L(x) = 2x - 2$　**41)** $L(x) = 8x - 12$　**43)** $L(x) = -6x - 3$　**Set C**　**45)** $x < 3$　**47)** $x > -4$
49) $x \le -3$　**51)** $x \ge -2$

Pages 544–546 (Section 13.3)

Set A　**1)** parabola　**3)** -3　**5)** -3　**7)** $5.5, -3$　**9)** $0, 9, 5.25$　**11)** $0, 1, 37$　**13)** $-6, -14, -7$
15) $R(-2) = -11$　**17)** $R(\sqrt{3}) = 10$　**19)** $T\left(\frac{1}{2}\right) = -2$　**21)** some points are $(-1, -2)$, $(0, 0)$, $(1, -2)$;
maximum is zero, root at $x = 0$　**23)** some points are $(-2, -1)$, $(0, -5)$, $(2, -1)$; minimum is -5, zeros at
$x = \sqrt{5}$, $x = -\sqrt{5}$　**25)** points are $(1, 8)$, $(0, 9)$, $(-1, 8)$; maximum is 9, zeros at $x = -3$, $x = 3$
27) $x = 7$ or $x = -7$　**29)** $z = 2$ or $z = -8$　**31)** $c = 3$ or $c = -3$　**Set B**　**33)** $x = -2$ or $x = 1$
35) $r = 0$ or $r = -4$　**37)** $t = \frac{1}{2}$ or $t = 4$　**39)** $q = \frac{1}{2}$ or $q = -\frac{1}{3}$　**41)** $m = 6$ or $m = -2$
43) $x = 2$ or $x = 8$　**45)** $z = 0$ or $z = -5$　**47)** $v = \frac{1}{3}$ or $v = -2$　**49)** $j = \pm\sqrt{2}$
51) $m = 1 \pm \sqrt{3}$　**Set C**　**53–55)** see graphs　**57)** **a** if $a > 0$, the graph has a minimum, if $a < 0$, the
graph has a maximum　**b** as a increases, the graph becomes narrower　**c** and **d** the value of c is the maximum or
minimum; it is the y-intercept

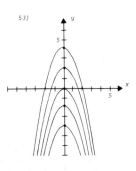

53)

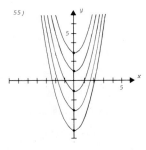

55)

Pages 548–551 (Section 13.4)

Set A　**1)** $2, 5$　**3)** $\frac{3}{2}, 7$　**5)** $7, 3$　**7)** $2, 2$　**9)** from $(-6, 0)$ through $(0, 6)$ and from $(-6, 0)$ through $(-12, 6)$.
The graph is V-shaped, opens upward, minimum at $x = -6$, range is $F(x) \ge 0$.　**11)** from $(2, 0)$ through $(0, 2)$ and
from $(2, 0)$ through $(4, 2)$. The graph is V-shaped, opens upward, minimum at $x = 2$, range is $H(x) \ge 0$.
13) from $\left(\frac{1}{2}, 0\right)$ through $(0, 1)$ and from $\left(\frac{1}{2}, 0\right)$ through $(1, 1)$. The graph is V-shaped, opens upward, minimum at
$r = \frac{1}{2}$, range is $F(r) \ge 0$.　**15)** from $\left(-\frac{1}{2}, 0\right)$ through $(0, 2)$ and from $\left(-\frac{1}{2}, 0\right)$ through $(1, 2)$. The graph is
V-shaped, opens upward, minimum at $x = -\frac{1}{2}$, range is $G(x) \ge 0$.　**17)** minimum at $x = -4$　**19)** minimum at
$x = \frac{1}{3}$　**21)** $y = 5$　**23)** $y = 8$　**25)** $y = 5$　**Set B**　**27)** from $(5, 0)$ through $(0, 5)$ and through $(10, 5)$;
V-shaped, opens upward, minimum at $x = 5$, range is $F(x) \ge 0$　**29)** from $\left(-\frac{8}{3}, 0\right)$ through $(0, 8)$ and through
$\left(-\frac{16}{3}, 8\right)$; V-shaped, opens upwards, minimum at $x = -\frac{8}{3}$, range is $G(x) \ge 0$　**31)** from $(3, 0)$ through $(0, 6)$ and
through $(6, 6)$; V-shaped, opens upward, minimum at $x = 3$, range is $H(x) \ge 0$　**33)** from $(0, 0)$ through $(-1, 8)$
and through $(1, 8)$; V-shaped, opens upward, minimum at $x = 0$, range is $F(x) \ge 0$　**35)** from $(-2, 0)$ through
$(0, -2)$ and through $(-4, -2)$; V-shaped, opens downward, maximum at $x = -2$, range is $F(x) \le 0$

Set C **37)** $F(x)$ has a minimum at $\left(\frac{5}{2},0\right)$; from there it passes through (0,5) and (5,5). $G(x)$ has a maximum at $\left(\frac{5}{2},0\right)$; from there it passes through (0,−5) and (5,−5). **39)** $F(x)$ has a minimum at $\left(\frac{1}{3},0\right)$; from there it passes through (0,1) and $\left(\frac{2}{3},1\right)$. $G(x)$ has a maximum at $\left(-\frac{1}{3},\ 1\right)$; from there it passes through (0,1) and $\left(-\frac{2}{3},1\right)$.

41) $F(x)$ and $G(x)$ are the same shape and both open upward; their minimums are $\dfrac{-b}{a}$ and $\dfrac{b}{a}$, respectively.

Set X **1)** all points on or above the rays from (2,0) through (0,2) and from (2,0) through (4,2) **3)** all points on or below the rays from (4,0) through (0,−4) and from (4,0) through (8,−4) **5)** all points above the rays from (5,−3) through (0,2) and from (5,−3) through (10,2)

Pages 554–558 (Section 13.5)

Set A **1)** 18,−9,4.5 **3)** $8,-\frac{5}{2},1$ **5)** −1,4,−4 **7)** one branch contains $\left(\frac{1}{10},1\right)$, $\left(\frac{1}{3},3\right)$, $\left(3,\frac{1}{3}\right)$, $\left(10,\frac{1}{10}\right)$; the other branch contains $\left(-\frac{1}{10},-1\right)$, $\left(-\frac{1}{3},-3\right)$, $\left(-3,-\frac{1}{3}\right)$, $\left(-10,-\frac{1}{10}\right)$. The asymptotes are $x=0$ and $y=0$. **9)** one branch contains (1,6), (2,3), (3,2), (6,1); the other branch contains (−1,−6), (−2,−3), (−3,−2), (−6,−1). The asymptotes are $x=0$ and $y=0$. **11)** one branch contains (1,−16), (2,−8), (4,−4), (8,−2), (16,−1); the other branch contains (−1,16), (−2,8), (−4,4), (−8,2), (−16,1). The asymptotes are $x=0$ and $y=0$. **13)** one branch contains (4.1,20), (5,2), $\left(8,\frac{1}{2}\right)$; the other branch contains $\left(0,-\frac{1}{2}\right)$, $\left(1,-\frac{2}{3}\right)$, (2,−1), (3,−2), (3.9,−20). The asymptotes are $x=4$ and $y=0$. **15)** one branch contains $\left(-12,\frac{1}{2}\right)$, (−7,3), (−6.1,30); the other branch contains (−5.9,−30), (−5,−3), $\left(0,-\frac{1}{2}\right)$. The asymptotes are $x=-6$ and $y=0$.

17) $g(-2)=9$ **19)** $f(-7)=1$ **21)** $h(-2)=0$ **Set B** **23)** 10,2,−10 **25)** one branch contains (−4,2) and (−2,14); the other branch contains $\left(0,-\frac{14}{5}\right)$ and $\left(2,-\frac{14}{11}\right)$. The asymptotes are $x=-\frac{5}{3}$ and $y=0$.

27) one branch contains $\left(-1,\frac{8}{7}\right)$ and $\left(0,\frac{8}{3}\right)$; the other branch contains (1,−8), $\left(2,-\frac{8}{5}\right)$, $\left(3,-\frac{8}{9}\right)$. The asymptotes are $x=\frac{3}{4}$ and $y=0$. **Set C** **29)** $\ell(w)=\dfrac{10}{w}$ **31)** domain: $\ell>0$ range: $w>0$ **33)** domain: n is a natural number range: $t>0$ **35)** asymptotes at $x=-\dfrac{b}{a}$ and $y=0$ **37)** $k=-10$ **39)** $k=1$

41) $k=17$ **43)** $k=15$ **45)** $k=-6$ **47)** $k=2$
Set X **1)** $x=4$ **3)** the graph contains (11, 1.898) and (12, 2.012); between $x=11$ and $x=12$
5) the graph contains (7, 0.478) and (8,0.430); between $x=7$ and $x=8$ **7)** $(1.075)^{15}=2.959$; $(1.075)^{16}=3.181$; sixteen years. **9)** 16,289; between 14 and 15 years.

Pages 563–565 (Section 13.6)

Set A **1)** parabola, opens downward, maximum at (0,4), zeros at $x=-2$ and $x=2$ **3)** V-shaped, opens upward, minimum at (0,0), zero at $x=0$. **5)** straight line, x-intercept between $x=-5$ and $x=-4$, y-intercept between $y=-4$ and $y=-3$ **7)** parabola, opens upward, minimum at $x=3$. **9)** a line with slope 4; the y-intercept is −1 and the x-intercept is $\frac{1}{4}$ **11)** hyperbola in upper right and lower left portions of the plane; asymptotes at $x=\frac{1}{4}$ and at $y=0$

13) the zero of $f(x)=4x-1$ is at $x=\frac{1}{4}$ **15)** $h(x)$ has no zeros **17)** $f\left(\frac{1}{2}\right)=1$

19) $h\left(\frac{1}{2}\right)=1$ **21)** 1 **23)** 10 **25)** $-\frac{1}{3}$ **Set B** **27)** a line with slope −3; the x-intercept is 2 and the y-intercept is −6 **29)** V-shaped, opens upward, minimum at (1,0) **31)** parabola, opens downward, maximum at (−1,−2), no zeros **33)** V-shaped, opens downward, maximum at (−1,0) **35)** parabola, opens downward, maximum at (0,0) **37)** hyperbola in upper right and lower left portions of the plane; asymptotes are $x=2$ and $y=0$ **39)** a line through the origin, slope is 1 **41)** $x=2$ **43)** $t=\frac{7}{2}$ **45)** $s=\frac{1}{2}$ **47)** $m=-10$

49) $x = -3$ **51)** $x = 2, -2, \sqrt{14}, -\sqrt{14}$ **Set C** **53)** hyperbola: branches contain (5,6) and $\left(6, \frac{7}{2}\right)$; $\left(1, -\frac{2}{3}\right)$ and (3,−1); asymptotes are $x = 4$ and $y = 1$ **55)** the graph is $y = 1$ for $x > 0$ and $y = -1$ for $x < 0$.
57) The graph has a relative maximum around (−2,−1) and a relative minimum around (0,−9). The zeros are near $x = -3$, $x = -2\frac{1}{2}$, and $x = 1\frac{3}{4}$. **59)** −64, −8, −1, 0, 8 **61)** −64, −8, −1, 0, 8 **63)** −64, −8, −1, undefined, 8 **65)** 0, 0, 9, 0, 0 **67)** 0, 0, 9, 0, 0

Page 570 (13/Chapter Test)

1) quadratic **3)** absolute value function **5)** quadratic **7)** $f(-3) = 13$; $f(2) = 3$; $f(0) = 7$
9) $f(-3) = -6$; $f(2) = 9$; $f(0)$ is undefined **11)** $f(-3) = 9$; $f(2) = 1$; $f(0) = 3$ **13)** $f(x) = x - 3$
15) $f(x) = \frac{1}{2}x - 1$ **17)** $(-\frac{2}{5}, 0)$ **19)** (3,0); (−5,0) **21)** straight line passing through points (0,−5) and (3,−3) **23)** straight line passing through points (0,0) and (2,1) **25)** V-shaped which opens upward, minimum at $(\frac{2}{3}, 0)$. The domain is all real numbers and the range is $f(x) \geq 0$.

Pages 577–579 (Section 14.1)

Set A **1)** x-axis **3)** opposite (over) adjacent **5)** 0.466 **7)** −2.078 **9)** 0.003 **11)** 31.7°
13) 53.1° **15)** 106.3° **17)** 7.616 **19)** 17 **21)** 50 **Set B** **23)** $tan\ Q = 0.625$, $\angle Q = 32.0°$
25) $tan\ Q = 1.875$, $\angle Q = 61.9°$ **27)** $\angle N = 67°$ **29)** $\angle B = 30°$ **Set C** **31)** $tan\ 2B = 1.192$
33) $tan\ 3D = 1.344$ **35)** $tan\ 30 = \frac{\sqrt{3}}{3}$ **37)** $\angle BAC = 21.8°$, $\angle BAD = 58.0°$, $\angle CAD = 36.2°$

Pages 583–588 (Section 14.2)

Set A **1)** $\sqrt{x^2 + y^2}$ **3)** opposite over hypotenuse **5) a** $\frac{BC}{AB}$ **b** $\frac{BC}{AB}$ **c** $\frac{BC}{AC}$ **d** $\frac{AC}{AB}$ **e** $\frac{AC}{BC}$ **f** $\frac{AC}{AB}$
7) $sin\ 86° = 0.998$, $cos\ 86° = 0.070$, $tan\ 86° = 14.301$ **9)** $sin\ 13.32° = 0.230$, $cos\ 13.32° = 0.973$, $tan\ 13.32° = 0.237$ **11)** $sin\ 95.59° = 0.995$, $cos\ 95.59° = -0.097$, $tan\ 95.59° = -10.217$ **13)** 68.2°
15) 53.2° **17)** 63.6° **19)** V-shaped, opens upward from (0,0) through (4,4) and through (−4,4). Minimum at (0,0), zero at $x = 0$; domain: all real numbers; range: $g(x) \geq 0$ **21)** V-shaped, opens downward from (−5,0) through (−10,−5) and through (0,−5). Maximum at (−5,0), zero at $x = -5$; domain: all real numbers; range: $h(x) \leq 0$ **23)** hyperbola in upper right and lower left portions of plane; asymptotes are $x = 1$ and $y = 0$.
Set B **25)** $sin\ \theta = 0.8$, θ is 53.1° **27)** $sin\ \theta = 0.583$, θ is 35.7° **29)** $tan\ 47° = \frac{12}{x}$ so x, the abscissa, is 11.2; $OP = 16.4$ **31)** $cos\ \theta = 0.917$, θ is 23.6° **33)** $cos\ \theta = 0.714$, θ is 44.4° **Set C** **35)** 70.5°, 70.5°, 39.0° **37)** $sin\ 2\theta = 0.889$ **39)** $cos\ 3\theta = 0.015$
Set X **1)** $sin\ 130° = sin\ 50°$ **3)** $sin\ 275 = -sin\ 85°$ **5)** $sin\ 225° = -sin\ 45°$ **7)** $sin\ -25° = -sin\ 25°$
9) $sin\ 125° = sin\ 55°$ **11)** the cosine curve has the same shape as the sine curve. It has maximums at (0,1), (360,1), (720,1) . . . and (−360,1), (−720,1) . . . , and it has minimums at . . . , (−540,−1), (−180,−1), (180,−1), (540,−1) . . . , the domain is unrestricted; the range is $-1 \leq cos\ \theta \leq 1$. **13)** $cos\ 340° = cos\ 20°$
15) $cos\ 105° = -cos\ 75°$ **17)** $cos\ 230° = -cos\ 50°$ **19)** $cos\ -50° = cos\ 50°$ **21)** $cos\ (-90°) = cos\ 90°$
23) $cos\ (105°) = -cos\ 75°$ **25)** $cos\ (-75°) = cos\ 75°$ **27)** $cos\ (-135°) = -cos\ 45°$
29) $cos\ (270°) = cos\ 90°$ **31)** $0.454 + 0.848 = 1.302$ **33)** no **35)** no **37)** 0.891
39) $0.788 + 0.978 = 1.766$

Pages 589–594 (Section 14.3)

Set A **1)** 102 feet **3)** 89.4 feet **5)** 186.6 meters **7)** 143.8 feet **9)** 264.5 feet **11)** −8 **13)** 5
15) 9 **Set B** **17)** $\angle C = 67.4°$ **19)** 1877.9 m **21)** 5.3 in. **23)** 802.1 ft. **25)** 1583.8 ft.
27) $\ell = 10.3$, $w = 61.9$, $p = 144$, $A = 638$ **29)** 1699.2 ft. **31)** $p = 43.2$ cm **Set C** **33)** 35.7°
35) 145 m
Set X **1)** 5.33 **3)** 5.56 **5)** 17.68 **7)** 14.50 **9)** 21.26 **11)** 17.25

Pages 597–600 (Section 14.4)

Set A **1)** vector **3)** 66.8° (the magnitude is 7.62 m/s) **5)** 453.15 kg **7)** 12.17 km/h at 9.4° from the south **9)** $\tan B = 0.75$, B is 36.9° **11)** $\cos X = 0.385$, X is 67.4° **13)** $\sin S = 0.882$, S is 61.9° **15)** $\cos E = 0.742$, E is 42.1° **Set B** **17)** 36.34 kg **19)** 89.9° **Set C** **21)** (answer in text) **23)** 21.15 at an angle of 19.9° with the longer component **25)** the resultant is 8.8 at an angle of 39° to the 22.1 component. **27)** the resultant is 55.8 at an angle of 43.7° from the vector with magnitude 27 (toward the vector with magnitude 29) **29)** the resultant is 81.1 at an angle of 52.8° from the vector with magnitude 42.

Page 605 (14/Chapter Test)

1) $\dfrac{y}{x}$ **3)** $\dfrac{x}{r}$ **5)** $\tan A = -1.3\overline{3}$, $\sin A = 0.8$, $\cos A = -0.6$ **7)** $\tan A = 0$, $\sin A = 0$, $\cos A = 1.0$

9) $\tan A = 0.5\overline{3}$, $\sin A = -0.471$, $\cos A = -0.882$ **11)** $\dfrac{RG}{GT}$ **13)** $\sin 62° = 0.883$,

$\cos 62° = 0.469$, $\tan 62° = 1.881$ **15)** $\sin 100° = 0.985$, $\cos 100° = -0.174$, $\tan 100° = -5.671$
17) $T = 81.5°$ **19)** $A = 35.3°$ **21)** $\theta = 62.1°$ **23)** 92 kg, 233 kg

Pages 606–609 (Cumulative Review 1–14)

Set A **1)** d **3)** d **5)** b **7)** a **9)** $x \le 54$ **11)** $x \le -3$ **13)** $x = \frac{3}{2}$, $x = 2$ **15)** $a = \frac{5}{4}$
17) $x = 34$ **19)** (2,0) **21)** **a** 600 **b** -16 **23)** **a** $x \le 8$ **b** $x \ge -1\frac{1}{8}$ **25)** **a** $x = -3$ **b** $x = 2\frac{1}{10}$
Set B **27)** answers may vary **29)** 41,43,45 **31)** **a** $>$ **b** $=$ **33)** **a** $2y(36 - 25y)$ **b** $3(x - 7)(x - 3)$
35) **a** $\dfrac{x^2y + x - 3y - 7}{y(x + 1)}$ **b** $\dfrac{3x + 4}{9 - x^2}$ **37)** $x = -4$ **Set C** **39)** $x = -3,0,3$
41) $f(x) = -3x + 2$; $f(-2) = 8$; $f(3) = -7$ **43)** **a** 4.0, **b** 3.5, **c** -1.5 **d** -0.333 **45)** tangent is 0.75, angle is 36.870° **47)** angle of 9.7° SW with speed 178 mph

Index

Credits

Senior Editor   Michael Green

Managing Editor   Kathleen Laya

Director of Design   Allen Carr

Designer   Randi S. Brill

Cover Photograph: Earl Glass

Photographs: James L. Ballard, frontispiece, chapters 1, 2, 4, 5, 7, 8, 9, 11, 12, 13, 14.
Photo Researchers, chapter 3.
Stock/Boston, chapters 6, 10.

Mechanical Art: ANCO/Boston
Artwork generated on ANCO Digital Illustration System

Additional Artwork: Carol Stutz, Illustrator
R&W Graphics

TE Consultants: JoAnn Rebollar
Cynthia Schaffer